£32-75 net

Hydrologic Applications of Space Technology

TITLES RECENTLY PUBLISHED BY IAHS

Hydrology of Humid Tropical Regions. Proceedings of the Hamburg Symposium, August 1983
Publ. no. 140 (1983), price $37

Dissolved Loads of Rivers and Surface Water Quantity/Quality Relationships. Proceedings of the Hamburg Symposium, August 1983
Publ. no. 141 (1983), price $37

World Catalogue of Maximum Observed Floods
Publ. no. 143 (1984), price $30

Challenges in African Hydrology and Water Resources. Proceedings of the Harare Symposium, July 1984
Publ. no. 144 (1984), price $48

Hydrological Applications of Remote Sensing and Remote Data Transmission. Proceedings of the Hamburg Symposium, August 1983
Publ. no. 145 (1985), price $48

Relation of Groundwater Quantity and Quality. Proceedings of the Hamburg Symposium, August 1983
Publ. no. 146 (1985), price $30

Scientific Procedures Applied to the Planning, Design and Management of Water Resources Systems. Proceedings of the Hamburg Symposium, August 1983
Publ. no. 147 (1985), price $48

New Approaches in Water Balance Computations. Proceedings of the Hamburg Workshop, August 1983
Publ. no. 148 (1985), price $20

Techniques for Prediction of Runoff from Glacierized Areas
Publ. no. 149 (1985), price $18

Hydrochemical Balances of Fresh Water Systems. Proceedings of the Uppsala Symposium
Publ. no. 150 (1984), price $44

Land Subsidence. Proceedings of the Venice Symposium, March 1984
Publ. no. 151, price $45

Experiences in the Development and Application of Mathematical Models in Hydrology and Water Resources in Latin America (mostly in Spanish). Proceedings of the HYDROMATH Tegucigalpa (Honduras) Symposium, September 1983
Publ. no. 152 (1985), price $30

Scientific Basis for Water Resources Management. Proceedings of the Jerusalem Symposium, September 1985
Publ. no. 153 (1985), price $42

Hydrogeology in the Service of Man, volumes 1-4. Proceedings of the IAH/IAHS Cambridge Symposium, September 1985
Publ. no. 154 (1985), price $40 the set

Proceedings of the symposia held during the Second IAHS Scientific Assembly, Budapest, July 1986

Modelling Snowmelt-Induced Processes
Publ. no. 155 (1986), $40

Conjunctive Water Use
Publ. no. 156 (1986), price $48

Monitoring to Detect Changes in Water Quality Series
Publ. no. 157 (1986), price $40

Integrated Design of Hydrological Networks
Publ. no. 158 (1986), price $40

Drainage Basin Sediment Delivery. Proceedings of the Albuquerque Symposium, August 1986
Publ. no. 159 (1986), price $45

Hydrological Applications of Space Technology. Proceedings of the Cocoa Beach Workshop, August 1985
Publ. no. 160, price $45

PLEASE SEND ORDERS TO:

Office of the Treasurer IAHS	IUGG Publications Office	IAHS Press
(Attn. Meredith A. Compton)	39 ter Rue Gay Lussac	Institute of Hydrology
2000 Florida Avenue, NW	75005 Paris	Wallingford, Oxfordshire
Washington, DC 20009, USA	France	OX10 8BB, UK

A copy of the latest Catalogue of IAHS Publications may be obtained free of charge from any of these addresses.

HYDROLOGIC APPLICATIONS OF SPACE TECHNOLOGY

Edited by

A. IVAN JOHNSON
7474 Upham Court, Arvada, Colorado 80003, USA

Proceedings of an International Workshop on Hydrologic Applications of Space Technology held in Cocoa Beach, Florida, USA, 19 – 23 August 1985. This workshop was convened by the IAHS International Committee on Remote Sensing and Data Transmission and the World Meteorological Organization. Cosponsors included the following USA Federal government agencies: Agricultural Research Service; Corps of Engineers; Geological Survey; National Atmospheric and Space Administration; and National Weather Service.

IAHS Publication No. 160

Published by the International Association of Hydrological Sciences 1986.
IAHS Press, Institute of Hydrology, Wallingford, Oxfordshire OX10 8BB, UK.
IAHS Publication No. 160.
ISBN 0-947571-85-X.

The camera-ready copy was assembled from author typescripts at IAHS Press, Wallingford. Particular thanks are due to Jo Bosley for her care and attention in doing the majority of the paste-up work.

Printed in Great Britain by Galliard (Printers) Ltd, Great Yarmouth

Preface

This volume presents papers selected from those that were originally presented orally or by poster at the International Workshop on Hydrologic Applications of Space Technology, held August 18-23, 1985 at Cocoa Beach, Florida, USA. The workshop was convened by the International Association of Hydrological Sciences (IAHS) International Committee on Remote Sensing and Data Transmission (ICRSDT) and the World Meteorological Organization (WMO). Cosponsors included the following United States government agencies: Agricultural Research Service; Army Corps of Engineers; Geological Survey; National Atmospheric and Space Administration; and National Weather Service.

In recent years, great strides have been made in the development and application of remote sensing and remote data transmission to the collection, interpretation, analysis, and near real-time communication of the huge amounts of hydrologic data being collected throughout the world. Thus, the purpose of the workshop was to bring together international specialists from a variety of disciplines to (1) present results of research and practice in the integration of remote sensing techniques, especially as related to relatively new applications to hydrologic models and geographic information systems, (2) to exchange the experiences of the specialists with others who need to know the capabilities and limitations of remote sensing and remote data transmission, and (3) to define some of the directions that future research and application should take in these techniques.

Probably the most important accomplishment of the workshop would be the transfer of information so there would be an increased awareness of current and future applications of remote sensing and remote data transmission in hydrologic problem solving. The workshop was not designed to make all participants instant experts on remote sensing and remote data transmission, but rather to prepare and encourage them to apply some of the ideas to their local problems and characteristics upon return to their home location. Participants, ranging from the inexperienced potential user to the highly trained and experienced researcher participated actively in this opportunity for information exchange.

Thirty-four countries were represented by the participants, with most of them providing authors discussing applications in their country. The workshop was preceded by a short course on geographic information systems, presented by Dr. Duane Marble of SPAD Systems, Ltd., Williamsville, NY, a course designed to introduce people to the subject in preparation for later discussions in the workshop. The workshop program consisted of approximately 75 oral and poster presentations concentrating on hydrologic applications of remote sensing and remote data transmission. Poster authors were given the opportunity to offer a full-length paper for publication if they so desired. In addition to the paper and poster sessions, the workshop offered exhibits of equipment and books related to the theme, actual demonstrations of data processing, and two field trips during the week, one of which was to the J.F. Kennedy Space Center where satellites are launched by the U.S. space shuttle.

Following review and any needed revision of the papers, over 50 were accepted and are published in this proceedings directly from author-prepared copy. The first section of this volume provides two overviews on present advances and future expectations of remote sensing and remote data transmission. Subsequent sections include six to eight papers each discussing applications of these techniques to precipitation and runoff, soil moisture and evapotranspiration, snow hydrology, miscellaneous applications, modeling and forecasting, remote data transmission, and geographic information systems. The final section consists of a summary, by Arthur Askew of WMO, of a panel discussion of today's problems and of remote sensing and remote data transmission developments of the future.

The workshop chairman was A. Ivan Johnson, President of the International Committee on Remote Sensing and Data Transmission, A. Ivan Johnson, Inc., Arvada, Colorado, USA. Other members of the Organizing Committee included Arthur J. Askew and J. Němec, World Meteorological Organization, Geneva, Switzerland; B.E. Goodison, ICRSDT Secretary, Atmospheric Environment Service, Downsview, Ontario, Canada; Tom Andersen, ICRSDT Vice-President, Norwegian Water Resources and Electricity Board, Oslo, Norway; G.A. Schultz, ICRSDT Vice-President, Ruhr University-Bochum, Bochum, Federal Republic of Germany; Serge Pieyns, ICRSDT Vice-President, ORSTOM, Paris, France; J.W. Trevett, Chairman, ICRSDT Remote Sensing Division, Hunting Technical Services, Ltd., Borehamwood, United Kingdom; Richard W. Paulson, Chairman, ICRSDT Remote Data Transmission Division, U.S. Geological Survey, Reston, Virginia, USA, who also served as the Representative of the co-sponsoring U.S. Geological Survey; Albert Rango, Representative of the U.S. Agricultural Research Service, Beltsville, Maryland, USA; Vincent V. Salomonson, Representative of the U.S. National Atmospheric and Space Administration, Goddard Space Flight Center, Greenbelt, Maryland, USA; Allen F. Flanders, Representative of the U.S. National Weather Service, NOAA, Silver Spring, Maryland, USA; and Harlan L. McKim, Representative of the U.S. Army Corps of Engineers, Cold Regions Research and Engineering Laboratory, Hanover, New Hampshire, USA. Local arrangements were chaired by Harry Rodis, U.S. Geological Survey, Orlando, Florida, USA.

Members of the organizing committee served as reviewers of abstracts and papers and posters for the program, and served as co-chairman for the oral paper sessions. Their contribution to the success of the workshop and this proceedings is gratefully acknowledged. On behalf of the Workshop Organizing Committee I express sincere gratitude to the co-sponsors WMO and the U.S. government agencies for their support through grants or services to the workshop. Appreciation also is expressed to the authors for their contribution to an interesting workshop and subsequent proceedings. A special thanks goes to Betty Johnson who provided the two years of secretarial assistance needed for organization of the workshop, carried out the registration in a most efficient manner, and assisted with many other duties related to the workshop and the proceedings. Finally, the proceedings would not have been possible without the assistance of the IAHS Editorial Office, particularly by Penny Kisby and her assistants.

The IAHS International Committee on Remote Sensing and Data Transmission recognizes that remote sensing and remote data transmission are not necessarily broadly applicable to all hydrologic problems. However, these techniques are relatively new and new or refined applications are developing rapidly. We therefore believe these techniques offer two potentially powerful new tools for use of the multi-disciplinary people working in the field of hydrology. Thus, the ICRSDT hopes this proceedings will encourage further research on remote sensing and remote data transmission for hydrologic applications.

A. IVAN JOHNSON
A.Ivan Johnson, Inc., 7474 Upham Court
Arvada, Colorado 80003, USA
Symposium Convenor and President ICRSDT

Contents

4 SNOW HYDROLOGY

5 MISCELLANEOUS APPLICATIONS

6 MODELING AND FORECASTING

TISON AWARD

Following the presentation by the Exeter Assembly Organizing Committee of the sum of $13 000 to the Association and the acceptance of the idea of an annual prize to recognize the scientific contributions of young hydrologists to IAHS, the Bureau established the Tison Fund. Investment income from the Fund will be used to provide an annual prize of $750 according to the terms of the Award set out below:

TISON AWARD – RULES

1. The IAHS Tison Award aims to promote excellence in research by young hydrologists. The award will be announced annually and will be presented in a public ceremony during either an IUGG/IAHS General Assembly or an IAHS Scientific Assembly.
2. The Tison Award will be granted for an outstanding paper published by IAHS in a period of two years previous to the deadline for nominations. Nominations should be received by the Secretary General of IAHS not later than 31 December each year. The award will be announced by 31 May of the following year.
3. Candidates for the award must be under 41 years of age at the time their paper was published.
4. The Award will consist of a citation in the name of L.J. Tison and an amount of US$750. (If the successful paper is jointly authored, the monetary award will be divided equally between the authors.)
5. Nominations for the Tison Award may be submitted by the National Committees of IAHS and also by any individual or group of persons. They should be sent directly to the Secretary General of IAHS and should contain a reasoned argumentation.
6. The award decision will be made by a committee of seven members, one from each of the IAHS Commissions and Committee. The members of the Award Committee will be hydrologists of outstanding research reputation. The IAHS Bureau will appoint the members of the Award Committee, membership lasting for a period of two years. The Chairman of the Award Committee will be rotated among the different representatives of the IAHS Commissions and Committee.
7. The Award Committee may not recommend an award in any one year if none of the papers submitted is of sufficiently high standard.

ADDRESS FOR NOMINATIONS: Dr. J.C. Rodda, Secretary General IAHS, Institute of Hydrology, Wallingford, Oxfordshire OX10 8BB, UK.

INTERNATIONAL HYDROLOGY PRIZE

The General Assembly of IAHS held at Canberra in 1979 endorsed the principle of an International Hydrology Prize awarded annually on an individual basis in recognition of an outstanding contribution to the science. Nominations for the Prize are made by National Committees and forwarded to the Secretary General for consideration by the Nomination Committee which consists of the President, the First and Second Vice Presidents and representatives of UNESCO and WMO according to the following criteria:

- The International Prize in Hydrology shall be awarded to a person who has made an outstanding contribution to hydrology such as confers on the candidate universal recognition of his international stature.
- The contribution should have an identifiable international dimension extending beyond both the country of normal work and the specific field of interest of the candidate.
- The contribution may have been made through scientific work, as evidenced by the publication in international journals of scientific literature of a high standard, and/or through practical work, as evidenced by reports of the projects concerned. Preference should be given to candidates who have contributed through both scientific and practical work.
- The Prize may be awarded to hydrologists of long international standing or to those who, while having gained such standing only recently, exhibit the qualities of international leadership in the science and practice of hydrology.
- An active involvement in the work of IAHS and other international organizations in the field of hydrology should be counted as an advantage.

LIST OF PRIZE WINNERS

1981 Prof. L.J. Tison (Belgium)
1982 Mr. W.B. Langbein (USA) and Dr. V.I. Korzun (USSR)
1983 Prof. J.C.I. Dooge (Ireland)
1984 Prof. A. Volker (Netherlands)
1985 Dr. J.A. Rodier (France)
1986 Dr. M.A. Kohler (USA)

1 Overview

Hydrologic Applications of Space Technology (Proceedings of the Cocoa Beach Workshop, Florida, August 1985). IAHS Publ. no. 160, 1986.

A European perspective on satellite remote sensing for hydrology and water management

E. C. BARRETT
Remote Sensing Unit, University of Bristol, Bristol, UK
R. W. HERSCHY
CNS Scientific and Engineering Services, Tresillan House, 20 Eldon Road, Reading, UK

Abstract
Hydrology and Water Management are key areas of applied science in the current world economy. Increasingly hydrologists are looking to satellite remote sensing to help meet their needs for near real-time data to measure, monitor and model water in the environment. However, progress has been hindered by the lack of a dedicated series of hydrological satellites. In 1985 an ESA-sponsored project undertaken by Working Group 10 of EARSeL reviewed the remote sensing state-of-the-art in Europe, and defined some future projects and possible sensor packages which could further advance such activity. This paper summarises its Final Report.

Introduction

Water is vital to mankind and its everyday activities. Its extreme significance has been grimly underlined in recent months and years by images and reports of hunger, famine, squalor and disease from drought-stricken areas in several parts of the world. Water is the essence of life; but when scarce, or contaminated, it can be the cause of disease or even death. It has been estimated that, at any given time 400 million human beings are suffering from gastroenteritis; 200 million have schistosomiasis (bilharzia, or 'snail fever'); 30 million have 'river blindness'. Half of all the hospital beds in the world are occupied by people suffering from water-borne diseases: tens of millions of women spend half their waking hours walking in the hot sun to fetch water - which will infect them and their families. Millions in Africa have died from water shortages in the last 12 months; many more will permanently suffer from the after-effects of drought-induced malnutrition.

The United Nations itself has recognised the key significance of water by designating the 1980s as the "International Water Decade." Its general objective is to provide clean drinking water (and sanitation) for everyone by 1990. But such water management, even on national or regional scales, often calls for a density and quality of water data which is only very rarely attained. Many of the data which are gathered are dubious; most are point measurements of parameters which vary continuously in space and/or time.

Remote Sensing, especially from satellites, affords new hope that more, and more homogeneous, data may be collected from even relatively inaccessible or poorly-developed regions of the world.

This paper summarises a Project intended to review present uses of satellite remote sensing for Hydrology and Water Management, and to draw up proposals for the future. It was undertaken by Working Group 10 (Hydrology & Water Management) of EARSeL (the European Association of Remote Sensing Laboratories), with financial support from ESA (the European Space Agency). Therefore its perspectives and proposals may be peculiarly

European. However, many of its conclusions will be of much wider interest and applicability. (See Herschy, Barrett & Roozekrans, 1985).

Terms of Reference

The objectives of the EARSeL/ESA study were sixfold, namely:

1). To identify the needs for remote sensing by addressing a broad community of hydrologists.

2). To review existing techniques and uses of satellite sensors in Hydrology and Water Management, as a reference for promotion and future work.

3). To draw existing techniques to the attention of potential users.

4). To identify limitations to existing techniques, and formulate possible solutions to them.

5). To provide inputs to conceptual studies of future remote sensing systems.

6). To formulate detailed practical proposals for future demonstration studies in regions covering a variety of hydrological problems.

Project Organisation

A number of special meetings were held so as to accomplish the objectives listed above. The chief working sessions were as follows:

1). Regional Workshops
   a) Humid Mid-latitude Regions: Bochum, FRG, 23-25 May 1984.
   b) Mediterranean Regions: Florence, Italy, 30 May - 1 June 1984.
   c) Arid and Semi-arid Regions: Athens, Greece, 7-10 June 1984.
   d) Montane Regions: Innsbruck, Austria, 10-12 July 1984.

2). Technical Workshop: Paris, France, 27-29 September 1984.

3). Reporters Meetings: Noordwijk, The Netherlands, 17 September 1984 and 2-4 January 1985.

As indicated by Table 1, advice and experience was culled from the expert community through a pyramidal approach. Apart from inputs from the Project Manager, Reporters, and Regional Workshop chairmen themselves, the views of a further 36 experts were crystallised from personal presentations and ensuing discussions. Responses to a general Questionnaire organised by L. Collin (UK) were gleaned from an additional 71 individuals, agencies, institutions or laboratories. A further 79 Questionnaires were distributed without response. However, the total input from over 100 individuals and bodies involved in Hydrology & Water Management is quite large enough for us to suppose that the profiles and conclusions drawn therefrom are at least broadly representative of remote sensing practices, problems and possibilities as perceived in Europe today.

The Present Status of Satellite Remote Sensing in Hydrology & Water Management.

Although no purpose-built hydrological satellite has yet been flown, many

Table 1 Project management and key personnel

Project Manager:	R W Herschy (UK)
Reporters:	E C Barrett (UK) J N Roozekrans (NL)
Area Workshop Chairmen:	V Cappellini (Italy) M Moutsoulas (Greece) H Rott (Austria) G A Schultz (FRG)
Area Workshop Participants:	29 Selected Remote Sensing Scientists and Water Data Users
The Hydrology & Water Management Community	71 Institutional Respondents to Widely-circulated Questionnaire

past and present satellites have yielded data or provided facilities of use in Hydrology. Pre-eminent amongst these have been the meteorological satellites (both geostationary and polar-orbiting), the Heat Capacity Mapping Mission (HCMM) and the Landsats. Of the satellites firmly planned for the future, the American N-ROSS & TOPEX, the Canadian Radarsat, and the ESA ERS-1 seem most likely to be of further interest and help. The most important areas of application in Hydrology & Water Management have included:

1). Rainfall monitoring, including severe storm and flash flood forecasting and evaluation.
2). Surface water inventory and monitoring, e.g. of rivers, lakes, marshes and reservoirs.
3). Snow mapping, measurement, and monitoring.
4). Soil moisture measurement, though mainly for un- or sparsely-vegetated localities.
5). Evapotranspiration estimation and monitoring.
6). Extremes of surface water presence or availability, i.e. through floods or droughts.
7). Sedimentation patterns and rates in reservoirs, and deposition in rivers.
8). Groundwater mapping and assessment, and discharge management.
9). Water pollution types and distributions.
10). Hydrological forecasting, of the above parameters and phenomena, and numerous dependent variables.
11). Data collection from *in situ* sensors &/or the relay of information from elsewhere.

Numerous individual and detailed examples of the above broad categories of applications were presented in the four Regional Workshops. Details are contained in the Project Final Report by Herschy et al. (1985), which also lists currently unsatisfied needs in satellite remote sensing as perceived by the European expert user community. Since these needs were largely coincident with many which were identified in the Questionnaire returns, it must suffice for present purposes and within the limited space available, to specify them more precisely through a listing of the chief conclusions from the Questionnaire. These can be summarised as follows:

1). Many operational requirements can only be fulfilled at present using traditional data collection methods (aerial survey included).

2). Very few existing satellite data analytical techniques are seen as fully or potentially operational. Much seems to depend on the enthusiasm of individuals.
3). The spatial resolution and frequency of information provided by existing sensors is inadequate for many applications. High incidences of cloud cover often exacerbate the imaging frequency problem.
4). Satellite remote sensing facilities are expensive to instal, and new specialist staff may be needed to operate them.
5). Knowledge and understanding of current and possible future satellite remote sensing systems and methods is low, implying needs for better publicity and education.
6). Optimism for the future is greatest where there is access to digital image processing equipment.

Perceived Needs for Future Advancement

On the global scale Hydrology is primarily a responsibility of the World Meteorological Organisation. The WMO Commission for Hydrology (CHy) is currently undertaking a review of observational requirements, in order to update a table first published by WMO in 1977 in "The role of satellites in WMO programmes in the 1980s". A draft copy of the revised table was available for detailed discussion in the Regional Workshops of the present project. Based upon that table, and a number of our own amendments to it, we have drawn up a summary of observational requirements not taking any account of the sources or methods by which such data might be obtained. We have then classified the requirements in terms of the feasibilities of meeting these needs with existing or firmly anticipated remote sensing data from satellites. The results are presented here in Table 2.

The "Resolution" and "Frequency" columns reveal very clearly that many observational requirements will remain unmet unless new satellites and sensor systems are developed for applications in Hydrology & Water Management. The "Accuracy" column may also be interpreted to confirm that further algorithm development is also required.

Future Satellite/Sensor Systems

Satellite-based research in hydrological science has been fragmentary, and the adoption of satellite remote sensing techniques in operational Hydrology has been slight and piecemeal when assessed on a global scale. The chief cause is clear and non-controversial: it is their enforced reliance upon systems designed primarily for other fields of application (e.g. in meteorology, oceanography, geology, land use). The configuration of a dedicated hydrological satellite ("Hydrosat") was first addressed by Dornier System (1975). The need was explored further by Barrett (1982), who felt it unlikely that such a satellite, much less a family of such satellites, could come about until much higher degrees of cohesion and organisation had been achieved in the user community, and until much stronger representations had been made thereby to the appropriate space agencies. Although the present study was sponsored by ESA, it has been very evident in recent public pronouncements by ESA personnel that the need for a more sharply and more consciously focussed approach to the measurement and monitoring of water in the environment has still gone largely unnoticed.

One outcome of the activity at the Regional and Technical Workshops of the present project was a set of outline specifications for satellite sensors thought likely to be of special value in Hydrology and Water Management programmes in the foreseeable future. These are summarised in

TABLE 2: Hydrological and water management observational requirements (summary giving main headings of table in Final Report)

	PARAMETER	RESOLUTION			FREQUENCY			ACCURACY		
		MAX	MIN	OPT	MAX	MIN	OPT	MAX	MIN	OPT
A	Precipitation	100m	10km	1km	5min	1M	1h	10%	30%	20%
B	Snow depth	30m	10km	1km	12h	1M	24h	2cm	10cm	5cm
C	Ice cover	10m	1km	25m	12h	7d	24h	1%	20%	10%
D	Glaciers -dimensions	10m	500m	25m	1y	10y	2y	1%	5%	2%
E	Surface water areal extent	10m	100m	30m	12h	7d	24h	1%	5%	3%
F	Groundwater -aquifer maps	50m	1km	100m	1y	5y	3y	5m	30m	10m
G	Evaporation	100m	10km	1km	12h	10d	1d	10%	30%	20%
H	Water quality -turbidity	30m	300m	100m	3h	24h	6h	10%	50%	20%
I	Drainage -drainage area	10m	100m	20m	3y	10y	5y	0.1%	1%	0.5%

LEGEND

FREQUENCY: h = hour; d = day; M = month, y = year.

FEASIBILITY ☐ = Requirement can be generally met by existing satellite(s)

____ = Requirement should be generally met by near future satellite(s)

Note: where a value is neither boxed nor underlined the observational requirement cannot generally be met either by existing or firmly expected future satellites, given the present state of the art.

Table 3. Further details of these sensors, and the reasons for their choice, are given in the Final Report by Herschy et al. (1985).

Expert opinion on the sensors described above is that the spectral requirements are by no means novel nor unexpected. Neither would the required spatial resolutions present undue engineering difficulties. However, the temporal frequency requirements are generally higher than previously achieved, and these might be more difficult to meet.

In general there would appear to be two possible scenarios in which these sensors could become available. One involves total reliance on existing and firmly anticipated satellites, the other, at least partial reliance on possible future programmes. In the case of the first, it is instructive to rank the seven types of sensors listed in Table 3 in the order in which they might be approximated by present or expected satellite systems.

1). Polar orbiter AVHRR-type imagery: obtainable from NoAA satellites until at least the mid-1990s though an improved spatial resolution would be required.
2). Geostationary imagery: good coverage is expected between about 60° N & S over all major land masses, though significantly higher spatial resolutions would be required especially in middle latitudes.
3). Space Shuttle/Spacelab "Modified Aerial Survey" camera photography: in this case the chief doubt is not over spectral or spatial resolutions, but over areas and frequencies of imaging cover.
4). Polar-orbiter thematic mapper imagery: expected data from Landsat

TABLE 3: Specification and justification for satellite sensors deemed likely to be of special value for Hydrology and Water Management in the foreseeable future

Satellite type	Orbit	Sensor type	Spectral Regions	Spatial Resolution	Imaging Frequency	Principal Applications
1 Environmental	Geostationary	Imaging Radiometer (GIR)	0.5- 0.9μm 5.7- 7.1μm 10.5-12.5μm	0.5 km* 4.0 km 0.5 km	48 d^{-1} 24 d^{-1} 48 d^{-1}	Meteorology, cloud systems, rainfall, flash floods, thermal inertia, surface water, ice & snow cover, aridity, drought
2 Environmental	Near-polar (Dual Polarized)	Scanning Microwave Radiometer (SMR)	90 GHz 37 GHz 25 GHz 19 GHz 10 GHz 5 GHz	5 km*) 10 km*) 10 km*) 10 km*) 10 km*) 15 km*)	At least 2 d^{-1} 4 d^{-1} preferable	Cloud liquid water contents, rain rates, snow cover, snow water equivalent, relative snow depth, snow melt, sea ice & polymas
3 Environmental	Near-polar	Imaging Radiometer (AVHRR)	0.55- 0.7μm 0.725- 1.3μm 3.55-3.95μm 10.5-11.5μm	0.33 km* 0.33 km* 0.33 km* 0.33 km*	At least 2 d^{-1} (03.15h) 4 d^{-1} preferable (03, 09, 15, 21 h)	Meteorology, cloud systems, rainfall, surface temperatures, ice & snow cover, major floods, aridity & drought, vegetation indices
4 Environmental	Near-polar	Synthetic Aperature Radar (SAR)	X-band C-band L-band	30 m) 30 m) 30 m)	Every 7-10 days; 5 days preferable	Extent of wet snow, lake & river ice, glaciers, surface water, soil moisture, measurement & monitoring
5 Environmental	Near-polar	Ocean Colour Monitor (OCM)	0.400 μm 0.445 μm 0.520 μm 0.565 μm 0.640 μm 0.685 μm 0.785 μm 1.020 μm 1.600 μm 3.700 μm 8.500 μm 10.800 μm 12.000 μm	0.25 km) 0.25 km) 0.25 km) 0.25 km) 0.25 km) 0.25 km) 0.25 km) 0.25 km) 0.25 km) 0.25 km) 0.25 km) 0.25 km) 0.25 km)	Every 3 days*	Water colour, quality & turbidity, suspended sediments, pollutants, phytoplankton, surface temperatures, land applications including vegetation and land use
6 Earth resources	Near-polar	Thematic Mapper (TM)	0.45-0.52μm 0.52-0.60μm 0.63-0.69μm 0.76-0.90μm 1.55-1.75μm 2.08-2.35μm 10.4-12.5μm	30 m) 30 m) 30 m) 30 m) 30 m) 30 m) 120 m)	Every 4 - 5 days*	Morphology, land cover, surface water extent & quality, glacier, lake & river ice, snow cover, ground water etc.
7 Space shuttle/ Spacelab	Various	MODIFIED AERIAL SURVEY Cameras (LFC)	+Visible +Infrared +False colour	c. 10 m) c. 10 m)) c. 10 m)	Occasional c. every 10 years	Relief, drainage, topographic mapping

* Represents significant advance on capabilities of earlier/present sensor systems

\+ Depending on films and filters used

and SPOT will be generally acceptable spectrally and spatially. However, there are doubts over the frequency of imaging cover which will be achieved, especially since SPOT is untested, and the future Landsat programme is so unsure. Extra provision might be necessary in this respect.

5). Polar-orbiter passive microwave imagery: data expected from USAF-DMSP satellites and N-ROSS should be very useful for research purposes, but serious doubts exist as to whether civilian operational programmes in Europe could be based on either. Therefore an independent passive microwave radiometer is urgently called for especially since satellite rainfall estimation techniques in the foreseeable future can only be significantly improved further through such means.

6). Polar-orbiter synthetic aperature radar imagery: it does not seem likely that planned systems will provide the spectral variety called for in Table 3. Thus a new instrument is required to advance both pure and applied science in this area of considerable significance to small-basin hydrology in areas like much of Europe where freeze-thaw processes and associated phenomena are so significant.

7). Polar-orbiter ocean colour monitor imagery: in the absence of any suitable sensor of this type, or firm plans for the same, special provision seems the only way in which such data may be assured for the future.

In summary, the first 3 above call for improvements of existing systems rather than entirely new satellites or sensors. In the case of (4) above the perceived needs might be met if the most optimistic scenarios for future Earth Resources satellites prove realistic. However, in the cases of the last 3 above it seems very unlikely that the required data will be forthcoming unless new satellite programmes or programme elements are established. It may strengthen the case for the 3 sensors in question (passive microwave imager, SAR, and OCM) that, as a package, they could contribute significantly to both land and ocean missions, and might therefore be suitable candidates for either type of programme. However, it is abundantly clear that the 3 together would comprise a distinctively hydrological package 'Hydrosat' or 'Watersat', since water (as precipitation, on the land surface especially as ice and snow, as well as in shallow water bodies) is central to the area of applicability of each sensor. The provision of one or two satellites carrying these 3 sensors would seem to be by far the simplest and neatest solution to the perceived Hydrology and Water Management data requirement problem. In this connection it would seem specially worthwhile to attempt to influence two new programmes now being defined for the 1990s.

1) The Earth Observing System (EOS) of NASA.
This is a planned NASA programme intended to further multidisciplinary Earth science through improved facilities for remote sensing from satellite altitudes. An important part of this will be the manned Space Station, a major engineering objective, one of whose purposes will be to make space more accessible for many remote sensing applications. However, the overall project plan also allows for a number of co-orbiting facilities, including unmanned polar-orbiting space platforms ('super satellites'?) to help provide long-term sets of Earth science data in various application areas, including several of interest to Hydrology. A number of "strawman" instrument packages are now being defined by working groups, on one of which the first author is serving. Currently it seems that possible American polar platforms in the mid-1990s might be so equipped as to reasonably meet about half the requirements identified in Table 2. However, neither

the SAR nor the SMR needs would be more than very partically met - and, more seriously, the provision of either type of instrument is in question because the High-Resolution Multifrequency Microwave Radiometer (HMMR) package into which they would naturally fit is under great threat in the competition for EOS project funding.

2) The Earth Observation Programme of ESA .
Although the Earth observation satellite activities of ESA have mainly focussed hitherto upon the Meteosat weather satellite programme, and the new ocean and ice applications mission ESR-1, ESA is now considering an expansion of its areas of concern. One element of current ESA thinking is that it should develop an advanced land observation mission, with an exphasis on microwave instrumentation, and that a start on this should be made as soon as possible. It further considers that "priority should be given to land resources monitoring rather than inventory." Recent presentations by ESA personnel have been remarkable for their lack of reference to water in the environment as a feature worthy of study by Earth observation or Earth resources satellites. However, it can be argued that a polar orbiter equipped with a multichannel passive microwave radiometer (for precipitation, ice and snow monitoring), a SAR (for ice and snow and soil moisture monitoring), plus an OCM (for water quality monitoring) could indeed constitute an "advanced land observation mission with emphasis on microwave instrumentation", and that such a satellite would greatly improve the chances that the requirements of Table 3 might be largely met before the end of this century. It is up to the hydrological community to organise its case, and present this effectively through the appropriate channels, bearing in mind that a number of governing decisions may be made very soon.

The Archiving, Retrieving and Processing of Satellite Data

Hydrologists and waterwork-engineers frequently need information on dynamic processes, like rainfall, flooding, erosion etc. over long periods. For design of waterworks, forecasting of runoff etc., many stochastic models have been developed. Stochastic models need long historical data. For many areas in the world such data are not available or are incomplete. Satellite Remote Sensing can be the only available data-source in such cases. In other cases remote sensing might be a cheaper data-source than a field measurement network.

It is therefore clear that archiving of remote sensing data over a long period is very important for hydrologists. Until now the organisations responsible for the operation of Earth-observation and meteorological satellites have archived much of the data received from the satellite-sensors on CCT, although not all at the full initial resolution. In the future this might not continue to be the case, for CCTs are a very space-consuming medium.

Even if archived the accessibility of remote sensing data to the user is conditioned by three factors: the effort to obtain the right data, time of delivery, and data costs.

From the Questionnaire and the four Regional Workshops in the present study we have learned that all three phenomena are important constraints on the operational utilisation of remote sensing techniques.

The ability to acquire data quickly is a first requirement. This assumes greatest importance when the user is involved with monitoring of dynamic processes. Even where regional data-centres are found it can, at the moment, take weeks before the user receives Landsat data which he has ordered. Before the user can order the requested data, he first has to ascertain if these data are available and if the quality is acceptable. Time of delivery can lengthen greatly when such data are ordered from receiving stations outside Europe and USA. Finally the interest of a potential user of remote sensing data might be highly diminished by the rapidly rising costs of satellite-data.

Most of the image processing facilities in Europe are located in government offices, mostly working in the research field. Those facilities in general embrace large, not very dedicated processing systems, and are available for use by outside users. However the costs for computer time are normally very high, especially when the user is not too familiar with the data handling procedures. Very few systems are dedicated to applications in Hydrology and Water Management. So a potential user working in the hydrology field first has to develop adequate software before he can actually use an image processing system.

Recommendations towards the improvement of archiving, retrieving and processing of satellite data are furnished in the Conclusions below.

Conclusions

The conclusions of this study may be briefly summarised as follows:-

1). Satellite remote sensing has many present applications for use in Hydrology and Water Management. The spatial, temporal and spectral information available from satellites is of great interest and value to hydrologists and water managers particularly when available in near real time and especially on account of the dynamic nature of the hydrological cycle and the inadequacy of *in situ* hydrological observations. However,

2). Penetration of satellite remote sensing techniques into operational Hydrology and Water Management has so far been relatively slight.

3). In Europe, many and varied applications of satellite remote sensing to hydrological problem-solving have been developed and tested. However a significant gap clearly separates the science of satellite remote sensing, as pursued and developed in research institutes, from the practices and needs of operational hydrologists and water managers.

4). It is possible to identify a number of new projects which, though dependent on existing satellite systems and/or future satellite data archives, could help to advance the scientific knowledge and understanding of the European hydrosphere and/or further the suitability of satellite remote sensing procedures for use in operational Hydrology and Water Management. These include broad integrative projects, necessitating multi-laboratory co-operation, more restricted area and/or theme-specific projects which could be undertaken by individual laboratories, and projects in the related fields of information, training and publications.

5). There is lively interest in the further development of satellite remote sensing for applications (both research and operational) in Hydrology and Water Management in both global and continental circles. However it is clear that many present data needs cannot be met, either wholly or in part, by existing and firmly planned satellites, none of which are dedicated to this field of activity.

6). In view of the likely configuration of satellites and satellite systems expected to be active in the late 1980s and 1990s, alternative scenarios have been drawn up to match anticipated data types and supplies with the key perceived needs of hydrologists and water managers. The strongly-recommended scenario is one which provides (for the first time) a dedicated international satellite system for

Hydrology and Water Management. Enforced dependence on satellite systems designed for other primary users seems unlikely to satisfy more than a small fragmentary proportion of our needs.

7). Associated recommendations in data processing and archiving call for centralised data-directories and data-banks and a computer centre to service the needs of local hydrological laboratories and authorities in possession of new, low-cost image processing systems.

8). It is clear from our investigations that the DCP telemetry facility available with the Meteosat system is significantly under-utilised. We are of the opinion that satellite telemetry for transmitting hydrological ground measurements is a cost-effective alternative to existing terrestrial radio and telephone systems. We therefore recommend that further efforts should be made by ESA to bridge the existing information gap to ensure that water organisations are made fully aware of this facility.

In view of 1 to 8 above, it is recommended that efforts be made not only to meet each identified need individually and, perhaps independently of one another, but also to ensure that there might be a suitable framework and mechanism for the considered balanced, and progressive development of Satellite Remote Sensing for Hydrology and Water Management. For this to be effective, a proper and continuing exchange of information, views, needs and possibilities will be essential, involving hydrologists, scientists, operational hydrologists and water managers, satellite systems engineers and software specialists. In such respects the near-term future may be especially decisive.

References

Barrett, E.C., 1982, Organizational Needs for Hydrological Applications of Satellite Remote Sensing in Developing Countries: Hydrological Sciences Journal, 28, 1983, p.273-281.

Dornier System, 1975, Mission Study for an Operational Remote Sensing Satellite System for Hydrology Observation in Developing Countries: Final Report, Contract, No.RV-21-V64/74-KA-50, Dornier System GMBH, Friedrichshafen, FRG, 132p.

Herschy, R.W., Barrett, E.C., & Roozekrans, J.N., 1985, Remote Sensing in Hydrology & Water Management: Final Report, EARSeL WG10/, European Space Agency, Paris, 225p.

NASA, 1984, Earth Observing Systems, Science & Mission Requirements Working Group Report, Vol. 1, Parts 1 & 2, NASA Technical Memorandum 86126, NASA Greenbelt, Md., 55p. & 51p.

Hydrologic Applications of Space Technology (Proceedings of the Cocoa Beach Workshop, Florida, August 1985). IAHS Publ. no. 160, 1986.

Development of a national real-time hydrologic information system using GOES satellite technology

W. G. SHOPE JR & R. W. PAULSON
U.S. Geological Survey, Water Resources Division, National Center, MS 460 Reston, Virginia 22092, USA

Abstract

The U.S. Geological Survey operates the basic hydrologic data collection system for the United States. The Survey is upgrading the collection system with electronic communications technologies that acquire, telemeter, process, and disseminate hydrologic data in real-time. These technologies include satellite communications via the Geostationary Operational Environmental Satellite, Data Collection Platforms in operation at over 1400 Survey hydrologic data collection stations, Direct-Readout Ground Stations at 9 Survey District Offices and a network of minicomputers that process and disseminate data quickly. The Survey is rapidly moving toward making the satellite telemetry system an integral part of the national hydrologic data collection network. Data telemetry via satellite provides valuable information to the water user community on a more timely basis, improves the operation of the data collection network, and enhances the quality of the hydrologic data. Further enhancement of the data collection system by the operational use of telemetry throughout the network will be based on cost effectiveness studies.

Introduction

The United States Geological Survey operates the basic hydrologic data collection program needed to provide an information base to support a wide variety of water resources planning and management activities in the United States. The data collection program and information base are in transition to much more automated technologies that speed the flow and analysis of data from thousands of remote field locations to user facilities. This transition includes upgrades to data collection and recording equipment at hydrologic stations, telemetry systems for automated data retieval and networks of computers to analyze and distribute the data to users across the nation.

National economic growth has meant an increase in the number of hydrologic data users who operate hydropower generating plants and irrigation systems and who manage flood damage prevention and navigational waterways. Growth has also generated interest from users such as environmentalists who are trying to clean up or prevent further environmental degradation. These additional requirements for hydrologic data have been translated into a need for more hydrologic data on a more timely basis which requires that data be collected and delivered to users through automated telemetry and computerized data processing and distribution systems.

Geological Survey Hydrologic Station Networks

The Geological Survey collects hydrologic data from about 13,000 stage and discharge stations, about 35,000 wells where water level and(or) pumpage data are collected annually or more frequently, and approximately 4,600 surface-water stations and 7,600 wells where water-quality information is collected. Data from the majority of these stations are collected through onsite visits by Survey personnel or observers who collect water samples and(or) make hydrologic measurements. Where continuous records are needed for computation of statistics such as daily means, maximums, and minimums, data are collected using automated recorders supplemented by manual measurements that are used for calibration, and correction. The Geological Survey collects continuous stage (water level) records at 8,000 stream sites and 1,000 lakes and reservoirs throughout the nation. Continuous records are also collected for about 2,000 wells and 1,000 stations (primarily surface-water) where water-quality data are obtained. For more information on the Water-Data Program of the Survey, the reader is directed to Gilbert and Buchanan 1982. The methods for automating the collection of data for continuous record stations have evolved over the last 40 years from spring driven mechanical devices to electronic instruments that take advantage of the new technologies developed for communications and computers.

Automated Hydrologic Instrumentation

The Geological Survey is collecting a variety of hydrologic data using automated instrumentation. The most prevalent types of data are stream and reservoir stage, water temperature, specific conductance, dissolved oxygen concentration, pH, rainfall and snow cover. These data generally are recorded at 15, 30, or 60-minute intervals by battery operated onsite recorders that have a mechanical or electrical connection to an onsite sensor. The sensors include a float with counter weight or a pressure equalizing manometer for stage measurement, a minimonitor for water-quality parameters, tipping buckets for precipitation and snow pillows for measuring snow cover.

Early recorders produced an analog graphical representation of the data (primarily stage vs. time). To facilitate inputting the data to a computer, analog to digital recorders were developed in the 1950's and remain as the primary method for on-site data recording at automated data collection stations. A clock periodically signals the recorder to punch the sensor readings on a 16-channel paper tape. The paper tapes are retrieved at intervals of 4 weeks to 6 weeks during visits to each site and are checked manually for time and data errors. The tapes are read by computers located at the Survey offices responsible for the data collection stations. After the data have been edited and processed by the Survey computers, they are available for retrieval through the Survey's national network of computers. Although the data are recorded in a timely manner, the collection and processing under this system includes a time lag of at least 4 weeks to 6 weeks because the data are manually retrieved from the stations.

Telemetry of Hydrologic Data

The procedures for acquiring data from the collection sites and entering the data into a computer are manpower intensive and time consuming. These two factors are causes for concern in terms of present and future demands for more and timely data.

The telemetry of data from remote data-collection sites is being accomplished by a variety of mechanisms. The major components of a telemetry system are: the sensors that measure or detect changes in an observation such as stream stage, encoders that convert the sensor output to forms suitable for transmission, a transmission system that provides the link from a remotely operated sensor to another location, and a data reception and distribution facility that receives, sorts, decodes, checks, and distributes the incoming data. The most important component, and the one that characterizes the communications system, is the transmission media. Conventional telemetry methods applied over the past 35 years include land lines (telephone) and high-frequency and ultrahigh-frequency (microwave line-of-site) radios. Extraterrestrial methods applied within the last 13 years include meteorburst and satellite data-collection systems. The reader is referred to Halliday 1979, for a more complete review of telemetry systems.

The selection of a telemetry system for an application calls for careful considerations of many factors such as cost, reliability, responsiveness, coverage, growth, and flexibility. The choice of a telemetry system for an area of limited size and uniform geographic characteristics could result in any one of the conventional or extraterrestrial systems best meeting the users needs. The telemetry system selected by the Geological Survey must support a national hydrologic information system that meets the needs of a variety of water users and collects data over a wide range of geographic conditions.

The evaluations conducted by the Survey and many other Federal agencies have shown satellite telemetry, when compared with other telemetry systems, to be generally cost-effective, reliable, easy to install and operate, able to cover vast areas, and extremely flexible in carrying a wide variety of data transmissions that can be scheduled to meet user needs. For reasons of compatibility with other federal agencies, economics (access is provided at no cost to users by the operating agency), flexibility, and large area coverage, the Survey has chosen to use the Geostationary Operational Environmental Satellite (GOES) Data Collection System (DCS) operated by the National Earth Satellite Data and Information Service (NESDIS). The GOES DCS is provided at no cost to the Survey and other Federal, State, and local government agencies under a Memorandum of Agreement with NESDIS, which is a component of the National Oceanic and Atmospheric Administration. This agreement specifies NESDIS as the operator of the satellites, Earth receive station, and a data distribution center. The reader is referred to National Oceanic and Atmospheric Administration, 1979, for detailed information on the GOES Data Collection System.

GOES Data Collection System

The GOES Data Collection System is built around Earth orbiting satellites that are used to relay transmissions from networks of dispersed data collection sites to one or more receiving sites. A satellite data collection system is made up of five major elements that include: (1) sensors linked to; (2) small radios called data-collection platforms (DCPs) that transmit data to; (3) satellites which immediately relay the data to; (4) Earth receiving site(s) that forward the data to; (5) data handling and distribution facilities.

The GOES DCPs currently on the marketplace can satisfy most needs for collecting and reporting hydrologic data. These DCPs can collect and temporarily store data from sensors at user-defined rates and transmit these data to the GOES satellite. Data collection normally occurs at 15-, 30-, or 60-minute intervals and the transmission intervals are normally set by the users at 3 to 4 hours. These self-timed transmissions are made up of messages that contain, at a minimum, all data collected from the sensors since the last transmission. In some cases the messages are extended to include data from one or more previous transmissions, thus providing redundancy in data transmission. Most of these DCPs also contain an alert feature that forces transmissions to occur soon after the detection of a data value that has exceeded a user-defined threshold or differential when compared with the previous sensor value. An example of this is a rapid change of stage or rate of precipitation during a critical hydrologic event. Alert messages normally contain the most recent set of values sampled. Third generation DCPs developed in the early 1980's, with costs reduced below $3,000, have significantly increased these capabilities. These new DCP's can provide on-site data conversion, calibration, and perform statistical summaries and other analytical tasks, if required.

The most significant concern now faced by the users is the lack of proper quality standards in the production and testing of the instrumentation associated with satellite telemetry. This is one of the key issues that will be addressed through the late 1980's as users seek standard quality control procedures, plus standards in data handling and formatting that will facilitate sharing of real-time hydrologic data collected via satellite telemetry.

Messages transmitted from the DCPs are received by GOES and are immediately retransmitted back to Earth at a higher frequency and data rate. Data are received from GOES by a primary satellite Earth receive station as well as user stations referred to as a Direct-Readout Ground Station (DRGS). NESDIS operates the primary receive station at Wallops, Virginia. This station is used as the centralized facility for all data reception and for monitoring, command, and control of the GOES spacecrafts.

Several users of the GOES system in an effort to reduce system complexity, increase timeliness of the data, and reduce dependence on land lines are turning to local passive (receive only) satellite DRGS. These DRGS', which can be obtained for $60,000-$100,000, provide a user with immediate access to the data transmitted from the satellite. The DRGS comprises an antenna, radio receiver, and decoding equipment, and a minicomputer that functions as a system controller. These controllers are powerful enough to manage the operation of the radio receiver, decode the DCP messages, flag and disseminate alert messages, store the decoded data in a temporary file, monitor the performance of the DCP transmissions, provide access for multiple users, and forward data to other computers colocated at the users offices.

During the early 1980's, the Geological Survey began to process and install satellite DRGS' at several district offices. These DRGS' are uncomplicated, and operate automatically. Since these DRGS' do not transmit to the satellite, monitor its health, command it and its sensors, copy imagery, or position the satellite, they can be dedicated to serve the single requirement of collection of real-time telemetered environmental data. Because the DRGS can be colocated with the user or data collection network field manager, responsiveness to user needs has been improved, control has been returned to the field manager, and system flexibility has increased considerably. As a result of these and other factors, the use of these stations has become increasingly attractive to users of the GOES telemetry system. The Survey is currently operating DRGS' at Harrisburg, Pennsylvania, Columbia, South Carolina, Fort Worth, Texas (for the U.S. Army Corps of Engineers), Denver, Colorado, Phoenix, Arizona and Tacoma, Washington. For additional information on the development of a distributive system for satellite telemetry see Shope and Paulson, 1985.

The major components of a satellite telemetry system are shown in Figure 1. Surface-water level data are collected at a continuous record station and relayed via the GOES satellite to a user-operated DRGS. Data are continuously acquired from the DRGS by one of the Survey's primary computers located near the DRGS and entered onto the Survey's telecommunications network addressed to the offices that operate the data collection stations. If the data are from stations operated by the office that also operates the DRGS, the data are processed locally with summaries forwarded (by all offices) to Reston, Virginia, to update the Survey's National Water Data Storage and Retrieval System and the National Water Data Index (NAWDEX).

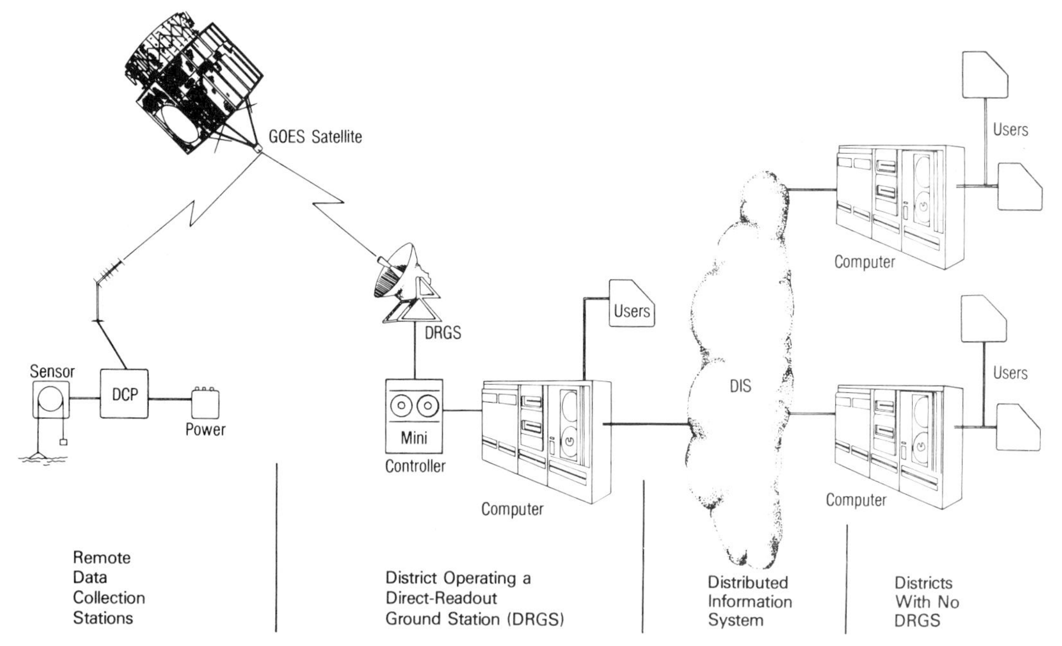

FIG.1 Hydrologic data collection using satellite telemetry and a distributed information system.

Please see Edwards 1980 for more more information on NAWDEX.

Cooperative Activities by the Geological Survey and Other Agencies in the Use of Satellite Telemetry

Many of the cooperative data collection programs that the Survey conducts with 800 Federal, State, and local government agencies support operation of automated hydrologic data collection stream gaging stations. The Survey normally constructs the stations, installs and operates the sensors and recorders, makes periodic measurements to determine the relationship between the streams' discharges and stage heights, retrieves and processes the stage data to compute instantaneous and mean discharges, and publishes the daily-mean-discharge values. In most cases, the Survey has not been involved in telemetry operations involving line-of-sight radio networks and landline telephone systems, except to provide space for the telephone or radios in the gage houses. The data collected by the traditional remote-acquisition systems are useful in monitoring conditions upstream and downstream of reservoir projects, but lack the content that the Survey requires for computing continuous records. For this reason, the Survey prior to the mid 1970's, did not participate actively in remote data-acquisition systems. However, with the advent of the use of satellites to relay an adequate stream of data from remote sites, the value in real-time data collection to the Survey has changed. Satellite relay not only provides the water data user with the timely data they need, but also provides the Survey with an opportunity to automate its data collection activities and remotely monitor the condition of on-site instrumentation.

The number of Geological Survey data collection stations supported by satellite telemetry has grown significantly over the past 7 years. At the end of 1978, the station count of sites using satellite telemetry was 120, and by 1985, it was up to 1,400. Based on forecasts for remote telemetry needs by the U.S. Army Corps of Engineers, Bureau of Reclamation, and

National Weather Service, station counts may exceed 2,500 and thus 25 percent of the Geological Survey's automated hydrologic data collection stations may be reporting through GOES by 1987. The Geological Survey is involved in the installation and operation of more than two-thirds of the telemetry operations at Survey operated data collection stations, with the majority of the equipment owned by the primary water data user (Corps of Engineers, Bureau of Reclamation). Examples of the operational application of hydrologic data collected via satellite telemetry are listed below:

- Flood Warning -- The National Weather Service acquires through the NESDIS central Earth receive station all hydrologic data transmitted via GOES for use in river and flood forecasting models. Flood forecasting represents the largest use of data telemetered via GOES.
- Reservoir Management -- The use of precipitation and stream stage data by the Corps of Engineers and Bureau of Reclamation represent the second largest use of hydrologic data transmitted via satellite DCS. The largest concentrations of DCPs for reservoir management are in the Ohio River basin, the Trinity River basin in Texas (Corps of Engineers), and the Snake River basin (Bureau of Reclamation) in Idaho and Oregon. Shope and Dreyer (1981) provide additional information on the Geological Survey's cooperative efforts with the Corps of Engineers.
- Monitoring Water Resources for Hydropower Generation by Various Federal, State, and Local Agencies -- An example of this application is a growing network of DCPs in the Columbia River Basin in the Pacific Northwest that are gradually being used to replace landline and terrestrial radio systems.
- Collection of Data for Irrigation and Water Management -- Examples include the use of telemetry in the Arkansas River basin in southeast Colorado. More than 70 DCPs are used for monitoring reservoir releases, stream flows, irrigation channel discharges, and diversions in the basin.
- Monitoring Water Allocations for Treaties and Legal Compacts -- DCPs are in use for continuous monitoring of streamflow across both State and international boundaries, and for enforcing treaties between various political jurisdictions, including Indian reservations.
- Data Collection Network Operation -- The primary utilization of satellite telemetry information in the Geological Survey today is providing near real-time data to users and the operation and management of portions of the hydrologic data-collection network. Because of manpower and transportation costs, it is often less expensive to invest in and operate a satellite telemetry system than to make frequent visits to remote sites to collect data and inspect the instrumentation. Sites that are difficult to access or require provisional data to be distributed more often than the normal 6-week manual acquisition cycle are good candidates for satellite telemetry.

Additional information on the use of hydrologic data collected via satellite telemetry for water management can be found in Shope and Paulson, 1981.

Cost Effectiveness of Satellite Telemetry

A cost-benefit study of the collection of hydrologic data by satellite telemetry was conducted by the Survey in 1978. This study concluded that benefits (flood forecasting and irrigation water management) other than those associated with the collection of data, outweigh the costs for satellite telemetry, but that the telemetry of water data could not, at that time, be justified based on cost effectiveness (for data collection operations) considerations alone. The issue of cost effectiveness is being restudied because of the increased interest in using telemetry supported by reduced costs in hardware, increased data processing and communications capabilities, and the omission from the previous study of the impact on data quality resulting from possible reduction in lost records.

Recent development of methods in network analysis techniques used to evaluate the cost effectiveness of the existing Geological Survey stream-gaging program will provide the tools required to estimate the cost effectiveness of converting all or part of the data collection network to satellite telemetry. These procedures will allow a comparison of error versus budget levels for varying degrees of network conversion against the current method of data collection. The investigation will consider the effect of possible reduction in record loss on accuracy and the optimum number of visits to sites required to maintain a given level of accuracy.

The outcome of the study will influence the level of installation of automated satellite telemetry in the Geological Survey's streamgaging network based on cost effectiveness. Providing automated telemetry from all of the Geological Survey's stream-gaging network would have a major impact on the types of services that the Geological Survey could provide to major cooperators and data users.

Distributed Information System

By the mid 1970's, the Survey had established a centralized National Water Data Storage and Retrieval System (WATSTORE) at the Survey's Headquarters in Reston, Virginia. Please refer to Showen, 1978, for further information on WATSTORE. During this period, the Survey also began to collect data via the GOES satellites for entry into WATSTORE. Data were acquired from the NESDIS data-collection system using various computerized telecommunications systems and entered into WATSTORE without manual intervention. This addition of data relayed via GOES represented an enhancement to the centralized WATSTORE system in making data available in a 1-day timeframe for a small number of stations.

Data in the WATSTORE files are frequently used as input to models that support the planning and operation of water-resources development projects. The data also are being increasingly retrieved directly from Survey computers by other agencies and the public. Although WATSTORE was a quantum leap forward over earlier technology, its batch-oriented central processing carries unacceptably high telecommunications costs and time delays, and it lacks the flexibility to serve a wide variety of local needs. The Survey determined that modern distributed computer technology would eliminate many of these problems.

The aging technologies that are being replaced in the water-data program often were becoming unresponsive to user needs and costly in manpower resources to operate and maintain. An investment in new technologies offered the Survey the opportunity to be more responsive to the needs of the water data user community. It also is anticipated that the capital investment in new technology will constrain operational and maintenance costs. These factors and others encouraged the Survey to plan a new generation of automated data collection instruments, communications facilities, and computer systems. The increased capabilities and lower costs of small computers encouraged the Survey to develop a nationwide network of minicomputers with the software and management control needed to operate a Distributed Information System (DIS).

The first step in the development of the DIS was a competitive procurement of a family of minicomputers. The second step in the development of the DIS was a telecommunications network based on a communication protocol known as "X.25", which was implemented in calendar year 1984. Figure 2 shows the backbone of the DIS telecommunications network that links the Survey's computers for processing hydrologic data with the DRGS'. The private network is controlled by high-speed message buffering and switching computers at Menlo Park, California, Denver, Colorado, Atlanta, Georgia,

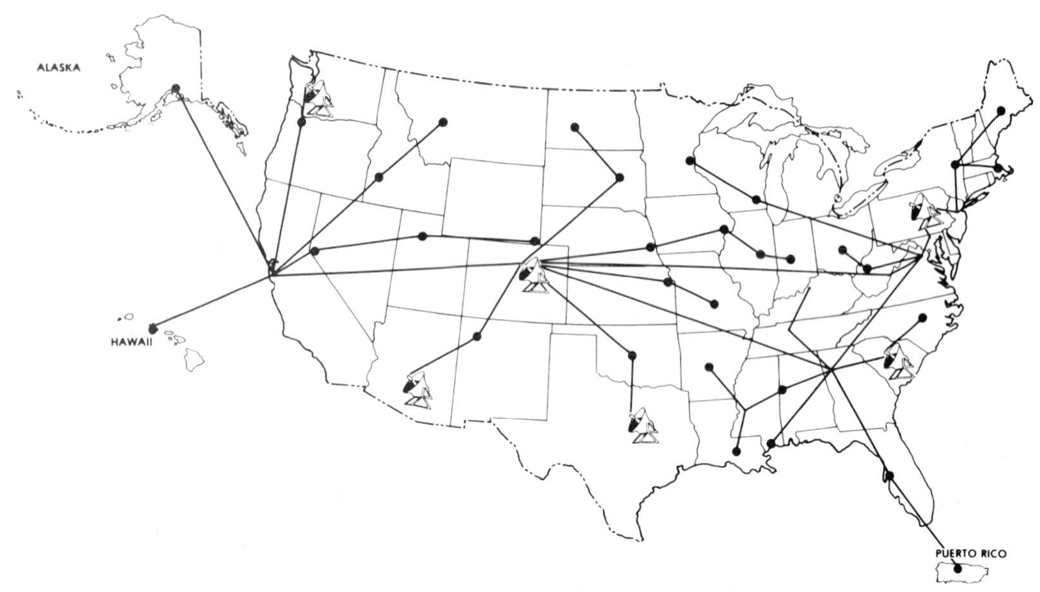

FIG.2 Backbone network of the Geological Survey's distributed information system linking district computers with direct-readout ground stations.

and Reston, Virginia. The Figure does not show all of the dedicated leased lines or terminal points that make up the complete network. For more information on the DIS see Posson, 1985.

WATSTORE has been redesigned from a centralized to a distributed data processing system. Integrated administrative data systems are also being designed to provide more efficient and streamlined schemes for budget and program planning. A variety of digital models for hydrologic data analysis have been reconfigured for the DIS system. Provisions for connecting the Survey's network of GOES satellite DRGS' to the DIS have been developed so that data acquired by the network can be shared by other users of the DIS, both within and out of the Survey. In June 1985, the Survey discontinued its reliance on the NESDIS Earth receive and data distribution facility and began acquiring all GOES telemetry data through the local DRGS' located at nine Survey field offices.

As the upgrade of the water-data program proceeds through the 1980's, collection, analysis, and processing of hydrologic data will no longer be handled by a centralized system of communications devices, computers, and data bases, but will occur on distributed computers in Survey field offices and on microprocessors in Survey gaging stations. Access to these data in real-time via satellite telemetry through the DIS will expedite the availability of information for water-data users.

Summary

The Geological Survey is implementing a national hydrologic information system using the GOES satellite. Data from over 1400 hydrologic stations now are being telemetered through the satellites and received at Survey or cooperating agencies' receiving stations. The Survey is automating the data analysis and distribution of GOES telemetered data to support data needs of water-resources management agencies and develop a more cost-effective operation. This effort has resulted from a need for more data on a more timely basis for reservoir management, hydropower generation, irrigation control, and water quality monitoring. The Survey is completing distribution to the field manager for of control and operation of data telemetry (transmission and reception), computer processing, and data distribution. This action has increased flexibility for providing more information in a more timely manner to Survey cooperators.

With the advent of the GOES Data Collection System, the use of telemetry by the Survey has become an important data collection tool. GOES telemetry provides a reliable means to provide critical hydrologic data to the water data community and allows the Survey to monitor its automated data collection network. By 1987, more than 25 percent of that network may be reporting through GOES. The cost effectiveness study now underway will determine how quickly the remainder of the network will be instrumented for satellite telemetry.

References

Gilbert, B. K. & Buchanan, T. J. (1982) Water Data Program of the U.S. Geological Survey. U.S. Geological Survey Circular 863, Reston, Va.

Halliday, R. A. (1979) The Use of Satellites in Hydrometry. In: Hydrometry: Principles and Practices, 427-447. R. W. Herschy, ed., John Wiley and Sons, Inc., New York, N.Y.

National Oceanic & Atmospheric Administration (1979) Geostationary Operational Environmental Satellite/Data Collection System. National Oceanic and Atmospheric Administration Technical Report NESS 78, Washington, D.C.

Shope, W. G., Jr., & Paulson, R. W. (1983) Development of a distributive system for handling real-time hydrologic data collected by the U.S. Geological Survey. In: Hydrological Applications of Remote Sensing and Remote Transmission (Proc. Hamburg Symp., August 1983). IAHS Publ. no. 145.

Edwards, M. D., (1980) NAWDEX: A key to finding water data, 15p, U.S. Geological Survey Pamphlet, Reston, Virginia.

Shope, W. G., Jr., & Dreyer, S. E. (1981) U.S. Geological Survey Cooperation with the U.S. Army Corps of Engineers for Hydrologic Data Collection Using the GOES Satellite. In: Remote Sensing Symposium (Proc. Nashville Symp., December 1981), 48-61. U.S. Army Corps of Engineers, Washington, D.C.

Shope, W. G., Jr. & Paulson, R. W. (1981) Real time data collection via satellite for water management. Transportation J., ASCE 107.

Showen, C. R. (1978) Storage and retrieval of water resources data. In: Collection, Storage, Retrieval and Publication of Water Resources Data. U.S. Geological Survey Circular 756, Washington, D.C.

Posson, D. R., Nethaway, C. D., Jr., and Harbaugh, A. W. (1985) Design and implementation of a nationwide distributed information system. In: Proceedings of the National Prime Users Group Meeting, June 1985.

2 Precipitation and runoff

Hydrologic Applications of Space Technology (Proceedings of the Cocoa Beach Workshop, Florida, August 1985). IAHS Publ. no. 160, 1986.

Interactive procedures for estimating precipitation from satellite imagery

JOHN F. MOSES*
Satellite Applications Laboratory, NESDIS, Washington, DC, USA
E. C. BARRETT
Remote Sensing Unit, University of Bristol, Bristol BS8 1SS, UK

Abstract

New interactive procedures combine satellite data, climatic data, local surface reports and numerical weather prediction outputs to monitor rainfall over data sparse regions of the world. A single meteorologist will be able to improve daily estimates of precipitation using an interactive image processing system. The procedures require a meteorologist to interpret raincloud pattern evolution from displays of satellite cloud images and conventional data at synoptic times. Three state-of-the-art precipitation algorithms have been selected for individual and combined operational application. Each algorithm offers unique advantages dependent on the type of satellite data available and the particular synoptic situation. Case studies over the U.S. Great Plains indicate that the interactive procedures provide a 10% improvement in the rainfall estimate field when compared to objective analyses of the surface reports alone. As part of the AgRISTARS program, an operational demonstration is planned to provide the best possible estimates covering the major crop growing regions in the U.S.A., Soviet Union and South America. Aside from denser automated surface networks, future improvements may be expected through refinement of meteorological interpretive skills, more effective use of climate data, and the addition of passive microwave observations from satellites.

Background

Accurate crop yield monitoring and harvest prediction have long been primary goals for nations and companies with economic needs for good food commodity forecasts. Recent events in Africa have drawn the attention of the world community to the significance of such monitoring and prediction for humanitarian purposes: food aid and famine relief could be mobilized more rapidly and appropriately if information on crop growth and productivity were more accurate and complete than hitherto.

Unfortunately, the assessment of crop yields and likely harvest volumes calls for many different types of information, of which key types are often difficult to obtain. Centralized production forecasting of major world crops requires accurate information not only on the areas planted, but also on agricultural practices, crop health, and crop condition. Environmental conditions during the growing season are specially significant in relation to crop performance, which is above average when conditions are good, and below average in times of stress. Perhaps the most important single parameters bearing on crop growth and performance is soil moisture. Mathematical models of soil moisture have been developed to help evaluate crop yield, and predict each year's production, through their use during each growing season. Since direct information on soil moisture is very sparse, and

*Present affiliation: SPACECOM, 1300 Quince Orchard Boulevard, Gaithersburg, Maryland 20878, USA.

satellite remote sensing methods for soil moisture monitoring are as yet partial and incomplete, heavy reliance is placed upon water budgetting to provide assessments of moisture in the soil. Of the quantities needed as inputs to such models, precipitation is the most variable, and the most difficult to obtain with sufficient accuracy because of its high variability both spatially and temporally.

Conventional rainfall data are characteristically too sparse within the time frame for routine rainfall monitoring over many of the important crop growing areas of the world. Consequently, hydrometeorologists have looked to weather satellites as a potentially valuable supplementary source of information on raincloud and rainfall distributions, especially for areas between surface rainfall station locations. Comprehensive summaries of research activities in such fields have been prepared by Barrett and Martin (1981) and Atlas and Thiele (1981). Although the development of appropriate techniques is by no means straightforward, there can be no doubt that effective combinations of routine satellite observations and conventional surface reports will provide the best possible rainfall data for direct inputs to soil moisture models for the foreseeable future.

Broadly speaking, satellite rainfall monitoring techniques can be grouped in three classes. These include:

1) Objective (automatic) techniques, e.g. that of Arkin (1979), based on a single IR temperature threshold to identify rain clouds and a simple weighting scheme to translate rain days into rainfall. Research results suggest that, for sufficiently large time and space scales, such simple methods may provide sufficient accuracy (e.g. for global climate studies);
2) Interactive (partly automated) techniques, e.g. the Bristol Method (see Barrett, 1984) which uses a manual analyst to differentiate between cloud areas which objectively appear to be similar, but which a trained meteorologist could separate into, say, raincloud and non-raincloud sections;
3) Manual techniques, based on the unique skill which can be developed by a specialized interpreter, e.g. to identify and evaluate convective clouds and cloud systems capable of prompting extreme rainfall events and associated potentially disastrous phenomena such as flash floods. (See Scofield, 1984).

In the context of crop monitoring, the first is too broad, and the third too detailed and too demanding in manpower, for either to be the presently preferred group of techniques.

The AgRISTARS Program

Agriculture and Resource Inventory Surveys Through Aerospace Remote Sensing (AgRISTARS) is a program designed to develop the uses of remote sensing primarily for the US Department of Agriculture. The AgRISTARS Program has sponsored development of three state-of-the-art rainfall algorithms either singly or together in a Large Scale Applications Test (LSAT) demonstration in support of crop monitoring. However, these techniques and the data they can provide are of interest in other contexts also, e.g. as potential sources of regional rainfall data for use in hydrology and/or water management.

The three techniques are the Bristol Method, the EarthSat Method (both "cloud indexing" techniques) and the ERL (Environmental Research Laboratory, or "Woodley-Griffith") Technique (a "cloud history" method designed primarily for use in convectional situations). Although some cross-fertilization of approach has already been engendered by earlier stages of the NOAA AgRISTARS rainfall initiative, each algorithm still offers its own unique advantages, dependent on factors including the skill of satellite meteorologists, the frequency of satellite data coverage, and the availability of surface weather station reports, climate fields, and Numerical Weather Prediction model outputs.

The chief purpose of this paper is to present the bases for these algorithms, explain the forms in which they are being used in the AgRISTARS Program, and present and discuss results from preliminary evaluations of them. First some common factors between the three chosen techniques will be summarized, after which their individual characteristics will be described.

Principles of Satellite Raincloud Analyses

Satellites such as the NOAA-7 polar orbiter take sun-synchronized cloud cover images by Advanced Very High Resolution Radiometers (AVHRR) twice each day, once during local morning and once local evening. Experience shows that the cloud imagery can be used as a guide to rain falling some time before or after the observation time, as well as at the observation time itself.

Taking R(t) to be a function between the cloud observed at time t and rainfall over a period centered at the same observation time t, then for any function (either linear or nonlinear) of R(t) the rainfall over a period ending at the satellite observation time can be approximated by the equation:

$$R(p) = 1/2R(t_1) + R(t_i) + 1/2R(t_2) \quad (1)$$

where $R(t_1)$ and $R(t_2)$ are the rainfall per unit periods centered at the satellite observation times t_1 and t_2. $R(t_i)$ is an allowance for rainfall from clouds analyzed to have developed or advected over an area between the times covered by the satellite cloud observations t_1 and t_2 when these are widely separated in time. It is necessary to give continuity to the analyses for fast-moving (e.g. cyclonic storm) systems or rapidly-changing (e.g. convective) situations. The means whereby the satellite cloud information is translated into rainfall estimates differs from technique to technique so these will be described in the technique specific sections.

Calibration with Surface Reports

Locally reported rainfall serves as a valuable constraint on satellite cloud/estimated rainfall relationships, and can be used to adjust the estimates for significant weather variations. However, before this can be done, persistent local influences (especially relating to position and topography) should be removed so that point observations can be applied to the cloud imagery to the maximum areal extent possible.

Thus the constraint on Equation 1 becomes:

$$Q(p) = R_0(p)/M \quad (2)$$

where $R_0(p)$ is the reported rainfall for the period p, M is the normalizing factor (a "morphoclimatic weight"), and Q(p) is the represented rainfall at the reporting station. The constraint is applied by setting Q(p) = R(p) over a suitable area of rain cloud for cases when the satellite observation time is near to the synoptic reporting time. In this way local effects can be removed from the array of reported rainfall observations so that the values used to guide the image analyst are more simply related to the nature and characteristics of the raincloud system itself.

The ERL Method

Griffith et al. (1978) derived an empirical relationship between calibrated radar echo areas and geostationary satellite-observed cloud areas over south Florida as part of the Florida Area Cumulus Experiment in the mid-1970s. This became the core of a satellite rainfall estimation technique which could run automatically or with a manual edit. A time/history relationship between the echo area and cloud area was obtained by normalizing each with respect to the maximum cloud area achieved during its

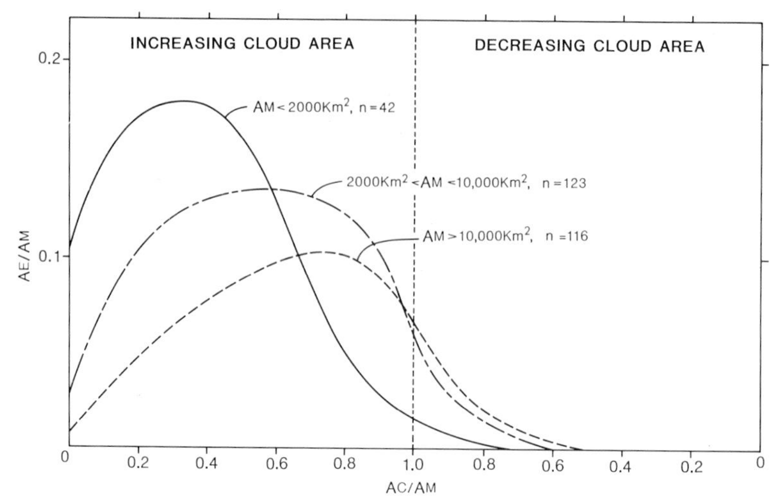

FIG.1 The cloud area/echo area relationships for infrared data over Florida. Both cloud (A_C) and (A_E) areas have been normalized to the relative maximum cloud area (A_M). The curves are subjective fits to the mean data (not plotted) and have been stratified by maximum cloud area (A_M).

lifetime. The diagram in Figure 1 shows the empirical relationship between normalized cloud area, normalized echo area, and the maximum cloud area achieved during the cloud's lifetime. The relationship between rain volume and echo area in the ERL technique can be written as follows:

$$R_v = I * A_E * \Sigma q_i b_i * \Delta t \qquad (3)$$

where
R_v is the rain volume (m^3)
I is the rain rate ($m^3/km^2/hour$)
A_E is the inferred echo area
i is an index of three temperature thresholds
q is the fraction of pixels at each threshold within the cloud
b is a dimensionless weighting factor dependent on temperature
Δt is the time interval in hours between successive satellite images

Table 1 lists the values of rain rate I as a function of echo growth trend and shows the equations used to generate the weighting coefficients.

The three temperature threshold groups are: $D<154$, $154<D<194$ and $194<D$ which corresponds to $T>-20°C$, $-20>T>-49°C$, and $T<-49°C$ (from the standard GOES IR calibration table).

The rain volume is computed for each cloud and apportioned over the cloud area to produce a grid array of hourly accumulations. The apportioning is done using the following relationship:

$$D_{ij} = R_v * b_{ij} * 10^{-3} / (\Sigma b) * g_{ij} \qquad (4)$$

where
D_{ij} is the rain accumulation at gridpoint i,j
R_v is the rain volume compiled for the cloud
b_{ij} is the weighting coefficient for gridpoint i,j
Σb is the sum of weighting coefficients
g_{ij} is the area associated with gridpoint i,j

Table 1 - Rain rate (mm/h) as a function of echo growth trend for south Florida echoes. A_E refers to echo area (defined by the 1 mm/h rain rate) and A_{EM} refers to the maximum area an echo attains in its life cycle.

Echo growth trend	Rain rate I (mm/h)
Increasing echo area	
$0.0 \le A_E/A_{EM} < 0.25$	13.3
$0.25 \le A_E A_{EM} < 0.50$	17.3
$0.50 \le A_E A_{EM} < 0.75$	21.1
$0.75 \le A_E A_{EM} < 1.00$	23.8
$A_E/A_{EM} = 1.00$	20.7
Decreasing echo area	
$1.00 > A_E/A_{EM} \ge 0.75$	21.1
$0.75 > A_E/A_{EM} \ge 0.50$	16.7
$0.50 > A_E A_{EM} \ge 0.25$	11.9
$0.25 > A_E A_{EM} \ge 0.00$	8.2

The weighting coefficients (b) as a function of digital count (D) for the standard calibration SMS-GOES infrared data.

$153 \le D < 176$:
$\bar{b} = \exp(0.026667 + 0.01547 \times D)/11.1249$
$176 \le D \le 255$:
$\bar{b} = \exp(0.11537 + 0.01494 \times D)/11.1249$

For use in AgRISTARS, the original computer programs were obtained from Griffith and converted to run on the NOAA Central Computer Facility, using GOES digital infrared imagery. The programs were modified so that they would produce estimates in the GOES satellite projection. This permits editing of the outputs when compared with GOES imagery, for example so as to reduce or eliminate rain estimates inadvertantly made for non-rain-cloud in the automatic stages (e.g. in areas of cirrus downwind from centers of strong convection). A further modification was seen to be necessary to better adjust results from contrasting climatic environments. Two procedures are being considered to accomplish this. One involves climatological differences between Florida (where the relationships were first derived) and the local area of interest, and using ratios of mean monthly rainfall per rain day morphoclimatic weights. The other involves ratios of observed precipitable water. The ERL technique remains the most completely automated of the three techniques selected for the AgRISTARS demonstration.

The EarthSat Method

Over a period of 10 years, Earth Satellite Corporation developed an operational satellite rainfall monitoring scheme to provide an improved precipitation analysis for input to their crop yield and commodity forecasting system. Evolving from the early work of Barrett, they derived regression relationships between cloud temperature and rainfall for the significant crop growing regions in the world, including the USSR, South America and the U.S.

As with other similar approaches, the regression models show a high variability and a relatively weak correlation. In order to improve upon these results and provide the best possible rainfall estimate EarthSat has investigated combinations of the satellite-rainfall relationship with synop-

Table 2 - Earth satellite-alone rainfall coefficients.

REGION	COUNTRY IDENTIFIER	RAINFALL COEFFICIENTS (Alpha, Beta) Morning	Afternoon
USA	1	-4.65, 1.88	-12.43, 3.23
S.A.	2	-4.90, 2.30	-14.53, 2.61
W. USSR	3	-2.65, 1.20	- 6.40, 2.03
E. USSR	4	-2.30, 1.31	- 6.20, 2.32

Table 3 - Image conversion chart.

COUNT VALUE	APPROX. TEMP. (C)	AVG. RAIN (MM)	BRIGHT-NESS LEVEL
>218	<-56	25.0	6
210 - 217	-51 - -55	16 0	5
199 - 209	-45 - -50	9.0	4
154 - 198	-25 - -44	4.0	3
125 - 153	-12 - -24	2 0	2
112 - 125	- 7 - -11	0.0	1
<112	< -6	0.0	0

Table 4 - Vertical motion classes.

CLASS	Vertical (cm/sec)
1	< -4
2	-3 - -1
3	-1 - 1
4	1 - 3
5	> +4

Table 5 - Cloud dynamics menu.

CATEGORY 1	CATEGORY 2	CATEGORY 3
Spreading Anvil	Typical "Synoptic Low" Clouds	Overshooting Tops
Decaying Cloud System	Normal T-Showers	Clouds Involved in Rapid Growth
Cirrus/Alto Stratus	Clouds at normal speed (20-30 KTS)	Hurricanes and Tropical Storms
Fast Moving System	Normal Life Cycles	Cloud System Associated with intense Upper Trough or Cut-Off Low Behind Front
Broken (Mostly BRI 4) Cloudi-ness with ill-defined edges	Care of Thunder-shower Exclu-ness with ill-shooting tops or Blowoff	Stratus that is producing Rain
Short-Lived Storms (<2 Hrs.)	Overrunning	Slow-Moving Rain
CU/SC Decks not raining	General FVA Rain	Thunderstorms with Long Life Cycles (> 6 Hours)

tic reports, output from numerical models and climate information. The current regression equation from EarthSat is:

$$R = [a+b*C*V*0.6]*M \tag{5}$$

when $V>3$ and $C\geq 5$ or
when $V\geq 4$ and $C\geq 3$

where R is the 6 hour accumulation of rainfall in millimeters
a,b are regression coefficients dependent on the time of day and region (see Table 2)
C is the local cloud brightness category determined from infrared satellite imagery (see Table 3)
V is the local vertical motion class determined from numerical model output and Table 4 or from interpretation of the imagery and
M is the morphoclimatic weight derived from the local mean monthly rainfall per rain day normalized by the average value over the region.

Using the Cloud Dynamics Menu in Table 5, category 2 areas are assigned vertical motion class 3 and category 3 areas are assigned vertical motion class 4. Category 1 areas and cloud free areas are assigned vertical motion class 1.

When warmer cloud tops (cloud category 2) are associated with strong vertical motion (class 4 or 5) the following rainfall estimation equation is substituted:

$$R = 1.4*M \tag{6}$$

After estimates are made using the satellite-alone regression equations, a second procedure was developed to calibrate the estimates in the vicinity of synoptic station reports. The satellite estimates surrounding a station report are adjusted by the ratio between the reported rainfall and the satellite estimate.

The area of influence for a particular station report can be defined automatically or by interpretation of the air mass characteristics of the storm system. The automatic method defines an area of influence according to the morphoclimatic weight in the vicinity of the report. The area of influence extends out from the station until the morphoclimatic weight changes by more than 10%. The calibrated rainfall estimate (R_C) at a particular point s between stations becomes:

$$R_C = R_S*(\Sigma O_i/D_i^2)/(\Sigma R_i/D_i^2) \tag{7}$$

where D_i is the distance from the gridpoint (satellite estimate) to the station i, R_i is the satellite alone estimate at station i, O_i is the observation from the station i, and R_S is the satellite alone estimate at point s. Defaults are used for special conditions:

$$R_C = R_S \quad \text{when} \quad \Sigma O_i/D_i^2 = 0 \tag{8}$$

and

$$R_C = (1/N)*\sum_{i=1}^{N} O_i/D_i^2 \quad \text{when} \quad \Sigma R_i/D_i^2 = 0 \tag{9}$$

The EarthSat method can be used to generate estimates automatically if acceptable vertical motion fields are available from the NWP models and if the cloud systems are slow moving with respect to the frequency of satellite observations (images every 6 hours are normally sufficient). In practice, meteorologists contribute significantly to the accuracy of the estimates by improving the vertical motion fields through interpretation of cloud development and dissipation in the satellite images, and through editing up or down the cloud brightness category in areas of raining stratus and non-raining cirrus.

The Bristol Method

The cloud indexing method from Bristol translates satellite cloud information (in the form of "cloud indices") into estimates of rainfall through empirical relationships between cloud type, mean monthly rainfall, and periodic (e.g. 12h) accumulations of rain. These relationships are depicted by Figure 2. The satellite cloud types and their common characteristics are shown in Table 6. Accumulated rainfall (in mm for a 12h

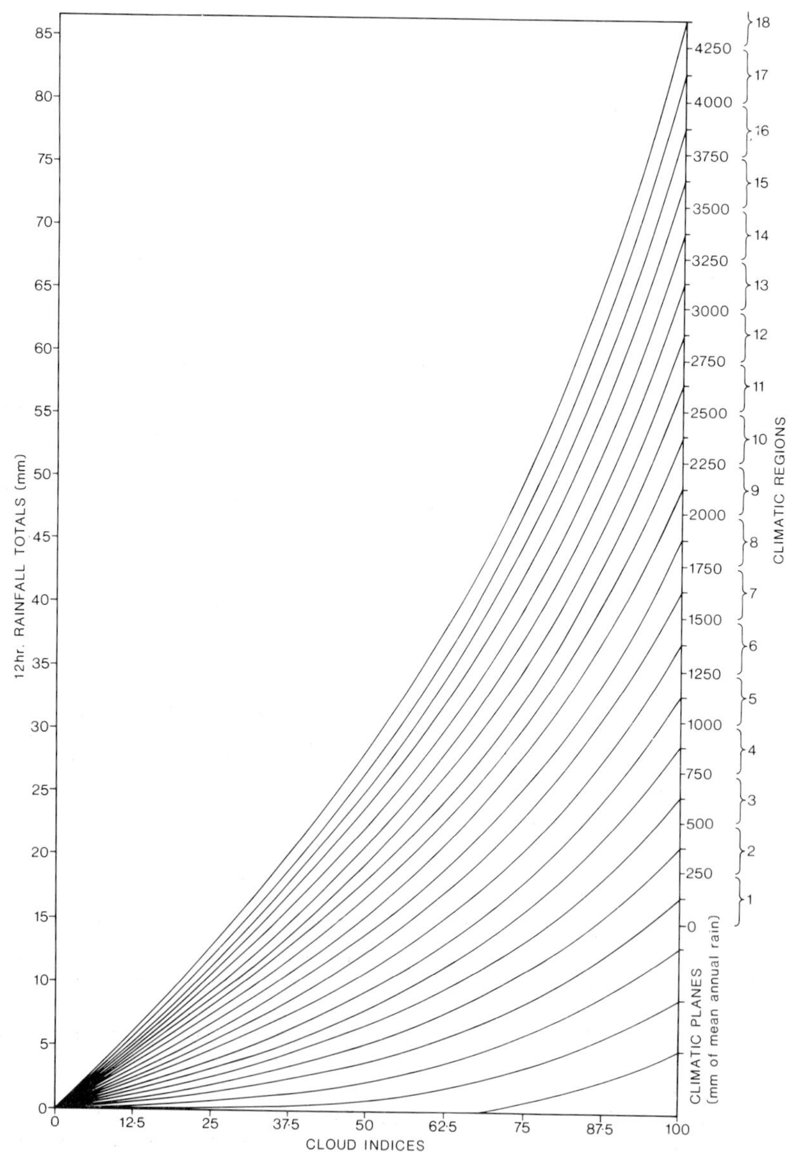

FIG.2 Bristol "global regression" diagram.

Table 6 - Bristol cloud types.

Name	Type	Common characteristics
Cu.Nb. with Ci.	10	Overshooting/colder tops. (Active area).
Cu.Nb.	8	Well developed convective clouds with/without anvils.
Layered St. with embedded Cu.Nbs.	7	Bright, banded frontal cloud cloud with pebbled texture in Visible.
Layered St.	5	Bright, banded frontal cloud.
Cu.cg. Layered Cu.	3	Patches of moderately bright convective clouds. Disintegrating frontal cloud.
Thick Al.St.	2	Downwind borders of warm fronts and warm occlusions.
St. St.cu. Debris	1	Thin, low-level cloud sheets. Decaying remains of deep convective rains.

period) is derived as a function of the satellite-observed cloud type and the local mean monthly rainfall through a "global regression" diagram or look-up table.

The family of curves in Figure 2 was derived from a variety of studies for specific areas and locations within the tropical and mid-latitudinal zones (Barrett, 1981). In those studies it was noted that rainfall accumulations from the range of cloud types listed in Table 6 increased from dry to hot humid regions, and that the accumulations from the higher intensity rainclouds (e.g. cumulonimbus) increased faster than those from moderate to lower intensity rainclouds (e.g. layered stratiform, and cumulocongestus, respectively). These characteristics were built into the hand-drawn "global regression" chart for widespread application.

In practice the chart in Figure 2 can be entered by either of two procedures depending on the availability of synoptic calibration stations:

1) The "climate entry" is used when station reports for a period are unavailable, unrepresentative of the raincloud areas, or otherwise suspect. The satellite cloud image is analyzed manually to provide information on raincloud coverage and raincloud type. An estimate is made for each location (e.g. pixel) in the analyzed rain area through the curve specific to that location because of its climatic mean monthly rainfall.
2) The "meteorological entry" is used when a surface station or stations report rainfall during the period of satellite raincloud coverage, and this information is deemed likely to be representative of rain from some or all of that cloud. The analyst assesses relationships between the raincloud area(s) and the available station reports in order to identify one or more station "areas of influence". Within each of these, the station rainfall reports are normalized through the application of mean monthly rainfall per rain day, morphoclimatic weights (as described in an earlier section); the colocated cloud type index is then used with the normalized station report to select the curve from Figure 2 which best represents conditions in that area of influence at that time. In this way adjustments can be made for raincloud performance either abnormally high or low compared to the local norm represented by the appropriate climate curve. Finally, the "met entry" estimates must be multiplied by the morphoclimatic weights specific to each rainy pixel so that terrain influences can be incorporated in the estimated rainfall field. For the AgRISTARS Program, the originally manual Bristol Method

was modified and developed for implementation on interactive image processing systems including VIRGS, VICOM, and I^2S. It remains the most heavily dependent on human interpretational skill.

Case Study Verification

Methods were developed by Research and Data System (1985) to evaluate the satellite interactive and automatic precipitation algorithms by measuring the relative contribution of the satellite information to the analysis of precipitation in the U.S. This was accomplished by separating the first-order stations into a set for calibration and a second independent set for verification. The calibration set was selected from the available stations to represent the density of stations reporting from the USSR or South America (about 300 km between stations). The verification set consisted of the remaining stations (about 150 km separation).

The calibration reports were analyzed objectively without the use of satellite data and compared to an analyses of the verification reports in order to provide a baseline statistic. Analyses were compared by Light (1-2 mm/12 hr) Moderate (3-12 mm/12 hr) and Heavy ($\geq$ 13 mm/12 hr) categories of rainfall and by a "Hit Cone" defined by:

$$|V-E| < .3*(V+1) \tag{10}$$

where V is the verification value (from the verification analysis) and E is the estimated value (from the calibration analysis). Results show that when (0,0) pairs are excluded, 47% of the gridpoints are correctly placed into the Light, Moderate, and Heavy category, and 30% are within the "Hit Cone".

These are considered the best possible results without the use of satellite data for the Soviet Union and South America because, unlike the stations in these regions, the calibration stations in the U.S. have been evenly spaced over the Great Plains and reported regularly.

Case studies conducted at NOAA's Interactive Computer Facility (NICF), World Weather Building, Washington, DC, showed that the Bristol "Climate Entry" procedure was the best performer providing an average of 13% improvement in the agriculturally significant Moderate rainfall category. The EarthSat "Satellite-Alone" method shows the most improvement at 14% while the Bristol "Climate Entry " followed by a small margin in the Heavy rainfall category. The ERL method did not show an improvement over the baseline in the Light, Moderate or Heavy category. This is attributed to relatively small areas of light rainfall estimates provided by this method.

Figure 3 shows an example of results from the three methods for one of the case study analysis periods. Estimates at the product resolution are shown for an enlarged area where the results from each technique differ most.

Calibration procedures, intended to provide an improvement over satellite-alone algorithms, often resulted in a deterioration in the test case results. This may be attributed to the fact that calibration station reports often differed significantly from nearby verification stations. Hence, adjusting the estimates based on these local calibration reports would introduce an apparent error when compared to an incorrectly analyzed "ground truth" field.

The EarthSat Automatic Calibration procedure showed better performance than the Bristol "Met Entry". Most of the test cases contained locally heavy rainfall events. Unfortunately, large "Areas of Influence" were analyzed for the "Met Entry" and as a result, the representative climate curves were incorrectly raised throughout the storm system, thereby raising the estimates in areas of light and moderate precipitation as well as the areas of heavy precipitation.

The Operational Demonstration

An operational demonstration of the ERL, EarthSat, and Bristol methods will be conducted for a period of two years beginning in September 1985. Specially trained meteorologists will prepare the best possible daily estimates covering the major crop growing regions in the Soviet Union and South America.

Estimates will be made over the U.S. crop growing regions in the Great Plains to allow for an evaluation and verification of the algorithms over an extended period. New interactive computer procedures have been designed and developed for the VICOM image processing system at the NICF to demonstrate the impact of advances in image processing on interactive meteorological analysis.

A weather data tape will be prepared daily at the NOAA Central Computer Facility (NCCF) at FB-4 Suitland, MD, and sent to the NICF for input to the Precipitation Estimation System on the VICOM. The weather tape will contain NOAA AVHRR visible and infrared imagery mapped by regions to a polar-stereographic grid (6.8 km @ 60°N) every 12 hours, GOES hourly infrared imagery and ERL estimates (unadjusted) over the U.S., 6, 12, and 24 hr. synoptic reports, and selected gridpoint analyses/forecasts from NMC global numerical weather prediction model (850 mb winds, 1000 mb - 500 mb heights, and vertical motion forecasts). In addition, ten years of climate data have been installed as part of a Climate Generation System on the VICOM.

The Precipitation Estimation System on the VICOM consists of Input, Setup, Process and Output functions (see figure 4). The individual estimation and calibration algorithms are options of the Processing function. The meteorologist will initiate the Input and Setup functions, selecting a region and a 12 hour period for making estimates. The VICOM will unpack

(a)

(b)

FIG.3 See next page for caption.

(c)

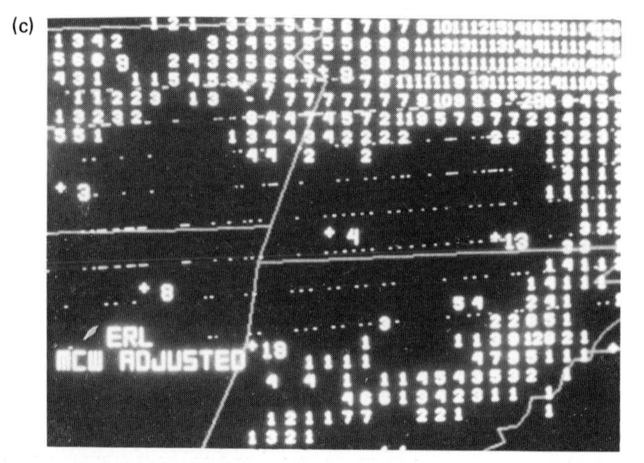

(d)

(e)

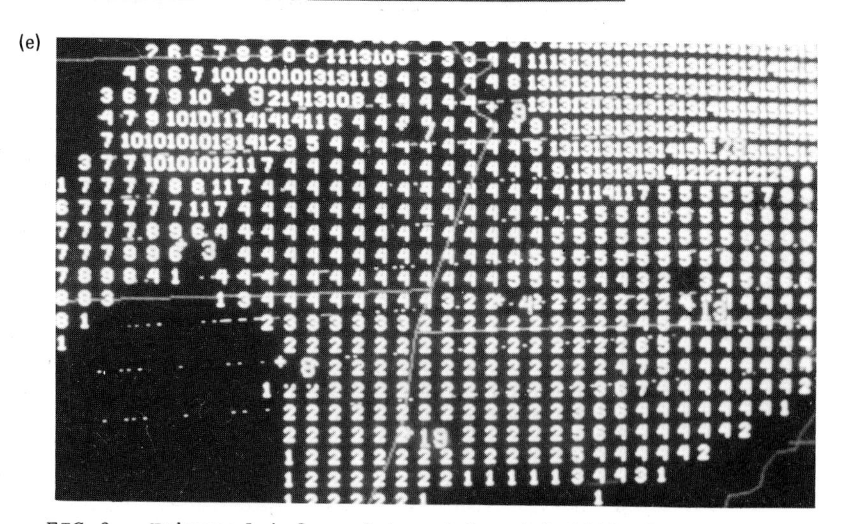

FIG.3 Enhanced infrared image for (a) 0200 GMT and (b) 1200 GMT, October 21, 1983, overlayed with calibration station reports in millimeters per 12 hours ending at 1200 GMT. (c) ERL estimates, (d) EarthSat estimates, and (e) Bristol estimates with verification station reports plotted in millimeters for 12 hour period ending 1200 GMT.

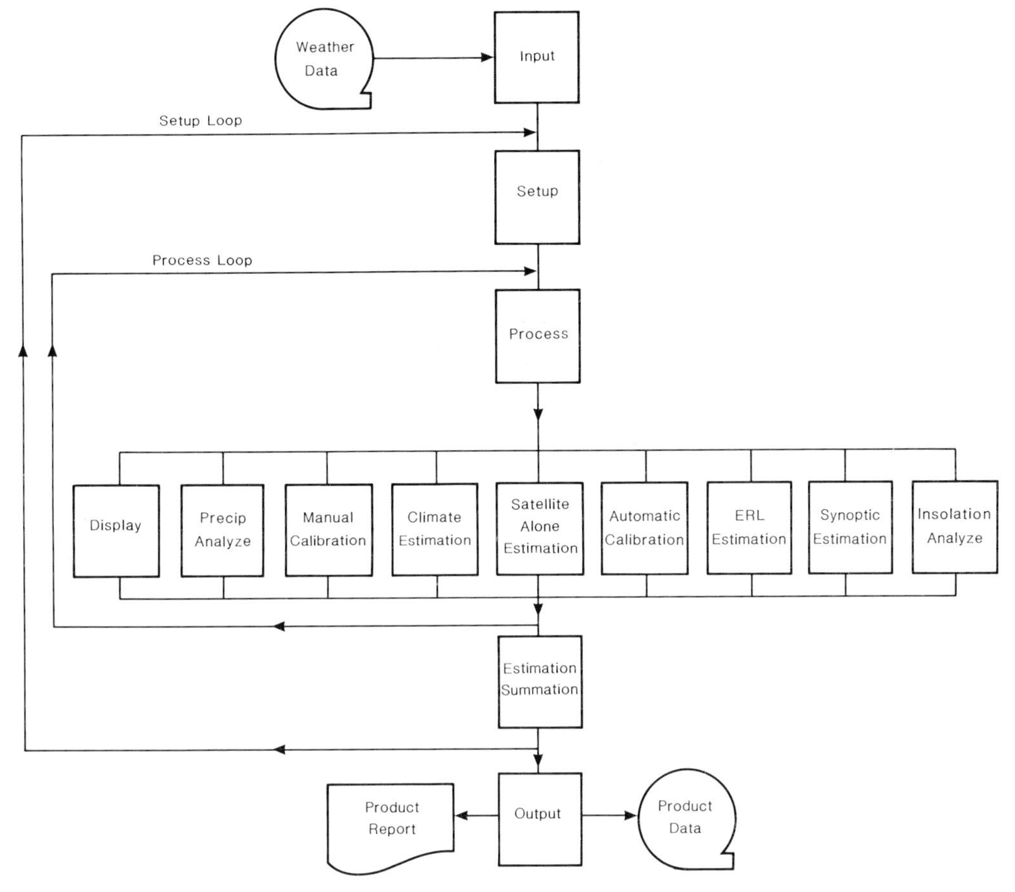

FIG.4 Precipitation Estimation System.

and plot the surface reports, contain the NMC gridpoint data, and prepare images and graphics for display.

As part of the Process function, the meteorologist may view first-guess estimate fields generated from fixed or adjustable cloud temperature - rain cloud type relationships for each of the three rainfall estimation methods. Using the trackball and the analyze option of the Process function, the meteorologist may draw new raincloud contours, amend existing contours for the Bristol and EarthSat methods, or may draw isohyets to edit automatic estimates from the ERL method.

When exiting the Process function, the 12 hour estimate field may be accumulated to provide a 24 hour total. Upon entering the Output function, estimates will be reduced from the image resolution (6.8 km @ 60°N for NOAA and 8 km for GOES) to the product resolution (47.6 km @ 60°N for NOAA at 24 km for GOES). As part of the operation, a precipitable product tape will be written and sent to the NCCF for mapping the U.S. estimates from GOES projection to the polar stereographic projection and for incorporation with other AgRISTARS products (i.e., max-min temperature, insolation, snow cover) before being sent to USDA.

In addition to preparation of the precipitation product, the Precipitation Estimation System will also save climate, NWP, calibration and satellite parameters that were available and used in preparing the estimate at selected U.S. verification station locations. Current plans call for conducting an operational evaluation of the methods over the U.S.

based on the verification techniques developed for the previous case study evaluation. A particular method and set of procedures will be used over the U.S. for periods of a month or more. These methods will most likely involve the meteorologist's interpretive abilities as much as possible. Automatic estimates can be generated from the data collected and compared later to evaluate the meteorologist's contribution.

Conclusions

For the future, it is expected that further improvements in the performance of the individual methods may be achieved through:

1) Refinement of the meteorological interpretive skills of analysts as a result of accumulated experience gained over extended periods of operation;
2) More effective use of background climatic data, e.g. through improvements to morphoclimatic weighting schemes; and
3) Through the exploitation of additional satellite information. In this respect, passive microwave data afford the strongest hopes. The first integrated tests of visible, infrared and passive microwave data are already being undertaken using historical data from the SMMR instrument on Nimbus 7.

However, it is also expected that the primary objective of providing improved rainfall inputs to soil moisture models for crop growth assessment and harvest prediction may be best met within NOAA operations through either a judicious use of the separate methods described in this paper in respect of particular regions or types of weather situations, or a single interactive rainfall monitoring method combining the best aspects of the three current techniques.

References

Arkin, P. A., 1979: The relationship between fractional coverage of high cloud and rainfall accumulations during GATE over the B-scale array. Mon. Wea. Rev., 107, pp. 1382-1387.

Atlas, D., and D. W. Thiele, 1981: Precipitation Measurements from Space: NASA, Goddard Space Flight Center, MD, 320 pp.

Barrett, E. C., 1981: AgRISTARS State I: Development and Application of the Bristol Method for Improved Rainfall Monitoring for Mid-latitudinal Use. Final Report, U.S. Department of Commerce Contract No. NA-80-SAC-00764, Univ. of Bristol, UK, 84 pp.

Barrett, E. C., 1984: An Interactive Technique for Satellite-Improved Rainfall Monitoring: Integrated Approaches in Remote Sensing. ESA SP-214, European Space Agency, Paris, pp. 191-199.

Barrett, E. C., and D. W. Martin, 1981: The Use of Satellite Data in Rainfall Monitoring. Academic Press, London, 340 pp.

Griffith, C. G., W. L. Woodley, P. G. Grube, D. W. Martin, J. Stout, and D. Sikdar, 1978: Rain Estimation from Geosynchronous Satellite Imagery - Visible and Infrared Studies. Mon. Wea. Rev., 106, pp. 1153 - 1171.

Hubanks, P. A., 1985: Evaluation of Interactive Precipitation Estimation Technique Using Polar-Orbiter and GOES Satellite Data. Final Report, U.S. Department of Commerce Contract No. NA-83-sAC-00117, Research and Data Systems, Inc., U.S.

Heitkemper, L. V., J. N. Cooper, E. S. Merritt, D. Masonis, 1982: An Interactive Meteorological Satellite Rainfall Diagnostic System Designed for Global Agricultural Applications. Final Report U.S. Department of Commerce, Contract No. NA-81-SAC-000714, EarthSat Corp., U.S., 86 pp.

Scofield, R. A., 1984: The NESDIS Operational Convective Precipitation Estimation Technique. Reprint from Prepint Vol.: 10th Conf. on Weather Forecasting and Analysis, June 25-29, 1984, Clearwater Beach, FL, 171-180.

Hydrologic Applications of Space Technology (Proceedings of the Cocoa Beach Workshop, Florida, August 1985). IAHS Publ. no. 160, 1986.

The NOAA satellite precipitation estimate program — with preliminary results of an operational test using estimates in a hydrologic river forecast model

DANE CLARK
Synoptic Analysis Branch, National Environmental Satellite, Data, and Information Service, Washington, DC, USA
DAVID G. MORRIS
West Gulf River Forecast Center, National Weather Service, Fort Worth, Texas, USA

Abstract

As part of the NOAA Flash Flood Program of the United States, the Synoptic Analysis Branch of the National Environmental Satellite, Data, and Information Service (NESDIS), is tasked with producing satellite-derived estimates and short-range outlooks of heavy precipitation for operational use by the National Weather Service (NWS). The precipitation estimates are produced in real-time by an experienced satellite meteorologist utilizing an interactive computer system known as the Interactive Flash Flood Analyzer (IFFA). The estimates are disseminated to NWS offices using the Automated Field Operational Services (AFOS) computer system.

The primary use of the precipitation estimate data is guidance information for NWS forecasters responsible for flash flood watches and warnings. The estimate data is also used by the Forecast Branch of the National Meteorological Center (NMC) to produce Quantitative Precipitation Forecasts.

In the early 1980's, hydrologists at the NWS West Gulf River Forecast Center (WGRFC) set up an operational experiment with the Synoptic Analysis Branch (SAB) to test the utililty of precipitation estimate data as input into a River Forecast Model. Precipitation estimate data were digitized at SAB and inputed to the NOAA 360 Computer where the WGRFC could access the data for inclusion in model runs. Preliminary results of the experiment are presented in this paper as well as suggestions for future application.

Introduction

NOAA, the U.S. Commerce Department's National Oceanic and Atmospheric Administration, keeps a round-the-clock, year round surveillance on the nation's rivers and streams and is prepared to issue warnings to the public when the threat of a flood is imminent. The official government river and flood forecasts and warnings are issued by the National Weather Service (NWS) through it's network of field offices. Within NOAA, the National Environmental Satellite, Data, and Information Service's (NESDIS) Synoptic Analysis Branch (SAB), provides direct support to NWS flash flood operations by providing real-time satellite pictures and products.

This paper will present an overview of the Satellite Precipitation Estimate Program including a description of the interactive computer system used operationally. Results from an operational experiment within NOAA to determine the utility of satellite rainfall estimates in a River Forecast Model will be discussed. Implications of this experiment and possible future applications will be presented.

The IFFA System

Video graphic display systems are rapidly replacing the traditional manual analysis operations in the meteorological community. These man-machine interactive devices provide meteorological analysts with the capability to assimilate real-time data from earth and remote-sensed observation systems and display parameters for simultaneous viewing in a time and space correlated, color-coded format. In addition, analysts have the capability to enhance, animate, track, and manipulate data fields to clarify the state and continuity of weather systems. These powerful diagnostic tools can also be used to interactively derive products for input into analysis and forecast models. One such system is the Interactive Flash Flood Analyzer, or commonly referred to as the IFFA.

The IFFA, which became operational in August 1983, represents a transfer of technology and techniques from NOAA research facilities to operational forecasters and meteorologists. The overall philosophy of IFFA is to convert digital satellite data, which are low in information and high in volume to a satellite product which is high in information and low in volume. The goal of IFFA is to improve the accuracy and timeliness of operational products called satellite precipitation estimates. The satellite meteorologist interacts with the computer, each performing tasks which they are best suited for. The meteorologists provide the intelligence and analysis functions while the computer provides the speed and accuracy of computing precipitation products in the required map formats.

GOES digital data are received in real-time through the Digital Interface Electronics, processed with a Harris/6 minicomputer, and stored on two 80 megabyte removable disks. The IFFA operational configuration consists of two complete, redundant systems. In case of hardware failure, the removable disks can be transferred to the back-up system and operational work resumed. The IFFA system also includes operator consoles, 1600 BPI 9-track tape drives, a card reader, line printer and two applications terminals. (fig. 1)

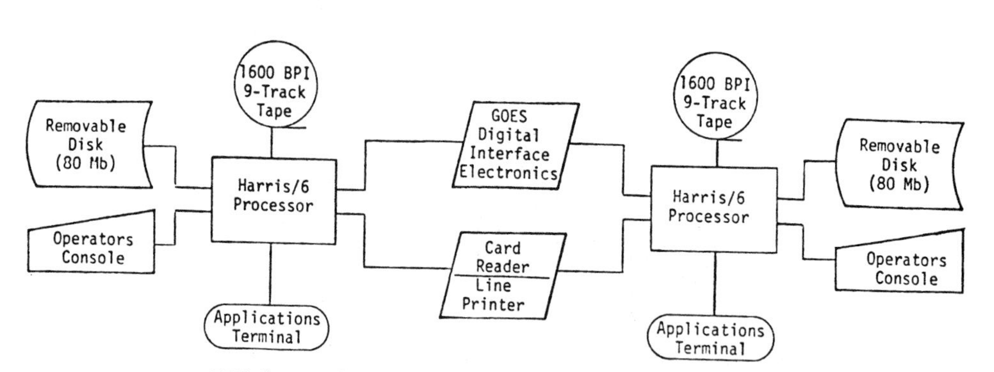

FIG.1 Schematic of the IFFA hardware configuration.

Each terminal consists of an Intel 8080 command processor connected to a color monitor and an alpha-numerical CRT screen with a key-board. A joystick and a data tablet are used to position the cursor on the screen to view enlarged areas and draw isohyets. A Versatec hard copy output device is used to produce a permanent image of the rainfall estimates. (Clark 1985)

Operational Procedures

Real-time GOES visible and infrared data are displayed every half-hour on the IFFA color monitor. The satellite meteorologist selects an event area with excessive precipitation potential to perform precipitation estimates. The GOES

(a)

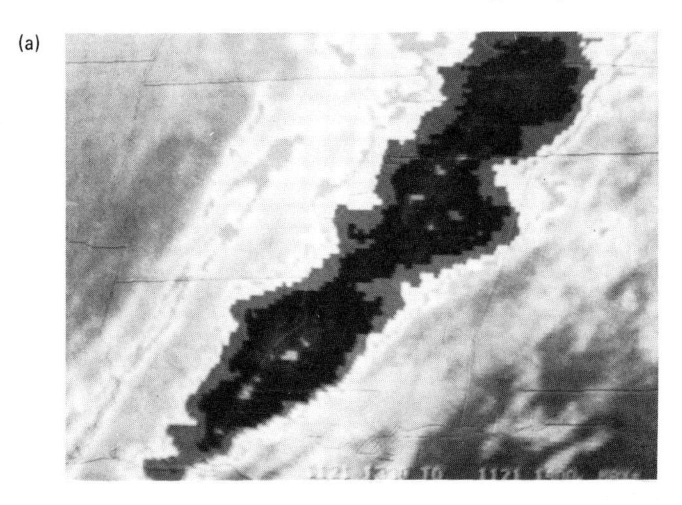

(b)

(c)

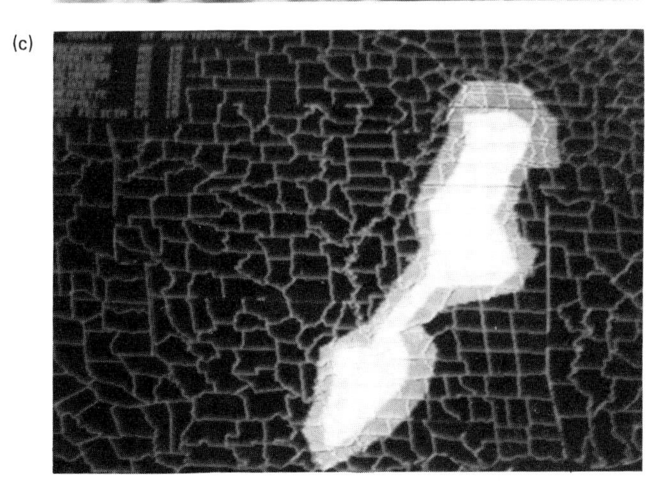

FIG.2 (a) IFFA display of a heavy rain event. GOES infrared (IR) image with Mb enhancement curve for 1400Z November 21, 1983. (b) GOES IR image from 1400Z November 21, 1983 with estimated precipitation (solid lines). (c) Satellite precipitation estimate product on state/county map.

data in the event area are enlarged and animation sequences of both the visible and infrared data are created. Current National Weather Service surface and upper air observations are also displayed on the color monitor. At this point, the meteorologist identifies and analyzes important cloud signatures producing heavy precipitation.

Three precipitation estimation techniques have been developed for interactive use on the IFFA. These are the Convective Technique for thunderstorms, the Winter Storm Technique for winter rain and snow, and the Tropical Cyclone Technique used for precipitation associated with tropical storms and hurricanes. Using the appropriate technique, the satellite meteorologist analyzes consecutive infrared (fig. 2a) and visible images by interactively drawing the estimated precipitation on the graphics screen of the color monitor using a data tablet system (fig. 2b). Each half-hour estimate can be summed with other half-hour estimates in the event area to produce precipitation totals. These products are annotated with state and county boundaries (fig. 2c) and hard copy prints are made.

NWS Forecast Offices use this message product as guidance information together with radar and conventional observations for the issuance of flash flood watches and warnings. Experience has shown that precipitation estimates are extremely helpful to Forecast Offices during night-time hours when many surface reports are not available. SAB meteorologists also provide satellite estimates to the Heavy Precipitation Unit (HPU) of the National Meteorological Center. HPU uses this information as guidance in preparing Precipitation Forecasts and Excessive Precipitation Outlooks.

Hydrologic Application

In 1982, hydrologists at the NWS West Gulf River Forecast Center (WGRFC) began an operational demonstration with SAB meteorologists to test the utility of precipitation estimate data as input to river prediction programs. WGRFC developed the capability to use remotely sensed rainfall point estimates and convert them to operationally usable precipitation data sets. This unique hydrologic application of satellite rainfall estimate data has been an important step in the utility of "event" defined data for the development of real-time river forecasts. (Morris 1985)

A grid point system was developed at WGRFC in the mid 1970's (Smith 1975) as a way of providing needed flexibility to cope with frequent rain gage network changes and observations from unplanned (unofficial) stations that so often report during storm periods. The resulting grid system is independent of gage location, and is therefore also ideally suited to geographically positioned estimates of rainfall from any source. The grid is latitude-longitude based, with six-minute intersection so that the report may be addressed and computer stored. The grid is sufficiently dense so that any report would be moved no more than approximately three miles, a data positioning accuracy well within that required to develop river forecasts for any basin other than a very small watershed.

SAB and WGRFC teamed up to develop IBM 360/195 computer programs (recently converted to NAS 9050) to move vast amounts of satellite estimated rainfall into the RFC hydrologic precipitation file. The WGRFC grid point system was programmed to load 3-hourly disk file estimation sums for each grid point within the storm area. Standard synoptic times were chosen: 00Z, 03Z, 06Z, 12Z, etc., for a total of eight files. With each data set messages are sent to the WGRFC line printer. The RFC then executes a program to sum the data into 6-hour totals (06Z, 12Z, 18Z, 00Z), for whatever periods are available, and store the 6-hourly grid point amounts. At this point the data are available for input to river forecast programs (fig. 3), depending on how the hydrologist wished to combine the data with other precipitation information. A large WGRFC precipitation processing program called ONECL allows the hydrologist to specify certain options at run times that will dictate how the data are handled.

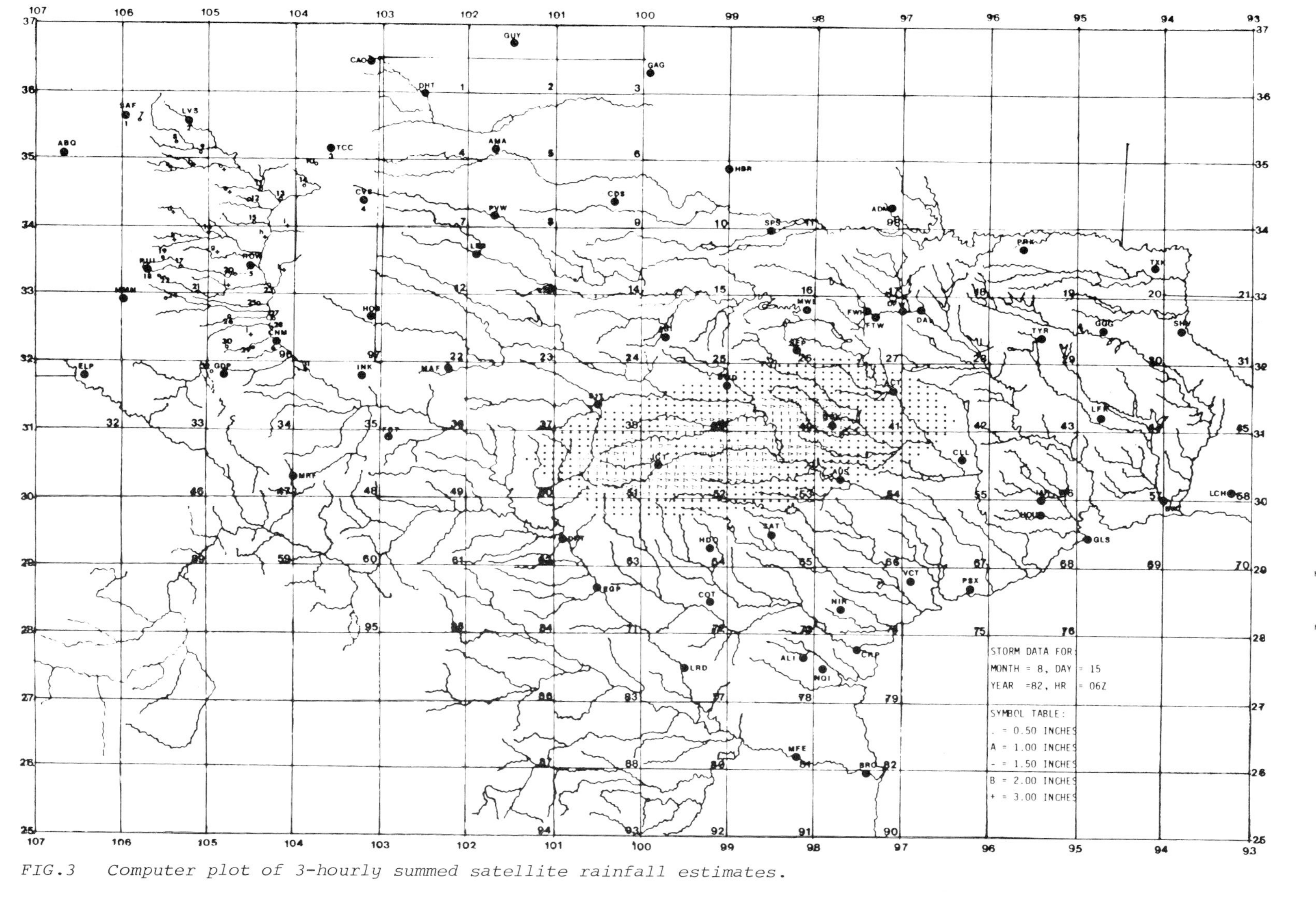

FIG.3 Computer plot of 3-hourly summed satellite rainfall estimates.

During the past two years SAB meteorologists have provided many satellite-derived precipitation estimate data sets of heavy precipitation to the WGRFC. Although several restricting factors, including time-consuming manual digitizing and other operational priorities, have limited the data sets considerably, preliminary conclusions have been drawn from the operational use of the data sets.

The WGRFC does not view satellite estimates as necessary input for routine predictions. However, satellite estimates can be critical inputs for severe rainstorms at night when the gage reporting network is largely inactive, and for sparsely populated basins anytime, since reporting networks in these areas are generally inadequate to describe heavy rainstorms. Therefore, the satellite estimates will undoubtedly prove invaluable to WGRFC forecast operations under certain circumstances. (Morris 1985)

Future

This pioneering effort by the WGRFC may serve to demonstrate the value of satellite estimate data to supplement conventional precipitation observations for the purpose of real-time river forecasting. As soon as problems can be solved with the IFFA hardware and software to allow a communications flow between IFFA and the NOAA NAS 9050 Computer, a real-time test and evaluation of satellite estimate data can be accomplished at other RFC's that have both the need and capability to handle such information.

References

Clark, J.D. and R. Borneman 1984, Satellite Precipitation Estimates Program of the Synoptic Analysis Branch: Proceedings from the Tenth Conference of Weather Forecasting and Analysis, June 25-29, 1984, Clearwater, FL, AMS, Boston, MA 392-399.

Clark, J.D. and M.O. Perkins 1985, The NOAA Interactive Flash Flood Analyzer: Proceedings from the International Conference on Interactive Information and Processing Systems for Meteorology, Oceanography, and Hydrology, January 7-11, 1985, Los Angeles, CA, AMS, Boston, MA 255-259.

Morris, David G. 1985, West Gulf River Forecast Center Operations Using Satellite Estimations of Rainfall: Proceedings from the NWS Fourth Southern Region Quantitative Precipitation Forecasting Workshop, January 28-30, 1985, San Antonio, TX.

Smith, D.T., 1975, River Forecast Application of Grid-Point Addressing: WGRFC Internal Documentation, non-published, 22 p.

Hydrologic Applications of Space Technology (Proceedings of the Cocoa Beach Workshop, Florida, August 1985). IAHS Publ. no. 160, 1986.

Satellite convective and extratropical cyclone cloud categories associated with heavy precipitation

RODERICK A. SCOFIELD
NOAA/NESDIS, Washington, DC 20233, USA

Abstract

Seven convective and five extratropical cyclone cloud categories have been developed for heavy precipitation systems over the U.S.A. These categories are based on satellite (visible and infrared), radar, rainfall characteristics and surface and upper air data. Each category has distinctly different cloud patterns and/or cloud top temperature characteristics, life cycles, precipitation characteristics, and mechanisms which initiate, focus and maintain the heavy precipitation system.

Introduction

The purpose of this paper is to present satellite convective and extratropical cyclone cloud categories associated with heavy precipitation. These categories are based on GOES (Geostationary Operational Environmental Satellite), imagery (visible and infrared (IR)), radar, rainfall characteristics and surface and upper air data. Each category has distinctly different cloud patterns and/or cloud top temperature characteristics and mechanisms which initiate, focus and maintain the heavy precipitation system.

Satellite Convective Cloud Categories

Seven convective cloud categories have heen developed for heavy precipitation systems over the U.S.A.

Satellite meteorologists do their best work in estimating rainfall (See Scofield, 1984) from Mesoscale Convective Complexes (MCC) observed in Figure 1. This MCC is embedded in a moderate vertical wind shear environment; heaviest rainfall is occurring along the upwind edge of the anvil (between A and A' in Figure 1).

Very frequently, flash floods are produced by subtle satellite observed cloud signatures. These thunderstorms with subtle signatures are quite different from MCC's; they usually have warm-tops (warmer than -62°C), are smaller, do not last as long and are often quite differently shaped as compared to MCC's. Most importantly, these thunderstorms share the same importance as MCC's with respect to producing heavy rainfall and flash floods. As a result, flash-flood producing thunderstorm systems were separated into various categories. The categories include: MCC's (Maddox, 1980), synoptic-scale tropical systems (Ward, 1981), large-scale wedges and linear multi-clustered systems (Clark, et al., 1980), single-clustered systems, regenerative, and circular multi-clustered convective

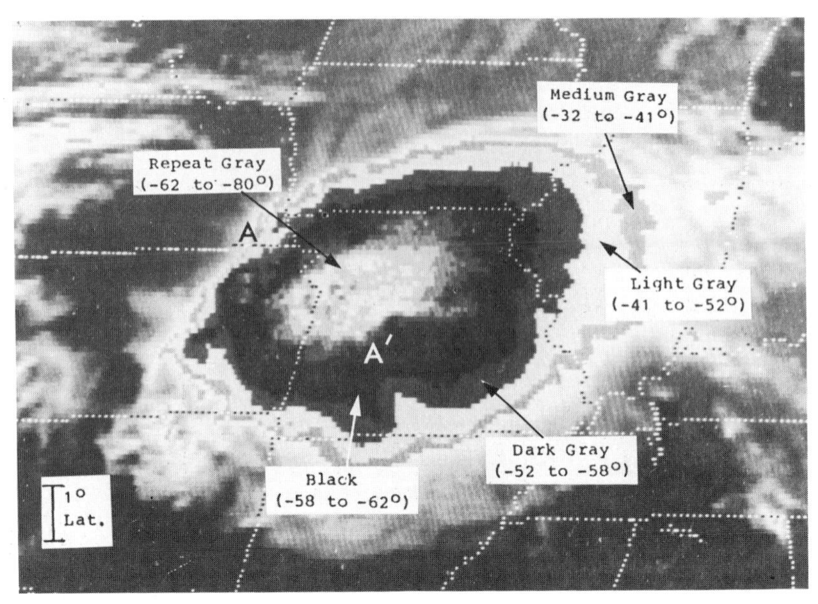

FIG.1 Enhanced infrared imagery (Mb curve), 0730 GMT, August 13, 1982.

systems and convection embedded in large/small-scale overrunning systems (Spayd, et al., 1983), synoptic-scale cyclonic circulations (Spayd, 1982) and squall lines (Fleming, et al., 1984). The categories along with characteristics in the satellite, conventional and radar data are presented in Figure 2.

As alluded to in the above, satellite meteorologists do their best work in estimating rainfall from categories I and II; their most difficult work is with categories III, V, VI, and VII. Flash floods occurred most frequently from milticlustered thunderstorms with warm IR cloud tops (category IV - tops warmer than -62° C).

Satellite Extratropical Cyclone Cloud Categories

In order to better estimate precipitation from extratopical cyclones (See Scofield and Spayd, 1984) various categories were developed. The categories evolved from studying many winter storm systems in the imagery and comparing these systems with radar data, rainfall reports and conventional data. The categories are presented as schematics of evolution of cloud patterns observed in IR pictures; the cloud patterns are frequently associated with moderate to heavy precipitation. The schematics can be used as an aid in analyzing the location and magnitude of continuous or showery precipitation within winter storm clouds. In addition, the schematics may be used to anticipate developments within the evolving winter storm cloud pattern for use in the short range prediction of precipitation. Five basic types of evolution schematics have been developed: the Comma Head category, Baroclinic Leaf category, Subsynoptic-scale Wave category, Cloud Band category and Overrunning Category.

CHARACTERISTICS OF SATELLITE-OBSERVED HEAVY CONVECTIVE RAINFALL SYSTEMS

TYPES	DIURNAL VARIATIONS	SATELLITE DATA	CONVENTIONAL DATA	RADAR DATA
Ia. TROPICAL SYNOPTIC SCALE TROPICAL	"Peripheral thunderstorms" develop in the afternoon in response to surface heating away from the circulation center. At night, boundary layer stabilizes and "core thunderstorms" develop at circulation center due to maximum moisture convergence. "Core thunderstorms" may form a MCC type system.	Cold tops, readily identifiable, persistent anticyclonic outflow aloft which causes cloud top growth to become quasi-constant. Weak jets in westerlies can cause elliptical elongation in outflow and convection. When system becomes extra-tropical the pattern may resemble that of an occluded frontal cloud structure and the maximum rainfall shifts north and east away from the center of the system. Outer rainbands and in dissipating stages the entire system may become warm-topped.	Remnant of Hurricane, Tropical Storm, or Tropical Depresson; initially-persistant forward motion and cyclone symmetry; occurs in extremely moist air mass (PW$\geq$ 2"), low to mid-level cyclonic vorticity focuses rainfall.	Outer curved rainbands may have a combination of convective and stratiform Z-R rain rates. Large persistent area of VIP 1-3, embedded but non-persistent VIP 4-6. New echoes may reappear hours after previous echos dissipate. Echoes may appear on periphery of circulation center during afternoon and reappear near circulation center at night. Echo movement is a combination of movement along the spiral band, propagation of spiral band around circulation center, propagation of circulation center.
Ib. TROPICAL MESOSCALE QUASI-TROPICAL (MESOSCALE CONVECTIVE COMPLEX -MCC)	Strong maximum in early evening to early morning; strong minimum in mid-morning.	Cold tops, overshooting tops, and numerous cell mergers observed. Large circular or oval anticyclonic outflow. Speed of movement of coldest tops most important for heaviest rainfall. Intensifying if coldest tops moves to central location in cloud pattern and cirrus outflow becomes increasingly anticyclonic in one or more quadrants. Most efficient precipitation producer 4 to 10 hours after initial convection develops, due to large area of light precipitation saturating the surrounding air mass. Usually produces mid-level cyclonic circulations and upper level mesoscale jet streaks which will alter surrounding and future convection.	Triggered by shortwave trough moving through upper level ridge and focused by low level axis of maximum winds overriding low level boundaries. Vertical circulation similar to Synoptic Scale Tropical system. Cyclonic vorticity in low to mid troposphere couples with anticyclonic outflow aloft. Winds veer strongly with height.	Large, persistent, trackable area of VIP 1-3 with embedded non-persistent VIP 4-6. Numerous echo mergers are detected. Highest VIP levels usually occur in first 5 hours of development when the precipitation efficiency is lowest.
IIa. LINEAR LARGE SCALE WEDGE	No distinct diurnal variation.	Large 50-90 degree angle pointing into the wind. Southern most cluster may be embedded in a N-S oriented squall line. Shortwaves rotating around longwave trough concentrate the convective outbreaks. Due to persistent low-level southerly inflow convection redevelops after weak shortwave passes and thunderstorms become increasingly efficient rainfall producers. As longwave trough approaches cloud tops may become warmer with time.	Forms where polar front jet and subtropical jet separate. Occurs east of deep 500 mb longwave trough with weak or neutral synoptic scale vorticity advection. Outbreaks concentrated by shortwave troughs. Wedges retard movement of 500 mb pattern. Fueled by strong low level axis of maximum winds over a low level boundary. Winds veer strongly with height.	Large areas of VIP 1 and 2 with embedded VIP 3-6. Echos may redevelop over same area or upwind in surges.

FIG.2 Characteristics of satellite-observed heavy convective rainfall systems.

CHARACTERISTICS OF SATELLITE-OBSERVED HEAVY CONVECTIVE RAINFALL SYSTEMS

TYPES	DIURNAL VARIATIONS	SATELLITE DATA	CONVENTIONAL DATA	RADAR DATA
IIb. LINEAR SQUALL LINE	Strong maximum (80%) in late afternoon through evening; minimum in morning.	Cold cloud tops in 75% of cases. Downstream convection may be masked by upstream anvil blowoff. Weakening usually occurs when squall line accelerates away from its initial triggering mechanism (i.e. frontal zone). When convection develops upwind, clusters may pass over the same area if the squall line is slow moving.	Occurs along or ahead of a slow moving cold frontal boundary. Winds veer only 40° with height; winds $<$ 35 knots, PW$\sim$1.6", mean RH$\sim$$\overline{80\%}$, triggered by a weak shortwave at 500 mb.	Line Echo Wave Pattern (LEWP) may be observed, an intense line of high VIP 3-6 echos. Echos may suddenly redevelop upwind in surges.
III SINGLE-CLUSTERED	Tied strongly to solar insolation; a strong maximum (80%) in late morning through early evening, and a strong minimum in nighttime and morning.	Very small, round, oval, or carrot shaped. Very rapid growth, stationary, overshooting tops. Usually warm tops. Since tops are so small the actual temperature of the tops may be colder than the resolution of the GOES-IR sensor indicates.	Fueled by solar insolation, anchored by topography, or mesoscale boundaries.	Small, stationary, echo, VIP 3-5.
IVa. MULTI-CLUSTERED CIRCULAR	Eighty percent occur from late afternoon through midnight; minimum in morning.	Warm tops in 70% of cases, round or oval shaped cloud tops, cluser mergers usually evident; usually quasi-stationary. Mergers of separate multi-clustered circular systems may evolve into a MCC-Mesoscale Convective Complex.	Weak upper level flow, develops due to low level forcing.	Quasi-stationary, VIP 3-6, echo mergers may occur.
IVb. MULTI-CLUSTERED LINEAR	Seventy percent occur from late afternoon through evening; weak minimum in morning.	Warm or cold tops, small wedge, carrot or diamond shaped, coldest tops in vertex (enhanced V pattern sometimes observed). Rapid growth and stationary, may build upwind. Much smaller than large scale wedge. The higher the speed shear from mid to high levels the narrower the wedge. Heaviest rain in extreme upwind portion of vertex although thunderstorm cells may stretch linearly from the vertex to the middle of the wedge (in the warmer IR temperatures behind the enhanced V pattern). Existence dependent on jet streak. If jet streak drifts away from wedge in a direction normal to flow, wedge dissipates and new wedges develop where jet subsequently intersects areas with favorable low level conditions. When second wedge develops upstream from the first, the initial wedge is shielded from jet and dissipates unless second wedge induces a mesoscale jet streak that interacts with the first system and intensification results. If another convective system develops upstream and blocks the environmental wind flow (reducing the mid to high level wind shear) the linear multi-clustered system could develop into a MCC.	Upper flow is zonal or weakly diffluent. Strong speed shear from mid to high levels present. May distort upper flow like Mesoscale Convective Complexes - MCC's and produce wind max on northern side. Development due to low level forcing and jet streak aloft.	Individual echo motion may be fast (15-30 knots) but repeated echo development in upwind of cluster may result in slow cluster speed. Persistent VIP 3's are common with embedded non-persistent VIP 4-6. In enhanced V patterns the highest VIP levels are usually at the vertex of the V extending into the warmer temperatures downwind of the vertex.

FIG.2 continued

CHARACTERISTICS OF SATELLITE-OBSERVED HEAVY CONVECTIVE RAINFALL SYSTEMS

TYPES	DIURNAL VARIATIONS	SATELLITE DATA	CONVENTIONAL DATA	RADAR DATA
V. SYNOPTIC SCALE CYCLONIC CIRCULATION	Moderate maximum in the evening into early morning; moderate minimum in mid-morning and afternoon.	Warm tops located in comma head of cyclonic circulation, cyclonic circulation moving E to NE at 2° latitude per 12 hours, rapid cloud growth, overshooting tops, mergers observed, either quasi-stationary or regenerative.	Occurs to north or east of slow moving circular 500 mb vorticity center. Occurs to north of 850 mb low with maximum isodrosotherms rapping around to north of low. Occurs to north and west of 850 mb axis of maximum winds. Occurs north of surface low in cool NE flow. When 500 mb center weak, no surface fronts; when stronger, surface fronts are evident. Winds veer 180° with height; winds < 40 knots. PW~1.3", mean RH~80%. Extremely "wet" when convection is focused along mesoscale surface convergence line.	If quasi-stationary, VIP levels are high, VIP 4-6. If regenerative, echos VIP 3-4.
VI. LARGE/ SMALL SCALE OVERUNNING	Strong maximum in early evening to midnight; strong minimum in early to mid-morning.	Warm tops locted in large anti-cyclonic flow of cirrus. Animation (IR) best for detecting convective bands from cirrus bands. Transverse banding in cirrus appears as textured areas on visible imagery. System doesn't weaken until strong shortwave passes through area.	Cool boundary layer, winds veer over 180° with height, air lifted isentropically until unstable and deep convection is released. Convective bands form perpendicular to 850 mb flow (low level axis of maximum winds), and nearly parallel to 500 mb flow. K index much better than Lifted Index for detection. Extremely moist environments RH ≥ 90%, PW ≥1.5" large area of weak maximum surface moisture convergence values, no defined surface low apparent.	Widespread persistent VIP 1 and 2, occasional VIP 3.
VII. REGENERATIVE	Moderate maximum in late afternoon through mid-evening; weak minimum in mid-morning.	Warm or cold tops. Single-clustered and multi-clustered convective systems develop along the upwind portion of a low-level boundary and transverse the same path downwind along the boundary. Animation is the best tool for detection. No cell mergers usually seen. Outflow from new cells may continually reinforce existing quasi-stationary outflow boundary. If regeneration of cells is very rapid (≥ 1/2 hour) system may resemble a small wedge (linear multi-clustered). Initial thunderstorm cells may saturate the local environment so new thunderstorm cells may be more efficient precipitation producers. The initial thunderstorm cells may also warm the local upper atmosphere causing a lowering (warming) of the equilibrium level; so new thunderstorm cells may have warmer tops. System weakens when triggering shortwave overtakes the quasi-stationary outflow boundary or low level convergence zone. Outflow from new cells may also accelerate existing quasi-stationary outflow boundary away from favored areas of development, so new cells stop regenerating.	Outflow boundary or convergence boundary apparent in surface mesoanalysis. Inflow perpendicular to boundary may be focused by mesolow. Extremely high mesoscale moisture convergence values.	Train echo effect. Individual echos may move at speeds of 15 to 40 knots. New echos may have higher VIP levels than previous echos.

FIG.2 continued

The Comma Head category shown in Figures 3a and 3b consists of three subcategories:

(1) rapidly deepening and occluding surface low development,
(2) weak surface low development
(3) no surface low development. Additional information about subcategory (3), "Comma heads with no surface low development," can be found in a paper by Kadin (1982).

The Baroclinic Leaf category is shown in Figure 3b. The baroclinic leaf is associated with frontogenesis aloft and is often the early, "pre-comma," stage of the comma head. Weldon (1979) describes the baroclinic leaf in detail.

The subsynoptic-scale Wave category is shown in Figure 3c and consists of two subcategories: (1) waves along the rear of a baroclinic zone and (2) waves in an overrunning zone. The subsynoptic-scale wave along the rear of baroclinic zone is often associated with a weak 500-mb vorticity lobe. Sometimes the lobe cannot be detected in the 500-mb vorticity analysis. At other times the wave appears to develop in an area of convection along the southern portion of the baroclinic zone and propagates northeastward along the zone.

The Cloud Band Category is depicted Figure 3d. Cirrus clouds comprise most of the cloud band. However, those bands which possess low-level tails are active (contain precipitation). In addition, when newer cloud bands develop in the rear portions of the baroclinic zones, the older bands in the front portions of the baroclinic zones often dissipate. Convective elements embedded within an active band will often become colder upwind and traverse along the band.

The Overrunning category is illustrated in Figure 3d. Precipitation elements and bands possess warm tops in the IR imagery and are embedded in a large anticyclonic flow of cirrus. Animation (IR) is best for detecting convective elements/bands from cirrus. Precipitation elements/bands often appear as bright textured areas in the visible imagery. Within the overrunning zone, the boundary layer is cold or cool, winds veer strongly with height and the air is lifted isentropically until unstable and deep convection is released. Convective elements/bands form perpendicular to the 850-mb flow (low-level axis of maximum winds) and nearly parallel to the 500-mb flow. Experience has shown that the more unstable and moist the overrunning air is, the heavier the precipitation.

Satellite meteorologists do their best work in estimating snowfall and rainfall from categories I, II, and III; their most difficult work is with categories IV and V. Heaviest snowfall (2-4 foot amounts) occurred most frequently from category IA.

Summary and Outlook

Various satellite convective and extratropical cyclone cloud categories associated with heavy precipitation were presented. Satellite meteorologists are most accurate in esti-

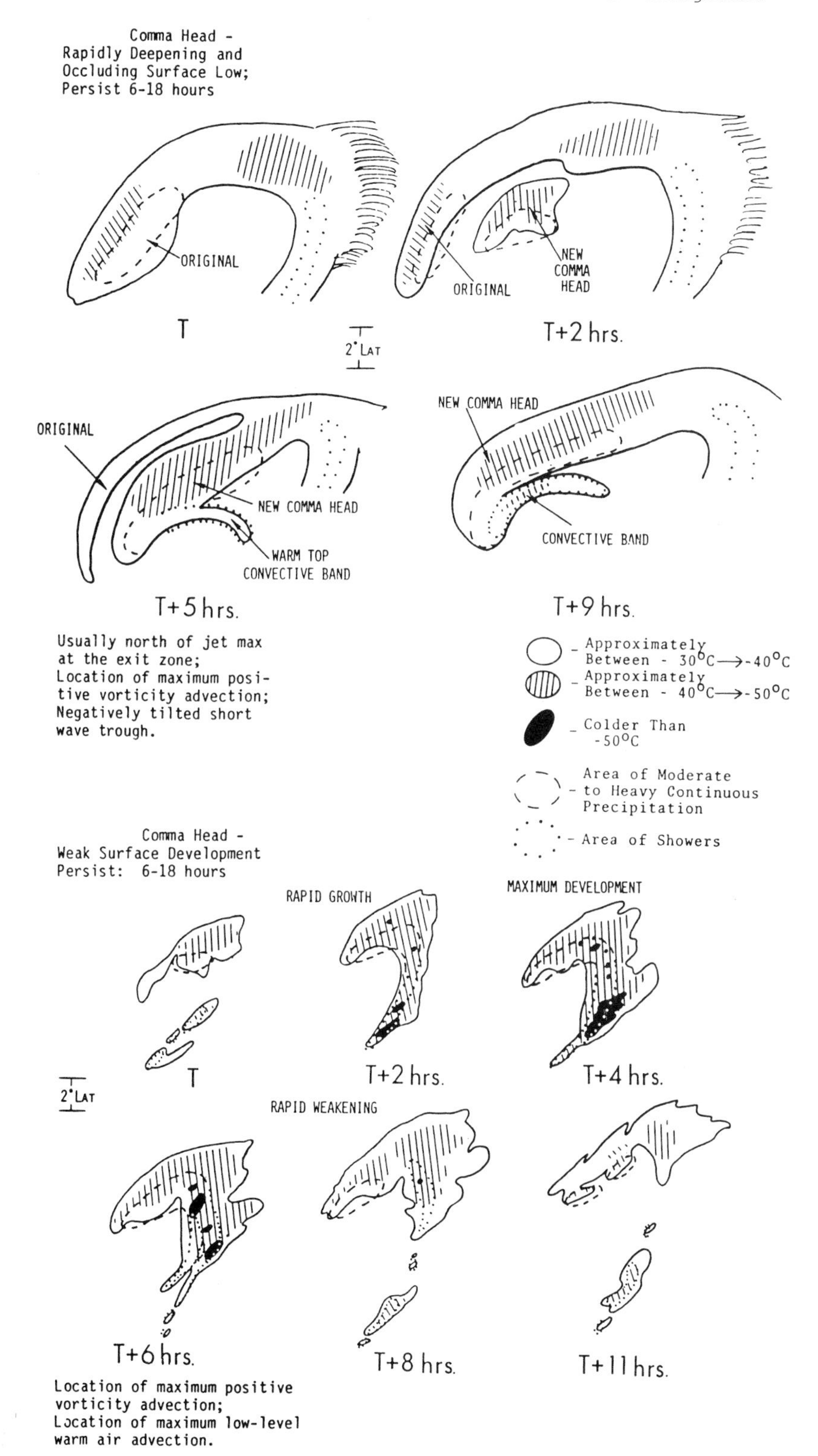

FIG.3a Characteristics of satellite-observed heavy extratropical cyclone precipitation systems.

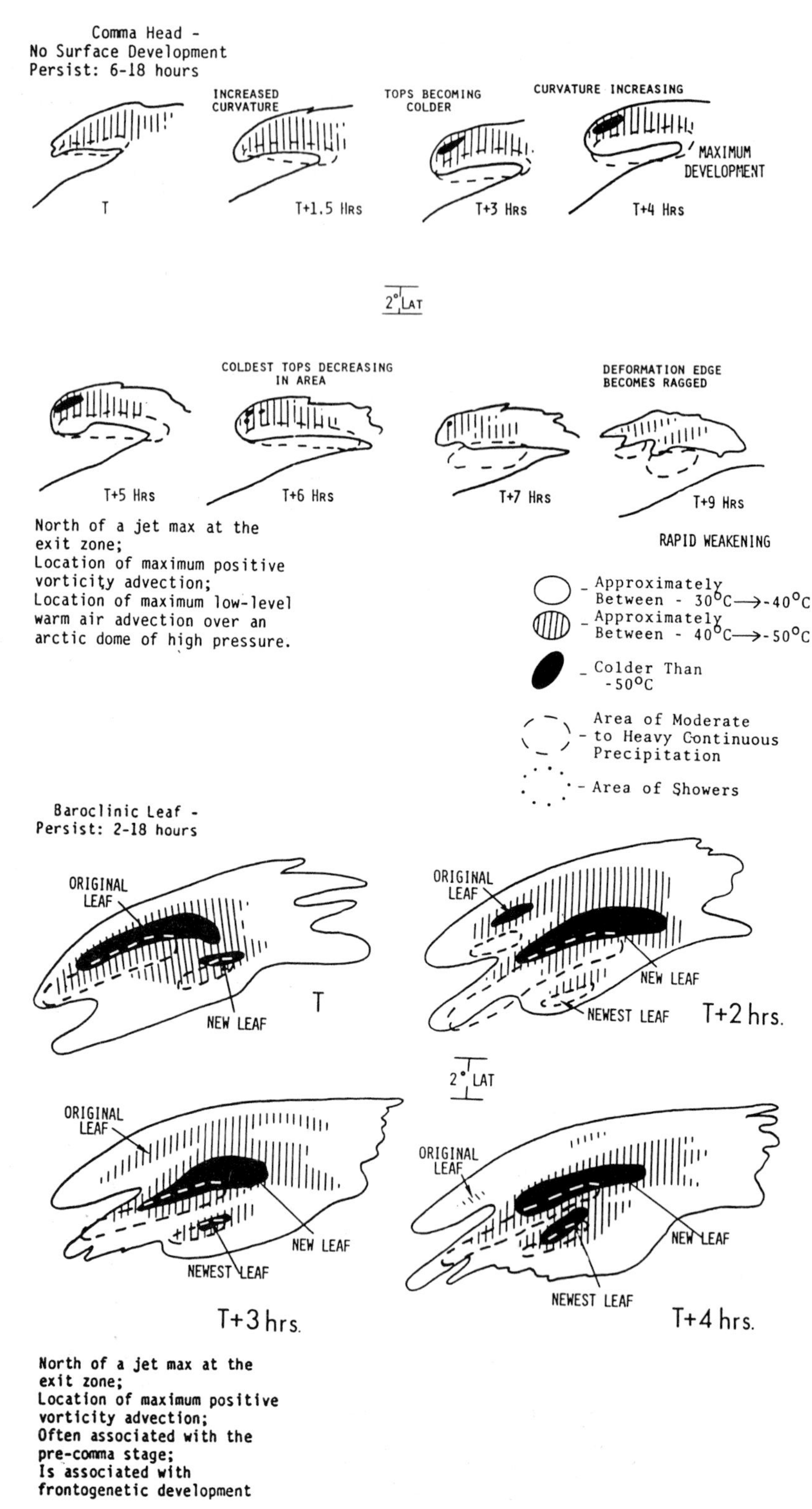

FIG.3b Characteristics of satellite-observed heavy extratropical cyclone precipitation systems.

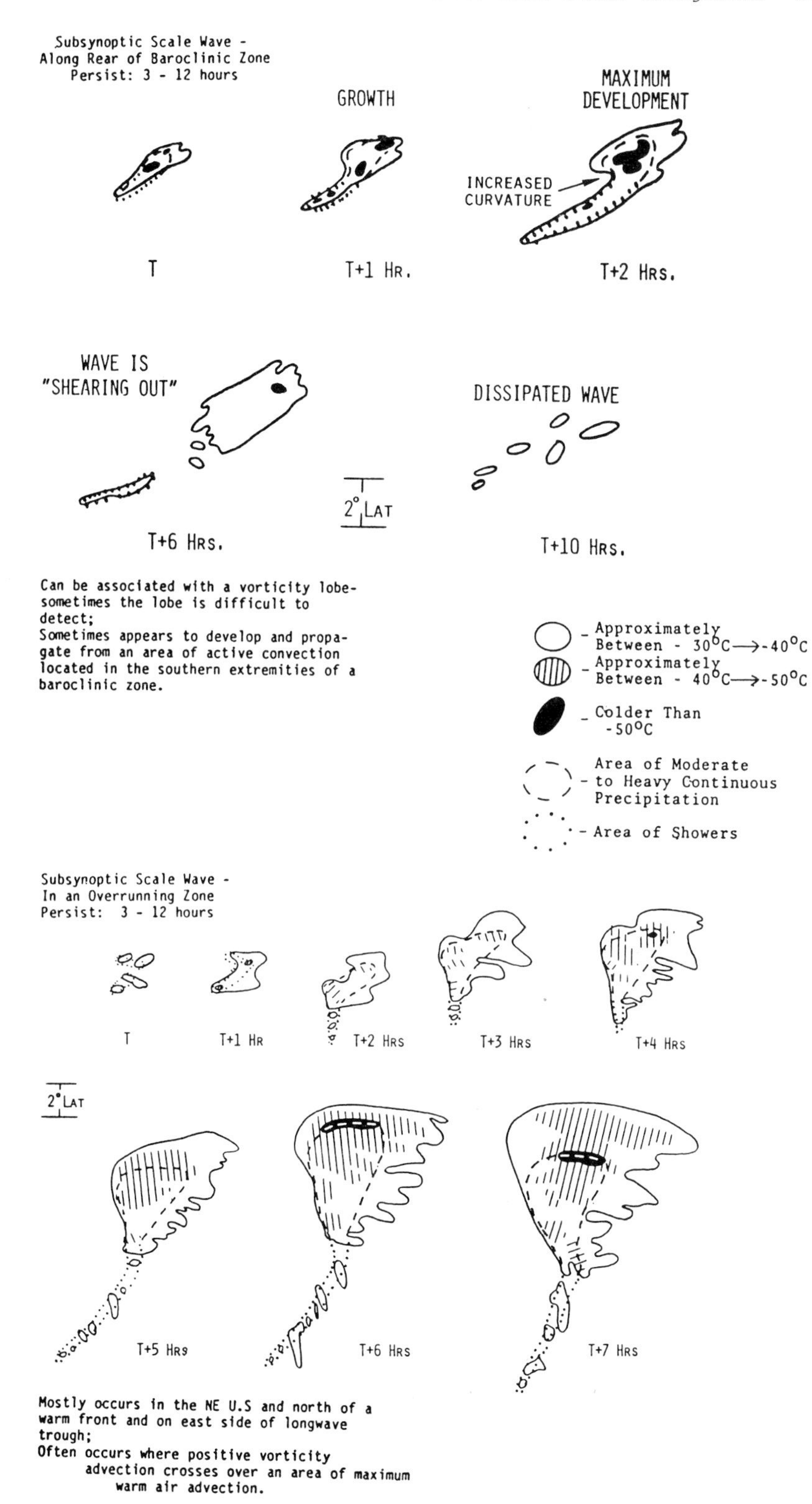

FIG.3c Characteristics of satellite-observed heavy extratropical cyclone precipitation systems.

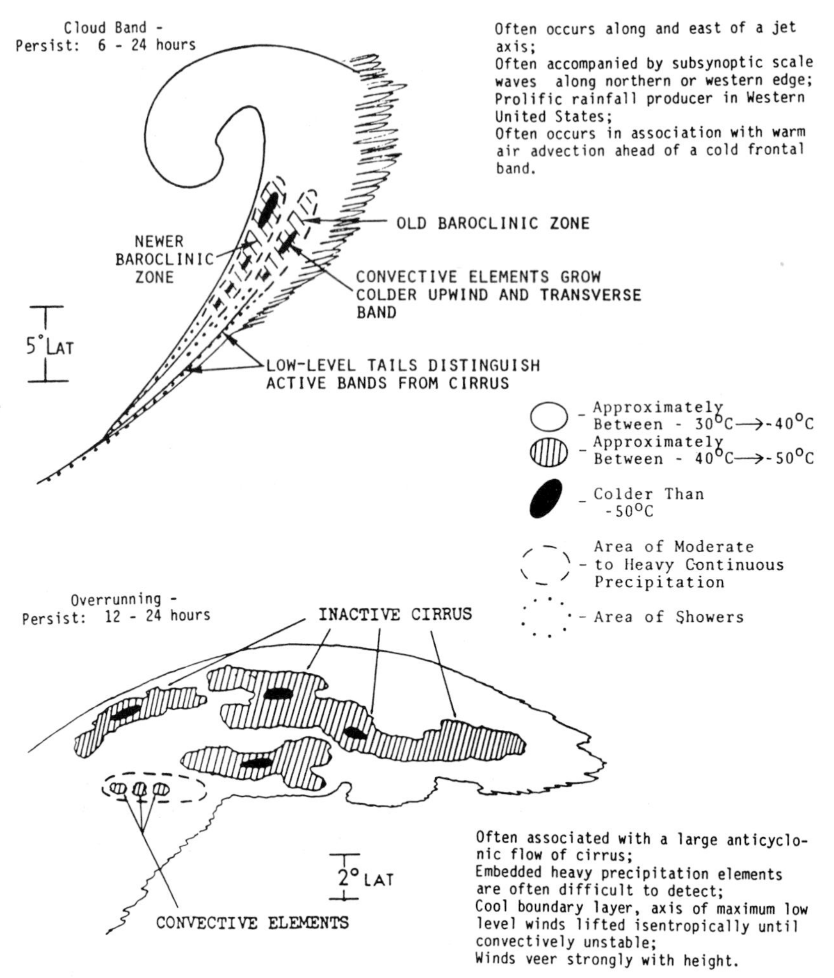

FIG.3d Characteristics of satellite-observed heavy extratropical cyclone precipitation systems.

mating convective rainfall from synoptic scale tropical systems, mesoscale convective complexes, squall lines and linear, large scale wedge systems. They are least accurate in estimating rainfall from single clustered, synoptic scale cyclonic circulation, large scale overrunning and regenerative systems. With respect to extratropical cyclone systems, most accurate estimates are produced from comma heads, baroclinic leafs and subsynoptic scale waves. Least accurate estimates are associated with cloud bands and overrunning systems.

The categories discussed in this paper are applicable to other parts of the world. The categories need to be fine tuned for each geographic location and may be used to anticipate precipitation amounts.

In the future, the categories will be refined as we develop a better understanding of satellite systems as they relate to heavy precipitation.

Acknowledgments

The author would like to thank Kim Beale for typing the manuscript, John Shadid for drafting the figures and layout of the manuscript and Gene Dunlap for reproduction of the satellite imagery.

References

Clark, J.D., A.J. Lindner, R. Borneman, and R.E. Bell, 1980: Satellite Observed Cloud Patterns Associated with Excessive Precipitation Outbreaks. Proceedings of the Eighth Conference on Weather Forecasting and Analysis, June 10-13, 1980, Denver, CO, AMS, Boston, MA, 463-473.

Fleming, E., L.E. Spayd, Jr., R.A. Scofield, 1984: Characteristics of East Coast Convective Flash Flood Events in GOES Imagery. Proceedings of the Tenth Conference On Weather Forecasting and Analysis, June 25-29, 1984, Clearwater Beach, FL, AMS, Boston, MA, 8 pages.

Kadin, Charles, 1982: The Minneapolis snow event--What did the satellite imagery tell us? National Weather Digest, 7, 13-16.

Maddox, R.A., 1980: Mesoscale Convective Complexes. Bull. Am. Met. Soc., 61, 1374-1387.

Scofield, R.A., 1984: The NESDIS operational convective precipitation estimation technique. Proceedings of the Tenth Conference on Weather Forecasting and Analysis, June 25-29, 1984, Clearwater Beach, FL, AMS, Boston, MA.

Scofield, R.A. and L.E. Spayd, Jr., 1984: A Technique That Uses Satellite, Radar and Conventional Data for Analyzing Precipitation from Extratropical Cyclones. NOAA Technical Memorandum NESDIS 8, U.S. Dept. Comm., Wash., D.C., 51 pp.

Spayd, L.E., Jr., 1982: Estimating Rainfall Using Satellite Imagery From Warm-top Thunderstorms Embedded in a Synoptic Scale Cyclonic Circulation. Proceedings of the International Symposium on Hydrometeorology, June 13-17, 1982, Denver, CO, AWRA, Minneapolis, MN, 139-146.

Spayd, L.E., Jr., and R.A. Scofield, 1983: Operationally Detecting Flash Flood Producing Thunderstorms which Have Subtle Heavy Rainfall Signatures in GOES imagery. Proceedings of the Fifth Conference on Hydrometeorology, October 17-19, 1983, Tulsa, OK, AMS, Boston, MA, 190-197.

Ward, J.D., 1981: Spatial and Temporal Heavy Rainfall Patterns Overland Associated With Weakening Tropical Cyclones. Proceedings of the Fourth Conference on Hydrometeorology, October 7-9, 1981, Reno, Nevada, AMS, Boston, MA, 174-180.

Weldon, R., 1979: Part IV, Cloud patterns and the upper air wind field. In-house publication of the Satellite Applications Laboratory, NESDIS/NOAA, 80 pp.

Hydrologic Applications of Space Technology (Proceedings of the Cocoa Beach Workshop, Florida, August 1985). IAHS Publ. no. 160, 1986.

Combined processing of meteorological information for very short-range weather forecasting in central Europe

DUSAN PODHORSKY
Czechoslovak Hydrometeorological Service, WMO Activity Centre for Very Short-range Forecasting, Bratislava, Czechoslovakia

Abstract
The geographic spatial complex (geographic landscape) is understood as the spatial dynamic system considered in the uniform cartographic projection which is optimum for the transformation of point and areal hydrometeorological data (e.g. satellite, radar, etc.) referring to the digital relief model.

For the purposes of efficient data collection and processing in operational service the purpose-made technological link and the specialized data bank METEOTREND'85 were established in Czechoslovakia enabling hydrologist and meteorologist to analyse real-time remote sensing data and very short-range weather forecasts, and at the same time the distribution of results obtained to users with the help of nowcasting technology.

The implementation of the METEOTREND'85 project affects the structure of both hydrological and meteorological forecasting services in Czechoslovakia and influences in positive way several branches of the national economy.

Introduction
Each mathematical forecasting model in meteorology and hydrology considers the relief influence on a studied process. Therefore, we have started with the mathematical description of the physiogeographic area; when investigating micro- and meso-scales we pay attention to their links with socio-economic factors. It follows from the work by Barrett E.C. and Curtis L.F. "Introduction to Environmental Remote Sensing" /3/ that the ecological analysis forms a core that joins geography with geology, biology with meteorology by

means of the study of rational exploitation of natural resources, environment and its protection applying cartographic and remote sensing methods. In this connection the term "ecological monitoring" appears with its two subsystems: geophysical and biological. The monitoring here represents that part of the control and information system which includes also geophysical, hydrological, and meteorological measurements enabling to analyse, observe, to give diagnosis and to forecast relationships - interactions between relief and atmosphere or hydrosphere with regard to the study of the degree of anthropogenic environmental impacts. Considering these presumptions we define the relief by a set of morphometric quantitative parameters, e.g. relief slope, relief orientation towards cardinal points (i.e. relief exposure, normal and horizontal curvature, relief insolation depending on time, etc.) and the state of the atmosphere and hydrosphere is characterised by a complex of individual quantities measured by conventional means and remote sensing methods and they are transformed subsequently into an optimum uniform cartographic system. In other words, with regard to the fact that the relief in Central Europe is an important spatial factor of differentiation from the viewpoint of the states of the atmosphere and hydrosphere, it is very important for the relief data to be included into an information system and to model the relief by means of the so called "complex digital model."

Now, when the efficient hardware is at our disposal, and the information system about atmosphere and hydrosphere is solved by the form of a data bank, it is possible to start with an operational processing of numerous data within separate elements of the physiogeographic sphere as the spatial complex system and in this system as a whole.

Geographic landscape as the geographic spatial complex is according to the works by Krcho /1/ considered a spatial dynamic system in a given system of coordinates.

In this system it is possible to express two basic subsystems i.e. the sub-system of the physiogeographic sphere and the sub-system of the socio-economic sphere. At present we load the data bank gradually with the data of the physiogeographic sphere's sub-system, i.e. with elements of the set: atmosphere, hydrosphere, litosphere, pedosphere, and biosphere. The structure of the sub-systems is expressed by nodal diagrams, individual elements of sub-sets are expressed by vectors and matrices, and thus inputs and outputs of each element of the physiogeographic sphere as well as its states are in the area considered in a given system of coordinates characterized by a set of quantitative parameters which form the parametric basis for the given physiogeographic sub-system. The area studied is expressed in the data bank in a discrete form - its units are created by areal elements of the square net.

An analysis of meteorological data in a given region of interest is needed not only in a term of observations but also in a site on the Earth's surface to which an observation is related to, i.e. it is necessary to know the territorial relevance of meteorological data. The geographical coordinates are usually used to locate meteorological stations. However, such approach is suitable for the point data only. The areal data generally require the division of the territory into areal units which correspond to the certain values of measured quantities. Since the areal units defined by the same differences of geographical coordinates have not equal areas, these coordinates are not suitable for expressing the territorial relevance of the areal data. A concrete selection of the appropriate cartographic system depends on the size and location of the given area of interest, resolution required and allowable coefficient of deformation on the boundaries of the area. Regarding the needs of the current but especially future investigations and practical use of meteorological data, the territory bounded by the following cartographic coordinates: $\varphi_N=60^\circ$, $\varphi_S=35^\circ$, $\lambda_W=-10^\circ$ and $\lambda_E=35^\circ$ has been defined as the maximum area of interest. The uniform cartographic system of the mentioned area was done by the planar projection onto a truncated cone which intersects the Earth's surface in the parallels $\varphi_1=54^\circ N$ and $\varphi_2=42^\circ N$. The way of addressing gives the possibility to work with 1x1 km^2 resolution, and furthermore it is possible to select any resolution of 2^n dimensions. Special transformation procedures provide data conversion from other cartographic systems into the uniform system and vice versa, and thus it is possible to process data in any of these cartographic systems.

Regarding up-to-now experience it can be stated that the above mentioned requirements on the territorial relevance of areal data are satisfied if these data enter the data base in a form of rectangular sectors of a certain network. The size of the sectors is defined so that the length of respective sentences corresponds to the size of physical blocks. Respective identifiers characterizing the territorial relevance of the sectors compensate for areal data identifiers of stations - sources of the point data. It is clear from the above that while the territorial access to the point data has to be realized by the station identifiers, the territorial access to the areal data can be realized directly.

The development of the technological link for nowcasting calls for a system approach as for example in proposing of automated systems in flight assistance. The basic principles of METEOTREND´85 have been formulated as follows:

-reliability - the principle of failure-free meteorological observations, their collection, processing, and distribution of data and information;

- continuous operation - the principle of continuous operation of all components of the technological link;

- readiness - the principle of optimal terms (frequency) of recovery, collection, processing, representation and distribution of all types of meteorological observations;

- efficiency - the principle of protection of results and operation of the technological link for nowcasting under real (optimal) economic conditions with the aim to serve all users of very short-range weather forecasts.

The beginning of the data bank development for the purposes of very short-range forecasts of cloudiness and associated phenomena is dated back to the second half of the 1970s when the computer centre EC 1040 (equivalent to IBM 360)was put into operation at the Regional Centre for Radar Meteorology on the Malý Javorník hill. The teams of specialists led by Dr Badíková, Dr Mičietová, Dr Vítek and Dr Vlčák have realized under the leadership of Dr Fuchs requirements and objectives stated by meteorologists at the Regional Centre (Dr Podhorský, Dr Wolek) as the basic philosophy of combined meteorological data processing.

Increasing number of meteorological data contributes to more and more tide connections among meteorological data and computing technique. Scientific research has brought complicated algorithms with many demands on input data, processing speed and flexibility in choosing methods and inputs. Substantial simplification and optimization of software can be achieved by an uniform data bank, archiving and data access. The data bank system METEOSYS/DB was built up at Slovak Hydrometeorological Institute after the preceding analysis of demands on meteorological data processing and, above all, demands on combined operational information for very short-range forecast of dangerous phenomena and precipitation. The contents and structure of the system satisfy the principle and the most frequent demands on data processing without duplicated creation on files which depend on individual users programs. Thus a desirable reduction and unification of communication procedures with the uniform system of data archiving and protection is possible.

System Description

METEOSYS/DB system consists of a data base and a programming data base management system. The system is based on the IDMS (Integrated Database Management System) from Cullinane Corp., USA. Since the product was designed for applications in other spheres (economic, social), its modified version METEOSYS/DB has been created on the basis of the analysis and experimental evaluations of specific meteorological models.

Data Base METEOSYS/DB

The formation of the data base was preceded by an analysis of data structure and correlations among the data themselves, and by the investigation of several characteristics of meteorological data.

Data Types

Meteorological observations at a certain time and in a certain place give us simultaneously several values of measured characteristics which belong due to their informative value and the way of observation to one logical unit. In connection with the above mentioned, the data type is an accurately defined structure in a programming language that collects coherent quantities of one type of observations, e.g. synoptic data, aerological data, etc.A record from the observation of a certain data type is done by writing one sentence with the structure of the respective data type.

Kinds of Data

With regard to the method of observations and territorial representation we differentiate the following kinds of data:
- point data
- areal data.

Point data represent observations at some fixed place on the Earth´s surface and they enter the data base above all from the network of ground, climatic and upper-air stations, etc. Areal data are those which belong to certain areal units of the Earth´s surface. Results of spatial measurements - after their appropriate projection into the plane of the Earth´s surface - are processed as the areal data, too. Such character is typical mainly for the results of remote sensing of the atmosphere, i.e. for radar and satellite data.

The kinds of meteorological data are of great importance to the definition of the inner structure of respective sentence types. While the sentence structures for the point data are simple in majority, sentences for the areal data are characterized by a matrix structure depending on the way of areal reference of such data.

Time Dependence

A notion of time for the structural sub-division of meteorological data is very important regarding the definition of their validity in time. From this point of view we differentiate:

- instantaneous data
- interval data
- time-independent data.

This division follows from the physical base of values and from methods of their measurement. Thus for example, air pressure and water temperature belong to instantaneous data; average daily temperatures and yearly precipitation totals belong to certain time intervals. Different station characteristics, relief data, etc. belong to data independent of time.

Data Base Contents

In spite of its original aim - to build up the data bank only for the purposes of very short-range forecasting based on combining the data from the remote sensing of the atmosphere, the METEOSYS/DB system has become the uniform data-base system for storage of all meteorological and hydrological data types obtained at Slovak Hydrometeorological Institute which are the subject of automated data processing and storage. At present the system operates storage and processing of the following meteorological and hydrological data: synoptic data, aerological data, radar data, satellite data, climatic data, precipitation data, soil temperature data, air pollution data, radiation data, data on surface waters, relief characteristics of the territory of Czechoslovakia, data defining administrative units on the territory of Czechoslovakia.

From the point of view of instantaneous weather analysis and very short-range forecast especially radar and satellite data are important, together with synoptic, aerological and relief data on an investigated region.

Data Inputs Into Data Base

Radar data enter the data base from hourly measurements of the dual-wavelength weather radar MRL-5 situated on the Malý Javorník hill with several hours delay due to the preliminary manual coding of radar data on punched cards.

At present we assume that an automated real-time processing of these data could be realized, and records are done for the square-like territorial units 100x100 km, 200x200 km, 300x300 km, and 600x600 km with the centre in the MRL-5 location and with resolutions 5x5, 10x10, 15x15, and 30x30km. The automated mode offers an optional resolution up to 2x2 km with four entries into the data base per hour.

Satellite data are primarily processed by the PDP 11-34 computer which forms one part of the receiving system. They enter the data base once per hour via magnetic tape which is transmitted off-line to the computer EC 1040. The record of one satellite orbit consists of several records from 32x32 km regions the sum of which forms a polygon covering the Czechoslovak territory and boundary regions.

Entries of the operational data from the meteorological stations are realized temporarily using punched telex tapes from the Regional Telecommunication Centre. A real-time input of these data can be realized on the assumption that a computer network will be formed during next year. Synoptic data enter the data base from all primary and secondary terms from 90 stations situated in the square of about 650x650 km with the centre on Malý Javorník. Aerological data from five stations (Prague, Poprad, Vienna, Warsaw, Budapest) are recorded at 00 and 12 GMT.

Operation of METEOSYS/DB System

It is clear that a quick and optimal access to meteorological and hydrological data can be ensured in the best way by means of direct access storage media. However, such media have not capacity enough for the whole fond of meteorological and hydrological data. So it is necessary to use magnetic tapes with sequential data organization only. The data base in the METEOSYS/DB system is from this reason divided into:

- operational part stored on magnetic discs;
- non-operational archived part stored on magnetic tapes.

Although it can be assumed that actual meteorological and hydrological data of appropriate types will be stored in the operational part of the data base, the operational utiliza- tion cannot be limited only to these data. In the case of inevitable processing of certain data from the non-operational part of the data base, it is possible to transport these data from archives into the operational part of the data base and to control, correct, or process them.

Generalization of Experience from Case Studies

Technological link METEOTREND'85 uses besides the data from the dense network of conventional hydrological and meteorological stations also information from the network of weather radars and data from the satellite receiving systems for NOAA and METEOSAT II satellites.

Based on the analysed case studies it is possible to conclude:

1) recognition of clouds associated with precipitation is much more effective using a complex - combined diagnosis based on radar and satellite data. At the same time it is necessary to use data from all spectral bands of a satellite and in the case of meteorological radars it is suitable to combine classical radar data with multiwave-length and Doppler radars data. Estimated rainfall intensities have to undergo a real-time calibration by radiopluviographs situated at various distances from the radar;

2) when estimating evolution of precipitation field it is not sufficient to use data on radar reflectivity measured at the boundary layer of the atmosphere (0 - 2 km). Of great importance from the viewpoint of very short-range precipitation forecasting is the vertical profile of radar reflectivity and its tendency depending on time, while the vertical step of measurement is recommended to be for convective cloud each two kilometers as minimum and every kilometer as optimum; for stratus clouds it is every kilometer as minimum and each 500 m as optimum (in this case, of course, the maximum range of radar observation is up to 60 - 80 km distance);

3) with cloud systems consisting of As - Ns - Cb it is important to estimate cloud tops in each pixel from satellite data and with the help of radars it is necessary to study in Ns clouds the connection between cloudless layers and location of the line of intensive crystallization (LIC) which must take place within the cloud mass if rainfall should be produced /2/;

4) uneven micro-structure of clouds and precipitation causes also an uneven distribution of radar reflectivity in space.

If we study the dependency of the average value of radar reflectivity $\overline{Z}$ on the measured maximum values of reflectivity Z_{MAX}, on the distance between the cloud and the radar R and the relationship between the beam width and horizontal and vertical thickness of cloud, we can see that in some cases it is necessary to correct the basic radar equation for the measurement of radar characteristics of clouds on the radar equation for point targets which is used for air traffic control, etc.

5) for precipitation occurrence at middle latitudes the presence of intensive crystallization is inevitable and

it takes place at the isothermic level (from $-10^{o}C$ to $-15^{o}C$) depending on the vertical velocity of parcel motion in stratus clouds. The level of intensive crystallization divides Ns clouds schematically into two zones:

A-zone - zone of active ice nuclei growth and formation of precipitation particles situated under LIC;

I-zone - zone of the intensive formation of natural ice nuclei situated above LIC.

In A-zone the natural process of cloud drops freezing almost does not occur. A-zone consists of supercooled drops, and ice crystals from I-zone quickly grow here as a result of coagulation.

So it can be said that I-zone determines the number of precipitation particles and A-zone their size.

Probability of precipitation falling from non-convective clouds depends on many parameters e.g., on cloud size, heights of cloud top and cloud base, etc. Intensity of the reflected signal depends on the structure and density of cloud particles. Moreover, these characteristics influence also the rate of particle growth in cloud. Weather radars operating in the wave length $\lambda < 3.2$ cm enable to determine with satisfying accuracy the height of cloud top ΔH and distribution of cloudless layers in non-convective clouds to the distance $R \leq 80$ km.

After changes in the inner structure of cloudiness also the radioecho parameters have to be changed. Then it is possible to determine indirect connections between radar parameters of cloud layer and formation of precipitation in stratus clouds.

In other words, it is necessary in our opinion to pay extra attention to the relationship between the values of precipitation intensities near ground and to tendencies, i.e. changes of quantities of radar reflectivity in the vertical profile above the line of intensive crystallization and, based on these new links, to give more precise methods of rainfall forecasts.

References

/1/ Krcho J. - Podhorský D., 1981, Dynamic model of landscape relief and remote sensing of environment, Meteorologické zprávy, 34, No.2, pp. 45-48.

/2/ Barrett E.C. - Curtis L.F., 1976, Introduction to environmental remote sensing, London, New York.

/3/ Podhorský D., 1985, Prognosis of precipitation evolution based on remote sensing, seminar Remote sensing applications in hydrology and water resources, Czechoslovakia, 10p.

Hydrologic Applications of Space Technology (Proceedings of the Cocoa Beach Workshop, Florida, August 1985). IAHS Publ. no. 160, 1986.

Future applications of GOES satellite VAS data to estimating and forecasting heavy precipitation

LEROY E. SPAYD JR
Satellite Applications Laboratory,
National Environmental Satellite, Data, &
Information Service, NOAA/Dept. of Commerce,
5200 Auth Road, Room 601, Camp Springs,
Maryland 20746, USA

Abstract
The purpose of this paper is to report on some preliminary applications of VAS data for estimating rainfall and short-range forecasting of heavy convective rainfall events. As part of the NOAA Flash Flood Program of the United States meteorologists in the Synoptic Analysis Branch (SAB) of the National Environmental Satellite, Data, and Information Services (NESDIS) routinely monitor on a half hourly operational basis GOES visible and infrared imagery on the Interactive Flash Flood Analyzer (IFFA) and produce estimates and short-range forecasts of maximum rainfall amounts by counties for flash flood threatening storms (Clark and Borneman, 1984). Satellite Precipitation Estimate (SPE) messages are disseminated through the Automated Field Operational Services (AFOS) computer system to hydrometeorologists in the National Weather Service (NWS) field forecast offices. In 1986 products from the GOES VISSR Atmospheric Sounder (VAS) data (Smith, 1983) will be operationally produced in the World Weather Building (WWB) in Washington, DC and available to SAB meteorologists.

1985 VAS Data Assessment

In the spring of 1984 VAS data was initially examined via the Man-Computer Interactive Data Access System (McIDAS) (Suomi, et al., 1983) terminal in the WWB for future applications to NOAA's IFFA (Spayd, 1985). In 1985, meteorologists in the Advanced Satellite Products Project of NESDIS processed VAS data on a daily basis beginning March 19 for real-time evaluation at the National Severe Storms Forecast Center (NSSFC) (Anthony and Leftwich, 1984) and to support the initial activities of the Program for Regional Observing and Forecast Services (PROFS) in preparation for the National Stormscale Operational and Research Meteorology (STORM) Program. Specific sets of VAS-derived products are produced at 1100 GMT, 1400 GMT, 1700 GMT, and 2000 GMT daily with an additional data set processed at 2300 GMT at the request of PROFS.

For each time period VAS derived fields of temperatures, dewpoints, heights, and gradient winds are produced at standard radiosonde reporting levels as 80 km gridpoint data. Atmospheric elements that relate to layers such as precipitable water, total totals and lifted indices are produced for each data set both as gridpoint data and as a high resolution (7 km) "image" (Smith, et al., 1985). The VAS 6.7 um channel water vapor imagery is produced on a half-hourly or hourly basis. Regression equations producing the Keller probabilities of severe weather (Keller and Smith, 1983) are solved for each VAS data set.

Daily evaluation of the VAS data in March and April 1985 revealed differences in the consistency of the VAS data sets from one time period to another and one day to another. According to Menzel and Schreiner (1985) the failure of the servo mechanism that maintains the VAS filter wheel temperature on GOES-6 at 40°C is allowing 10°C to 15°C daily temperature fluctuations of the VAS instrument. These temperature fluctuations are caused externally by solar heating and internally by friction associated with the filter wheel movement. This means it is very difficult, if not impossible, to differentiate between changes in the atmospheric state and changes in the spectral response of the VAS instrument.

With the VAS instrument on GOES-6 producing varying quality of data with time it would be premature to state any firm conclusions about the contribution of the VAS data to increased accuracy of satellite rainfall estimates. Instead, this paper will concentrate on the evaluation of the operationally produced VAS data sets in a pre-convective environment prior to a significant convective outbreak in the Midwest United States.

Case Study

On the afternoon of April 23, 1985 a large convective outbreak occurred from Texas northeastward through Wisconsin. Although no reports of flash flooding were received, numerous areas received over three inches of rain (Figure 1). Meteorologists in SAB began estimating rainfall from thunderstorms developing in Arkansas at 1800 GMT. Continuous rainfall estimates were computed from 1800 GMT through 0600 GMT April 24 with over 3 inches estimated in Arkansas. Twelve separate SPE messages were sent to NWS field forecast offices.

FIG.1 Twenty four hour rainfall reports ending at 1200 GMT April 24, 1985.

Synoptic Overview

An atmospheric composite chart (Figure 2) at 1200 GMT on April 23, 1985 shows the wind fields at 300, 700, and 850 mb, contours of 850 mb dewpoints, 700 mb moisture areas, and trough axes as determined from the standard upper air charts. Features of the 500 mb vorticity analysis are also shown: axes of high vorticity called vorticity lobes and axes of low vorticity called vorticity ridges. Note the vertically deep trough over Nebraska, with a large diffluent area at 300 mb along the Mississippi

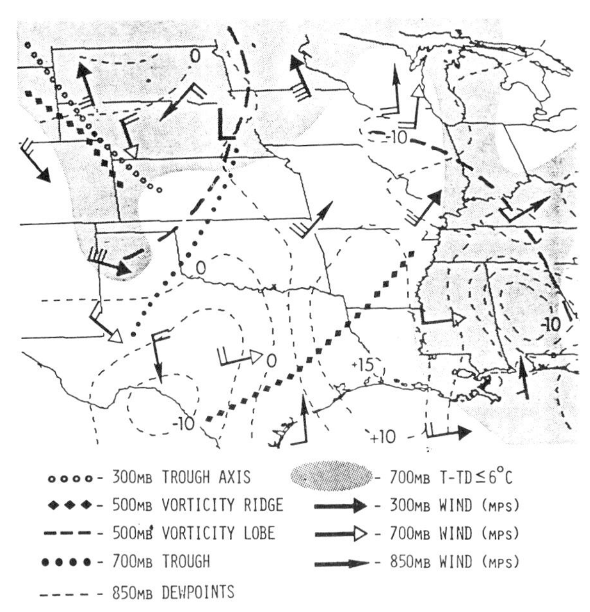

FIG.2 Atmospheric composite chart at 1200 GMT April 23, 1985. The wind barbs are in meters per second & contours of 850 mb dewpoints at 5 degrees Celsius intervals.

River. Also note the dry air at 700 mb overlaying the high 850 mb dewpoint area from eastern Texas to Missouri. At 500 mb a strong vorticity lobe extended southwestward from the cutoff low in Nebraska to the Texas Panhandle.

The McIDAS-analyzed surface wind field and dewpoint contours at 1100 GMT (Figure 3) show a cyclone in eastern Nebraska which had a central pressure of 999 mb. The convergence in the streamline field depicts frontal zone locations from Minnesota to Nebraska and southward to central

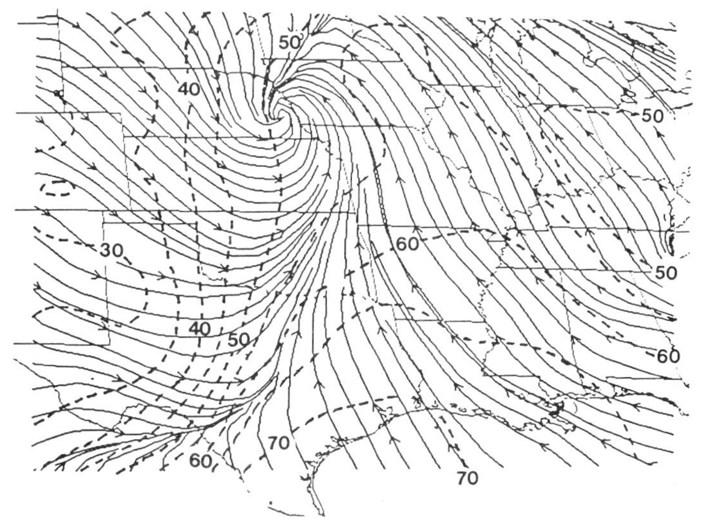

FIG.3 Surface streamlines & dewpoint contours at 1100 GMT April 23, 1985.

Texas. A sharp dewpoint gradient is observed across central Texas and Oklahoma with significant dry air advection across western and central Texas and moist air advection in eastern Texas.

VAS Data Sets

VAS dwell sounding data was processed on April 23 at 1100 GMT, 1400 GMT and 1700 GMT. The NSSFC requested rapid VISSR scans just after 1800 GMT on April 23 to monitor the convective development so VAS data collection was interrupted and the 2000 GMT VAS data set was not produced.

VAS Low-level Gradient Winds

The VAS gradient wind fields accurately depicted the magnitude and direction of the axis of maximum winds at 850 mb in southwestern Missouri (see figure 2). Throughout the day the VAS data showed an eastward progression of these maximum winds into eastern Missouri and Illinois (Figure 4) where the northern line of convection developed. The line of convection in eastern Texas to central Arkansas developed along the axis of confluence from the moist flow from the Gulf of Mexico and the dry flow from western Texas as seen from the VAS 850 mb gradient winds (Figure 4). The VAS data allowed the meteorologist to continually monitor the progression and evolution of the axis of maximum winds and the confluence zone. Accurately

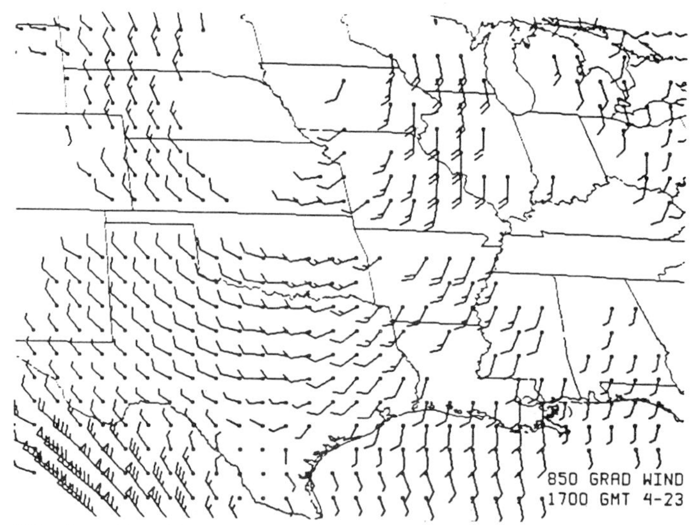

FIG.4 VAS 850 mb gradients winds at 1700 GMT April 23, 1985.

monitioring the changes in the low-level wind field is important for forecasting heavy rainfall events.

VAS-Derived Keller Probabilities of Severe Weather

Keller and Smith (1983) developed a statistical procedure that estimates probabilities of future severe local storm occurrence using polar orbiting atmospheric soundings and radiosonde data. This work was subsequently adapted to use GOES VAS soundings (Anthony and Leftwich, 1984). Current research involves deriving a similar set of regression equations for forecasting heavy rainfall events. These equations would be called the Flash Flood Index and would include some of the Keller probability predictors. The ten best predictors of the Keller probabilities in order of importance are lifted index, 850 mb dewpoint, a vertical wind shear term, precipitable water, 850 mb three hourly temperature advection, 850 mb wind speed, 850 mb moisture divergence, 300 mb wind speed, 500 mb three hourly temperature advection and three hourly change in the Showalter stability index. According to Keller and Smith (1983) probabilities greater than 20% in the Keller index indicate severe weather may occur in the next several hours.

On April 23 the NSSFC issued the first severe thuderstorm watch area at 1817 GMT for central Arkansas to northeastern Texas and five additional severe weather watch areas were issued by NSSFC within the next six hours. There were unofficially 95 separate reports of severe weather including 23 tornadoes from 1810 GMT April 23 to 0215 GMT on April 24 (Figure 5). Many of these reports were collocated and post-analysis may reveal that some of these reports were produced by the same storm.

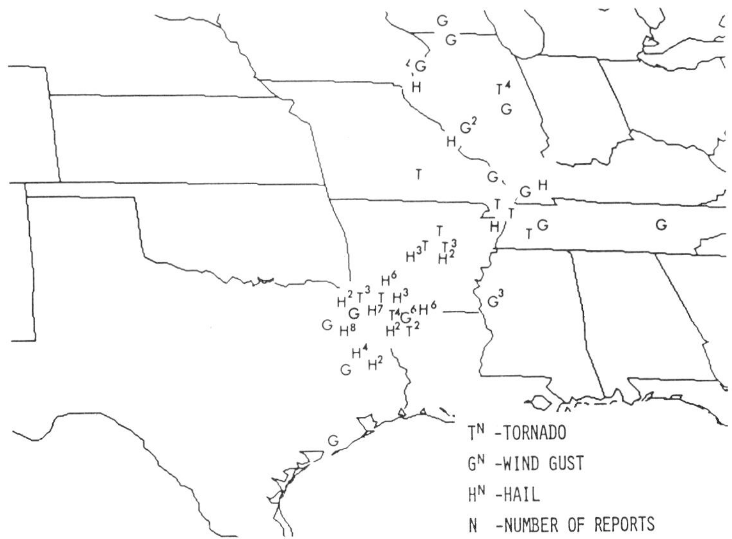

FIG.5 Unofficial severe storm reports from 1810 GMT April 23 to 0215 GMT April 24, 1985.

The Keller probabilities at 1130 GMT are shown in Figure 6. Note that the axis of the maximum 30% probabilities at 1130 GMT corresponds very accurately to the severe weather reports from southeastern Missouri through northeastern Texas.

VAS Stability Fields

Lifted indices and total total indices are routinely produced by the VAS retrieval algorithms. The lifted indices appeared to more accurately reflect the stability differences across the baroclinic zone in the southern plains than the total totals index. The plotted lifted indices at 1100 and 1700 GMT are shown in figure 7. Due to solar insolation the lifted indices decrease throughout the region during the day, however a sharp gradient is evident at 1700 GMT across eastern Texas with values of -5 appearing from central Arkansas into eastern Texas. Although low lifted

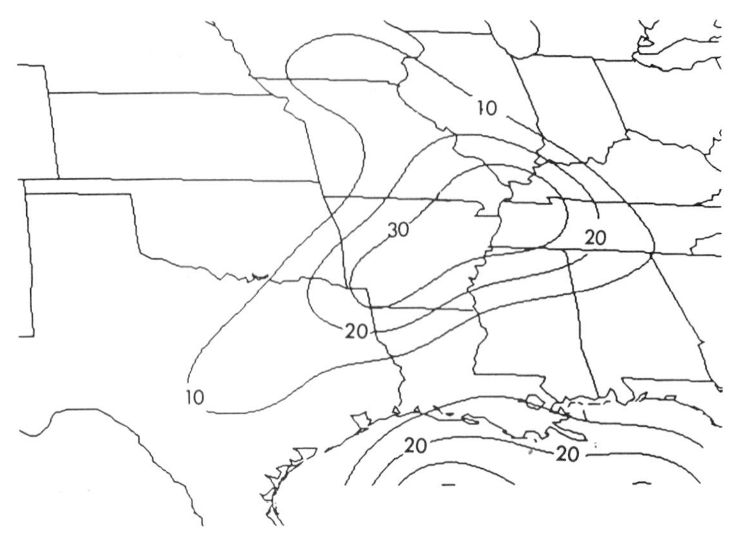

FIG.6 VAS-derived Keller probabilities of severe weather at 1130 GMT April 23, 1985.

indices exist throughout southern Texas, Louisiana, and offshore it is along the gradient of lifted index values that the line of convection in Arkansas and Texas formed. It is hoped that VAS data will allow short term monitoring of stability changes important in forecasting heavy rainfall producing convection.

VAS Precipitable Water

Accurately monitoring the changes in low-level moisture is extremely important in forecasting heavy rainfall events and it is hoped that the short-term changes in the VAS precipitable water fields will allow a continual "calibration" of the moisture correction factors to rainfall estimation techniques. The total precipitable water amounts can be displayed as gridpoint values and the gridpoints can be contoured. Contours of the 1100 GMT precipitable water values are shown in figure 8 along with the plotted RAOB surface to 500 mb precipitable water values. Because the contouring program contours across the cloudy (sounding void) areas, the plotted gridpoint values were compared to the 1200 GMT RAOB precipitable water amounts. For this time period sixteen comparisons were made and in 75% of these comparisons the VAS values were higher than the RAOB values. The average difference between the RAOB and VAS values was 6.3 mm with a RMS difference of 7.0 mm. The largest differences were in central Texas at Stephensville and Del Rio, Texas. The RAOB sounding at Stephensville (dotted line) and the nearest VAS sounding (solid line) are plotted in figure 9. Note that the VAS sounding has much more moisture between 900 and 600 millibars even though the surface dewpoints are very similar. Also note that the VAS temperatures between 850 and 300 mb are higher than the RAOB temperatures. The actual values of the RAOB and VAS soundings at the mandatory levels are shown respectively in figure 10. The third column of figure 10 shows the algebraic differences of (VAS - RAOB) for temperatures, dewpoints and heights. The VAS/RAOB sounding differences at Stephensville were larger than the other fifteen VAS/RAOB comparisons for this time period. There has been a consistent bias of the VAS sounding retrievals to overestimate the total precipitable water in areas of high surface dewpoints overlain by a deep layer of dry air. This bias has been observed on many separate days

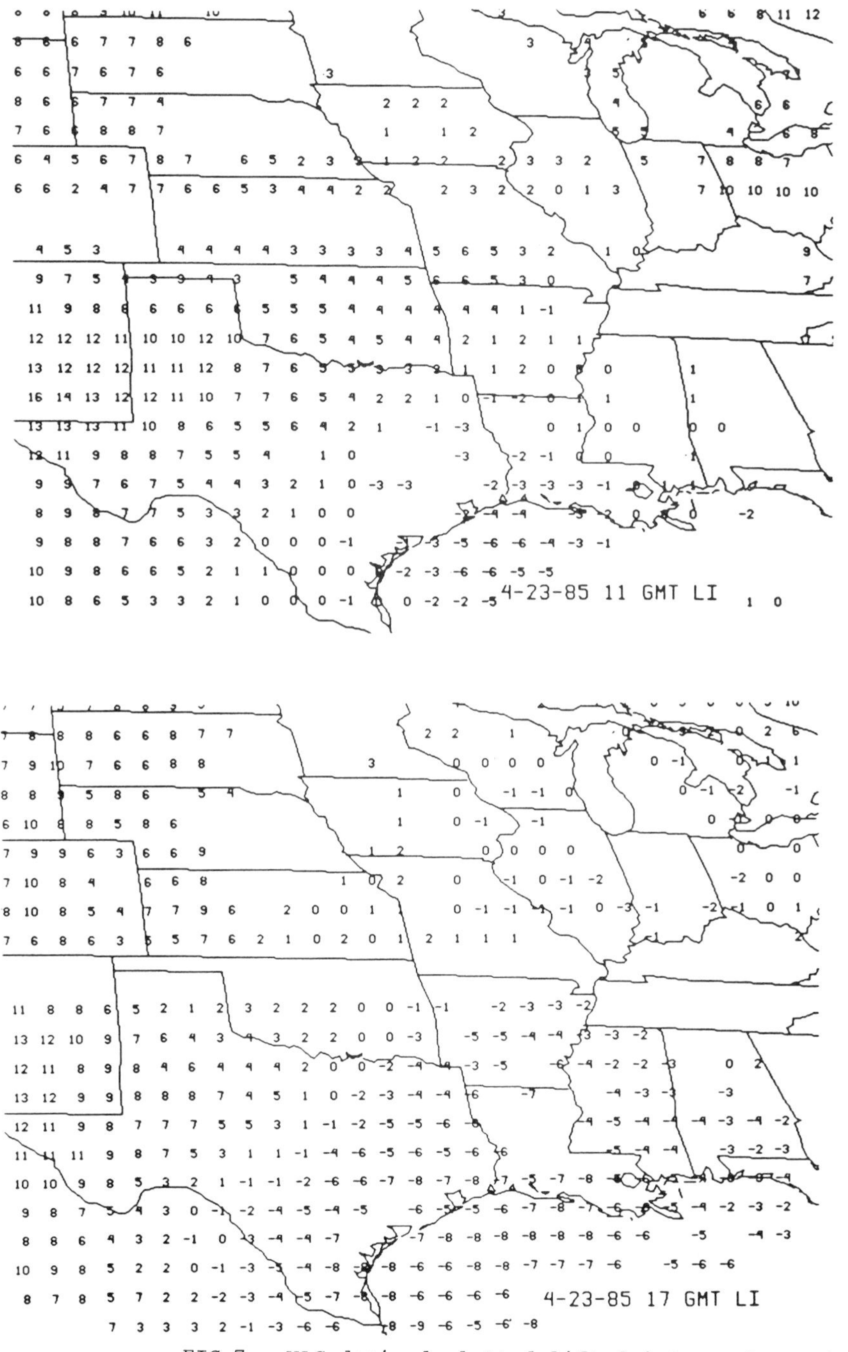

FIG.7 VAS-derived plotted lifted index values at 1100 & 1700 GMT April 23, 1985.

and different synoptic conditions. This bias is revealed in figure 10. Forecasters should be cautious in using the VAS precipitable water amounts for moisture correction factors to rainfall estimation techniques in areas with deep layer dry air and high shallow surface moisture until efforts in improving the VAS retrieval algorithms remove this bias.

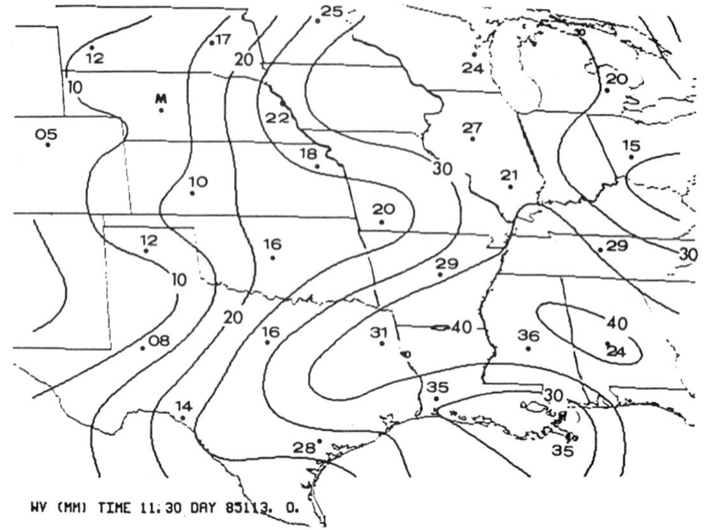

FIG.8 Contours of VAS-derived total precipitable water amounts at 1100 GMT and plotted RAOB observed surface to 500 mb precipitable water amounts in millimeters at 1200 GMT April 23, 1985.

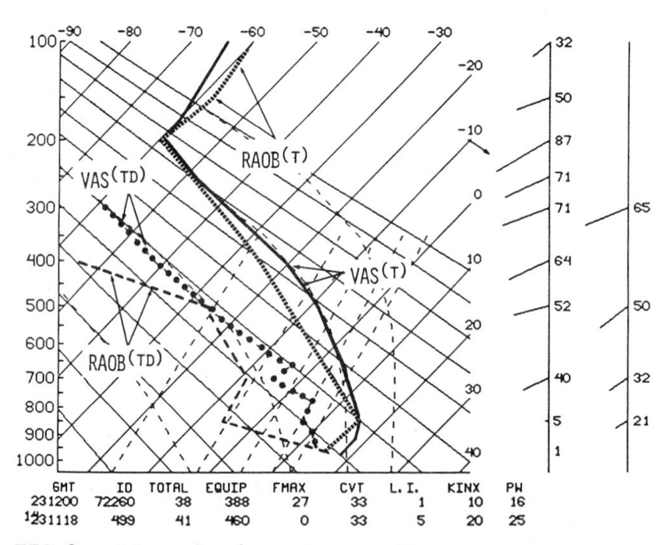

FIG.9 Atmospheric RAOB sounding at 1200 GMT at Stephensville, Texas and nearest VAS sounding at 1100 GMT April 23, 1985.

Conclusions and Outlook

This paper presented a case study showing the usefullness of GOES VAS data in detecting, monitoring and tracking atmospheric features responsible for initiating, focusing and maintaining a line of heavy rainfall producing convection. In an operational environment it would be impossible to review all the VAS data fields for each set of VAS retrievals. This paper has presented a few of the most useful VAS data sets that may be used by opera-

	RAOB					VAS					VAS - RAOB		
P(MB)	T(C)	TD(C)	Z(M)	DIR	MPS	T(C)	TD(C)	Z(M)	DIR	MPS	T	TD	Z
970						18.2	15.3	326					
982	15.0	14.8	399	310	1								
850	16.2	-5.8	1461	260	3	16.2	6.6	1454	239	11	-.0	12.4	-7
700	4.8	-9.2	3074	245	21	6.7	-5.0	3079	235	17	1.9	4.2	5
500	-13.7	-26.7	5720	255	27	-9.0	-27.7	5768	233	26	4.7	-1.0	48
400	-25.5	-55.5	7380	245	33	-21.4	-42.2	7455			4.1	13.3	75
300	-40.1		9400	250	37	-38.6	-58.3	9504	248	34	1.5		104
250	-49.3		10620	245	37	-49.1		10729			.2		109
200	-60.3		12050	240	45	-59.6		12159			.7		109
150	-58.3		13830	250	26	-60.8		13953			-2.5		123
100	-60.5		16380	230	17	-63.7		16457			-3.2		77

FIG.10 Printout of Stephensville, Texas RAOB sounding at 1200 GMT, the nearest VAS sounding at 1100 GMT April 23, 1985 and the VAS-RAOB differences.

tional meteorologists responsible for estimating and nowcasting heavy convective rainfall. Developmental work is underway to combine the VAS data fields to produce statistical probabilities of heavy rainfall occurrence called the Flash Flood Index.

Acknowledgements

The author would like to thank Ralph Anderson for reviewing this manuscript and John Shadid for producing the figures.

References

Anderson, R.K., J.J. Gurka, and S.J. Steinmetz, 1982: Application of VAS multispectral imagery to aviation forecasting. Proceedings of the Ninth Conference on Weather Forecasting and Analysis, June 28-July 1, 1982, Seattle, Washington, AMS, Boston, MA. 227-234.

Anthony, R.W. and P.W. Leftwich, Jr., 1984: Operational VAS applications in identifying regions with potential for severe thunderstorm development. Proceedings of the Tenth Conference on Weather Forecasting and Analysis, June 25-29, 1984, Clearwater Beach, Florida, AMS, Boston, MA, 358-364.

Clark, D. and R. Borneman, 1984: Satellite precipitation estimates program of the Synoptic Analysis Branch. Proceedings of the Tenth Conference on Weather Forecasting and Analysis, June 25-29, 1984, Clearwater Beach, Florida, AMS, Boston, MA, 392-399.

Hayden, C.M., W.P. Menzel, and A.J. Schreiner, 1984: The clouds and VAS. Proceedings of the Conference on Satellite Remote Sensing and Applications, June 25-29, 1984, Clearwater Beach, Florida, AMS, Boston, MA, 49-54.

Keller, D.L. and W.L. Smith, 1983: A statistical technique for forecasting severe weather from vertical soundings by satellite and radiosonde. NOAA Technical Report NESDIS 5, Department of Commerce/NOAA/NESDIS, 35 pp.

Menzel, P. and R. Schreiner, 1985: Effects of filter wheel temperature excursions on VAS radiative transfer calculations. NOAA Memorandum for the Record dated April 30, 1985, 8 pp.

Scofield, R.A., 1984: The NESDIS operational convective precipitation estimation technique. Proceedings of the Tenth Conference on Weather Forecasting and Analysis, June 25-29, 1984, Clearwater Beach, Florida, AMS, Boston, MA, 171-180.

Smith, W.L., 1983: The retrieval of atmospheric profiles from VAS Geostationary radiance observations. Journal of the Atmospheric Sciences,

Vol. 40, No. 8, August 1983, AMS, Boston, MA, 2025-2035.

Smith, W.L., G.S. Wade and H.M. Woolf, 1985: Combined atmospheric sounding/cloud imagery-a new forecasting tool. Bulletin American Meteorological Society, Vol. 66, No. 2, February 1985, 138-141.

Spayd, L.E. Jr., 1985: Applications of GOES VAS data to NOAA's interactive flash flood analyzer. Proceedings of International Conference on Interactive Information and Processing Systems for Meteorology, Oceanography, and Hydrology, January 7-11, 1985, Los Angeles, California, AMS, Boston, MA, 240-247.

Suomi, V.E., R. Fox, S.S. Limaye, and W.L. Smith, 1983: McIDAS III: A modern interactive data access and analysis system. Journal of Climate and Applied Meteorology, 22, 766-778.

Hydrologic Applications of Space Technology (Proceedings of the Cocoa Beach Workshop, Florida, August 1985). IAHS Publ. no. 160, 1986.

Spatial relationship between cloud-cover and rainfall fields: a statistical approach combining satellite and ground data

J. D. CREUTIN, P. LACOMBA & CH. OBLED
Institut de Mécanique de Grenoble, LA n° 6,
BP 68, F-38402 Saint Martin D'Hères,
Cedex, France

Abstract

This study is devoted to the spatial estimation of rainfall depths over a region of the Middle-East using both the measurements from a scarce raingage network and images from meteorological satellites.

In a first step, a nephanalysis is performed on IR and VIS images. A regression between the ground measurements and the cloud-cover due to the different cloud types allows to derive guess-fields at time steps from 5 to 15 days, corresponding to rainy events.

A second step consists in an optimal combination of the measurements from the two devices through the so-called cokriging system which is a simple extension of kriging interpolation when several measurement sets are available.

Introduction

A rainfall estimation study has been carried out over a region of the Middle-East, in order to assess the replenishment rate of an aquifer. As the scarce raingage network did not allow an accurate evaluation of the rainfall amounts, an attempt was made to assess rainfall with the help of both ground data and images of meteorological satellites.

Various studies on rainfall estimation by satellite (E.C. BARRETT, 1977 ; A. VAN DIJK, 1981 ; D. ATLAS et al., 1982) use rainfall production coefficients related to different cloud-types.

This work is an attempt to complement this classical approach by a geostatistical combination of satellite and ground measurements. Thus, after a brief description of the data set that has been used, the implementation of a mean square regression between cloud-cover and ground measurements is shown to produce a first estimation of the rainfall depths which can be considered as a guess-field ; then, cokriging systems is detailed and shown to be appropriate to combine the satellite guess-field and the gage measurements ; finally the improvement provided by the use of remote sensed data is illustrated comparing maps yielded on one hand by cokriging and on the other hand by simple kriging of the gages measurements alone.

Data set used

Image set. The year 1979 was retained for the study because a geostationary satellite, GOES Indian Ocean, was on orbit at that time. Additional images were provided by a polar orbiting satellite, DMSP (Defense Meteorological Satellite Program). Both sets were available only as paper prints.

The images that were purchased, cover a period of 6 months of 1979 only, because during the rest of the year, nearly no precipitation occurred. As the series provided by the two satellites let appear numerous gaps, they had to be merged, in order to get a greater daily frequency of images. Even so, no more than 6 IR and/or VIS images could be used within a day,usually 3.

Raingage records. As for the ground data, 45 raingages recorded continuously the daily rainfall amounts during the whole year 1979 (Fig. 5). Their distribution over the region was irregular, leaving some large areas without any measurement.

Satellite data conditioning (derivation of rainfall guess fields from nebulosity)

Cloud cover digitalization. As images were available as paper prints, the information they contained has to be digitalized. However, prints allow a visual classification of clouds into different types (nephanalysis), which would be difficult to implement automatically because of the accounting of parameters such as pattern, texture... Then simple relationships between rainfall depths and digitalized cloud-cover can be derived, providing a first estimation of rainfall fields.

The implementation of nephanalysis implies using a grid of digitalization. A set of square cells of 1° width was considered as sufficiently accurate. The classification of clouds in this study led to the identification of 3 types related to rainfall occurence : isolated convective clouds, convective areas of cyclonic disturbances and heterogeneous patterns of clouds. Each cloud-type was quantified separately as percent coverage of each cell by this cloud type.

Method used to identify rainfall parameters. The simplest relationship between rainfall depth and cloud-type that may be found is linear, such as :

$$z = \sum_{i=1}^{N} p_i C_i + \varepsilon$$

where z is the rainfall amount, C_i the cloud cover for the ith cloud-type among N and ε the residual error, each of these values being measured over a cell of the grid, within a day of a period.

Such parameters can be found by minimizing the error according to a criterium. The least square criterium has been chosen in this case-study.

As raingage measurements are not spatially representative values, they had to be averaged over the cell by taking the arithmetic mean of the inside point values. However, the number of gages per cell had to be considered as a weight attributed to each cell, in order to privilege well instrumented cells. The number of images per day was given a similar weighting role in the attempt to favor well sampled days.

Once the regression has been performed, its quality can be assessed through the correlation coefficient and through the pattern of the regression plot which has to conform to the linearity hypothesis.

If a significant relationship can be found, it allows a rainfall estimation even in the cells that are unprovided with ground measurements.

Implementation of linear and non-linear regression over various time-steps. First, daily data were processed for each month separately. This led to very low correlation coefficients (less than 0.6) and plots (fig. 1) with many outlayers.

Such a result reflects the poor representativeness of gages, whose number is 4 at most, in meshes about 10 000 km^2 wide. In addition, an uncertainty of several days in rainfall records was evidenced in several cases, through it could not be systematically detected.

In order to counter-balance recording errors and to obtain rainfall

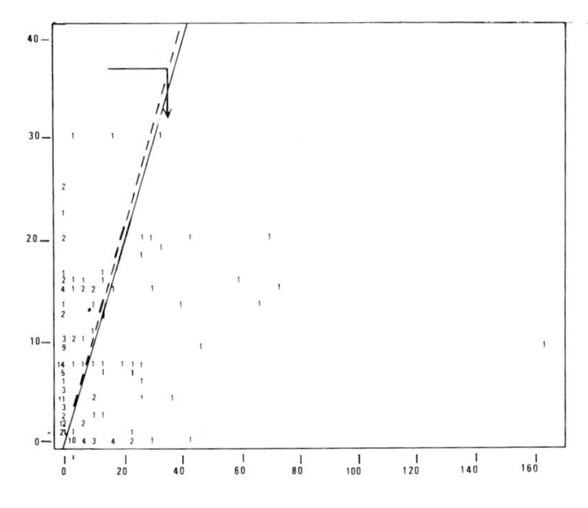

FIG 1 Daily amounts; three images a day 931 events and 31 meshes gaged giving 961 dots).

unit=mm

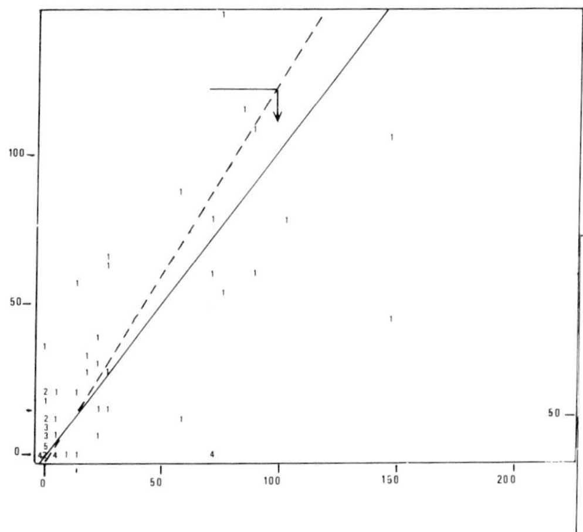

FIG.2 Amounts of rainy events; three images a day (93 dots).

FIG.3 Amounts of rainy events; one image a day (93 dots).

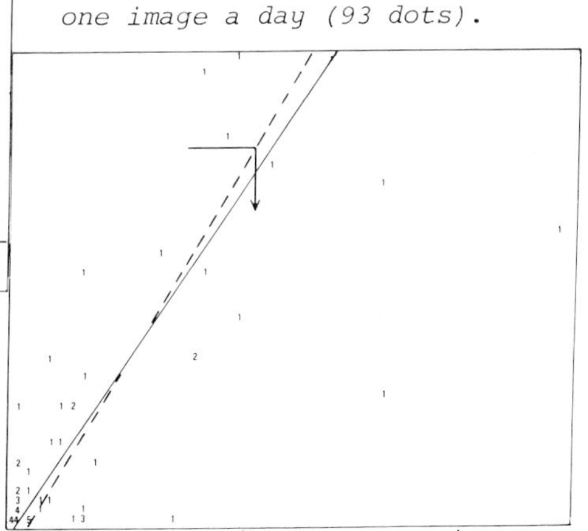

FIGS 1,2 & 3 Regression plots between observed (X-axis) and estimated (Y-axis) rainfall for Jan. 1979. Dashed lines are the best linear relationships computed by regression method; solid lines show perfect agreement.

depths of better spatial structure, monthly regressions were performed with sets of data cumulated over periods of various length. For 4 months among 6, the correlation coefficients and plotted patterns improved, presenting an optimum for rainy periods, 5 to 15 days long and separated by dry days (Fig. 2).

Further improvements were awaited from non linear relationships such as :

$$z = \sum_i p_i C_i^2 + \varepsilon \quad \text{or : } z = (\sum_i p_i C_i + \varepsilon)^2$$

in order to account for the greater variability of rainfall compared to that of cloud-cover. However, as table 1 shows, none of these methods produced markedly improved results, and so the linear model can be considered as sufficiently suitable to this case-study.

As more images were available for the month of January 1979, the sensitiveness to image frequency was tested for this period. As clouds appeared mostly as isolated cumulonimbi, the cloud-cover was assessed with one, two or three images for each day when they developed. Regression performed with such cloud-cover values provided correlation coefficientsgrowing from 0.75 to 0.82 as image frequency increased from 1 to 3 a day (Fig. 3). This is due to a better accounting of growth and motion of isolated cumulonimbi.

Table 1 - Correlation coefficients measuring the quality of the described regressions; (1) linear regression, (2) square root of rainfall depth and (3) square of cloud-cover unlinear regressions.

		(1)	(2)	(3)
Oct.	Daily data	0.57	0.56	0.46
	Monthly cumulated data	0.88	0.80	0.86
Jan.	Daily data	0.46	0.55	0.39
	Data cumulated over 3 periods	0.82	0.85	0.74

Spatial gage-satellite rainfall estimation combination

After the above appropriate satellite data conditionning step two sets of measurements are now available to estimate the rainfall depth at the ground level : the gage network that ponctually provides direct measurements and the satellite that provides a rainfall guess-field regularly distributed in space. These two devices appear to be complementary : the ponctual precision of the gages allowing satellite guess-field calibration and satellite coverage compensating for ground network scarcity.

A geostatiscal approach seems to be a good way to combine these two sources of information since the rainfall estimation derived from it would take into account the statistical properties of each measurement set and of their combination.

After a brief description of the so-called cokriging system-simple extension of kriging (now a well known technique in hydrosciences, see J.P. DELHOMME, 1978 or P. DELFINER, 1975) when several measurement sets are available, the statistical structure of the gage and satellite measurements will be analysed ; finally a comparison will be performed from the various maps corresponding to the interpolation derived from gages only or to a combination of satellite and gages data.

Cokriging : theoretical background. The purpose of this objective analysis technique is to provide an unbiased linear estimator minimizing the mean squared error of reconstitution.

Let $z^*_G(x_o)$ be the estimated value, at a given point x_o of the studied area, given by the following linear combination :

$$z^*_G(x_o) = \sum_{i=1}^{n} \lambda^i z_G^G(x_i^G) + \sum_{\alpha=1}^{N} \lambda^\alpha z_S(x_\alpha^S) \qquad (1)$$

where z_G and z_S represent the two types of measurements (ground and satellite) and (x_i^G , i=1,n) and (x_α^S α= 1,N) the corresponding networks of points or cells.

If this estimated value is required to be unbiased, its expectation must fit the expectation of the true value of the phenomenon :

$$E\, z^*_G(x_o) = E\, z\,(x_o) \qquad (2)$$

Since expectation is linear, replacement of (1) into (2) leads to:

$$\sum_{i=1}^{n} \lambda^i E\, z_G(x_i^G) + \sum_{\alpha=1}^{N} \lambda^\alpha E\, z_S(x_\alpha^S) = E\, z_G(x_o) \qquad (3)$$

When the variables z_G and z_S are supposed to be intrinsically stationary (i.e. second order stationarity of the first order increments of the variables) their expectations can be assumed locally constant in space ($E\, z_G(x) = m_G$ and $E\, z_S(x) = m_S$) and equation (3) yields the following system

$$\sum_{i=1}^{n} \lambda^i = 1 \qquad \sum_{\alpha=1}^{N} \lambda^\alpha = 0 \qquad (4)$$

If the estimated value (1) is also required to be optimal, in the sense of the minimization of the estimation variance, then the following partial derivatives must be set equal to zero :

$$\frac{\partial}{\partial \lambda^i} E(z^*_G(x_o)-z(x_o))^2 = 2\sum_{i=1}^{n} \lambda^j C_G(x_i^G,x_j^G) + 2\sum_{\alpha=1}^{N} \lambda^\alpha C_{GS}(x_i^G,x_\alpha^S) - 2C_G(x_i^G,x_o) \qquad (5)$$

and

$$\frac{\partial}{\partial \lambda^\alpha} E(z^*_G(x_o)-z(x_o))^2 = 2\sum_{\beta=1}^{N} \lambda^\beta C_S(x_\alpha^S,x_\beta^S) + 2\sum_{i=1}^{N} \lambda^i C_{GS}(x_i^G,x_\alpha^S) - 2C_{GS}(x_\alpha^S,x_o) \qquad (6)$$

the various direct and cross covariance are denoted C_G, C_S and C_{GS} (for instance $C_{GS}(x,x') = E\, z_G(x).z_S(x')$.

Annulation of the above derivatives combined with equations (4) gives the cokriging system where represents Lagrangian multipliers :

$$\left[\begin{array}{cc|cc} C_G(x_i^G,x_j^G) & C_{GS}(x_i^G, x_\alpha^S) & 1 & 0 \\ C_{GS}(x_\alpha^S,x_j^G) & C_S(x_\alpha^S, x_\beta^S) & 0 & 1 \\ \hline 1 & 0 & 0 & \\ 0 & 1 & & \end{array}\right] \cdot \left[\begin{array}{c} \lambda^i \\ \lambda^\alpha \\ \hline \mu_G \\ \mu_S \end{array}\right] = \left[\begin{array}{c} C_G(x_i^G,x_o) \\ C_{GS}(x_\alpha^S,x_o) \\ \hline 1 \\ 0 \end{array}\right] \qquad (6)$$

If the conditions of system (6) are fulfilled, the estimation variance can be written as follows :

$$E(z^*(x_o)-z(x_o))^2 = C_G(x_o,x_o) - \sum_{i=1}^{n} \lambda^i C_G(x_o,x_i^G) - \sum_{\alpha=1}^{N} \lambda^\alpha C_{GS}(x_\alpha^S,x_o) - \mu_G \qquad (7)$$

providing a good indicator of the expected precision of the estimator.

If only intrinsic stationnarity is assumed the covariances have to be replaced by variograms, in the same way as in the simple kriging context; for instance the cross variogram gets the following formulation :

$$\gamma_{GS}(x,x') = \tfrac{1}{2} E\,(z_G(x) - z_G(x')).(z_S(x)-z_S(x'))$$

When the covariances exist and are symetrical, the classical relationship:

$$\gamma_{GS}(x,x') = C_{GS}(x,x) - C_{GS}(x,x')$$

also valid for direct variograms, allows to demonstrate simply that an equivalent system to system (6) can be obtained replacing C by $-\gamma'$. This remark is also valid for expression (7).

Structure analysis. The different rainfall fields studied have, as a strong common characteristic, a general shape presenting a peak value located on the South East part of the region and a large rainfree area covering the North West remainding part.

This general trend of the phenomenon (also called drift) is consistently evaluated by both ground and satellite devices.

The most appropriate way to reduce the effect of such a drift on the structure identification would be to normalize the data using the climatological mean values over a large period. Unfortunately the available sample of events is too small to exhibit ensemble results for such a multirealization approach. So, each field is considered separately and, in order to cancel drift effects, the less affected direction is chosen (generally N45E) to compute the experimental variograms (i.e. only the couples of measurement points approximately oriented in that direction are selected).

As shown in table 2 and illustrated in Figure 4, the experimental

Table 2 - Description of the fitted models for the direct and cross variograms (for each variogram the sill, the range and the nugget effect are to be read succcessively).

	Direct variograms		Cross variogram
Event	Ground	Satellite	Ground vs sat.
Jan. 1-14	500 300 0	300 400 0	140 300 0
Jan. 15-26	40000 150 0	40000 400 0	30000 450 5000
Jan. 27-31	1500 200 900	4000 400 1000	1600 400 600
Mars	2500 250 0	2500 300 0	2500 300 0
Octobre	15000 300 0	3300 400 1800	5000 300 2000

cross and direct variograms have been modelled using a spherical model (i.e. showing a stabilization of its variations after a given distance-the range, around a given value-the sill).

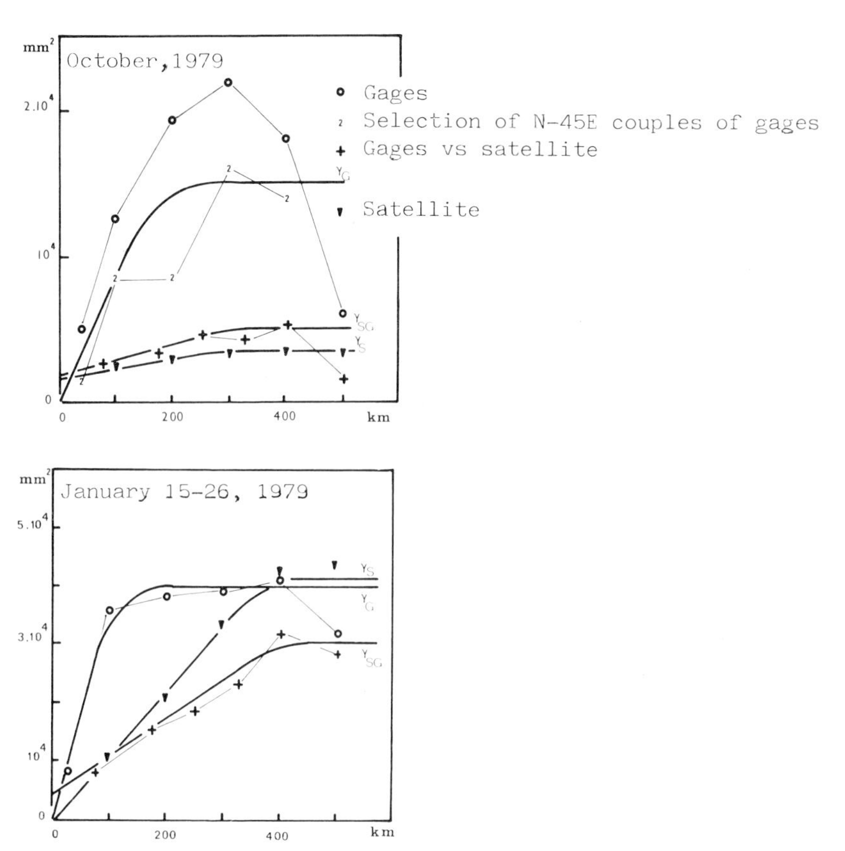

FIG.4 Experimental direct and cross variograms for two events; solid lines represent the theoretical model fitting experimental values.

It can be noted that ranges for satellite variograms are systematically larger than for ground variograms ; this fact is connected with the integrated or block averaged nature of the satellite measurements ; this should also lead to systematically lower sills : this is less evident in this experiment context where drift effects are certainly not fully filtered.

The cross structure is generally significant in the sense that sill values of cross variograms are of the same order magnitude that for the direct variograms ; the range values are consistent.

This structure analysis indicating a fairly good cofluctuation of the two signals, enables to foresee a good efficiency of the following attempt to combine these two kinds of rainfall measurements (i.e. there is a good chance that satellite data would help to fill the gap between the ground values).

Results. The various results obtained from the different steps of this study may be compared through contour maps of the rainfall fields estimated by (i) an appropriate processing of the satellite pictures (see part III), (ii) a classical interpolation of the ground measurements (actually performed by kriging) and (iii) a combination of these two estimations through cokriging.

For practical display reasons, figure 5 only shows the maps corresponding to one of the most caracteristic events (1979 january 15-26).

On one hand, a good agreement can be noted between the general shapes of the ground and satellite estimations even if satellite significantly

FIG.5 Contour maps of rainfall depths for a selected event. Map (1) is derived from satellite picture, (2) from gage only interpolation & (3) from a combination of data from both devices.

overestimates the rainfall in the Eastern part of the study area (comparison of maps 1 and 2). On the other hand, the introduction of satellite information in ground interpolation leads to significant modifications of the isolines in the regions where the ground network density in the lowest.

The addition of satellite information may also be appreciated by the plot of standard deviations of estimation provided either by kriging or cokriging (see formula 7). This indicator of the expected error of prediction is mapped for the selected event (see figure 6) showing, after the introduction of satellite information, a significant reduction of the area where the standard deviation exceeds 20 mm.

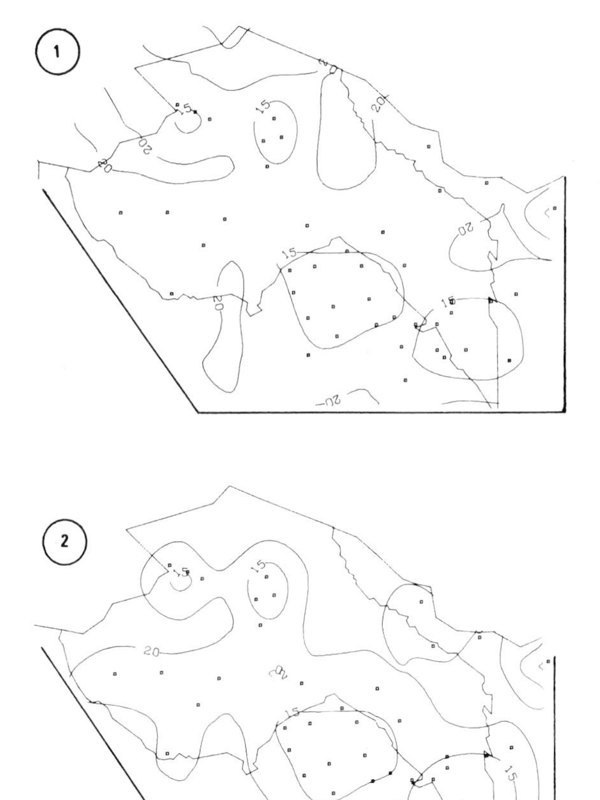

FIG.6 Contour maps of the estimation standard deviations predicted by (1) cokriging and (2) kriging for a selected event.

Concluding remarks

This study confirms that rainfall depth assesment from satellite data produces coherent results even when the rainfall parameters are computed by simple linear regression provided that the considered time step is large enough.

However, this classical statistical approach appears to be suitably complemented by using geostatistical concepts in order (i) to appreciate the coherence between satellite and gage measurements (by means of structure analysis) and (ii) to provide,. at unrecorded points, an "optimal" estimation of the rainfall depth (using the cokriging system).

Acknowledgments
We are grateful to Bureau de Recherches Géologiques et Minières, which provided us the opportunity of carrying out this study. It supplied us satellite images as well as raingage recordings.

The DMSP images were provided by the NOAA-CIRES World Data Center for Glaciology in Boulder (United States). As for the GOES I.O. images, they are collected by CMS-Météorologie Nationale de Lannion (France) during the GATE experiment.

References

Atlas, D., Eckerman, J., Meneghini, R., Moore, R.K., 1982, The outlook for precipitation measurements from space: Atmosphere Ocean, 20, p. 50-61.

Barret, E.C., 1971, The assessment of rainfall in north-eastern Oman through the integration of observations from conventional and satellite sources: Consultant's report to the Food and Agriculture Organization, 55 p.

Delhomme, J.P., 1978, Kriging in hydrosciences: Advan. Water ResourcesimO, 1(5), p. 251-266.

Delfiner, P., 1975, Linear estimation of non stationary spatial phenomena: Advanced geostatistics in the Mining Industry, M. Guarascio et al. Ed., Hingham- Mass., p. 49-68.

Van Dijk, A., 1981, Precipitation assessment from environmental satellite data for north-west Libya including the Grefara Plain: Consultant's report to the Food and Agriculture Organization, 45 p.

Hydrologic Applications of Space Technology (Proceedings of the Cocoa Beach Workshop, Florida, August 1985). IAHS Publ. no. 160, 1986.

Comparison of ELAS classification and density slicing Landsat data for water-surface area assessment

S. F. SHIH
Agricultural Engineering Department, University of Florida, Gainesville, Florida 32611, USA

Abstract

The techniques of density slicing and the Earth Resources Laboratory Application Software (ELAS) classification of the Landsat data were used to assess water-surface area. Landsat data dated 9/16/72, 4/19/73, 2/27/74, 3/17/74, 10/19/74. 1/22/76 and 2/9/76 were used to assess the water-surface areas in Lake Washington, Florida. The results showed that both techniques were quite applicable for assessing the water-surface area. The pixel-subset size (i.e. number of pixels displaying on the CRT screen for analysis) should be chosen as less pixels as possible without missing the coverage of the area of interest for improving the accuracy of density slicing. Using Band 5 and Band 7 in ELAS system can successfully classify the water surface of a lake. The deviation of the water-surface area assessment between the density slice method and ELAS classification was within 3%.

Introduction

Water-surface area assessment is an important information for improving the flood-plain management, flood insurance program, wetland assessment and management, lake storage estimation, and open channel flow computation, etc. The water-surface area can only be obtained if accurate data exists as to the area contours in conjunction with water stage. Such data rarely exists because of the extensive time and cost associated with conventional transect survey methods of collecting such data and the fact that they are subject to change over an extended period of time. Therefore, the assessment of the water-surface area poses many unique and difficult problems that warrant the use of recently developed Landsat remote sensing techniques to improve the water-surface area assessment.

Fortunately, the General Electric Image 100 located to the National Aeronautics and Space Administration (NASA), Kennedy Space Center, was relocated to the Institute of Food and Agricultural Sciences (IFAS) Remote Sensing and Image Analysis Laboratory (RSIAL), University of Florida, in January 1982. About 1300 Landsat computer compatible tapes were also relocated with the Image 100 facility. Within this large number of available tapes, water researchers have an opportunity to utilize these facilities for studying some water resources problems (Shih, 1984).

In 1982, Shih had used these Image 100 system and tapes to study the water-surface area assessment in the Lake Washington, Florida, by density slicing the spectral response in the near infrared Band 7 (0.1-1.1 μm) of the Landsat Multispectral Scanner (MSS) data. He concluded that the upper limit of 25 spectral response is the most suitable selection in his study. The density slicing is a procedure used to carry out the enhancement of the spectral response data. Quatization noise or spurious contouring may result if the slices are not chosen carefully. Particularly, for water bodies having shallow depths, marsh shores, and water quality problems, such measurement could be not only sensitive to the pixel-subset size selection (i.e. number of pixels displaying on the CRT screen for analysis), but also varying with time. The questions remain as to how the density slicing is affected by the pixel-subset size, and whether the spectral response within a lake water would be varied with the time. In the meantime, the Earth Resources Laboratory Application Software (ELAS) (Graham et al., 1980) has been adapted to the Image 100 to process the Landsat data, it is interesting to know whether the performance is different between the density slice method and the ELAS classification for assessing the water-surface area. Therefore, the purposes of this study were: (1) to evaluate the statistical parameter of density slicing the Landsat data with different pixel-subset sizes; (2) to compare the performance difference between the density slice method and the ELAS classification for assessing the water-surface area; (3) to investigate the spectral response within a lake water varying with time.

Materials and Methods

Study Site and Landsat Data: The Lake Washington, Florida was chosen in this study. Connor and Belanger (1981) reported that the water surface of the Lake Washington was 11.53 km^2 at the stage of 4.45 m. Seven Landsat data dated 9/16/72, 4/19/73, 2/27/74, 3/17/74, 10/19/74, 1/22/76, and 2/9/76 were used in this study.

Landsat Pixel-Subset Size Selection and Density Slicing: Three Landsat pixel-subset sizes were chosen in this study, i.e. 512x512, 256x256, 128x128 pixel data in the form of computer compatible tapes (CCT). Each size was tried twice for density slicing the water-surface area of the Lake Washington by using the Image 100 system. The statistics parameters in each trail included the spectral bounds (i.e. the lower and upper bands, respectively, assigned by the program such that the area of the histogram between the limits is equal to the percentage defined by the Histogram Kejection Levels), delta (i.e. the inclusive difference between the lower and upper bounds expressed in terms of effective resolution), peak (i.e. the maximum histogram value expressed in pixels), mean, variance, and training area (i.e. the number of pixels contained within the training site), and the alarmed area (i.e. the number of pixels in the entire scene which fall within the lower and upper bounds defined previously). Three dates of 9/6/72, 1/2/76, and 2/9/76 Landsat data were analyzed in this study.

ELAS Classification: Computer classification of Landsat data using CCT's was also achieved at the Remote Sensing and Imaging Analysis Laboratory of the Institute of Food and Agricultural Sciences. A complex set of computer algorithms were used to classify pixels (picture elements) from the digital number reflecting the spectral response. The General Electric Image 100 was used in conjunction with the Earth Resources Laboratory Applications Software (ELAS) for Landsat data classification. ELAS has been specifically designed to analyze digital data such as those assembled from digitized maps or any airborne MSS data (Graham et al., 1980). The algorithm that was used is the maximum likelihood, or Gaussian distribution approach. As the name implies, the algorithm determines classes by associating all pixels to the normal distribution. The classifier quantitatively evaluates both the variance and correlation of the category spectral response patterns when classifying an unknown pixel. Use of the GE Image 100 in conjunction with the ELAS to identify the land use category from the Landsat CCT data is designated as the ELAS classification method. A cloud-free scene of 6 September, 1972 was chosen for the analysis.

The spectral response of each 0.45 ha pixel represents an average reflectance from all land use and land cover. Thus, grouping or categorizing helps to eliminate spatial disturbances. Our interest was to minimize those disturbances to the point where the data is useful. According to the characteristics of each band of the MSS system (Shih, 1984 and Still and Shih, 1984), the Band 5 (0.6-0.7 μm) emphasizes cultural features and exposed soil and rock surfaces and assists in the analysis of the surface water conditions, and the Band 7 (0.8-1.1 μm) penetrates best through haze and light clouds and also emphasizes live vegetation and land-use boundaries. Thus, the spectral response from Bands 5 and 7 are used in this study for classifying the water-surface area of the Lake Washington.

Spectral Response Varying With Time: Seven dates of 9/6/72, 4/19/73, 2/27/74, 3/27/74, 10/19/74, 1/22/76, and 2/9/76 Landsat CCT tapes were chosen for studying the spectral response changing over time for assessing the water-surface area in the Lake Washington. The 128x128 pixel data size was used. The spectral bounds, mean, and variance expressed as effective resolution were computed for each band.

Results and Discussion

Statistical Parameters Difference Between Pixel Subset Size: The statistical parameters of spectral bounds, delta, peak, mean, variance, training area, and alarmed area of each trials are listed in Table 1. Several observations can be made from Table 1. First, the spectral bounds, delta, mean, and variance appear to be similar to all three pixel-subset sizes. Second, the peak and training area are inversely related to the pixel-subset size, i.e. the larger size in pixel-subset selection, the lower response in peak and training area. This could lead to an unstable condition for estimating the water-surface area which will be discussed in the following section. Third, the alarmed areas are not much different except that 128x128 pixel subset had about three times larger than other two sizes. Fourth, one of the major differences between two trails within the same pixel subset is the training area.

Water-Surface Area Assessed by Density Slicing: The results of water-surface area in Lake Washington as density slicing the Landsat data dated 9/6/72, 1/22/76, and 2/9/76 for two trails in each pixel subset are listed in Table 2. The deviations (D) between two trails were inversely related to the pixel-subset size (PS), i.e.

For 9/6/72 data

$$D = -0.023 + 0.339\ PS \qquad r = 0.88 \qquad [1]$$

For 1/22/76 data

$$D = -0.126 + 0.531\ PS \qquad r = 0.95 \qquad [2]$$

For 2/9/76 data

$$D = 0.071 + 0.789\ PS \qquad r = 0.99 \qquad [3]$$

where PS = 1, 0.5, and 0.25 representing the pixel-subset size of 512x512, 256x256, and 218x218, respectively. As far as the stability of the density slicing is concerned, the smaller deviation indicates that the more stabilized technique is implemented. Thus, the pixel-subset size should be chosen as less pixels as possible without missing the coverage of the area of interest. The lake water stage recorded on 9/6/72 was 4.51 m which was very close to the stage of 4.45 m as reported by Connor and Belganer (1981). They also reported that the lake surface area was 11.53 km^2 which was respectively about 6, 4, 5% larger than the area estimated from the Landsat data dated 9/6/72, 1/22/76, and 2/9/76 (Table 2). These discrepencies could be due to the lake stage differences, inherent limitation of the density slicing technique, and/or, the accuracy of the ground-truth information. But it can be concluded that the density slicing is quite applicable for assessing the water-surface area.

Water-Surface Area Assessed by ELAS Classification: The pixel size used in the ELAS Classification was 128x128 pixels of the Landsat data dated

Table 1. Statistical parameters difference between pixel subset sizes on the Landsat data 6 September 1972.

Pixel subset sizes	No. of trails	Bands	Spectral bounds	Delta	Peak	Mean	Variance
512x512	1	4	0-12	13	525	8.56	13.04
		5	5-7	3	556	5.69	0.22
		6	0-21	22	419	4.19	15.18
		7	1-5	5	553	2.19	0.32
		Training Area = 812, Alarmed Area = 14125					
	2	4	0-12	13	390	8.98	10.43
		5	5-7	3	432	5.77	0.19
		6	0-35	36	271	4.90	21.20
		7	1-6	6	394	2.18	0.34
		Training Area = 572, Alarmed Area = 14626					
256x256	1	4	0-12	13	1262	8.40	14.72
		5	5-7	3	1524	5.78	0.18
		6	0-21	22	1020	4.55	15.60
		7	1-6	6	1327	2.21	0.34
		Training Area = 1980, Alarmed Area = 12512					
	2	4	0-12	13	848	8.82	11.46
		5	5-7	3	934	5.73	0.20
		6	0-35	36	674	4.82	20.19
		7	1-6	6	904	2.15	0.33
		Training Area = 1292, Alarmed Area = 12670					
128x128	1	4	0-12	13	7428	8.37	14.62
		5	5-7	3	8476	5.73	0.20
		6	0-21	22	5972	4.46	15.34
		7	1-6	6	7900	2.21	0.35
		Training Area = 11716, Alarmed Area = 41690					
	2	4	0-12	13	3728	8.69	12.52
		5	5-6	2	4076	5.71	0.21
		6	0-35	36	2880	4.84	21.04
		7	1-6	6	3994	2.17	0.33
		Training Area = 5740, Alarmed Area = 39694					

9/16/72. The Landsat scene used for this study produced 8 spectrally different classes, i.e., A, B, C, D, E, F, G, and H (Fig. 1). These classes were plotted on a scatter diagram of Band 7 against Band 5. This diagram with the aid of the CRT was used to determine to which land cover belongs. The class F was identified as the water-surface area of the Lake Washington. The spectral response in Band 7 as estimated ELAS classification was 2.29 which was very close to the value of 2.19 as estimated by the density Slicing method (Table 1). However, the spectral response in Band 5 was 11.88 which was almost twice the value of 5.72 as estimated by the density slicing method (Table 1). This difference is mainly due to a digital num-

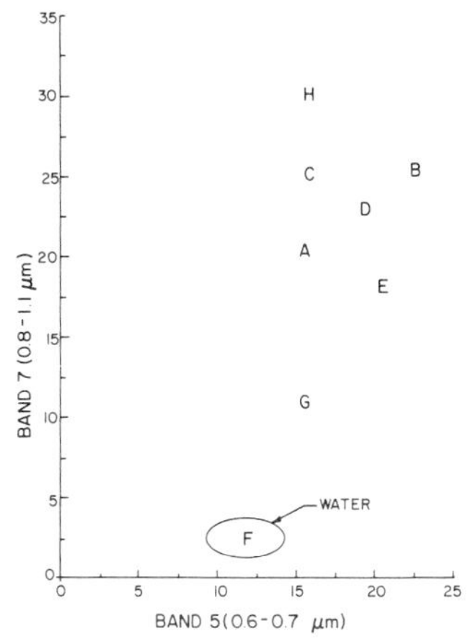

FIG.1 Scatter diagram between Band 5 (0.6-0.7µm) and Band 7 (0.8-1.1µm) for the Landsat scene on 16 September, 1972.

ber in Band 5 ranging from 0 to 63 was used in density slicing and ranging from 0 to 127 was used in the ELAS approach. The ELAS program is also able to compute the area of each class. The water-surface area assessed by the ELAS approach was 11.13 km^2 which was about 3% larger than the 10.82 km^2 as assessed by the density slicing method, but it was about 3% less than the ground truth information of 11.53 km^2. This slight discrepancy could be due to the same causes as mentioned above. This result indicates that the ELAS classification appears to be quite an applicable tool for assessing the water-surface area.

Spectral Radiance Varying Over Time: The spectral bounds, mean, and variance expressed as effective resolution for seven dates during the period of 9/6/72 to 2/9/76 are shown in Table 3. Although several variables can influence the magnitude of spectral response, the mean values during four-year period (Table 3) show a tendency that the magnitude of the spectral

Table 2. Water-surface-area difference between training size and number of trails with 4-bands on different dates of Landsat data.

Pixel subset sizes	No. of trails	Water-surface area of Lake Washington, Fla.		
		9/6/72	1/22/76	2/9/76
		km^2		
512x512	1	10.610	11.542	11.198
	2	10.900	11.112	12.044
	Diff.	0.290	0.430	0.846
256x256	1	10.705	11.109	10.853
	2	10.931	11.173	11.360
	Diff.	0.226	0.064	0.507
128x128	1	10.811	11.099	10.862
	2	10.820	11.042	11.102
	Diff.	0.009	0.057	0.240

Table 3. Spectral radiance varied with time in Lake Washington, Florida

Dates	Bands	Spectral bounds	Mean	Variance	Lake stage (m)
9/6/72	4	0-12	8.37	14.62	4.51
	5	5-7	5.73	0.20	
	6	0-21	4.46	15.34	
	7	1-6	2.21	0.35	
4/19/73	4	9-11	9.48	0.28	4.45
	5	4-7	5.38	0.25	
	6	3-5	3.67	0.24	
	7	1-3	1.80	0.33	
2/27/74	4	8-11	9.19	0.23	3.89
	5	4-7	5.81	0.19	
	6	3-6	4.47	0.32	
	7	1-4	2.21	0.36	
3/17/74	4	8-10	8.29	0.21	3.79
	5	4-6	5.20	0.37	
	6	2-4	3.31	0.24	
	7	0-3	1.11	0.32	
10/19/74	4	7-9	8.16	0.19	4.83
	5	3-5	3.96	0.13	
	6	2-4	2.38	0.24	
	7	0-3	0.74	0.34	
1/22/76	4	2-4	3.55	0.25	3.68
	5	1-4	2.89	0.17	
	6	0-3	1.39	0.35	
	7	0-3	0.59	0.31	
2/9/76	4	3-5	4.01	0.10	3.68
	5	2-5	3.67	0.23	
	6	1-3	2.05	0.35	
	7	0-4	0.12	0.14	

response is decreasing as the time progresses. As the lake stages show in Table 3, it is obvious that the spectral response decrease is not related to the lake stage change. The reason for causing this decrease is unknown, perhaps the water quality or other environmental conditions have been changed over four-year period. A further study is needed to confirm this statement.

Summary and Conclusions

Water-surface area assessment is an important information for improving the flood-plain management, flood insurance, wetland assessment and management, lake storage estimation, and open channel flow computation, etc. Assessment of water-surface area by conventional methods is expensive and time consuming, thus, an alternative method should be developed. Two techniques of density slicing and the Earth Resources Laboratory Application Software (ELAS) classification of the Landsat data were used in this study. Landsat data dated 9/16/72, 4/19/73, 2/27/74, 3/17/74, 10/19/74,

1/22/76, and 2/9/76 were used to assess the water-surface area of Lake Washington, Florida. Several conclusions are made as follows.

The pixel-subset size (i.e. number of pixels displaying on the CRT screen for analysis) not only can influence the stabilization of the density slicing but also it should be chosen as less pixels as possible without missing the coverage of the area of interest.

The peak and training area involving the number of pixel are inversely related to the pixel-subset size, i.e., the larger size in pixel-subset selection, the lower response in peak and training area.

Using Band 5 (0.5-0.7 μm) and Band 7 (0.8-1.1 μm) in ELAS system can successfully classify the water-surface area of a lake.

Both density slice method and ELAS classification are quite applicable tools for assessing the water-surface area. The deviation between these two methods was within 3%.

Although several variables can influence the magnitude of spectral response, the mean values during four-year period (1972-76) show a tendency that the magnitude of the spectral response is decreasing as the time progresses. The reason causing this decrease is unknown, perhaps the water quality or other environmental conditions have been changed over four-year period. A further study is needed to confirm this statement.

Acknowledgments

The author wishes to thank Mr. D. Jordan for his assistance in this study and to the IFAS's Remote Sensing and Image Analysis Laboratory for analyzing the Landsat data.

References

Connor, J. N. and T. V. Belanger. 1981. Groundwater Seepage in Lake Washington and the Upper St. Johns River Basin, Florida. Water Resources Bulletin., Vol. 17(5): 798-805.

Graham, M. H., B. G. Junkin, M. T. Kalcic, R. W. Pearson, and B. R. Seyforth. 1980. ELAS - Earth Resources Laboratory Applications Software. Vol. 2, A-14 - A-17.

Shih, S. F. 1982. Using Landsat Data to Estimate Reservoir Storage, Proc. of Eighth Intl. Symposium on Machine Processing of Remotely Sensed Data. Purdue University, Laboratory for Applications of Remote Sensing, Purdue University, West Lafayette, Indiana, USA. pp. 321-326.

Shih, S. F. 1984. IFAS Landsat Data Availability and Its Potential Applications. Soil and Crop Science Society of Florida Proceedings, Vol. 43: 21-25.

Still, D. A. 1984. Classification of Landsat Data and Rainfall Analysis For Use In Runoff Estimation. M.S. Thesis, Agricultural Engineering Department, University of Florida, Gainesville, Florida.

Hydrologic Applications of Space Technology (Proceedings of the Cocoa Beach Workshop, Florida, August 1985). IAHS Publ. no. 160, 1986.

Water levels of a sahelian lake (Mare d'Oursi — Burkina Faso)

P. CHEVALLIER
Centre Orstom, B.P. V51, Abidjan, Ivory Coast
M. LOINTIER
Centre Orstom, B.P. 165, 97323 Cayenne, French Guyana
B. LORTIC
Centre Orstom, 70, rte d'Aulnay, 93140 Bondy, France

Orstom: Institut Français de Recherche Scientifique pour le Développement en Coopération

Abstract
The authors present a modelisation of the water levels as daily computed of the "Mare d'Oursi", a sahelian lake (Burkina Faso), on the basis of a "space-gridded model". This deterministic model uses a grid to divide the catchment into several squares. A mean production (rainfall and runoff) function is alloted to each squares. A certain number of natural or artificial pools may be introduced and taken into consideration for the transfer function to the catchment outlet.

Two original methods have been brought into the model elaborated and fitted to the specific conditions of the "Mare d'Oursi":
(1) Runoff simulation : The characteristics of the production function are deduced directly from measures of runoff and rainfall on experimental plots using a rainfall simulator.
(2) Remote sensing : The surface features of the soils are the main factors of the rainfall-runoff function. A map of these surface features for the whole catchment is drawn from a multispectral classification of LANDSAT data. Thus, the physiographical characteristics of each square are automatically deduced from this numerical representation.

This method has been tested three years running through field observations. Extremely dry and humid conditions, as well as a mean condition were simulated.

Introduction

Classical hydro-pluviometric observations have been carried out during six years (1976-1981) on the representative watershed of "Mare d'Oursi". The use of rainfall simulation on the watershed of Polaka (9,14 km2) and Jalafanka (0,80 km2) enabled us to draw up a first attempt at reproduce flooding from the results obtained from the representative plots of the morpho-structural units (Valentin, 1981 ; Chevallier, 1982).

It seemed interesting to employ two other recent tools of hydrology in combination with rainfall simulation :
(1) remote sensing for the mapping of the morphostructural units.
(2) the Orstom-Ecole de Mines's space gridded model the determinism of which is particularly well adapted.

It seems unnecessary to detail the site and the environment of the "Mare d'Oursi"'s basins which have been fully described by Chevallier and al. (1985), except to mention that the study site is located in the north of Burkina Faso in the heart of the Sahelian climatic zone. The average annual rainfall is about 400 mm. The varied landscapes are representative of the region known as the "Boucle du Niger".

Rainfall Simulation and Space Gridded Modeling

Space gridded modeling has been improved since 1972 by Girard (ORSTOM) with, at first, collaboration of scientists of Institut National de la Recherche Scientifique du Québec (INRS-Eau) (Girard, Morin, Charbonneau, 1972). Later, the E.N.S.M. of Paris hydrologists worked with them, introducing underground component.

The first step of space gridding is the representation of the watershed by squares. The size of the squares being adapted to the basin physiology and morphology.

On this set of representative squares of the hydrological system, we define five interconnected functions wich modelise the water cycle :

(1) input function representing contributions to the system (mainly rainfall, occasionally external contribution from surface or underground flows).

(2) production function (for each kind of soil) defining the hydro-assessment, i.e. the distribution of inputs between evaporation, runoff and infiltration (superficial and underground storage).

(3) surface transfer function defining the surface water transit conditions, from one square to another.

(4) underground transfer function defining underground water transit conditions.

(5) surface/underground crossing function giving mutual exchange conditions.

These five functions must be perfectly defined in space and time (choice of period of calculation compatible with the problem to be solved).

The production function is the essential element in modeling. Each surface feature unit determines its own function. Several production functions may be found in a single square. They contribute proportionally to the surface occupied by each feature unit on the square.

To study the "Mare d'Oursi", it seemed interesting to employ a production function obtained directly from the results on the experimental plots with a rainfall simulator (Chevallier, 1982). Priority is given to runoff since, for a given plot, the simulator produces a depth of flow depending of the height and the antecedent precipitation index (API).

A characteristic equation for an experimental plot can be drawn up from rainfall simulation, and consequently for a unit of surface (an experimental plot represents one unit or "theme").

The equation can be writen :

$$QR = AA * P + AB * API1 + AC * P * API1 - AD$$

where QR is the depth of flow,
AA, AB, AC, AD are constant characteristics,
P the height of rainfall,
API1 the value of the antecedeant precipitaion index at the onset of the shower which produce runoff.

Girard and Rodier (1979) suggest an equivalent calculation for short periods of time with a slightly different characteristic equation.

Two versions of the space-gridded model have been used for the

"Mare d'Oursi" :
(1) A "coupled" model (Girard, Ledoux, Villeneuve, 1981) was developed jointly by the "Laboratoire d'Hydrologie de l'Orstom" and the "Centre d'Informatique Géologique de l'Ecole des Mines de Paris". It uses the fives interconnected base functions to model the water cycle. In the Mare d'Oursi case , this model was used for the simulation of flood of the Polaka basin. The recorded outflows are entirely due to runoff and only the production function and transfer function have been used. The selected period of calculation was 36 mins (1/40th day) corresponding to the relatively short periods of flooding which last 3-5 hours without increasing the number of iterations in order to keep costs low.
(2) The main inconvenience of the "coupled" model is that it doesn't take into account hydraulic development of the surface area or of natural changes. The MODLAC model was design to counterbalance this and to help in the planning of the rational management of surface water (Girard, 1982). This space-gridded model simulates the flows on a hydrological system made up of a set of basins. Each basin may include a certain number of natural or artificial reservoirs. It was selected to simulate the filling of Mare d'Oursi, taking into account the vast flood plains which are comparable to reservoirs.

Landscape Mapping and Satellite Remote Sensing

LOTERIE Procedure Used for Surface Feature Mapping (Lointier and Lortic, 1984).--In space-gridded model, production functions are defined for a surface unit which presumed to have a homogeneous surface. The production function is a linear combination of production functions for each of the surface units present in one square, obtained in proportion of the types of surfaces).It is therefore necessary to draw up an accurate, exhaustive map of the studied area.

To study the origin of floods with the help of a rainfall simulator, (Chevallier, 1982) and Valentin (1981) a map of the morpho-structural differentiations of the Polaka watershed was required. This approach has been repeated since in other basins in Burkina Faso, Ivory Coast, Congo, Niger and Togo.

This map (fig. 1) shows 11 units and directly fits for the keying space gridded models. However, this method is only possible for small areas such as the Polaka watershed (9,14 km2) and requires an experienced pedologist and as surface areas increase, the problem quickly becomes insoluble.

Satellite remote sensing is therefore an ideal new technique for the constitution of landuse data base (Lointier and Pieyns, 1981). The Sahel with its ground easily visible by satellite, clearly defined landscapes, sparse vegetation and few human settlement appears as a particularly interesting region for such studies.

The mapping of morpho-structural differentiations of the Polaka basin provides an excellent "ground truth" for the keying of MSS data obtained from satellites.

For the "Mare d'Oursi" region there are many views (covering a surface of 180 x 180 km centred on a point just West of the town Dori) taken by the scanners of the American satellites Landsat.

The image selected for analysis is that of 4th feb. 76. The 4 bands of the MSS are available.

By image processing, two new band are available (7-5 and 7+5) made up from the original bands 5 and 7. The neo-band 7-5 gives the state of the vegetation (but not only that) and 7+5 gives the surface brightness, relief and hydrographic network (Lortic, 1982).

A "multivariate" analysis using these two new bands with the LOTERIE procedure (Lointier and Pieyns, 1981) enabled us to determine a certain number of "lots" by using the "ground truth" map and knowledge of the environment. These 48 lots can be classified under 9 headings :

(1) Shifting sands, e.g. the Oursi dune.
(2) Rocks (gabbros, green rocks and hardpans).
(3) Hardpans debris.
(4) Fragments of various rocks.
(5) Gravels.
(6) Granitic and coarse sands.
(7) Surface crust.
(8) Fine sand, dune bar.
(9) Vegetation.

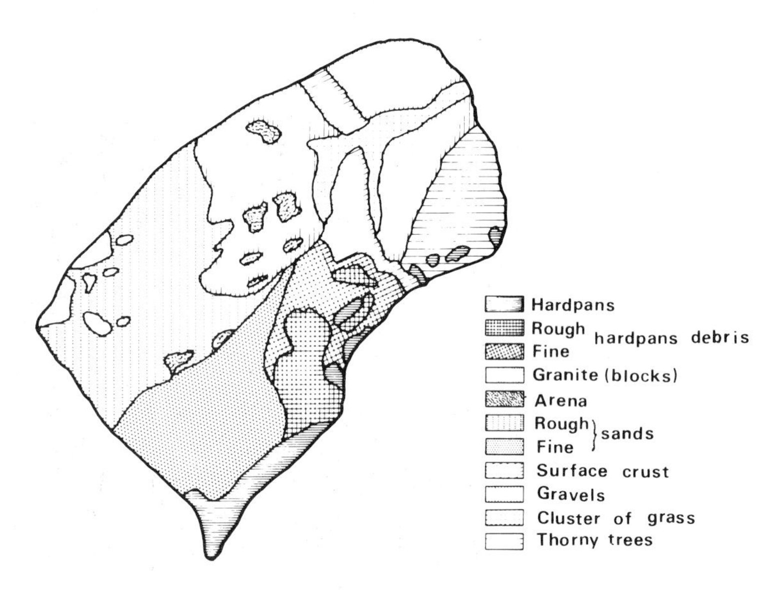

FIG.1 Morpho-structural differentiations of Polaka watershed.

The map of these 9 ground surface types for the Polaka watershed can be compared with that drawn up on the ground by Valentin (1981). It demonstrates that the extension of this "ground truth" method to the whole of Mare d'Oursi basin may be used with very little error.

For easy reading, class # 9 was artificially divided into a class # 9 (vegetation and low ground) and a class # 10 (areas of free water, covered or not by aquatic vegetation) from previous knowledge of the natural environment.

This image processing was done directly on screen of the

specialize computer Pericolor 1000 which has a certain number of preprogrammed functions for image analysis. The LOTERIE procedure is automatically used from parameter introduced by the operator.

Automatic Space Gridding.--The following processing is linked to the technical possibilities of P 1000 and we are interested mainly in the final results. The ground survey satellites Landsat give images made up of parallelograms (pixel) 56x79 m (approx. 0,45.10-2 km2). The result of the LOTERIE classification is to give each pixel a class number wich can be materialized on the screen by a colour. One characteristic of Pericolor is to visualize a square pixel. The image (256x256 pixels) is geographically false : a square on the ground becomes a parallelogram on the screen lying on an axis WSW/ENE. In order to represent the whole watershed of the "Mare d'Oursi" it is necessary to divide it into two parts (east and west), each part covering a surface of 14,3x20,2 km. Markers can be used on the Pericolor to define various limits. These markers are used to draw the basic squares of the space gridded model. The main difficulty is the necessary correction of the geographical distortion. The drawing of straight lines is carried out automatically by a program. The result of east half of the "Mare d'Oursi" watershed is shown in fig. 2.

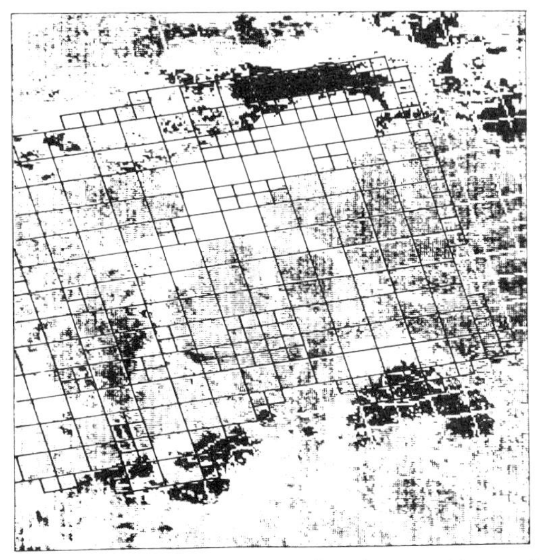

FIG.2 East part of the "Mare d'Oursi" watershed; copy of the Pericolor screen.

A manual slide is used to pick out each square and to obtain instantaneously the percentage of the 10 classes comprised in each. These results can be transferred as they are to the routine GEOCOU. This program characterizes the average production function of a given square by composing.

For example the following table gives the characteristics of a few squares selected from the "Mare d'Oursi".

Table 1 : Correspondence of selected squares :

number of square	percentage for each lot								
	1	2	3	4	5	6	7	8	9
14	97							3	
95									100
208				5		38	40		17
234					43	38	8	10	
345			1	47			47		5
405		82	11						7

Square # 14 represents the Oursi dune ;
95 the lake of Oursi ;
208 the flat open country of Taïma ;
234 the middle of Taïma watershed ;
345 the lower part of Tchalol watershed ;
405 the hillock of Kolel.

Results

The Model Adjustment.--The space-gridded model is adjusted mainly from the parameter of the production function , but it is difficult to achieve. Although the production function is quite representative of the hydrodynamics of the soil unit, the response curve of the model must be adequate.

As far as the "Mare d'Oursi" is concerned, the production functions are entirely defined by the results of the rainfall simulation which are used without any modification (Chevallier, 1982). The observations made from the study of the Polaka watershed are applied to the whole watershed of the "Mare d'Oursi".

Comparison Between the Levels Observed and the Modelized Levels in the "Mare d'Oursi".--The production functions of the space-gridded model were not subjected to any basic modification from the Polaka watershed (9,14 km2) to the "Mare d'Oursi" watershed (263 km2). It is easy to shift from the coupled model to the model with reservoirs since the production functions are evaluated in a similar way.

The model was tested in order to evaluate the water levels of the "Mare d'Oursi" in 1978, 1979 and 1980 using an initial readings of 2,88 m on January 1st, 1978 (it must be added that the drying level is close to 1,00 m).

Figure 3 shows the comparative results of the observed and modelized levels of the "Mare d'Oursi". The time interval used to make evaluations is the days, but in order to make the interpretation easier, the readings considered are those corresponding to the first day of each month.

One can note that the model is quite adequate, except maybe for the maximum value observed in 1978 along with its consequences on the following low value. This difference can be accounted for only by the monthly evapotranspiration the mean value of which remained unchanged over the three years. The latter ranges from 7 to 10 mm/day and owing to a drier and more windy climate, it can be subjected to variations which can be notable, when cumulated.

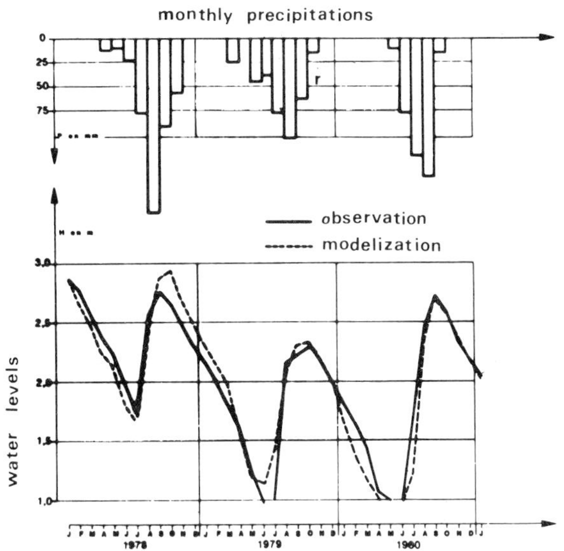

FIG.3 Observed and modeled levels of the "Mare d'Oursi".

Simulation of Levels in the "Mare d'Oursi" under Different Extreme and Mean Rainfall Conditions.--It is interesting to use modelization in order to simulate the variations of the levels of the "Mare d'Oursi" under specific conditions. Three fictitious rainfall events were selected from the Gorom Gorom raingauge station. It is a question of repeating three times the same annual rainfall sequence and of observing the evolution of the water levels in the "Mare d'Oursi".

(1) First hypothesis (extremely humid) : the year 1958 is repeated three times and the total rainfall amount to 691 mm, which corresponds to a humid 50-years return period.

(2) Second hypothesis (mean) : the year 1967 is repeated three times and the total rainfall amount to 465 mm and are roughly equal to the interannual mean.

(3) Third hypothesis (extremely dry) : the year 1971 is repeated three times and the total rainfall amount to 200 mm, which corresponds to a dry 100-year return period.

The simulation was applied in the three hypotheses on the basis of the rather low reading of 2,88 m (corresponding to January 1st, 1978).

Figure 4 shows the results obtained and leads to the following conclusions :

(1) First hypothesis.-- The general level of the "Mare" increases regularly up to 6,00 m and above it, wich is considered as the overflowing level (levelling amounts to 6,33 m, but such amounts of rainfall are likely to lead to erosion at the potential outlet). Therefore, it is possible that the "Mare d'Oursi" overflow over the last years.

(2) Second hypothesis.-- The levels of the "Mare d'Oursi" tend to reach an equibrium ranging from 2,50 m to 4,30 m, wich would make the illusion during the periods of mean or balanced rainfall and urge the people to believe that the "Mare" was perennial, thus leading them to use it. A return to sucessions of rainfall closer to the interannual mean would allow the "Mare d'Oursi" to recover its equilibrium.

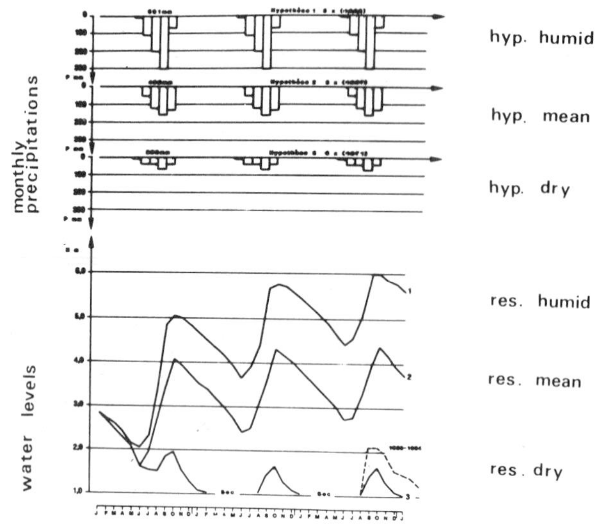

FIG.4 Simulation of levels in the "Mare d'Oursi".

(3) Third hypothesis. -- The figure speaks for itself. The "Mare" is drying up from February to July, such was the case over the last years. It can be observed that the variations recorded in the 1983-1984 year (maximum level amounting to 2,17 m in August and drying up in early March) are hardly better than those recorded for the extreme simulation.

Conclusion

Therefore, one can realize that the comparison of these new methods of research in surface hydrology, namely the rainfall simulation and the satellite remote sensing with a rather efficient determinist model gives quite satisfactory results in the Sahelian zone where the green cover exerts a small influence.

It is encouraging, but there are still some difficulties in applying this type of approach to much more complex environments such as the forest or the dense savannah where vegetation tends to prevail over the soil surface.

As part of the Hyperbav Project carried out in the Ivory Coast since 1983, in a humid savannah zone, one plans to test again the method by using the SPOT satellite data if they are of good quality.

References

Chevallier, P., 1982, Simulation de pluie sur deux bassins versants sahéliens (Mare d'Oursi - Burkina Faso): Cah. Orstom, sér. Hydrol., vol. XIX, n°4.

Chevallier, P., Claude, J., Pouyaud, B., Bernard, A., 1985, Pluies et crues au Sahel. Hydrologie de la Mare d'Oursi. Burkina Faso. (1976-1981).: Travaux et Documents de l'Orstom n°190, Paris.

Girard, G., 1975, Application du modèle à discrétisation spatiale au bassin de l'Oued Ghorfa (Mauritanie).: Cah. Orstom, sér. Hydrol., vol. XII, n°3.

Girard, G., 1982, Modélisation des écoulements de surface sur des bassins hydrologiques équipés de réservoirs. Modèle MODLAC.: Cah. Orstom, sér. Hydrol., vol. XIX, n°2.

Girard, G., Ledoux, E., Villeneuve, J.P., 1981, Le modèle couplé. Simulation conjointe des écoulements de surface et des écoulements souterrains dans un système hydrologique.: Cah. Orstom, sér. Hydrol., vol. XVIII, n°4.

Girard, G., Morin, G., Charbonneau, R., 1972, Modèle précipitation-débit à discrétisation spatiale.: Cah. Orstom, sér. Hydrol., vol. IX, n°4.

Girard, G., Rodier, J.A., 1979, Application de modèles mathématiques déterministes à l'étude des crues et de l'écoulement annuel en zone sahélienne.: Proceedings of the Canberra Symposium, dec. 1979, IAHS/AISH Publication n°128.

Lointier, M., Lortic, B., 1984, Mare d'Oursi. Traitement numérique de la vue Landsat du 4 février 1976.: Orstom, Cayenne.

Lointier , M., Pieyns, S., 1981, Télédétection n°4. Méthodologie de constitution d'une base de données d'occupation du sol par télédétection.: Orstom, Initiation et documents techniques n°47, Paris.

Lortic, B., 1982, Création de nouveau canaux par méthode photographiques.: Actes du Symposium International de la Commission VII de la SIPT, Toulouse, sept. 1982.

Valentin, C., 1981, Esquisse au 1/25 000 des différenciations morpho-structurales de la surface des sols d'un petit bassin versant sahélien (Polaka - Oursi, Nord Haute-Volta).: Orstom, Adiopodoumé.

3 Soil moisture and evapotranspiration

Hydrologic Applications of Space Technology (Proceedings of the Cocoa Beach Workshop, Florida, August 1985). IAHS Publ. no. 160, 1986.

Assessment of preplanting soil moisture using airborne microwave sensors

T. J. JACKSON
USDA-ARS Hydrology Laboratory, Beltsville, Maryland, USA
M. E. HAWLEY
University of Virginia, Charlottesville, Virginia, USA
J. SHUIE, P. E. O'NEILL & M. OWE
NASA Goddard Space Flight Center, Greenbelt, Maryland, USA
V. DELNORE & R. W. LAWRENCE
NASA Langley Research Center, Hampton, Virginia, USA

Abstract

Preplanting soil moisture assessment is necessary for agricultural management and has a significant influence on crop yield in the Texas panhandle region. The Texas High Plains Underground Water Conservation District invests considerable time and money in developing a soil moisture deficit map each year in the hopes of achieving optimal water use for irrigation. Microwave sensors are responsive to surface soil moisture and, if used in this application, could provide much more timely and detailed information than is currently available. For this reason, an experiment was conducted in 1984 to evaluate the potential of passive microwave aircraft mounted sensors. Microwave radiometer data were collected over a 2700 km^2 area near Lubbock, Texas, with a processed resolution of 0.32 km^2. These data were ground registered and converted to estimates of soil moisture using an appropriate model. Analyses indicate that the system provides an efficient means for mapping variations in soil moisture over large areas.

I. Introduction

Soil moisture information is valuable in agricultural applications ranging from on-farm irrigation and trafficability decisions to large area water management and drought assessment. In order to be useful to regional water managers, as well as to individual farmers, this information must be collected in a timely manner over an extensive area, yet still provide accurate information on specific fields.

An example of regional soil moisture assessment is the preplanting survey conducted in the spring of each year by the U. S. Department of Agriculture Soil Conservation Service (SCS) and Texas High Plains Underground Water Conservation District No. 1. in the Texas Panhandle. These agencies collect over 180 point samples over a 240,000 km^2 area and produce a soil water deficit map as shown in Figure 1 (Risinger, 1984). This map is developed from the point measurements by interpolation and contouring techniques. The mapping process takes about a month; the resulting map shows general patterns of variability, but does not provide field-specific information. Important causes of soil moisture variation, such as soil texture and land cover, are not considered in developing these regional maps.

Water conservation is critical in this region of the U.S., not only to

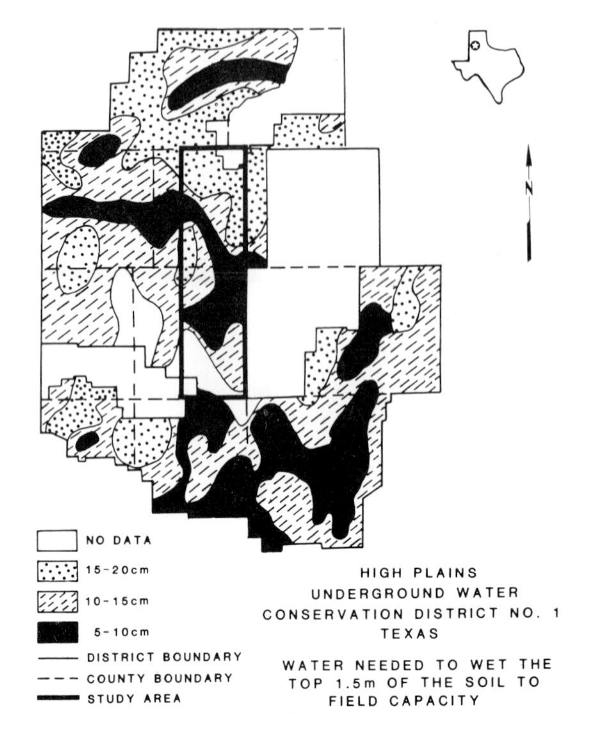

FIG.1 Adaptation of the 1984 preplanting soil water deficit map issued by the USDA Soil Conservation Service.

individual farmers but also to the general population. Almost all of the irrigation water used in this area is drawn from the Ogallala Aquifer, which is rapidly being depleted. Efficient use of irrigation water requires field-specific information that is not provided by the current regional mapping program.

The purpose of this study was to determine the feasibility of using a microwave remote sensing system for mapping soil moisture on an operational basis. Remote sensing systems are ideally suited to the problem of mapping soil moisture over large areas for two reasons. First, by mounting the sensor on an airborne platform, the necessary data can be collected very quickly. Second, the sensor system can be designed to provide spatial resolution such that field specific information can be gathered and distributed to individual farmers.

Microwave sensors are useful because the magnitude of the microwave emission from a soil surface is related to the near-surface moisture content. Although the depth of measurement of these sensors is generally only a few centimeters, extrapolation of root zone moisture content is possible in some cases (Jackson, 1985). Given a knowledge of the strength of the microwave emission, the soil texture, and land surface conditions, it should be possible to develop field-specific maps of root zone soil moisture conditions.

II. Study area description

The feasibility of an operational system was investigated by developing a field-specific soil moisture map for a study area in the Texas Panhandle. This site is a portion of the area mapped by the Texas High Plains Underground Water Conservation District No. 1. The specific portion selected for this investigation is shown in Figure 2 (24 km wide

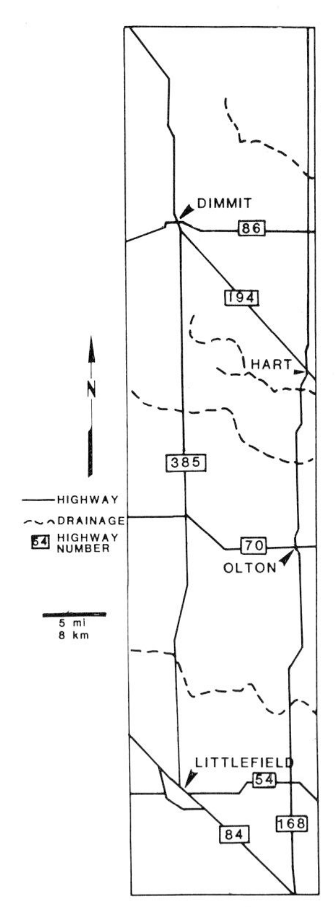

FIG.2 Texas High Plains study site.

and 112 km long). It was selected because of the diversity of soil textures and the large amount of irrigated agriculture that is present, as shown in Plate 1. Soils in the study area vary from fine sands to clay loams, with most of the sandy soils located in the southern portion. One feature of particular interest is the Sand Hills (see Plate 1) which is entirely fine sands. Most of this area is brushy rangeland. Numerous center pivot irrigation farms are located on the north and south borders and the eastern portion of the area.

The aircraft experiment coincided with a period when most of the farms were in stubble or fallow prior to being planted in corn, cotton and grain sorghum. All irrigation water is pumped from wells which tap the Ogallala Aquifer. Most of the irrigation is done using surface furrows; however, there are many center pivot sprinkler systems.

Soil characteristics and general land cover information for this area have been digitized by the SCS and were available on magnetic tape at a 6.25 hectare resolution. Plates 1A and 1B were produced from these data tapes by reprocessing to a 32 hectare resolution. Roads and section lines run both North-South and East-West on a 1.6 km (1 mile) spacing throughout most of the study area.

Ground measurements of gravimetric soil moisture, bulk density and soil temperature were collected concurrent with the aircraft flights in 18 fields within the area. These data indicated that most of the soils were dry with a typical volumetric soil moisture between 10 and 15%.

III. Sensor systems and flightlines

The principal sensor used in the Texas experiment was the pushbroom passive microwave radiometer (PBMR) developed at the NASA Langley Research Center. The PBMR operates at 1.4 GHz (21 cm wavelength) and provides simultaneous crosstrack radiometric measurements. The radiometer is a switching noise injection system providing a very stable response by reducing the effects of receiver noise and gain fluctuations. Additional details on the PBMR can be found in Harrington and Lawrence (1985). The PBMR was flown on a NASA Skyvan aircraft. Additional instruments on this aircraft include a navigational system, photographic camera, a video camera, and a thermal infrared radiometer (single beam 20° field of view).

The PBMR was used in a four beam configuration with beam centers at both 8° and 24° to the left and right of nadir. The total swath covered is roughly 1.25 times the aircraft altitude. Cross track resolution is 0.29 times the altitude at 8° and 0.34 times the altitude at 24°. Along track resolution is 0.29 times the altitude. The nominal ground speed was 50 mps.

Roads running North-South through the study area were used as the center of the flight lines. The altitude of the aircraft was 1000 m which resulted in total swath of 1.25 km. and 15 contiguous North-South flightlines.

Microwave measurements were recorded at intervals of 0.5 seconds, giving a nominal resolution along the flight line of about 25 m. However, because the geometry of the sensor and altitude of the aircraft, the length of the instantaneous footprint is approximately 350m. along the flightline. Thus, there was considerable overlap between the areas represented by successive microwave measurements.

Since the thermal infrared instrument was set up to scan left to right on a 1 second interval, these data were not sampled at every beam position. Analyses indicated very little variation during any one second interval; therefore, an average thermal value was assigned to all four microwave beam positions.

IV. Data processing

Microwave data were processed by first calibrating the raw data based on internal standards and a water body near the test site. The data tape includes a time record, as does the video tape. A detailed map of the study area was used to digitize ground coordinates at selected control points. The time at which the aircraft passed over each control point was determined from the videotape. These control points were used to determine a ground location for each microwave observation. The same procedure was used to process the thermal infrared data.

The microwave instrument provides a measurement of the brightness temperature and the thermal instrument measures the thermal temperature. By assuming a uniform vertical soil moisture profile, the microwave emission from the soil is approximated by dividing the brightness temperature by the effective thermal temperature (Choudhury et al., 1982). The effective thermal temperature is estimated using a weighted average of the surface thermal temperature and the estimated soil temperature at a depth of 15 cm. During the experiment the thermal infrared temperature changed dramatically as a function of time of day, while soil temperatures at 15 cm were relatively stable throughout the day.

The emissivity data obtained by processing the microwave and thermal data were used to obtain average values for each 32 hectare unit (0.8 km along track and 0.4 km across track). In most cases, between 10 and 20 samples were available. The resulting emissivity map is shown in Plate 1C.

V. Results

The main objective of this study was to produce a synoptic map of soil moisture from microwave emissivity data that also contained field-specific information. The emissivity map shown in Figure 3c meets these requirements because each map cell represents an area typical of the region's field sizes.

Theoretical and experimental analyses of microwave remote sensing have indicated that the accurate interpretation of microwave data in terms of soil moisture also requires some knowledge of vegetation type, vegetation biomass, tillage practice and soil type (Choudhury and Schmugge, 1980, Dobson et al., 1985, Jackson et al., 1982, Jackson et al., 1985, and Wang and Schmugge, 1982). Due to the time of year in which the experiment was conducted, vegetation was minimal throughout the study site. While tillage practice and soil type may affect the microwave response from a given field, these effects are much less important than surface soil moisture conditions.

Data collected in previous experiments with the PBMR (Jackson et al., 1984) were combined with limited ground observations of soil moisture collected during the Texas flights. The Texas ground soil moisture data turned out to be of little value due to site location and variability problems. However, the few soil moisture-emissivity pairs that were available did prove useful in adjusting and verifying the use of the relationship established by Jackson et al. (1984). The equation used was

$$\text{Volumetric Soil Moisture (\%)} = 135.0 - 137.0\,(\text{emissivity}) \qquad (1)$$

The resulting soil moisture map is shown in Plate 2. Based upon a visual inspection, the map provides a good representation of the overall soil moisture patterns expected. Some of these patterns are the result of land cover and soil texture variations illustrated in Plate 1.

Figure 1 is based on the measured soil moisture values and the estimated field capacity (0.33 bar moisture content) of the soils. With the exception of a few areas including ephemeral streams, the pattern of soil water deficit corresponds to the fineness of the soil textures. The total available water capacity of a soil increases with an increase in the fineness of the texture. Under uniform areal meteorological conditions, which local records for the study area verified, and no near surface water table conditions, the pattern of soil water deficit should be controlled by the soil texture.

The surface soil moisture is also influenced by the soil texture under the same assumptions mentioned above. The pattern of dry to wet from South to North in Plate 2 corresponds to the change from sandy to loamy soils over the study site. Most ephemeral drainage channels are distinct from the surrounding area.

A comparison of the emissivity values with land cover and soil texture information for each map pixel was performed using a two-way Analysis of Variance. The results indicate significant relationships between emissivity and both land cover and soil texture. Based on 6503 observations (pixels) with six different soil types and nine different land covers, variations in land cover alone accounted for 13.3% of the variation in emissivity. Variations in soil texture alone explained 19.9%; and the combination of these two factors explained 33.2% of the total variation in emissivity. No significant interaction effects were detected, indicating that the effects of soil texture and land cover are independent. However, due to the distribution of the 503 emissivity values among the 32 different combinations of soil texture and land cover, this test of the interaction effects may be flawed. The mean emissivity values are shown for each category of soil texture and land cover in Table 1. The total of 6503 map pixels was obtained by deleting those pixels for which either emissivity or soil texture and land cover

TABLE 1

Mean emissivity values as a function of soil texture and land cover (Numbers in parenthesis are number of observations)

	Soil Texture						
Land Cover	Sands & Fine Sands	Loamy Fine Sands	Fine Sandy Loams	Loams	Clay Loams	Clays	Land Cover Means
Urban	(0)	(0)	.898 (18)	.861 (16)	.869 (21)	(0)	.876 (55)
Dry Cropland	(0)	.925 (2)	.942 (314)	.932 (13)	.883 (389)	.901 (1)	.910 (719)
Irrigated Cropland	.907 (151)	.922 (122)	.922 (1339)	.912 (1329)	.903 (2102)	.890 (5)	.911 (5048)
Dry Pasture	(0)	(0)	(0)	.880 (2)	.893 (3)	(0)	.888 (5)
Irrigated Pasture	.912 (24)	(0)	.922 (24)	.905 (1)	.907 (3)	(0)	.916 (52)
Feedlots	(0)	(0)	.899 (3)	(0)	.860 (1)	(0)	.889 (4)
Open Range	.892 (2)	(0)	.891 (10)	.871 (17)	.870 (346)	.865 (9)	.871 (384)
Brushy Range	.914 (218)	.919 (2)	(0)	.881 (6)	(0)	(0)	914 (226)
Playas	(0)	(0)	(0)	(0)	.918 (5)	.899 (5)	.908 (10)
Soil Texture Means	.911 (395)	.922 (126)	.925 (1708)	.911 (1384)	.896 (2870)	.882 (20)	

information was not available; also, those pixels in which the mean emissivity value was not reliable were deleted.

This analysis of variance established a significant relationship between emissivity and soil texture and land cover. This is expected because soil moisture is also related to these variables. The mean emissivity values shown in Table 1 vary with soil texture and land cover in a predictable fashion; i.e., in much the same way that soil moisture might be expected to vary. Thus, adjustment of the emissivity values to reflect the soil texture and land cover in each pixel will not result in a better soil moisture map; in fact, this would tend to remove some of the actual variation in soil moisture.

Further analysis included locating those map pixels that had exceptionally high or low emissivity values for the combination of land cover and soil texture represented by the pixel. The videotapes and airphotos were examined to determine whether these anomalies could be explained.

Detailed evaluations of the microwave response in specific fields showed that the system detected all center pivot irrigation systems that were verified to be in operation. In most cases these were fallow fields which could be easily identified due to color changes in the photography. However, the sensor system detected many other "wet" areas that could not be verified through photography.

IV. Summary

A product such as Plate 2 could be of great value to both the farmer and the regional manager. The value of this information would be even greater if it were available in conjunction with land cover, soil texture and deep profile soil moisture data bases such as those shown in Figure 1 and Plate 1.

A direct comparison of the point sampled soil water deficit map, Figure 1, and the remotely sensed data will be conducted. An algorithm developed by Rawls et al. (1982) will be applied to the soil texture data base, Plate 1B, and soil survey information to generate field capacity soil moisture values by depth for each data cell. Surface soil moisture, Plate 2, will be extrapolated to profile moisture using a procedure developed by Jackson (1980). Profile moisture will be subtracted from profile field capacity to obtain the soil water deficit.

Presowing soil moisture condition assessment is a one-time analysis. However, soil moisture data are valuable throughout the growing season. Collecting these data by point surveys is impossible. An operational remote soil moisture sensor could collect these data easily and could probably provide the information the same day. Daily surface soil moisture observations combined with a deep survey such as Figure 1 might allow us to compute the changes in the areal water balance.

References

Choudhury, B. J., Schmugge, T. J., Chang, A., and Newton, R. W., 1979, Effect of Surface Roughness on the Microwave Emission from Soils: Journal of Geophysical Research, v. 84, p. 5699-5706.

Choudhury, B. J., Schmugge, T. J., and Mo. T., 1982, A Parameterization of Effective Soil Temperature for Microwave Emission: Journal of Geophysical Research, v. 87, p. 1301-1304.

Harrington, R. F. and Lawrence, R. W., 1985, An Airborne Multibeam 1.4 GHz Pushbroom Microwave Radiometer: International Geoscience and Remote Sensing Symposium Digest, in press.

Jackson, T. J. 1980. Profile Soil Moisture from Surface Measurements: Journal of the Irrigation and Drainage Division, American Society of Civil Engineers v. 106(IR2), p. 81-92.

Jackson, T. J., 1985, Soil Water Modeling and Remote Sensing: IEEE Trans. on Geoscience and Remote Sensing, in press.

Jackson, T. J., Shuie, J., O'Neill, P., Wang, J., Fuchs, J., and Owe, M., 1984, L Band Push Broom Microwave Radiometer—Soil Moisture Verification and Time Series Experiment, Delmarva Peninsula: Data

Report: NASA Technical Memo. 86068, Goddard Space Flight Center, Greenbelt, MD, 71 p.

Jackson, T. J., Schmugge, T. J., and Wang, J. R., 1982, Passive Microwave Remote Sensing of Soil Moisture Under Vegetation Canopies: Water Resources Research, v. 18, p. 1137-1142.

Jackson, T. J., Koopman, G. J., O'Neill, P. E., and Wang, J. R., 1985, Effects of Soil Tillage on Microwave Emission: International Geoscience and Remote Sensing Symposium Digest, in press.

Rawls, W. J., Brakensiek, D. L., and Saxton, K. E., 1982, Estimation of Soil Water Properties: Trans. of the ASAE, v. 25, no. 5, p. 1316-1320.

Risinger, W. M., 1984, Measuring Pre-Plant Soil Moisture Deficits: Conference on Water for the 21st Century: Will It Be There?, Southern Methodist University, Dallas, Texas.

Wang, J. R. and Schmugge, T. J., 1980, An Empirical Model for the Complex Dielectric Permittivity of Soils as a Function of Water Content: IEEE Trans. on Geoscience and Remote Sensing, v. GE-18, p. 288-295.

Hydrologic Applications of Space Technology (Proceedings of the Cocoa Beach Workshop, Florida, August 1985). IAHS Publ. no. 160, 1986.

Integration of remote sensing with a soil water balance simulation model (SWATRE)

G. J. A. NIEUWENHUIS
Institute for Land and Water Management Research (ICW), Wageningen, The Netherlands

Abstract

A method has been developed for the automatical mapping of evapotranspiration from digitally taken reflection- and thermal images. This method has been tested in combination with conventional methods in a remote sensing study project performed in the eastern part of The Netherlands. For this project different remote sensing flights were performed in the summer of 1982 and 1983. The images acquired after a very dry period were especially relevant to demonstrate that an important improvement of the hydrological description of an area could be achieved by combining the remote sensing approach with conventional methods.

1. Introduction

Information about regional evapotranspiration of crops is important for an optimal water management in agriculture and for the determination of the effect of man-made changes in the overall hydrological situation. Remote sensing can be very helpful in obtaining the necessary information (Heilman et al., 1976; Soer, 1980), although only the situation at one particular moment, c.q. time of overflight, is obtained. With the so-called SWATRE soil water simulation model for local conditions the use of water by agricultural crops can be simulated during the entire growing season (Feddes et al., 1978; Belmans et al., 1983). Since 1981 the applicability of Multi Spectral Scanning (MSS) techniques has been tested, in combination with the SWATRE approach, in a regional study project of an area (East Gelderland) in the eastern part of The Netherlands (Fig. 1). Crop temperatures derived from heat images can be transformed into daily evapotranspiration values with surface energy balance models (Jackson et al., 1977; Soer, 1980 and Hatfield et al., 1984). Jackson et al. proposed an empirical relation between midday surface-air temperature differences and actual daily evapotranspiration.

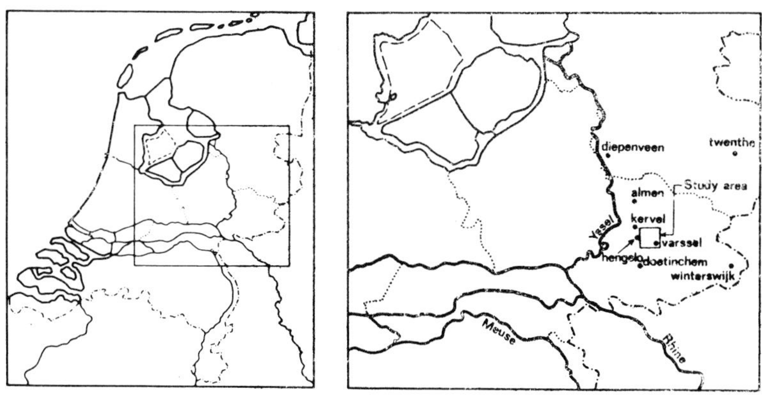

FIG.1 Location of the study area.

Nieuwenhuis et al. (1985) proposed some modifications to the method of Jackson. With the modified method differences in radiation temperature of a certain crop as derived from heat images can be directly transformed into differences in evapotranspiration.

The presently developed linear relationship between crop temperature and daily evapotranspiration is crop dependent. Therefore mapping of the thermographic evapotranspiration values was combined with automatic crop classification. Crop classification was performed by means of reflection images taken with a multi spectral scanner.

In the present study especially the effect of groundwater extractions on the water supply of agricultural crops has been emphasized.

2. Theory

2.1. Instantaneous crop temperature and evapotranspiration

The temperature of objects at the earth surface is determined by the instantaneous equilibrium between gains and losses of energy. At the earth surface net radiation R_n equals the sum of latent heat flux into the air LE, sensible heat flux into the air H and heat flux into the soil G:

$$R_n = LE + H + G \qquad (W\ m^{-2}) \tag{1}$$

where L is the latent heat of vaporization ($J\ kg^{-1}$) and E the evapotranspiration flux ($kg\ m^{-2}s^{-1}$).

The term R_n can be split up in a net short wave and a net long wave radiation term:

$$R_n = (1 - \alpha)R_s + \varepsilon(R_l - \sigma T_c^4) \qquad (W\ m^{-2}) \tag{2}$$

where α is the surface reflection coefficient, R_s the incoming short wave radiation flux ($W\ m^{-2}$), ε the emission coefficient, R_l the long wave sky radiation flux ($W\ m^{-2}$), σ the constant of Stefan Boltzmann ($5.67.10^{-8}$ $W\ m^{-2}K^{-4}$) and T_c the crop surface temperature (K).

When the crop is well-supplied with water, the net radiation energy is mainly used as latent heat for vaporization. When the latent heat flux decreases, the surface temperature increases, resulting in a rise of the sensible heat flux H. Considering the transport of heat from the crop surface with temperature T_c (K) to a certain height z_{ref} (m) with air temperature T_a (K) the transport equation can be expressed as:

$$H = -\rho C_p\ (T_a - T_c)/_{rah} \qquad (W\ m^{-2}) \tag{3}$$

where ρ is the density of moist air ($kg\ m^{-3}$), C_p the specific heat of moist air ($J\ kg^{-1}K^{-1}$) and r_{ah} the turbulent diffusion resistance for heat transport ($s\ m^{-1}$) from the crop surface to $z = z_{ref}$.

Combining the eqs (1), (2) and (3) the relation between latent heat flux LE and surface temperature T_c can be found (Brown and Rosenberg, 1973 and Stone and Horton, 1974):

$$LE = \rho C_p\ (T_a - T_c)/r_{ah} + (1 - \alpha)R_s + \varepsilon(R_l - \sigma T_c^4) - G \qquad (W\ m^{-2}) \tag{4}$$

From eq. (4) it can be seen that LE depends on a number of meteorological and crop surface parameters. For a certain regional area, T_c can be remotely sensed by thermal infrared line scanning. When T_a, r_{ah}, α, R_s, ε, R_l and G are known (or estimated) LE can be computed.

The resistance r_{ah} depends on wind velocity u, roughness of the crop surface z_o and atmospheric stability (Dyer, 1967 and Webb, 1970).

For clear sky conditions T_a, R_s, R_l and u can be taken constant over a certain area. This means that standard meteorological measurements can be used. The parameter α, has to be determined from field measurements or from reflection images. With more indirect procedures ε and z_o can also be estimated by combining field observations with interpretation of reflection images.

2.2. Relation between instantaneous crop temperature and 24 hour evapotranspiration rate

For the translation of instantaneous to daily values Soer (1977) developed the TERGRA-model. However, interpretation of thermal images with the aid of the TERGRA-model is rather complicated because of the large number of input parameters that are required.

Jackson et al. (1977) related midday surface-air temperature differences linearly to 24 hour evapotranspiration and net radiation values. To estimate the slope of this relationship a crop-dependent analytical expression has been derived by Seguin and Itier (1983).

Nieuwenhuis et al. (1985) proposed to replace the surface-air temperature difference by the temperature difference ($T_c - T_c$*) that exists between the crop that is transpiring under the actual restriction of the soil moisture condition and that transpiring under optimal soil moisture conditions. The net radiation term was replaced by the 24 hour potential evapotranspiration rate of the crop. With these adjustments they obtained:

$$LE^{24}/LE_p^{24} = 1 - B^r(T_c - T_c^*)_i \tag{5}$$

where LE^{24} and LE_p^{24} are respectively the actual and potential 24 hour evapotranspiration rate (mm day^{-1}), B^r (K^{-1}) is a calibration constant and the subscript i indicates instantaneous values. By means of eq. (5) differences in radiation temperature of a certain crop derived from thermal images can be directly transformed into reductions in evapotranspiration.

From TERGRA-model calculations Thunnissen (1985) found that B^r can be described by a linear function of the wind velocity (u) at a height of 2.0 m above groundsurface:

$$B^r = a + b.u \quad (K^{-1}) \tag{6}$$

Values for the regression coefficients a and b are given in Table 1 for different type of crops and crop heights.

For agrohydrological purposes heat images are usually taken on clear days in the summer period. It was found that for such days eqs (5) and (6) can be applied for the meteorological conditions prevailing in The Netherlands.

TABLE 1--Values for the coefficients a and b in eq. (6) for a number of crops with crop height H (after: Thunnissen, 1985).

Crop	H (cm)	a (K^{-1})	b ($K^{-1}m^{-1}s$)
Grass	<15	0.050	0.010
Grass	>15	0.050	0.017
Potatoes	60	0.050	0.023
Sugar beet	60		
Cereals	100	0.090	0.030
Maize	200	0.100	0.047

2.3. Simulation of the water balance of a cropped soil with the SWATRE-model

Remotely sensed images characterize the conditions at one time. For several agrohydrological applications, however, determination of cumulative effects in time on the total crop yield is required. As an example one can think of the effects of groundwater extraction for domestic purposes on the growing conditions of grassland and arable crops. The amount of water available for transpiration strongly influences dry matter production.

With a model such as SWATRE (Feddes et al., 1978 and Belmans et al., 1983) the use of water by agricultural crops can be simulated during the entire growing season. SWATRE is a transient one-dimensional finite-difference soil-water-root uptake model, that applies a simple sink term and different types of boundary conditions at the bottom of the system. When the soil system remains unsaturated, one of three bottom boundary conditions can be used, namely pressure head, zero flux or free drainage. When the lower part of the system remains saturated, one can give either the groundwater level or the flux through the bottom of the system as input. In the latter case the groundwater level is computed. At the top of the system, 24 hour data on rainfall, potential soil evaporation and potential transpiration are needed.

The SWATRE-model can be sued to simulate actual transpiration, hence it can be used to investigate how far the moisture conditions at particular times are representative for the entire growing season.

3. Description of the study area and remote sensing flights

The study area covers about 36 km^2 and is situated in the eastern part of The Netherlands around the pumping station 't Klooster (Fig. 1). Most of the study area is covered by grassland, but the cultivation of maize becomes more and more important.

The area is geohydrologically characterized by a coarse sandy aquifer overlying a more or less impermeable layer of fine silty sand at a depth of about 35 m. The most important soil types in the study area are the Typic Haplaquods (Gleyic Podzols, about 45%), the Typic Humaquepts (Humic Gleysols, about 20%) and the Plaggepts (Plaggen soils, about 20%). The soils show differences in drainage class resulting from small variations in elevation and soil texture (fine sand and loamy fine sand). In The Netherlands on soil maps the drainage classes are indicated as so-called groundwater table classes (Table 2). Each class is a combination of a mean highest groundwater table (winter situation) and a mean lowest groundwater table (summer situation). In the study area classes III till VII are found.

In 1982 and 1983 a number of remote sensing flights were performed in the eastern part of The Netherlands. Digital reflection and heat images were taken with a Daedalus digital scanner (DS1240/1260) by Eurosense (The Hague), simultaneously with false colour photographs. Especially the images taken after a relatively dry period show important information about the regional hydrological situation. Results are presented from a flight performed on 30 July 1982 at a height of about 3000 m resulting in a pixel size of about 7.5 x 7.5 m.

TABLE 2--Drainage classes indicated on soil maps in The Netherlands.

	I	II	IIIa	III	IV	V	VI	VII
MHG	-	-	<20	<40	>40	<40	40-80	80-140
MLG	<50	50-80	80-120	80-120	80-120	>120	>120	>160

MHG = Mean Highest Groundwater depth (cm - groundsurface)
MLG = Mean Lowest Groundwater depth (cm - groundsurface)

4. Applied methods

The image processing was performed on the remote sensing datahandling system (RESEDA) of the National Aerospace Laboratory (NLR) in Amsterdam.

A crop map was composed from the reflection bands 5 (0.55-0.60 μm), 7 (0.65-0.69 μm) and 9 (0.80-0.89 μm) by applying a more or less standard supervised classification procedure. The classification result was checked with field measurements and was compared with results obtained by interpretation of the simultaneously taken false colour photographs. It was found that a distinction between tall grassland and maize was impossible with standard classification procedures. Therefore it was decided to improve the classification result interactively by indicating all the maize plots on the videoscreen of the datahandling system in order to obtain a reliable crop map.

Depending on the height, grassland was divided into three classes by applying the Vegetation Index (VI), which is defined as (Tucker, 1977):

$$VI = (IR - R)/(IR + R) \tag{7}$$

For IR and R the radiation intensities in respectively wavelength band 9 and 7 have been applied. The relation between the Vegetation Index and the crop height has been determined by measuring on flight days the crop height on several plots. It was found that about 90% of the considered plots was correctly classified.

With eqs (5) and (6) for maize, middle high (5-15 cm) and tall (>15 cm) grassland the heat image was automatically converted into a map with estimates of relative 24 hour evapotranspiration rates.

With the SWATRE-model (Feddes et al., 1978 and Belmans et al., 1983) the water balance terms weresimulated during the entire growing season with actual weather data of that particular year and for three typical soil types present in the study area. For 30 July 1982 results obtained with the SWATRE-model have been compared with the remote sensing approach.

5. Results and discussion

5.1. Interpretation of the evapotranspiration map

The evapotranspiration map of the study area composed from the reflection and heat images of 30 July 1982 is presented in Fig. 2.

Because of irrigation by means of sprinkling irregularly distributed over the area, plots are present with crops well supplied with water. On these plots crops are more or less potentially transpiring (dark in Fig. 2).

Under natural conditions crop evapotranspiration depends on the moisture availability in the root zone, which is determined by:

- the depth of the root zone;
- the available moisture capacity in the root zone;
- the hydraulic conductivity of the subsoil;
- the groundwater level during the growing season.

The first three factors are mainly dependent on the soil properties. By comparing the evapotranspiration map with the available soil map the occurrence of drought could be explained for several soil types (Nieuwenhuis, 1985).

As phreatic groundwater is extracted by the pumping station 't Klooster (indicated with a 'P' in Fig. 2) the groundwater level and therefore the occurrence of drought damage is influenced by the groundwater extraction in the shown area. Around the centre of the extraction a more or less conical depression of the groundwater table occurs. The isoline indicating a 10 cm drawdown according to calculations reported by De Laat and Awater (1978) is also shown in Fig. 2.

FIG.2 Evapotranspiration map of the study area (see Fig.1), situated around the pumping station 't Klooster (P) composed from reflection and heat images taken on 30 July 1982 at 12.00 MET. The isoline represents 10 cm groundwater table drawdown. Crop evapotranspiration decreases from potential (dark grey) till a level of about 30% of the potential one (white). Black is not classified.

The evapotranspiration of crops has been studied in relation to the distance from the centre of the groundwater extraction. As crop evapotranspiration depends on soil type and groundwater level a systematic analysis has been performed for each soil type and each groundwater table class separately. Fig. 3a and b show two typical results.

Fig. 3a shows that the evapotranspiration rate for grassland on a Typic Haplaquod soil in combination with a relatively high groundwater table under natural conditions, decreases in the direction of the centre of the extraction. Natural conditions are defined as the situation without groundwater extraction. At distances of more than 1300 m from the centre of the extraction the drawdown of the groundwater table is negligible and because of sufficient water supply by capillary rise from groundwater crops are transpiring potentially.

Fig. 3b shows a quite different result. For maize on a Typic Haplaquod soil with a relatively deep groundwater table the evapotranspiration rate is very low and independent on the distance from the centre of the extraction. This means that under these circumstances even without lowering of the groundwater table the water delivery to the root zone by means of capillary rise can be neglected.

5.2. Calculations with the SWATRE-model

Calculations with the SWATRE-model were performed to obtain information about the effect of a lowering of the groundwater table on the total crop yield.

Evapotranspiration was simulated during the entire growing season of 1982 for grass and maize grown on a Typic Haplaquod soil with groundwater table class V. In the calculations measured groundwater depths were taken for

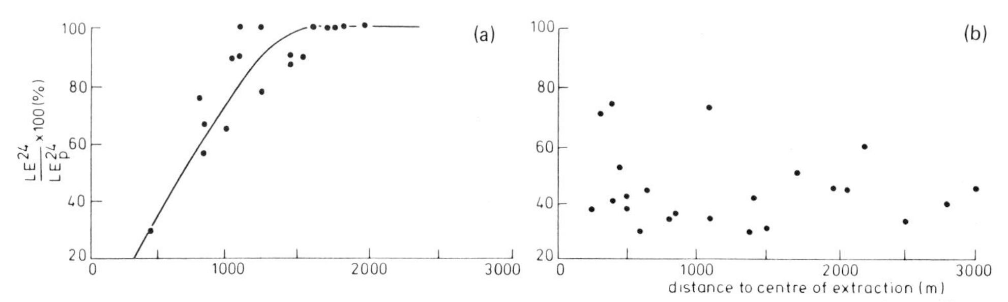

FIG.3 Relative 24 hr evapotranspiration rate (LE^{24}/LE_p^{24}) on 30 July 1982 derived from the evapotranspiration map shown in Fig.2 for (a) grass on Typic Haplaquod soil with drainage class V and (b) for maize on the same soil with drainage class VI depending on the distance to the centre of the groundwater extraction. Drainage classes are given in Table 2 (after: Thunnissen, 1984).

situations without extraction. Moreover, model calculations were performed assuming a constant drawdown during the entire growing season. Fig. 4 shows that for the growing season of 1982 the cumulative effect of a lowering of the groundwater table can amount to 15% for grass and 20% for maize.

Except cumulative effects for 30 July 1982 also the effect of a lowering of the groundwater table on crop daily evapotranspiration was studied. Fig. 5a and b show respectively the results for grass on a Typic Haplaquod soil with drainage class V and maize on the same soil with drainage class VI.

In a dry period the water supply of crops depends on suppletion from groundwater by means of capillary rise. The effect of a lowering of the groundwater table could be serious if a relatively shallow groundwater table is present under natural conditions (Fig. 5a). For a relatively deep groundwater table crop evapotranspiration of maize is even under natural conditions very low on 30 July 1982 and the effect of a lowering of the groundwater table is than limited (Fig. 5b).

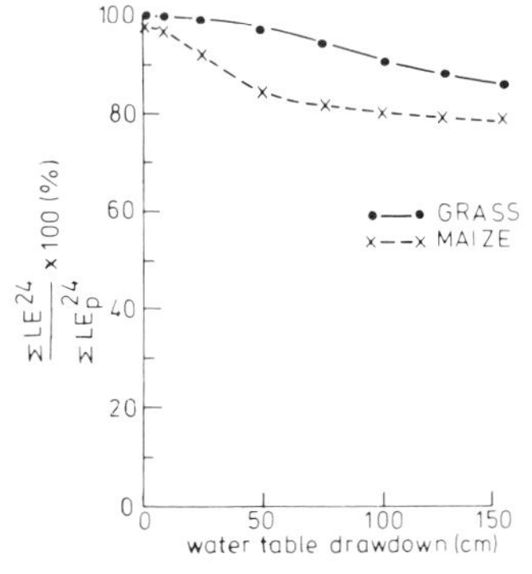

FIG.4 Ratio of cumulative actual to potential 24 hr evapotranspiration over the entire growing season of 1982 ($\Sigma LE^{24}/\Sigma LE_p^{24}$) for grass and maize on Typic Haplaquod soil with drainage class V (see Table 2) depending on groundwater table drawdown (after: Thunnissen, 1984).

5.3. Comparison of remote sensing results with SWATRE-model calculations

According to the remote sensing approach crop evapotranspiration strongly decreases on 30 July 1982 in the direction of the centre of the extraction in case of shallow groundwater tables under natural conditions. This is shown in Fig. 3a. Fig. 5a shows that also according to SWATRE-model calculations for the concerning conditions crop evapotranspiration strongly decreases with lowering of the groundwater table.

Also for relatively deep groundwater tables under natural conditions both results show good agreement (Fig. 3b and 5b). If no suppletion from groundwater occurs crop evapotranspiration is very low on 30 July 1982 and a lowering of the groundwater table has no perceptible influence on crop evapotranspiration.

For specific locations, where the groundwater level was measured, crop evapotranspiration was simulated with the SWATRE-model during the entire growing season of 1982. For 30 July 1982 model results have been compared with results obtained with the remote sensing approach. Table 3 shows some examples. For Typic Haplaquod and Typic Humaquept soils results are in good agreement. For Plaggept soil, however, crop evapotranspiration is overestimated by the SWATRE-model in relation to the remote sensing approach. The model results are determined by the applied soil physical properties. Probably for Plaggept soil an overestimation of crop water supply occurs with the applied properties. In general results obtained with the SWATRE-model are in good agreement with the remote sensing approach.

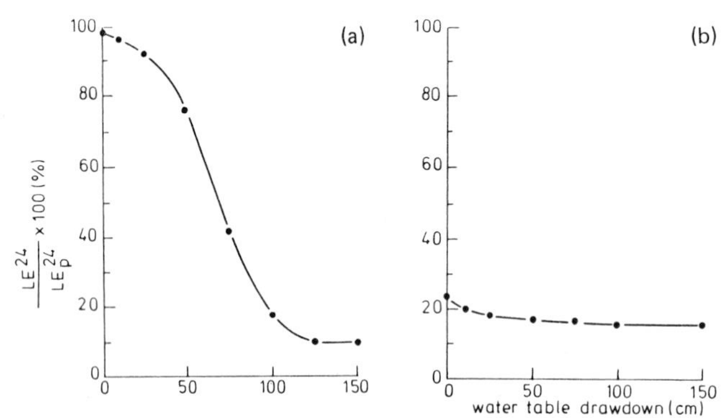

FIG.5 Relative 24 hr evapotranspiration rate (LE^{24}/LE_p^{24}) on 30 July 1982 for (a) grass on Typic Haplaquod soil with drainage class V and (b) for maize on the same soil with drainage class VI depending on groundwater table drawdown. Drainage classes are given in Table 2 (after: Thunnissen, 1984).

6. Conclusions

With remote sensing detailed information about the regional distribution of evapotranspiration on flight days is obtained. With agrohydrological simulation models like SWATRE for a restricted number of locations crop evapotranspiration can be simulated during the entire growing season. For the explanation of drought patters on the evapotranspiration map determined with remote sensing, such model calculations are indispensable.

Moreover, with model calculations effects of certain drought periods during the growing season on total crop yield can be determined. It can be concluded that an important improvement of the hydrological description of an area can be achieved by combining SWATRE-model calculations with remote sensing.

TABLE 3--Relative 24-hour evapotranspiration rates (LE^{24}/LE_p^{24}) for 30 July 1982 according to the remote sensing approach and calculated with the SWATRE-model for 14 grassland plots and 3 different soil types (after: Thunnissen, 1984).

Soil type	$(LE^{24}/LE_p^{24}) \times 100$ (%)	
	remote sensing approach	SWATRE-model
1. Typic Haplaquods	85	98
2. Typic Haplaquods	<30	14
3. Typic Haplaquods	60	70
4. Typic Haplaquods	78	74
5. Typic Haplaquods	<30	38
6. Typic Haplaquods	50	26
7. Typic Haplaquods	70	70
8. Typic Haplaquods	100	92
9. Typic Haplaquods	84	90
10. Typic Haplaquods	76	72
11. Typic Humaquepts	100	100
12. Typic Humaquepts	100	98
13. Plaggepts	66	94
14. Plaggepts	52	72

References

Belmans, C., J.G. Wesseling and R.A. Feddes, 1983, Simulation Model of the Water Balance of a cropped Soil: SWATRE: J. Hydrol., v. 63, p. 271-286. Techn. Bull. n.s. 21. ICW, Wageningen, The Netherlands.

Brown, K.W. and N.J. Rosenberg, 1973, A Resistance Model to predict Evapotranspiration and its Application to a Sugar Beet Field: Agron. J., v. 65, no. 3, p. 341-347.

Dyer, A.J., 1967, The turbulent Transport of Heat and Water Vapour in an unstable Atmosphere: Quar . J. Roy. Meteorol. Soc., v. 93, p. 501-508.

Feddes, R.A., P.J. Kowalik and H. Zaradny, 1978, Simulation of Field Water Use and Crop Yield: Simulation Monographs, Pudoc, Wageningen, The Netherlands, 189 p.

Hatfield, J.L., R.J. Reginato and S.B. Idso, 1984, Evaluation of Canopy Temperature-Evapotranspiration Models over various Crops: Agric. and Forest Meteorol., v. 32, p. 41-53.

Heilman, J.L., E.T. Kanemasu, N.J. Rosenberg and B.L. Blad, 1976, Thermal Scanner Measurements of Canopy Temperatures to estimate Evapotranspiration: Remote Sensing Env., v. 5, p. 137-145.

Jackson, R.D., R.J. Reginato and S.B. Idso, 1977, Wheat Canopy Temperature: a practical Tool for evaluating Water Requirements: Water Res. Res., v. 13, p. 651-656.

Laat, P.J.M. de and R.H.C.M. Awater, 1978, Groundwater Flow and Evapotranspiration; A Simulation Model. Part 1: Theory: Basisrapport Commissie Bestudering Waterhuishouding Gelderland, Provinciale Waterstaat van Gelderland, Arnhem, The Netherlands, 64 p.

Nieuwenhuis, G.J.A., 1985, Thermography: Principles and Application in the Remote Sensing Studyproject 'Oost-Gelderland': Proc. 4th Int. Symp. ISSS (in press).

Nieuwenhuis, G.J.A., E.H. Smidt and H.A.M. Thunnissen, 1985, Estimation of regional Evapotranspiration of Arable Crops from thermal Infrared Images:

Int. J. Remote Sensing (in press).

Seguin, B. and B. Itier, 1983, Using midday Surface Temperature to estimate daily Evaporation from Satellite thermal IR Data: Int. J. Remote Sensing, v. 4, p.371-383.

Soer, G.J.R., 1977, The TERGRA model - a mathematical Model for the Simulation of the daily Behaviour of Crop Surface Temperature and actual Evapotranspiration: Nota 1014. ICW, Wageningen, The Netherlands, 44 p.

Soer, G.J.R., 1980, Estimation of regional Evapotranspiration and Soil Moisture Conditions using remotely sensed Crop Surface Temperatures: Remote Sensing Env., v. 9, p. 27-45. Techn. Bull. 116. ICW, Wageningen, The Netherlands.

Stone, L.R. and M.L. Horton, 1974, Estimating Evapotranspiration using Canopy Temperatures: Field Evaluation: Agron. J., v. 66, p. 450-454.

Thunnissen, H.A.M., 1984, Hydrologisch Onderzoek: Toepassing van hydrologische Modellen en Remote Sensing. Deelrapport 4, Remote Sensing Studieproject 'Oost-Gelderland'. Nota 1542. ICW, Wageningen, The Netherlands, 85 p.

Thunnissen, H.A.M., 1985, Eenvoudige Methode voor de Bepaling van de regionale Gewasverdamping. Deelrapport 6, Remote Sensing Studieproject 'Oost-Gelderland'. Nota 1580. ICW, Wageningen, The Netherlands, 39 p.

Tucker, C.J., 1977, Use of near infrared/red Radiance Ratios for estimating Vegetation Biomass and physiological status: Proc. 11th Int. Symp. of Remote Sensing of Env., v. I, p. 493-494.

Webb, E.K., 1970, Profile Relationships: the log-linear Range, and Extension to strong Stability: Quar. J. Roy. Meteorol. Soc., v. 96, p. 67-90.

Hydrologic Applications of Space Technology (Proceedings of the Cocoa Beach Workshop, Florida, August 1985). IAHS Publ. no. 160, 1986.

Practical application of remote sensing techniques in water management problems: state of the art

J. M. M. BOUWMANS
Ministry of Agriculture and Fisheries,
Government Service for Land and Water Use (LD)
Utrecht, The Netherlands

Abstract

Since a method is available to derive crop evapotranspiration maps from digital reflection- and thermal remotely sensed images, several projects have been started to investigate the practical applicability of this technique for the determination of the effects of changes in the agro-hydrological system on crop production. From two projects, concerning respectively soil improvement and groundwater extraction, the state of the art is presented in this paper.

In this stage the conclusion can be drawn that the availability of actual crop evapotranspiration maps makes it possible to check the output of hydrological models. Besides it is possible to estimate the spatial variation in soil physical characteristics more accurately.

Remote sensing techniques can be used to determine effects of man-made changes in the agrohydrological situation. On a regional scale reliable quantitative results can be obtained. On field scale, however, the reliability is less due to the variability in hydrological and soil physical characteristics. With a multitemporal comparison of the same object in the changed and unchanged situation this variability problem can be avoided and an improvement of the results on field scale seems likely.

1. Introduction

The main activities of the Government Service for Land and Water Use are the design, preparation and execution of land consolidation projects and redevelopment programmes. In these projects among others the agricultural infrastructure is adapted to the present demands. An improvement of the watermanagement system is often an important part of these projects. Measures are designed and evaluated to prevent crop damage due to both water excess and shortage of water as much as possible. The experience of the Government Service for Land and Water Use in agrohydrology is also applied to determine effects of planned and operational groundwater extractions on among others crop production.

For the determination of the effects of improvements of watermanagement systems and groundwater extractions, hydrological models or standard tables are applied.

The possibility to derive actual crop evapotranspiration maps from remotely sensed images (Nieuwenhuis, 1985), means that an accurate overall view of local differences in crop water supply can be obtained for the point of time that the remote sensing images were recorded. Therefore these evapotranspiration maps are in principal very useful for inventories and studies on subjects concerning crop water supply. As crop water supply depends on more factors, additional information is necessary to explain differences in actual evapotranspiration.

In cooperation with the Institute for Land and Water Management Research (ICW) the practical applicability of this remote sensing technique is investigated in several projects. The costs and benefits of the application of remote sensing in comparison with traditional methods and the determination of yield depression due to water excess have not yet been studied. Therefore in this paper only attention is paid to the use of remote sensing techniques in relation to the availability of soil moisture for crop evapotranspiration. Of two projects preliminary results are discussed.

2. Theory

2.1. Crop production and evapotranspiration

The potential yield of crops Q_P (t ha-1) in a certain year under given growth conditions depends on the level of the potential evapotranspiration E_T (mm). If crop water supply is the limiting factor, the actual crop production Q_A can be derived from the potential production. For arable crops there is a linear relationship between evapotranspiration and crop yield, known as the Stewart-model (Feddes, 1979), that can be written as

$$(1-E_A/E_T) = \beta_o (1-Q_A/Q_P) \quad (1)$$

In this formula β_o is a dimensionless parameter dependent on the type of crop and E_A (mm) is the actual evapotranspiration.
For grassland a non-linear relationship was found (van Boheemen, 1981) between yield and crop water consumption as given in figure 1.

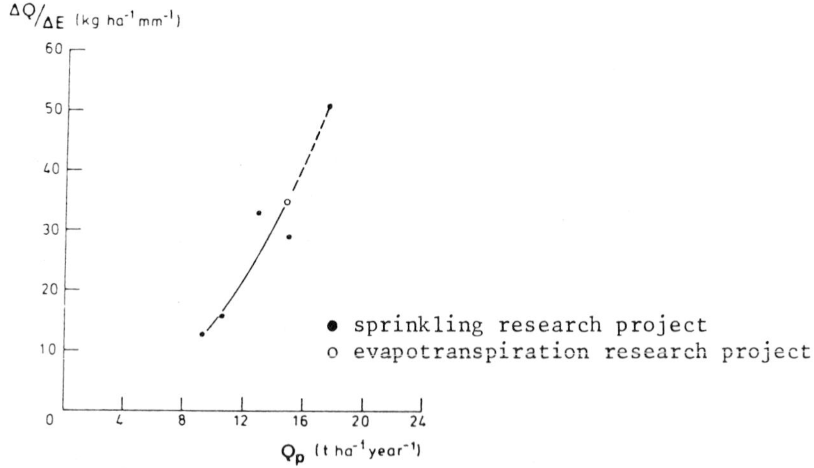

FIG.1 Ratio between the additional dry matter production (ΔQ) and the additional evapotranspiration (ΔE) in relation to the potential production for grassland. (After: van Boheemen, 1981).

So crop production is related to the total amount of evapotranspiration during the growing season.

2.2. Available water for crop evapotranspiration

Water supply of crops is dependent on soil moisture that can be taken up by plant roots during the growing season. The terms of the soil moisture balance of the root zone are schematicly presented in Fig. 2.

Flow in the unsaturated zone is assumed to be in the vertical direction only and is taken to be positive upwards. The upper boundary flux (q_s) consists of precipitation (P), sprinkling (Ir) and actual evapotranspiration (E_A). A negative flux across interface root zone-subsoil (q_{rs}) represents percolation and a positive flux capillary rise. An upward lower boundary

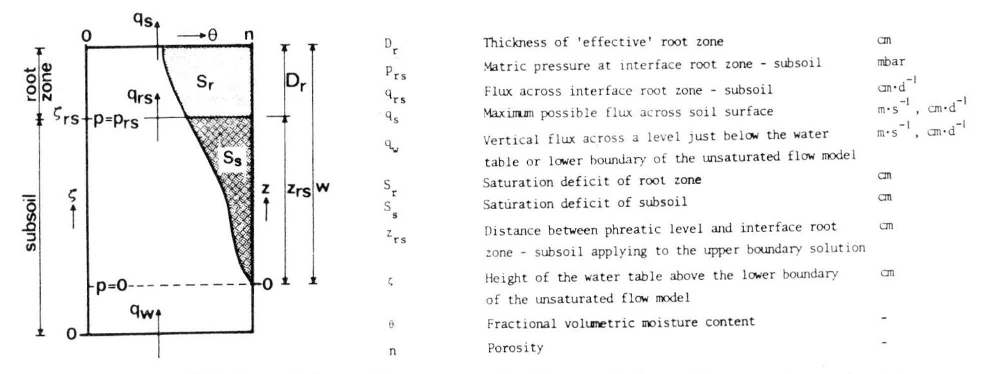

FIG.2 Schematic presentation of the flow system in the unsaturated zone. (After: De Laat, 1980).

flux (q_w) represents seepage and a downward flux leakage.

The amount of actual crop evapotranspiration during the growing season can be calculated by adding the several fluxes into the root zone and the change of the saturation deficit of the root zone. For the flux q_{rs} the difference between capillary rise and percolation is taken. This relation can be written as

$$\int_{t0}^{t1} E_A.dt = \int_{t0}^{t1} P.dt + \int_{t0}^{t1} Ir.dt + \int_{t0}^{t1} q_{rs}.dt + (Sr(t1)-Sr(t0)) \qquad (2)$$

In a year with average meteorological conditions in The Netherlands there is a precipitation deficit during the growing season (1 April - 1 October) as is illustrated in Fig. 3. To prevent reduction in crop evapotranspiration it is necessary that the maximum precipitation deficit can be fully covered by available soil moisture in the root zone and capillary rise. Otherwise without supplemental irrigation the actual evapotranspiration will be lower than the potential, which results in a reduction of crop production.

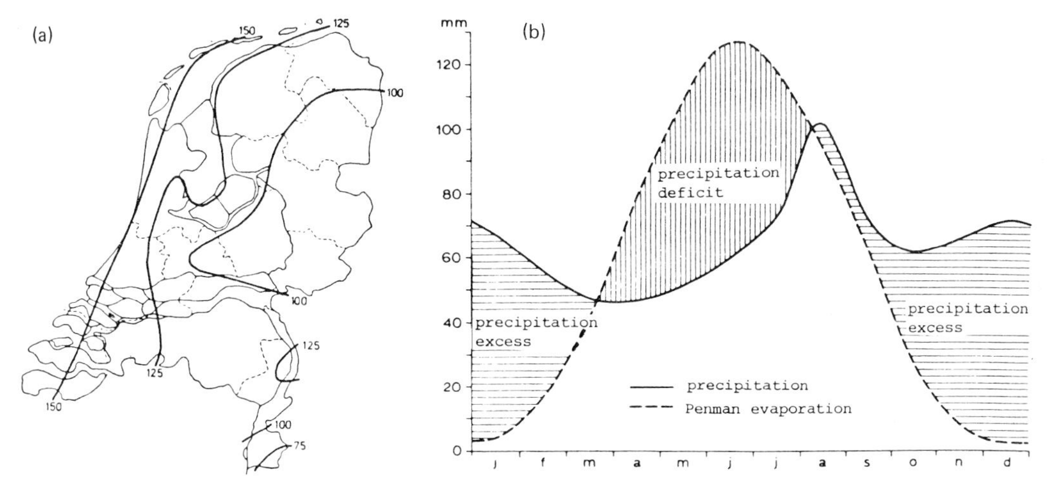

FIG.3 (a) Maximum precipitation deficit $P-E_T$ (mm) for grassland in the Netherlands during the growing season in a year with average meteorological conditions (after: van Boheemen, 1980). (b) Precipitation and evaporation in an average year.

2.3. Soil moisture content and capillary rise

The available soil moisture for crop evapotranspiration is determined by

- the depth of the effective root zone (Dr)
- the moisture capacity of the root zone
- the hydraulic conductivity of the subsoil
- the phreatic level during the growing season

For crops the available amount of soil moisture in the root zone can be determined from the thickness and its soil moisture characteristic (pF-curve). Generally the moisture stored between pF 2.0 and pF 4.2 is assumed to be available for the crop. In agrohydrological models often a sink-term and hysteresis factor are applied to adapt the available amount of water for crop and soil depending effects (De Laat, 1980).

The capillary flux across interface root zone - subsoil (q_{rs}) is determined by the matric pressure at this interface (p_{rs}), the depth of the groundwatertable below this interface (z_{rs}) and the hydraulic conductivity of the homogeneous or layered subsoil (K(h)-relation). The height of capillary rise in a subsoil or layer of loamy medium fine sand and very heavy clay for several fluxes and matric pressures at interface root zone - subsoil is presented in figure 4.

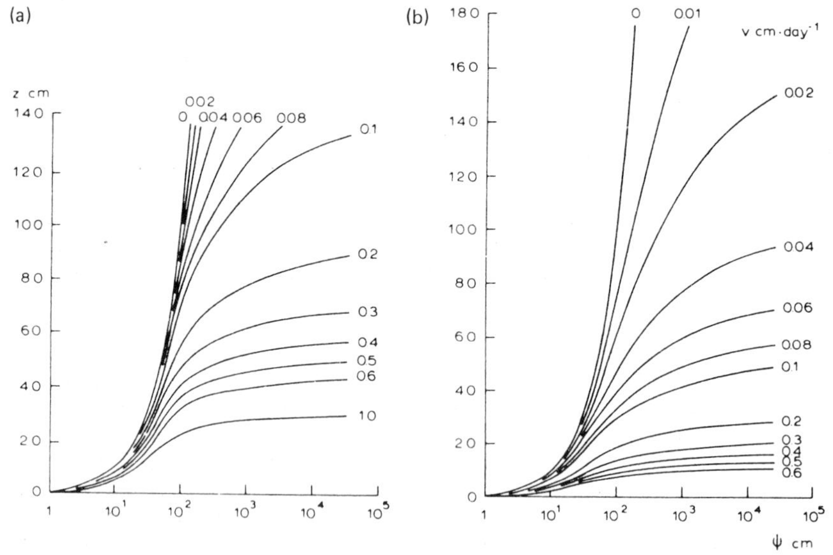

FIG.4 Height of capillary rise for loamy medium fine sand (a) and very heavy clay (b).

If capillary rise becomes less than 0.2 cm/day by a matric pressure p_{rs} of pF 4.2, crop water supply is considered to be independent from the groundwater depth. The distance z_{rs} by which this occurs is dependent from the K(h)-relation of the subsoil and the groundwater depth.

On grounds where the groundwater table remains within a distance that enables a capillary rise greater than 0.2 cm/day during the entire growing season hardly any drought damage occurs. On grounds where the groundwater table at the start of the growing season already is at a depth that capillary rise is less than 0.2 cm/dag drought damage occurs when moisture content in the root zone expires and new supply by precipitation or sprinkling stays away.

The amount of available soil moisture can be increased by:

- enlargement of the root penetrable zone as far as the actual thickness is smaller than the maximum rooting depth of the crop. This also implies to a smaller z-distance
- improvement of the hydraulic conductivity of the (layered) subsoil
- raise of the groundwater table. (infiltration, soil excavation)
- supplemental irrigation (sprinkling).

The amount of available soil moisture can be decreased by:

- drawdown of the groundwater table
- soil degradation (irreversible dry up, plough sole, etc.).

3. Methods

3.1. Usual approach to quantify the effects of changes in the agrohydrological situation

Usually the effects of changes in the agrohydrological situation are determined with the aid of geohydrological, agrohydrological and farm economic models (Werkgroep Landbouwkundige Aspecten, 1984).

First of all the change in depth and fluctuation of the groundwater table is estimated. When it concerns a former change in the agrohydrological system the change of groundwater depth is determined either by applying a numerical geohydrological model, or by statistiscal correlation of groundwater depth measurements in the changed and unchanged situation, or by studying the hydromorphic characteristics of the soil profile. For designed measures of course only the first method can be applied.

The next stage is the inventory of the soil physical characteristics of the agricultural land in the area where the phreatic groundwater table is or will be influenced.

In the final stage the effect of the planned or realized change is quantified by comparing the amount of actual evapotranspiration during the growing season in the changed and unchanged situation. For that the pseudo steady-state soil waterbalance simulation model LAMOS (Reuling, 1983) is applied. This model is an adapted version of the model UNSAT (De Laat, 1980).
Besides the effect of the concerned measure on crop evapotranspiration also the consequence of this measure with respect to the occurrence of water excess in the changed and unchanged situation is estimated. For the estimation of damage caused by water excess empirical relations are applied. The most important parameters in these relations are soil type, groundwater table fluctuation class, organic matter content of the topsoil and crop type. For the determination of the difference in crop production in the changed and unchanged situation the net yield in both situations are compared.

When only a reasonable indication is required of the effects of planned measures often standard tables are applied. These standard tables are based on calculations with the LAMOS-model for a great number of typical soil profiles and for the usual groundwater table fluctuation classes, and give mean values for reduction in production due to excess and shortage of water.

3.2. Remote sensing approach

Since actual crop evapotranspiration maps can be derived from remotely sensed images (Nieuwenhuis, 1985), differences in evapotranspiration at the point of time that the images were acquired, can be made visible. By applying this method information about spatial differences in crop water supply due to natural causes or human interference can be obtained.

For the estimation of the effects of man-made changes in the hydrological situation on crop water supply the unchanged and changed situation must be compared. As it is not possible to observe the object in the unchanged and the changed situation at the same time another way to compare both situations must be followed. In principal there are two possibilities:

- Study the same object in different periods
- Study the object simultaneously with unchanged hydrologically and soil physically comparable reference-objects.

The first method is to prefer when changes in crop water supply due to differences in meteorological and other growth conditions during the growing season until the moment of acquisition are negligible or can be quantified. Until now only for a few regions digital multi spectral and thermal infrared images with sufficient geometrical resolution have been acquired. Therefore a multitemporal approach could not be applied in the present projects.

The second method to study the effects of changes in the agrohydrological situation by comparing the changed object with comparable but unchanged reference objects, implies that the result is dependent on the "quality" of the reference objects. The differences in hydrological and soil physical characteristics between both the object and the reference object need to be negligible. Fields that belong to the same soil map unit and groundwater table fluctuation class and which are situated within the same small area (comparable subsoil characteristics) are considered to satisfy this condition.

By means of statistical analyses of derived evapotranspiration values of fields, that originally would belong to the same distinguished class and which are divided in groups with and without changes, the effect of a certain measure is estimated. Fields with additional water supply by sprinkler-irrigation are left out of consideration as much as possible.

The accuracy of this method is mainly determined by the variability of soil physical and hydrological characteristics within the distinguished soil map units and groundwater table fluctuation to which the objects and reference objects belong. When this variability is low, good and reliable results may be expected.

4. Description of the remote sensing projects

4.1. Determination of the effect of soil improvement on crop water supply

The Veenkoloniën is a former peat and swamp area in the north-eastern part of The Netherlands that has been reclaimed. The excavation of peat for domestic use and land reclamation purposes already started in the 12th century and lasted until a few decades ago. Because domestic use was considered more important than the need to reclaim, the land was not well suited for modern agricultural use. A cross-section in outline of the reclaimed grounds is given in fig. 5.

The hydraulic conductivity of several layers in the subsoil, in particular the muck- and cemented B-horizons, was very low and caused water excess in wet periods. In dry periods these layers limited capillary rise.

In the past on several locations in the Veenkoloniën soil improvement works have been carried out but according to the present standards the soil physical condition of many of these grounds was still bad. In the last decade new and renewed soil improvement works have been achieved to reduce crop damage due to excess or shortage of water.

Effects of the soil improvement works on crop production have been studied on experimental fields. Moreover it is investigated if this information also could be derived with the aid of remote sensing images.

For this case-study heat-images and simultaneously taken false colour

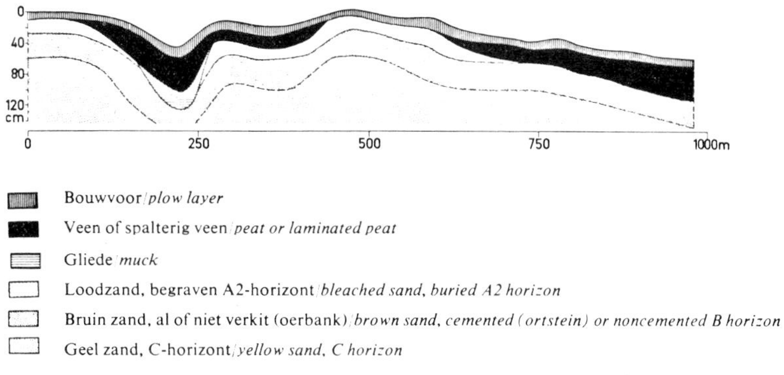

FIG.5 Cross-section in outline of old peat-reclamation soils. (After: de Smet, 1969).

photographs (Scale 1: 30.000) were used. The acquisition of the remote sensing images was performed from an airplane at an altitude of 5000 m on August 8, 1983 at 14.30 hrs. For the IRLS-recording a Daedulus DS1240/1260 digital scanner was used. The ground resolution of the heat images amounts about 12,5 x 12,5 m.

4.2. Determination of the presence and the effect of a loam-layer in the environment of a groundwater extraction

For the estimation of the influence of a groundwater extraction on crop growth in a cover sand area in the south-western part of The Netherlands, the drawdown of the phreatic groundwater level was calculated with the aid of a regional geohydrological model. Problems were encountered because of the local appearance of a loam-layer of variable thickness in the subsoil. As the hydraulic resistance of this layer varied considerably within short distance, the drawdown of the phreatic groundwater level could not be calculated accurately. A very intensive soil survey program (2-3 bore-holes/hectare) for an area of about 67km^2 would be necessary to obtain a good image of the presence and characteristics of the loam-layer.

Because of the high costs of such an intensive soil survey program of an area of this size, it was decided to try to obtain the necessary information by the application of remote sensing in combination with an extensive soil survey program (1 bore-hole/5 hectare). The soil survey program was carried out in 1982. The RS-flight was performed on July 21, 1983. From an altitude of 3000 m digital multi spectral and thermal infrared images were recorded with a Daedalus DS1240/1260 scanner and also false colour photographs were taken (Scale 1:20.000). The ground resolution of the multi spectral and thermal infrared images amounts about 7.5 x 7.5 m.

5. Results and discussion

5.1 "Soil improvement project"

The effect of soil improvement works on crop water supply was studied with the aid of heat images and false colour photographs, the existing soil map, a map with locations of improved fields and production measurement data of a number of improved fields with potatoes.

Differences in crop temperatures derived from the heat image of August 8, 1983 of improved and unimproved fields for four soil map units were compared. To prevent differences in groundwater depth and subsoil characteristics within the distinguished soil map units as much as possible, only improved and unimproved fields situated directly next to each other were used for this comparison. In total 35 improved and 35 unimproved fields were selected.

It appeared that crop temperatures for plaggeptic Medihemists (iVz),

(a)

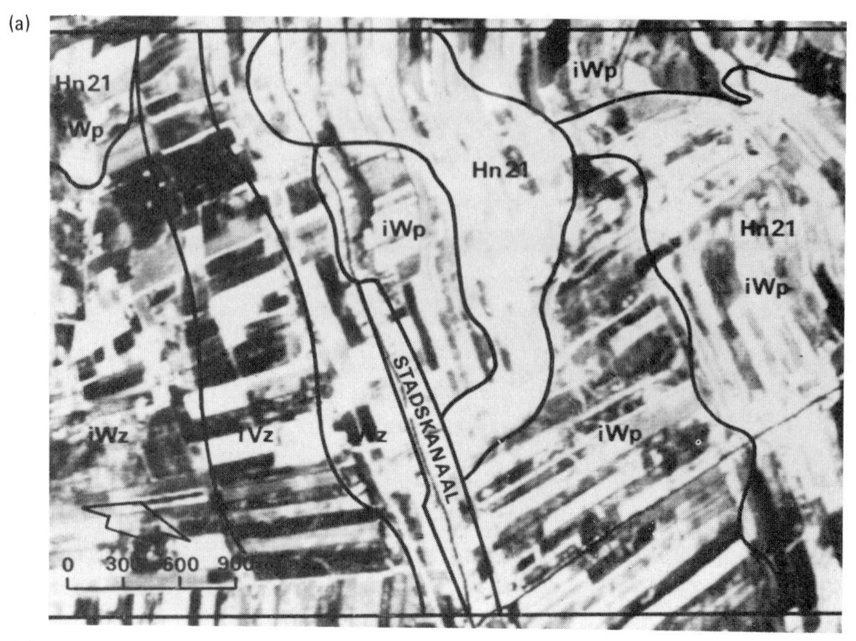

(b)

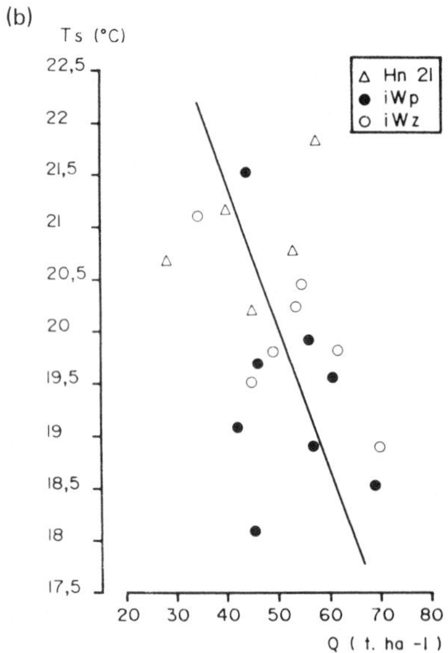

FIG.6 (a) Heat image recorded on August 8, 1983 of a part of the project area with an overlay of the soil map. (After Kok, 1984)

(b) Relation between crop temperatüre and final yield for some improved fields with potatoes on August 8, 1983. (After: Kok, 1984).

mesic hystic Haplaquods (iWp) and mesic hystic Haplaquepts (iWz) at improved fields were always lower than at unimproved fields within the same soil map unit. For podzol soils (Hn21, typic Haplaquod) no systematic temperature differences were found between improved and unimproved fields. The results are given in table 1.

TABLE 1--Comparison of crop temperatures of improved and unimproved potato fields within four soil map units. (After: Kok, 1984)

soil map unit	average temperature T (°C) improved	unimproved	ΔT (°C)	ΔE (%)	number of pairs
iVz	18.7	20.1	1.4	33	7
iWz	19.1	20.1	1.0	25	4
iWp	19.3	20.9	1.6	37	12
Hn21	(19 - 22)		-	-	12

From these figures it can be concluded that crop water supply at the time acquisition was better at improved fields except for the fields within soil map unit Hn21. This can be explained by the deeper groundwater tables of these soils. Capillary rise is as well in the improved as in the unimproved situation negligible. Soil improvement on these soils is predominantly applied to avoid perched water tables resulting in crop damage due to water excess. The effect of the soil improvement measures to prevent water excess has not been studied with remote sensing images. In fig. 6A a heat image of a part of the study area is presented with an overlay of the soil map. Dark tones represent relatively low crop temperatures and bright tones relatively high crop temperatures. Differences in crop water supply for the several soil types are clearly visible on the heat image.
During 1983 at a number of improved potato fields production measurements were performed for a factor-analyses project that was carried out by a number of institutes. The final production figures were combined with momentaneous crop temperatures derived from the heat image of August 8, 1983.

It appeared that the test fields within the three distinguished soil type classes showed a rather large variation in yield. Also the momentaneous crop temperature in respect to the final yield measurements showed a rather large variation (Fig. 6B).

Although only a low correlation between the momentaneous crop temperature and final production was found, the determined relationship was applied to estimate the yield at the unimproved potato fields. For this rather dry year the yield for improved fields was calculated to be about 15-25% higher than for unimproved fields. This agrees reasonably well with results obtained from experimental fields.

From this project the conclusion can be drawn that with remote sensing techniques important information on regional scale can be obtained that is hardly obtainable with any other method. The reliability and accuracy with which information on field scale can be obtained is unpredictable because of the variability in soil physical and hydrological characteristics within the same soil map unit. If the differences in crop water supply due to th s variability within a distinguished class are relatively small in comparison with the differences in crop water supply as a result of the investigated factor, reliable results are to be expected. In this area the variation in crop water supply within a distinguished class was only less smaller than the increase in crop water supply due to soil improvement works. For that reason the raise of crop production as a result of these works for a certain field could not be determined accurately.

5.2. "Loam-layer project"

In the extensive soil survey program at about 1100 locations information was collected about soil type, presence and thickness of the loam-layer, actual groundwater depth and groundwater table fluctuation class. From the multi spectral and heat images acquired on July 21, 1983 information was derived about crop type, sprinkling and relative evapotranspiration ($E_A/E_T * 100\%$). By statistical correlation the actual groundwater depth on the flight date was estimated from the groundwater depth measurements in 1982. Groundtruth data were combined with the data derived from the remote sensing images.

For the estimation of the effect of the loam-layer on crop water supply, only fields with maize or grass were used. Sprinklered fields were left out of consideration as much as possible.

Comparison of the estimated relative evapotranspiration-values between the distinguished classes with and without loam-layer showed that the evapotranspiration-values were almost equal in both situations. The presence of the loam-layer had obviously none or just a very slight positive effect on crop water supply. The same conclusion could be drawn from calculations with the LAMOS-model. The K(h)-relationship of the sand- and loam layer turned out to be almost identical.

In the study area, however, one sub region could be distinguished where the relative evapotranspiration-values were significant lower than the average values for the concerned classes. This especially occured for classes with very shallow groundwater tables. From field observations it was found that the soil physical characteristics of the loam-layer in this sub region differed a lot from those of the loam-layer that was found at other places in the project area. The hydraulic conductivity was much lower and therefore capillary rise was less for comparable groundwater depths. This resulted in larger reductions in evapotranspiration. With the aid of the evapotranspiration map this sub region could be mapped more accurate.

For several soil type classes the relative evapotranspiration and the calculated actual groundwater depth were compared. The result for two podzolic soils, respectively with a 20-30 cm (Hn) and a 30-50 cm (cHn) thick topsoil is given in figure 7A. The points falling at the right hand side of the curve in figure 7A are possibly influenced by sprinkling.

Obviously the rooting depth is for both soil types about the same as there is hardly a difference in evapotranspiration for equal groundwater depths. It also appeared that the determined relationship between relative evapotranspiration and groundwater depth agreed reasonably well with the capillary flux derived from the k(h)-relation of the subsoil. On July 21, 1983 the potential evapotranspiration for maize and grass amounted about 5 mm. When it is considered that the moisture content in the root zone is not expired wholy, than the matric pressure at interface root zone - subsoil is somewhat lower. The curve-fitting will even be betten in that case.

Furthermore the importance of capillary rise for crop water supply in The Netherlands is well illustrated in figure 7.

From this case-study it can be concluded that with the aid of remote sensing images the hydrological description of an area can be improved. Moreover, the output of agrohydrological models can be checked for the point of time that the remote sensing images were recorded. Besides it seems possible that under certain conditions the hydraulic conductivity of the subsoil can be checked or perhaps even can be determined with the aid of evapotranspiration maps. A more detailed study on this subject has not been carried out yet.

Also in this study the variability within distinguished classes caused problems for an accurate interpretation on field scale. The results on regional scale were positive because of the large number of sample sites that were available.

6. Preliminary conclusions

Actual crop evapotranspiration maps derived from remotely sensed images give an accurate overall view of spatial differences in crop water supply for the point of time that the images are recorded. This overall view is very useful for inventories and investigations concerning crop water supply.

Results obtained with the aid of hydrological models can be checked with these maps and the hydrological description of a region can be improved.

The variability of hydrological and soil physical characteristics within a certain soil map unit and groundwater table fluctuation class causes problems

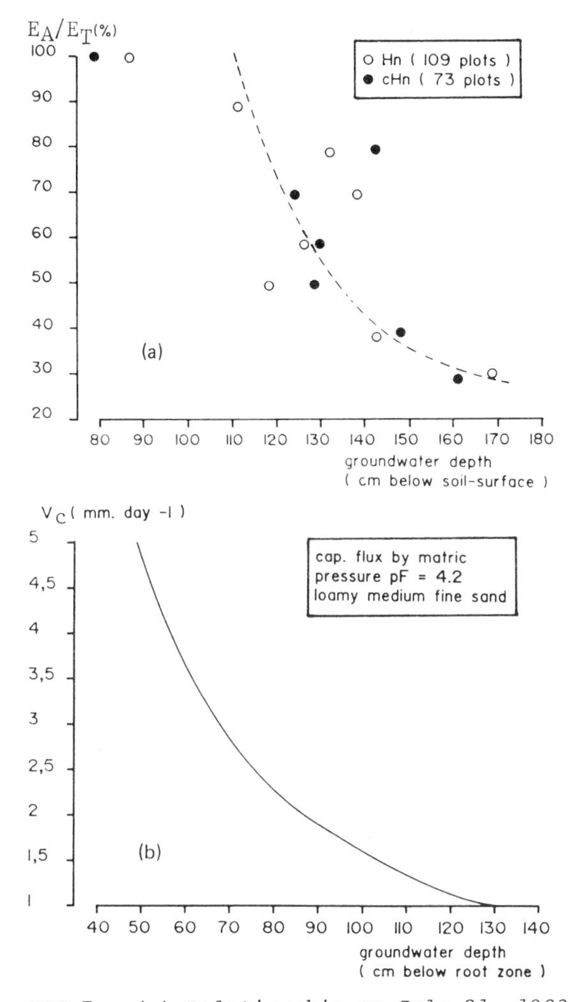

FIG.7 (a) Relationship on July 21, 1983 between groundwater depth and relative evapotranspiration for two podzols with different thickness of topsoil.
(b) Maximum capillary flux by a matric pressure of pF 4.2 at the interface root zone - subsoil derived from the K(h) - relation of the subsoil.

for the estimation of effects of man-made changes on crop water supply. On regional scale positive results can be obtained but on field scale the accuracy and reliability are insufficient for practical use.

Problems occur if no reliable reference objects are present. Then a multitemporal remote sensing approach has great advantages. For a multi temporal approach it is necessary that frequently digital multi spectral and heat images are recorded around midday with at least a spatial resolution of 15 - 20 meter. The availability of a space born crop monitoring system with such a device ("CROPSAT") would be a preferable solution to realize this. In The Netherlands the applicability of remote sensing techniques in practice would come importantly closer if frequently and routinely CROPSAT-images would come available.

References

Boheemen, P.J.M. van, 1980, Seizoen- en piekbehoefte aan kunstmatige watervoorziening bij gras, aardappelen en tuinbouwgewassen, nota 1211. ICW, Wageningen, The Netherlands, 51 p.

Boheemen, P.J.M. van, 1981, Toename van de produktie van grasland bij verbetering van de watervoorziening. nota 1298. ICW, Wageningen, The Netherlands, 68 p.

Feddes, R.A., 1979, Gewasproduktie en waterverbruik, nota 1118. ICW, Wageningen, The Netherlands, 39 p.

Kok, A., 1984, Studie naar de effecten van de grondverbetering in de Veenkoloniën met remote sensing, nota 1532. ICW, Wageningen, The Netherlands 51 p.

Laat, P.J.M. de, 1980, Model for unsatured flow above a shallow watertable, applied to a regional sub-surface flow problem. Thesis. Agric. Res. Rep. 895. Pudoc, Wageningen, The Netherlands, 126 p.

Nieuwenhuis, G.J.A., 1985, Integration of remote sensing with a soil water balance simulation model (SWATRE), paper of this workshop, 10 p.

Reuling, T.H.M., 1983, Gebruikershandleiding voor het model LAMOS, nota LD. Landinrichtingsdienst, Utrecht, The Netherlands, 20 p.

Smet, L.A.H. de, 1969, De Groninger Veenkoloniën (westelijk deel). Verslag landbouwkundige onderzoekingen nr. 722. Stiboka, Wageningen, The Netherlands.

Werkgroep Landbouwkundige Aspekten, 1984, Landbouwkundige aspekten van grondwateronttrekking. LAGO-rapport, Commissie Grondwaterwet Waterleidingbedrijven Utrecht, The Netherlands, 154 p.

Hydrologic Applications of Space Technology (Proceedings of the Cocoa Beach Workshop, Florida, August 1985). IAHS Publ. no. 160, 1986.

Regional transpiration assessment by remote sensing

J. BALEK
Stavebni Geologie, Prague, Czechoslovakia
J. CERMAK, J. KUCERA & A. PRAX
Institute of Forest Ecology, Brno, Czechoslovakia
M. PALOUS
Meta, Prague, Czechoslovakia

Abstract

An in situ method for the measuring of the transpiration rate of single trees was developed and described earlier (Balek et al. 1983). For the extrapolation of the results to the region a remote sensing was applied, based on the analysis of the optical density in bands 4,5 and 7. From a model airplane flying less than 200 metres above the soil surface the images were obtained with pixels representing the actual areas size of less than 20 cm. This was sufficient to obtain results statistically significant for tree crowns of single species.

A relationship between the optical density of band 7 and the transpirational rate was found to be most significant for measured plants and for the lysimeter grass covered surface as well.

General

Methods of transpirational measurement of plants have become available only recently. Ground measuring methods as evaluated by Čermák et al (1973, 1976, 1982, 1984) can be characterised as one-point in situ measurements, however, when extending the results from trunks to the tree crowns, they can be considered as representative for an area. An interpretation of the results outside the tree crowns is rather subjective, even if it is based on a joint analysis of meteorological data, soil moisture regime and biometry. Remote sensing method appears to be more objective for such a purpose.

Remote sensing method

In general, the method is based on the presumption that the surface reflecting the same amount of energy at a certain wavelength have at least some of the physical properties similar. In the case of the vegetation this principle is extended to the surface of the plants. By earlier measurements (Heller, 1971) there was proved that the plants reflect more energy in the infrared than in the visible bands of the spectrum. For some coniferous species the ratio was found 4:1 at the peak of the growing season, it dropped at the end of it. A maximum ratio 5:1 was found for angiosperms.

The emitted energy is influenced by molecular structures. Some authors expected that the leaf chlorophyl reflected mainly at the wavelength 0.38 - 0.65 μm, while for the infrared it was nearly transparent. Heller concluded that the reflectivity at the wavelength 0.8 - 1.1 μm was higher for leaves with higher content of mesophyllous cells. It means that very likely the water content in the cellular walls plays an important role.

Therefore a presumption has been established that the measurement of the plant transpiration should be based on the measurement of the infrared energy reflected from the plant surface; however, at least the seasonal pattern of the leaf color and density is detectable at the visible part of the spectrum. Therefore also the structural effect of the leaf area development should be considered when the images are analysed.

The ground measurements were taken on the adult species of spruce (Picea abies (L) Kars) and oak (Quercus sessilis Ehrh.) with crown areas of $41 m^2$ and $46 m^2$ respectively. Both species were located on a hillside covered by light alluvial soil, underlined by sandstone formations. The transpiration measuring device was described by Balek et al. (1983). It consists of a power generator, a series of thermocouples, electrodes and a recording instrument. Power is supplied to the tree trunk through five stainless-steel electrodes installed in the hydroactive xylem. Assessment of the transpiration is based on the heat balance method of direct heating of stems, developed by Čermák et al. (1973, 1982) and Kučera et al. (1977). The temperature difference between heated and nonheated parts of the stem, the power input, the distance and number of the electrodes together with the tree circumference enter in the formula.

For the assessment of the grass transpiration a lysimeter constructed around a natural soil block 3x3x3 metres was set up. Here the data acquisition system HP 3052A was used for a continuous monitoring of the soil moisture balance in the zone of aeration.

The soil moisture under the grass cover in the lysimeter was measured at the depths 10, 30, 50, 80 and 120 cm by using Soiltest sensors calibrated for a particular soil type.

An example of the continuous transpiration measurement during the growing season 1983 is in Fig. 1. Here P is for precipitation (mm day^{-1}), E_t for potential evapotranspiration (mm day^{-1}) and Q for the sum of daily transpiration (kg day^{-1}). W is the soil moisture development (mm) for each soil profile.

The pictures of the crowns and of the lysimeter surface were taken by a double lens reflex camera installed in a model airplane operated by radio. The weight of the device with camera is approximately 7 kg. It can reach the altitude 3000 metres. Kodak IE 135-20 film which can detect so called blue part of the spectrum (wavelenght 0.5 - 0.6 μm), green part (0.6 - 0.7 μm) and near infrared (0.8 - 1.1 μm) was used. Corresponding bands are 4,5 and 7, respectively. In general, film used for such a pupose should be sensitive to the energy emitted from the vegetation surface and supress the impact of the atmospheric emissions. Kodak Wratten filter No. 16 was used to eliminate secondary effects of the atmosphere.

The pictures were taken during cloudless days at noon. In the attempt to avoid any optical deformation, only pictures with the objects in the central part were used. For the analysis of the diurnial regime several pictures were taken during other hours.

After the visual evaluation, selected photographs were digitalised in each particular band on the Photomotion drum scanner. The optical density in bands 4,5 and 7 was determined in pixels

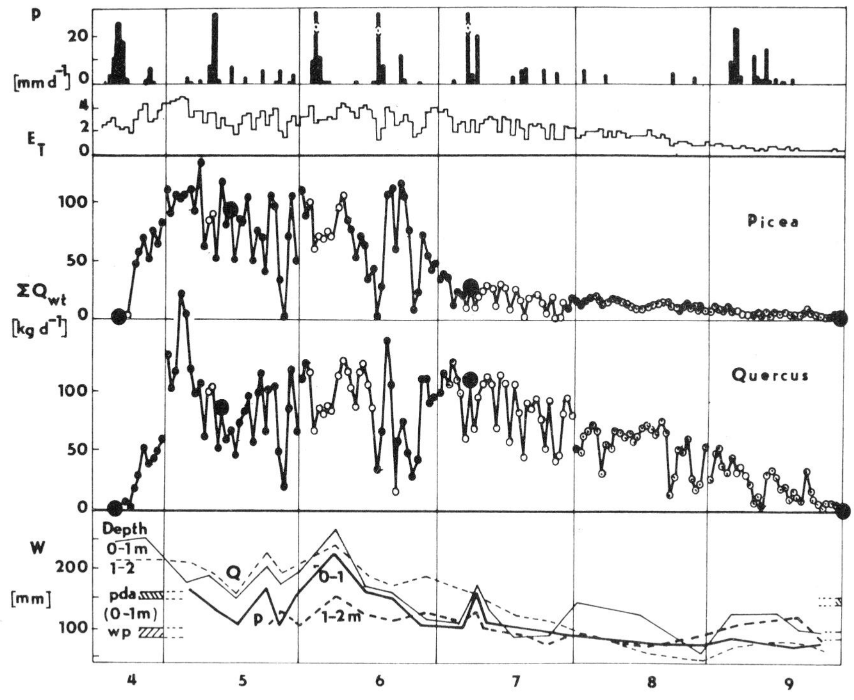

FIG.1 Ground measurement of transpiration.

corresponding to the actual plots size of about 20 x 20 cm. General principles of the digitalisation as described by Cracknell (1981) were applied; a methodological approach of NASA was followed (Juday 1979) and modified methodology set up by Balek and Palouš (1983).

The data stored on the magnetic tape were processed on the Eclipse computer and selected statistical values for each object were calculated. Most difficult part of the procedure is a proper identification of the relatively small observed objects. For this purpose black and white enlarged photographs were used with the square network corresponding to 50 x 50 pixels and from the magnetic tape a three-dimensional graph was plotted for selected objects in which z-axis corresponded with the optical density given in the range of 0-255 grey levels.

Discussion of the results

An example of a three-dimensional image of the optical density in band 7 for a lysimeter and experimental plots is given in Fig. 2. The bright color of the roof of the house attached to the lysimeter (a) has rather stable optical properties and can be used for an orientation. The variability of the optical density of the lysimeter surface is rather low (b), which indicates uniform transpiration. The optical density of the surrounding grassland (c) is more variable because the grass is not well maintained. Also the optical density of the grassland is slightly higher, which indicates a lower transpiration than that in the lysimeter.

On the adjacent surface runoff measuring plots the optical density is higher for bare soil (d) than for the grass (e).

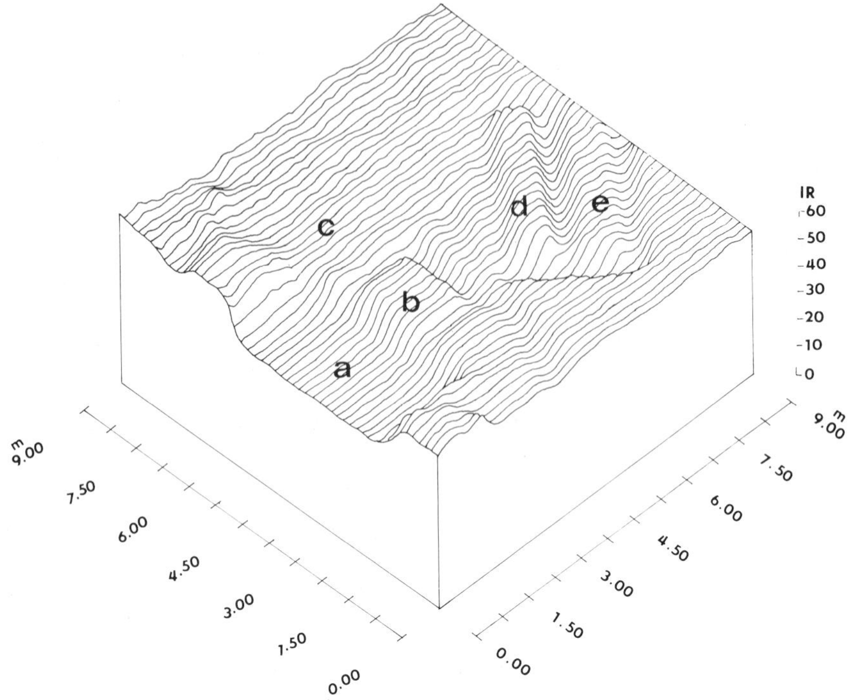

FIG.2 A three-dimensional image of the lysimeter, grass and bare soil. Optical density at band 7.

Does this indicate a higher transpiration from grass than from bare soil? Low optical densities around the plots are for concrete walls.

In Fig.3 there is an image of the wetland at the band 5. For such a type of the vegetation the optical density is rather monotonous. At the band 7 even more uniform optical density confirmed a uniform transpiration.

Finally an image of the crown of measured oak, as obtained at the end of the growing season at the band 7, is given in Fig. 4. The variability of the optical density is produced by a nonhomogeneous leaf area of the crowns and by a combined effect of the branches and leaves as seen from the airplane.

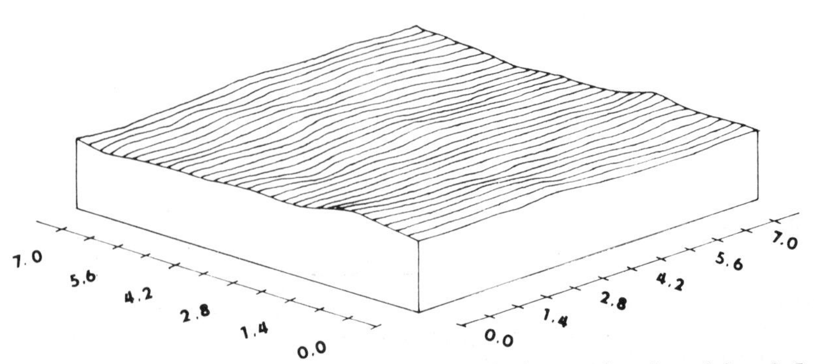

FIG.3 A three-dimensional image of the wetland and band 5.

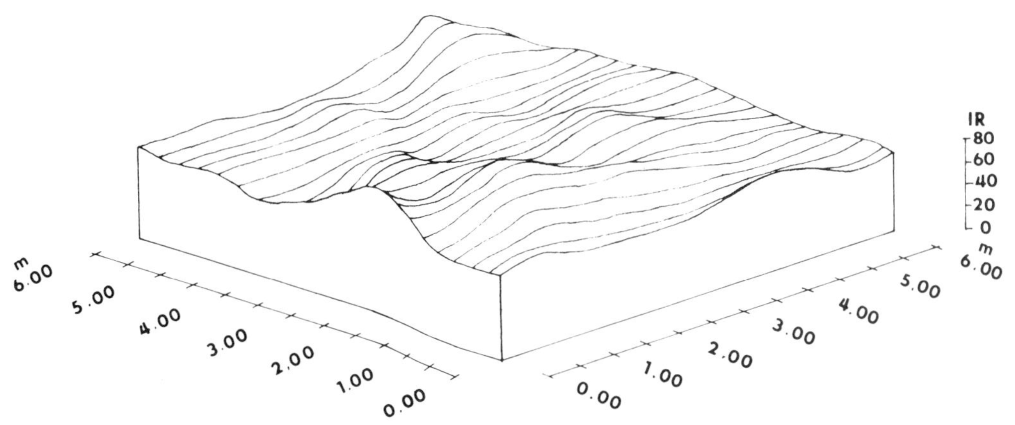

FIG.4 An image of the oak crown at the end of growing season; band 7.

A similar effect is certainly incorporated in the images obtained for more extensive forest areas.

An analysis of the results has proved that the most significant indicator of the transpiration rate is the optical density at band 7. The optical densities as obtained for bands 4 and 5 have been found far less significant.

For mature oak the highest correlation coefficient (R = 0,96) was found for the relationship

$$E_t^{oak} = -52.8 + \frac{8806}{IR} \text{ litres day}^{-1} \tag{1}$$

where IR is the optical density at the band 7.

For spruce the correlation coefficient R = 0.85 was found for the relationship (Fig. 5):

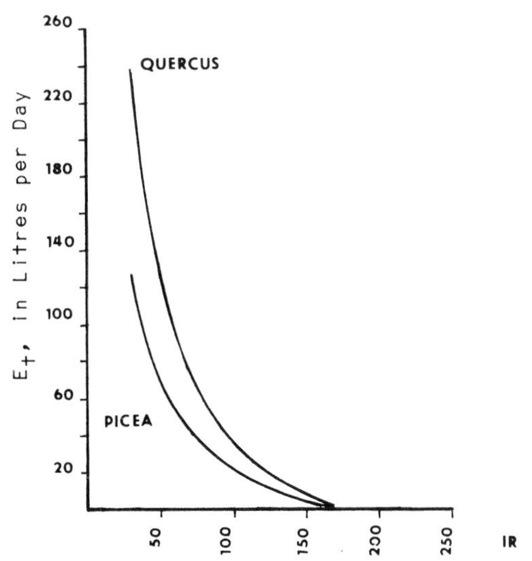

FIG.5 Optical density/transpiration rate relationship for oak and spruce.

$$E_t^{spruce} = -27.3 + \frac{4654}{IR} \text{ litres day}^{-1} \quad (2)$$

By a multiple regressional analysis and the transpiration rate as a dependent variable and optical densities at bands 4,5 and 7 as the independent ones, the following relationship was found for the spruce:

$$E_t^{spruce} = 61.2 + \frac{5729}{IR} + \frac{7724}{IG} + \frac{6046}{IB} \text{ litres day}^{-1} \quad (3)$$

where IG and IB are optical densities at the band 5 and 4 respectively. For oak transpiration, the optical densities at bands 4 and 5 have not been proved as significant at 90 % level.

For the transpiration of grass a relationship was found in the following form:

$$E_t^{grass} = \frac{1}{0.08\ IR - 0.024} \text{ litres m}^2 \text{ day}^{-1} \quad (4)$$

Again, the optical density at bands 4 and 5 was not proved as significant.

Conclusion

It is assumed that a linear combination of the optical densities at each band may supply more convenient results and future effort will be directed toward such an approach.

A comparison of the diurnial fluctuation of the transpiration during a cloudless day (Fig. 6) and during a day with cloudy afternoon (Fig. 7) indicates problems which can be expected when the remote sensing results obtained at noon need to be applied in general. Actually,a comparison of such a type of graphs is utilised when a reduced transpiration during other than cloudless days is calculated and deviation from hypothetical cloudless conditions occurs.

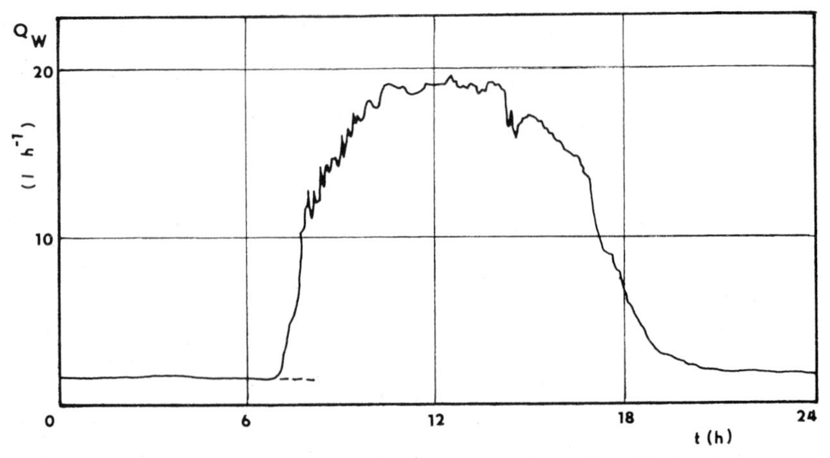

FIG.6 Transpiration rate during a summer cloudless day.

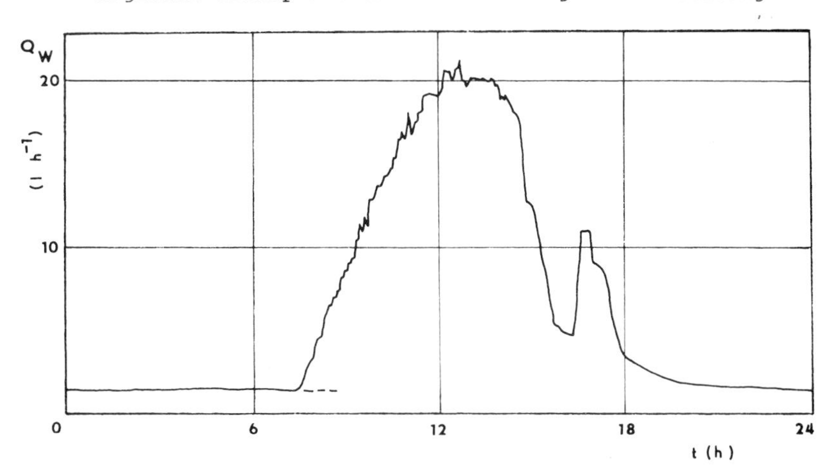

FIG.7 Transpiration rate during a summer day with a cloudy afternoon.

The mean value of the optical density at the band 7 for an area, watershed or region can be obtained from satellite images in a way similar to that used for measured single plants. Thus the validity of the relationships (1) - (4) can be regionally extended, providing the area is covered by the same family of species or composed by their mixture.

A solid ground measurement is always essential for a successful measurement of the transpiration rate. A further extension of statistical chracteristics of the images obtained for each measured plant and for the region may contribute to a better understanding of the transpirational process.

References

Balek, J., Čermák, J., Kučera, J., Prax, A., 1983, A Direct Method For Forest Transpiration Measurement: Journal of Hydrology 66 (1983), 123 - 131.

Balek, J., Palouš, M., 1983: An Assessment of the Transpiration Through an Analysis of Infrared Images on a Computer (Russian) Proceed. of Academy of Science, USSR, Khabarovsk.

Čermák, J., Deml, M., Penka, M., 1973: A New Method of Sap Flow Rate Determination in Trees. Biologia Plantarum, Prague.

Čermák, J., Kučera, J., Penka, M., 1976: Improvement of Method of Sap Flow Rate Determination in Adult Trees Based on Heat Balance With Direct Electric Heating Of Xylem. Biologia Plantarum (Prague) 18 (2): 105 - 110, 1976.

Čermák, J., Úlehla, J., Kučera, J., Penka, M., 1982: Sap Flow Rate and Transpiration Dynamics in the Full-grown Oak (Quercus robur L.) in Floodplain Forest Exposed to Seasonal Floods, as Related to Potential Evapotranspiration and Tree Dimension. Biologia Plantarum, Prague, 24 (6): 446 - 460, 1982.

Čermák, J., Jeník, J., Kučera, J., Žídek V., 1984: Xylem Sap Flow in a Crack Willow Tree (Salix fragilis L.) in Relation to Diurnial Changes of Environment. Oecologia - in print.

Cracknell, A. P., (Edit.), 1981: Remote Sensing in Meteorology, Oceanography and Hydrology. Ellis Horwood Ltd., Chichester, 451 p.

Heller, J., 1971: Application of Remote Sensing in Forestry. Int. Union of Forest Research Organisations, Sect. 25, Freiburg, 189 p.
Juday, R. D., 1979: Colorimetric Principles as Applied to Multichannel Imagery. NASA Tech. Memorandum 58215, Sioux Falls, 66 p.
Kučera, J., Čermák, J., Penka, M., 1977: Improved Thermal Method of Continual Recording the Transpiration Flow Rate Dynamics. Biologia Plantarum (Praha) 19 (6): 413 - 420.

Hydrologic Applications of Space Technology (Proceedings of the Cocoa Beach Workshop, Florida, August 1985). IAHS Publ. no. 160, 1986.

Use of GOES digital data to estimate land-use land-cover for hydrologic applications

S. I. SOLOMON
Department of Civil Engineering, University of Waterloo, Waterloo, Ontario, Canada N2L 3G1
K. D. HARVEY
Inland Waters Directorate, Environment Canada, Ottawa, Ontario, Canada K1A 0E7

Abstract
The first of the GOES satellites was launched in 1974 primarily to monitor meteorological conditions. However, digital data sensed by GOES in the visible wavelength band of 0.55-0.75 μm has since also been used to roughly assess the land-use land-cover of cloud-free areas. In regions where an almost permanent cloud cover prevails, the frequent coverage by the geostationary satellites provides for at least a few opportunities per year of obtaining cloud-free imagery and, hence, assessing land-use land-cover. From a hydrologic perspective, a so-called "fractional" classification of GOES data can provide useful land-use land-cover input to both distributed and lumped hydrologic models, provided that the size of the watershed under study is in the order of 1000 km^2 or more. The attractiveness of the GOES technique over alternative methods increases with the cloudiness of the study area, the closeness to the sub-satellite point, and also with the size of the watershed being modelled, because the amount of data requiring analysis is minimized.

Introduction
The hydrologic response of a watershed is a complex function of many factors, including those related to the land-use land-cover characteristics of the watershed. Some of these characteristics, such as surface storage, imperviousness, and forest-cover, are subject to significant variations with time. Such variations could result naturally or from man's interference; the construction of dams and reservoirs, urban development, forest fires, logging operations, and mining practices can drastically change the hydrologic regime from year to year. Recognition of and proper accounting for the temporal variation of land-cover are extremely important to the proper assessment of the watershed hydrology. Modern remote-sensing techniques provide the means to monitor changing land-use land-cover. The use of conventional remote sensing techniques and of Landsat for this purpose has been well-documented in the literature. However, meteorological satellites such as the Geostationary Operational Environmental Satellite (GOES) can also be used for this purpose, particularly in the case of larger river basins. Digital processing techniques have been developed for use with GOES data (Solomon and Swain, 1981), and this provides the possibility of using such data beyond the purely meteorological applications for which GOES was originally designed.

One such non-meteorological application is the use of GOES data to estimate land-cover parameters for hydrologic models. The main advantage of using GOES data is that it is collected year-round on an hourly basis, so estimates can be made and regularly updated in almost all areas of the world. A further advantage relates to the fact that GOES is operational. However, an obvious disadvantage is its relatively poor spatial resolution, particularly in the thermal infrared band. For small watersheds (e.g. urban), such poor resolutions are obviously restrictive. For large watersheds, however, it has been shown (Harvey, 1983; Harvey and Solomon, 1984) that interpreted GOES visible data can be of use as land-cover inputs to hydrological models, as such data are usually averaged for areas larger than the resolution achieved in the GOES visible band.

The intent of this paper is to describe more fully the analysis of GOES data to provide such input. An example is presented using the Serpent River Watershed in northern Ontario, Canada.

GOES Digital Data

Each GOES satellite is equipped with a Visible Infrared Spin Scan Radiometer (VISSR). This radiometer senses the electromagnetic energy radiated by the earth in two spectral bands. The visible band (VISIBLE) covers the 0.55-0.75 micrometer (μm) band, while the thermal infrared band (IR) covers the 10.5-12.6 μm band.

Data is collected using a systematic scanning process. The satellite rotates continuously at a rate of about 100 revolutions per minute, its spin axis nearly parallel to the spin axis of the earth. With each rotation, the radiometer's eight VISIBLE and one IR sensors scan a swath of the earth in the west-east direction. At the sub-satellite point, each picture element, or "pixel", thus obtained has a ground resolution of about 0.8 km by 0.8 km, while each infrared pixel has a ground resolution of about 3.2 km by 6.4 km. Due to both the fixed position of the satellite relative to the earth and the curvature of the earth, these resolutions decrease as the distance from the sub-satellite point increases.

Under normal conditions, the satellite collects data twice per hour. The data is sent via analog signal to a ground receiving station, where it is converted and recorded in digital form onto computer compatible tapes (CCTs).

Users may request copies of the CCTs or the photographic imagery (Figure 1) produced from the data. With a CCT, it is possible to use a computer line-printer to produce a relatively large-scale image of a specific study area. Such an image, or "graymap", is produced by overprinting to obtain shades of gray which are inversely proportional to the intensity of back reflectance of light. Figure 2(a) is a photo-reduced VISIBLE graymap of the northern Lake Huron region of Ontario. The data used to produce this graymap was also used to produce the photograph of Figure 1.

Fractional Method of Land-Use Land-Cover Classification

Given the relatively coarse resolution of the GOES VISIBLE pixel, the reflected energy sensed for each pixel by the GOES radiometer is in many cases some weighted average amount of the energy radiated by two or more landcover classes of interest. When carrying out attempts to classify land-use land-cover using GOES data, it is obviously tempting to employ techniques based on those developed for the classification of Landsat data. However, development of signatures based on the two GOES bands are not very productive in non-homogeneous areas because one pixel in the infrared band corresponds to 32 pixels in the visible band. Earlier attempts to apply such approaches have indicated that the technique could be of use to roughly map land-use land-cover in an area (Plate 3). However, the use of the technique for hydrological purposes leads to

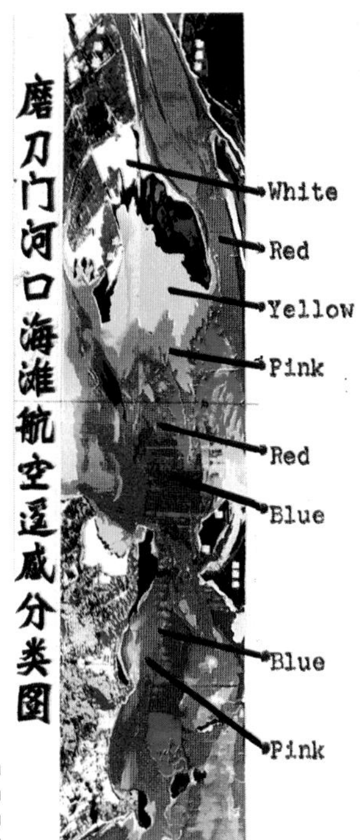

White: 0.5 m
Yellow: 1.0-1.3 m
Pink: 1.3-1.5 m
Blue: 1.5-3.0 m
Dark red: 3.0-5.0 m

PLATE 4 The water depth of the coast at Pearl River.

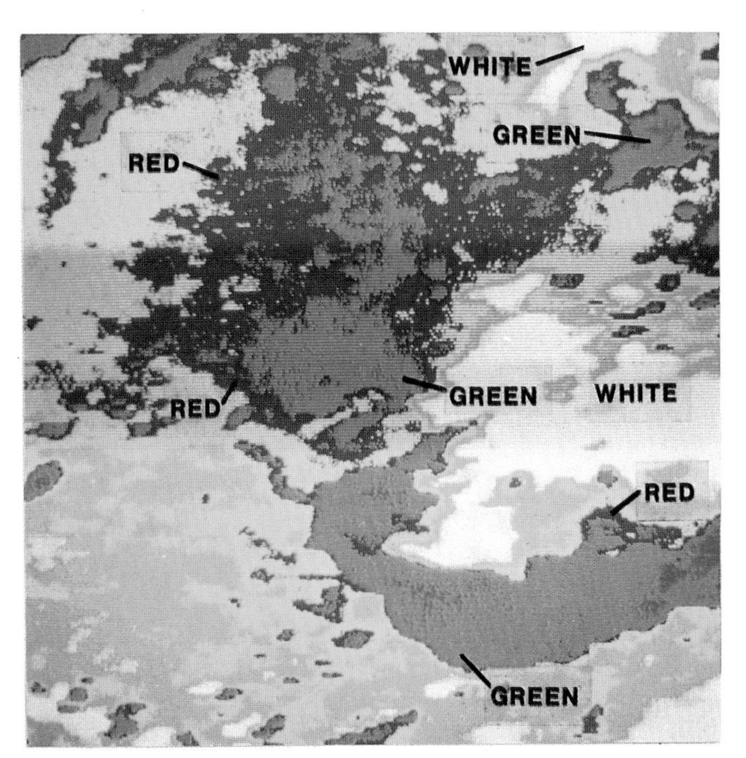

Red: damp soil
Green: water
White: cloud

PLATE 5 Digital image processing of Meteosat NOAA 7 image. At the right-hand side below the cloud is a big lake. The central green area is the Hefei City of inundation.

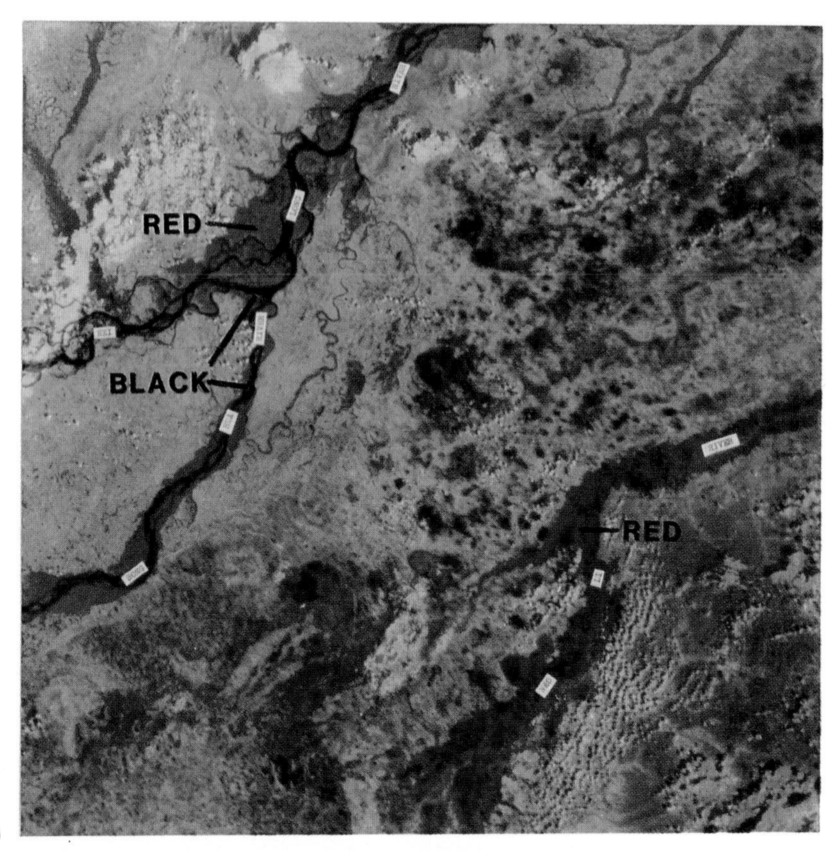

Red: flooded area
Black: river in dry season

PLATE 6 False color composite image utilizing same region and two different time images in San Jiang Plain with flood period in 1981 and dry season in 1976 overlapping.

Red: exit of electric power plant, 32°C
Light blue: inlet of electric power plant, 17°C

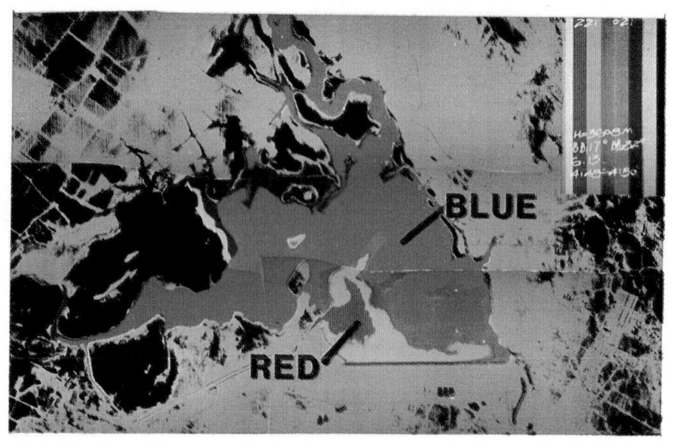

PLATE 7 The surface temperature distribution of Dou He reservoir.

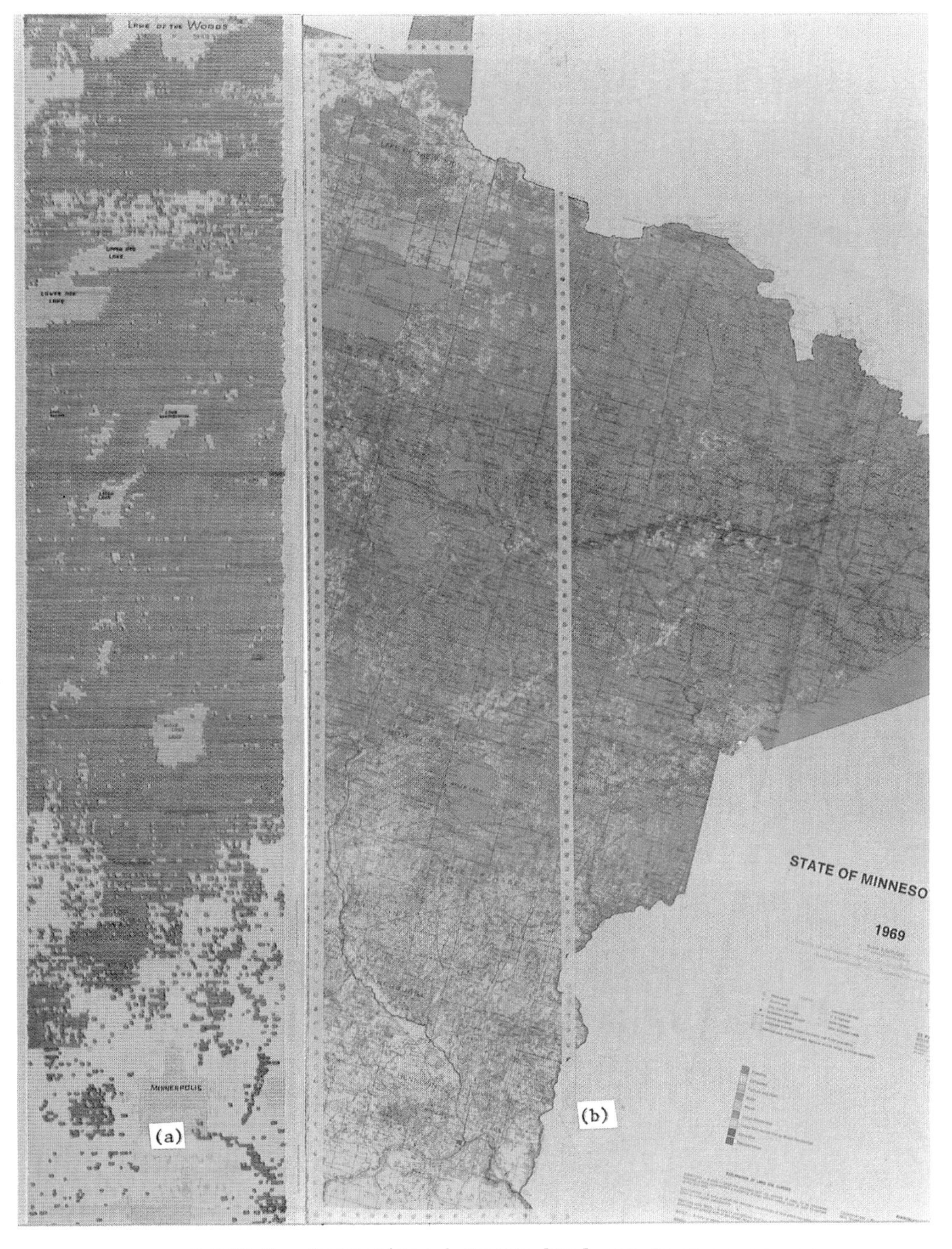

PLATE 3 Comparison between land-use land-cover maps obtained from GOES (a) with conventaional land-use land-cover map (b) for the area of Minnesota.

N

COLOR CODES

	LAND USE	SOIL TEXTURE	EMISSIVITY
	-	-	<.801
	-	-	.801-.823
	FEEDLOT	CLAY	.824-.844
	RANGE	-	.845-.866
	IRRIGATED PASTURE	CLAY LOAM	.867-.887
	DRYLAND PASTURE	LOAM	.888-.909
	IRRIGATED CROPS	FINE SANDY LOAM	.910-.930
	DRYLAND CROPS	LOAMY FINE SAND	.931-.951
	URBAN	SAND	>.951

LAND USE A   SOIL TEXTURE B   EMISSIVITY C

PLATE 1 Digital data bases for the Texas High Plains study site: A - landcover, B - soil texture, and C - emissivity derived from microwave data.

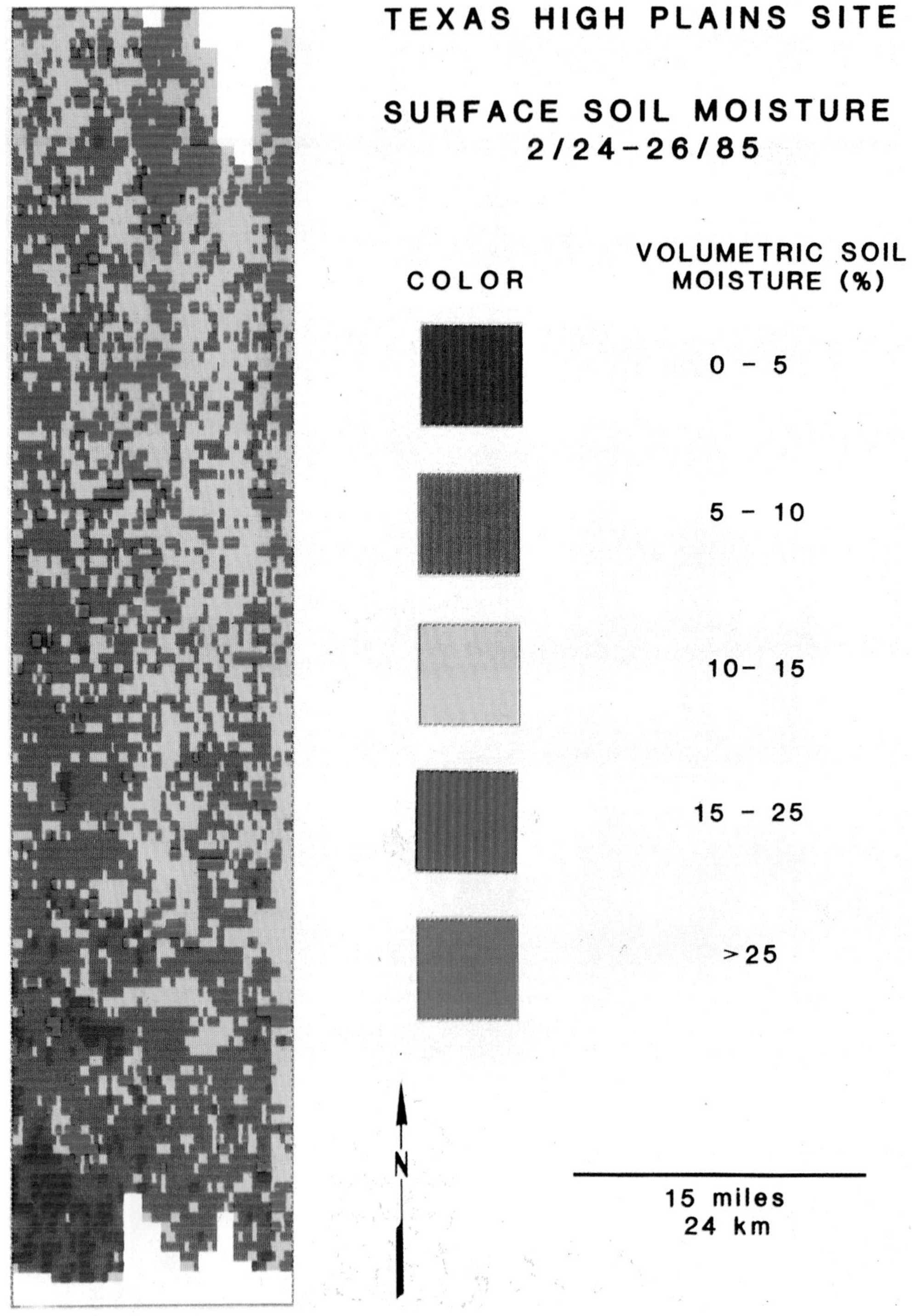

PLATE 2 Surface soil moisture map for the Texas High Plains study site derived from microwave data.

FIG.1 GOES photographic image (visible-band) October 3, 1976 (1800 hrs GMT).

excessive errors in classification (Harvey and Solomon, 1984). In view of this, a different land-use land-cover classification technique, based exclusively on the digital data obtained in the visible band, was developed and applied for hydrological purposes. In this approach, which is applicable basically only in areas in which the number of land-use land-cover classes is limited and known, the combination of percentages of land-cover classes which produces a specific VISIBLE spectral response can be defined for the purpose of classification. If one assumes that, in each pixel, there are only two known classes of land-use land-cover, the amount of each class in an area may be indirectly estimated, although the relative location of each class within a pixel remains unknown. Some of the restriction due to poor resolution of the data is therefore eliminated. This technique has been designated as the "fractional" method.

Defining each spectral response (reflectance) value in terms of a combination of land-cover classes is achieved by first registering the GOES VISIBLE data grid (extracted from the CCT) onto so-called "ground-truth" maps using an affine transformation for the area. An affine transformation provides a linear relationship between conventional

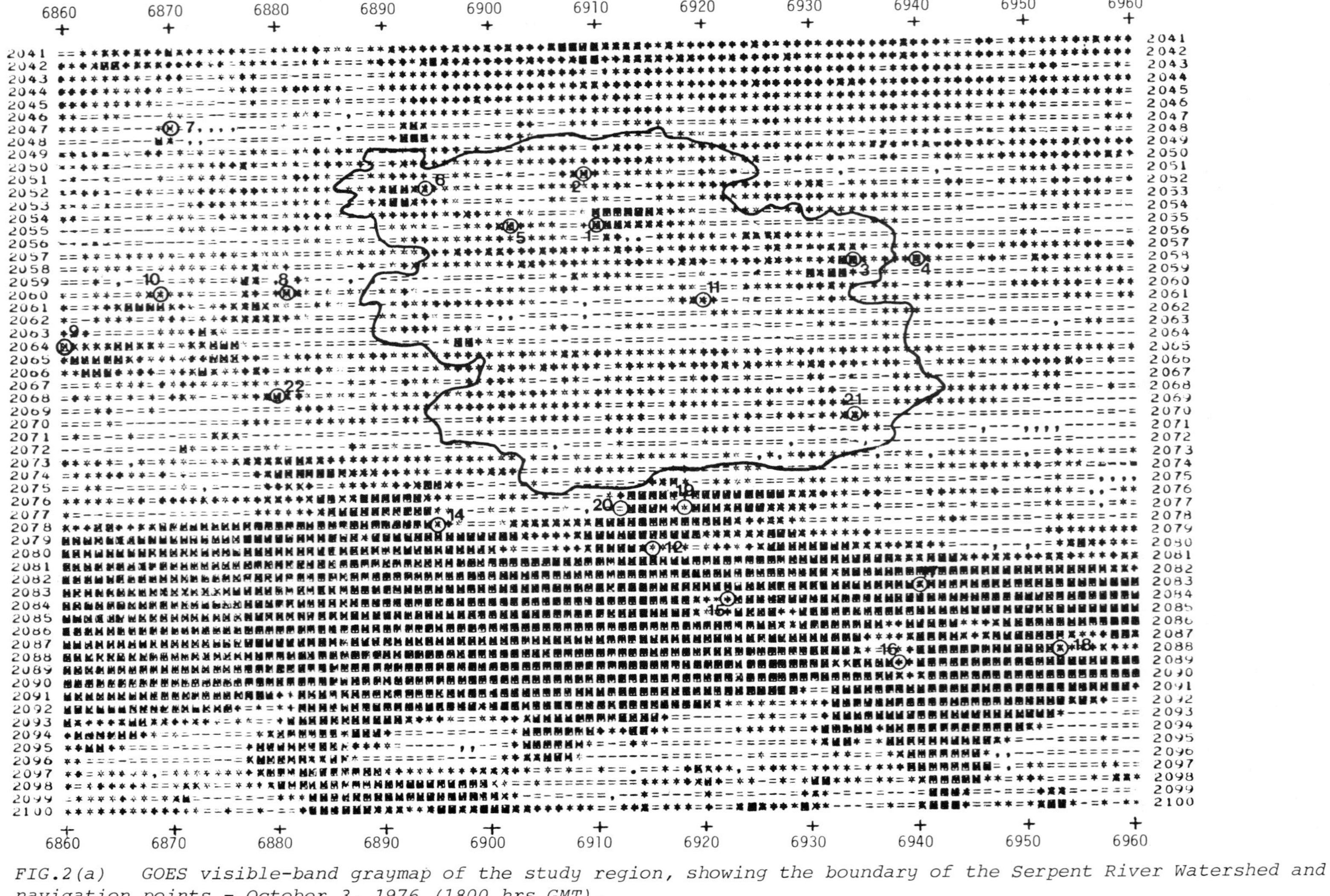

FIG.2(a) GOES visible-band graymap of the study region, showing the boundary of the Serpent River Watershed and navigation points - October 3, 1976 (1800 hrs GMT).

cartographic co-ordinates and the GOES VISIBLE co-ordinates (lines and columns). For each reflectance value, several pixel areas are identified on the maps and analyzed for patterns regarding the types of land-cover which are present and the proportions (percentages) of the pixel area which they cover. Once such patterns are identified, each reflectance value can be assigned to a particular combination of percentages of land-cover classes, or "land-cover composition".

To quantify the land-cover of a study area, a composite land-cover map is first produced by computer, assigning a unique line-printer character to each reflectance value. The area of interest is then located on this map using the previously developed affine transformations. The relative

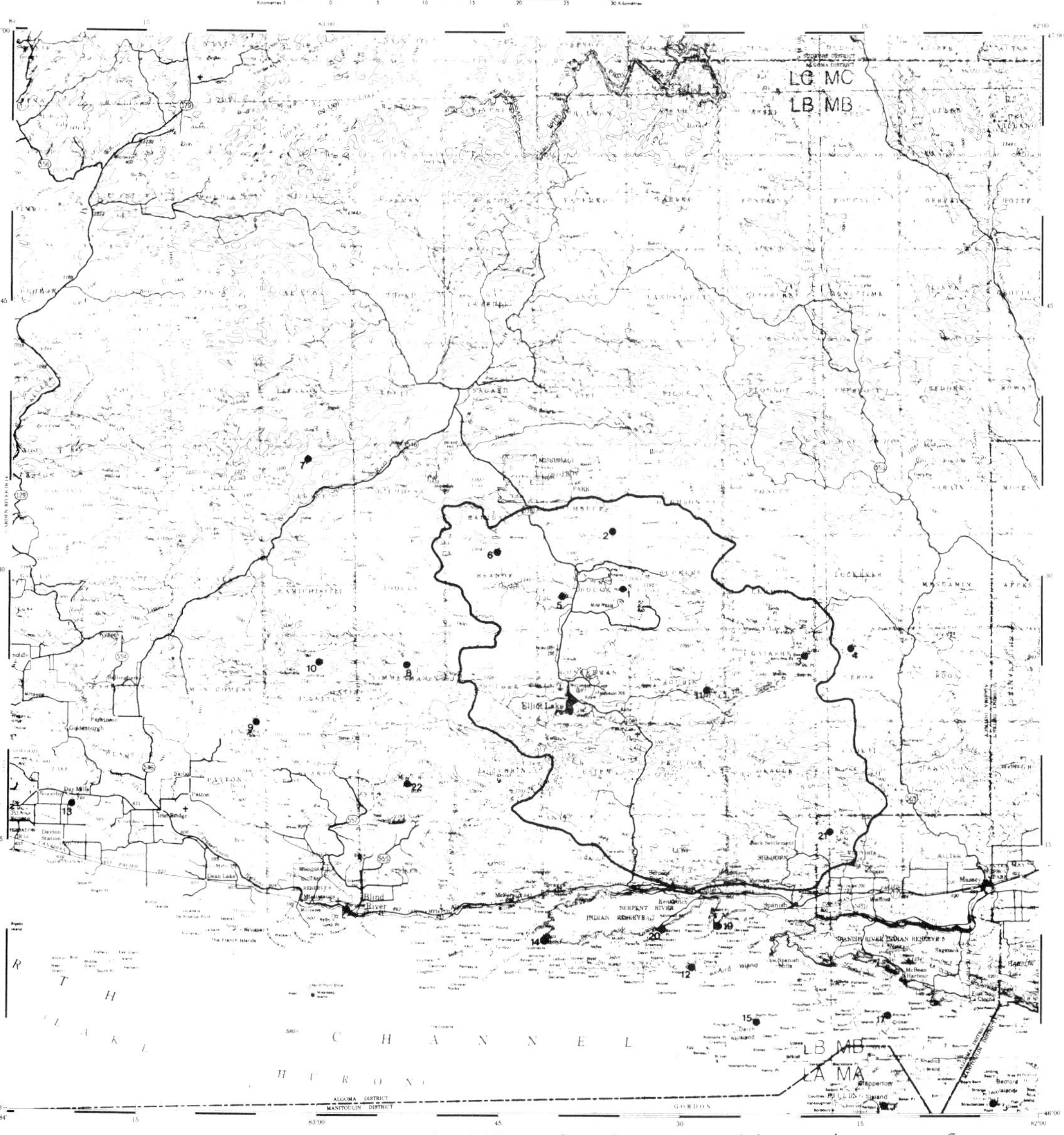

FIG.2(b) 1:250 000 National Topographic Series map of the study region, showing the boundary of the Serpent River Watershed and navigation points.

percentages of land-cover which are present within the study area are then estimated on the basis of the land-cover compositions corresponding to the pixels within the study area. Figure 3 illustrates the estimation of a single land-cover class for a given area. The results obtained can be used as inputs to lumped hydrological models, as well as to distributed hydrologic models, provided that the resolution elements of the model are larger than those of the GOES visible data.

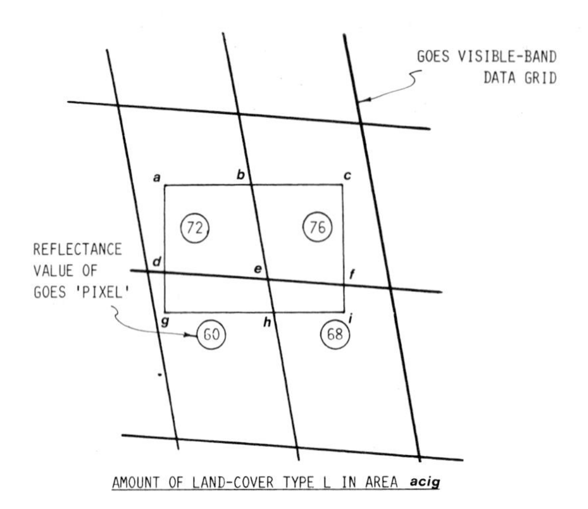

$L_N = L_{72} \cdot abed + L_{76} \cdot bcfe + L_{60} \cdot dehg + L_{68} \cdot efih$

WHERE L_N = PROPORTION OF LAND-COVER TYPE L OCCURRING AT REFLECTANCE VALUE N

FIG.3 Estimation of land-cover using GOES visible-band data and the fractional method.

Example

The Serpent River Watershed (Figure 2) is situated on the north shore of Lake Huron, in northeastern Ontario. This 1350-km^2 basin is fairly representative of watersheds found in this region of the rugged Canadian Shield, a region characterized by a generally humid climate with uniform annual precipitation and subject to climatic extremes - cold winters, warm summers. There is little major topographic relief in this area. Glacial deposits and recent alluvium constitute the shallow, sandy soils which mantle the pre-Cambrian bedrock, outcrops of which are common throughout the area. The watershed is covered by a considerable number of lakes, which tend to have a moderating effect on streamflow variations.

GOES Navigation

In order to locate the watershed boundary and other points of interest onto the VISIBLE graymap (Figure 2(a)), and to register the GOES data grid onto the topographic and ground-truth maps, affine transformations were developed using linear regression techniques. Conventional co-ordinates were obtained using the Universal Transverse Mercator (UTM) grid found on the 1:250 000 National Topographic Series map (Figure 2(b)). A total of twenty-two landmarks, or navigation points, were identified on each map, as shown in Figure 2.

Although for large areas a complex "navigation" model (Goertz, 1982) based upon orbit parameters and the earth's geometry is necessary to determine such relationships, a simpler model can be used when the area of interest is small. In such areas, the transformation can be considered to be approximately linear and the co-ordinate relationship can be readily estimated by an affine transformation.

The success of the fractional method relies heavily on the accuracy of the co-ordinate transformation used to locate the GOES data grid onto the ground-truth and topographic maps. Originally, a single affine transformation had been used to register the GOES grid over the entire area of interest (about 50 km x 50 km). However, there appeared to be discrepancies with grid location in the north-south direction. These discrepancies were attributed to pixel distortion at higher latitudes, in this case, about 46° N. As a result, two distinct affine transformations were developed, one for the northern portion of the watershed and one for the southern portion. The two sets of equations obtained were:

(a) For the northern section,

EASTING = - 5394.9805 + (0.110886) LINE + (0.802494) COLUMN
NORTHING = 8723.2422 - (1.601366) LINE - (0.041116) COLUMN

(b) For the southern section,

EASTING = - 5512.3242 + (0.105132) LINE + (0.821263) COLUMN
NORTHING = 8543.1406 - (1.498541) LINE - (0.045784) COLUMN

Resulting standard errors of estimate for these simple navigation models were less than one half of one GOES visible-band pixel. This appears to be the acceptable error limit in navigation for the application of the fractional method.

Land-Use Land-Cover Classification

From a hydrologic viewpoint, the basin under investigation can be considered to contain basically only three major classes - water, forest, and urban-barren. Tailing areas, which are significant in this basin, can be assimilated from the viewpoint of reflectance to the urban-barren class. In fact, some of these tailings areas have very high reflectances, as discussed below. Land-cover classification of the study watershed using the fractional method was performed using GOES VISIBLE data obtained on October 3, 1976 (Figures 1 and 2). The technique could be applied in a similar manner to both VISIBLE and IR data. However, due to the fact that each IR pixel corresponds to 32 VISIBLE pixels, the huge number of class combinations that would be required when using both bands would make the technique impractical.

Forest Resource Inventory maps (1:15,840-scale) produced by the Ontario Ministry of Natural Resources (Figure 4) were used as ground-truth maps to perform the classification. These maps covered three townships in the eastern portion of the Serpent River Watershed. Using the affine transformations, the GOES VISIBLE data grid was superimposed upon these maps (Figure 4) and also onto 1:50 000 National Topographic Series maps (Figure 5). The very large reflectance of the tailing disposal areas noted in Figure 5 (on which the GOES data were indicated for each pixel) provided a good validation of the navigation results. (See points A and B on Figure 5).

Using initially the ground-truth maps, each GOES reflectance value was analyzed to determine an average land-cover composition that could be attached to the corresponding value. Several pixels were analysed for each of nine GOES VISIBLE reflectance values ranging from 52 to 84, in increments of 4, which were found to correspond to land areas in the GOES imagery. These nine values covered all land-cover classes of interest, including water, forest, barren and urban areas. When information from the ground-truth maps was insufficient, the topographic map (Figure 5)

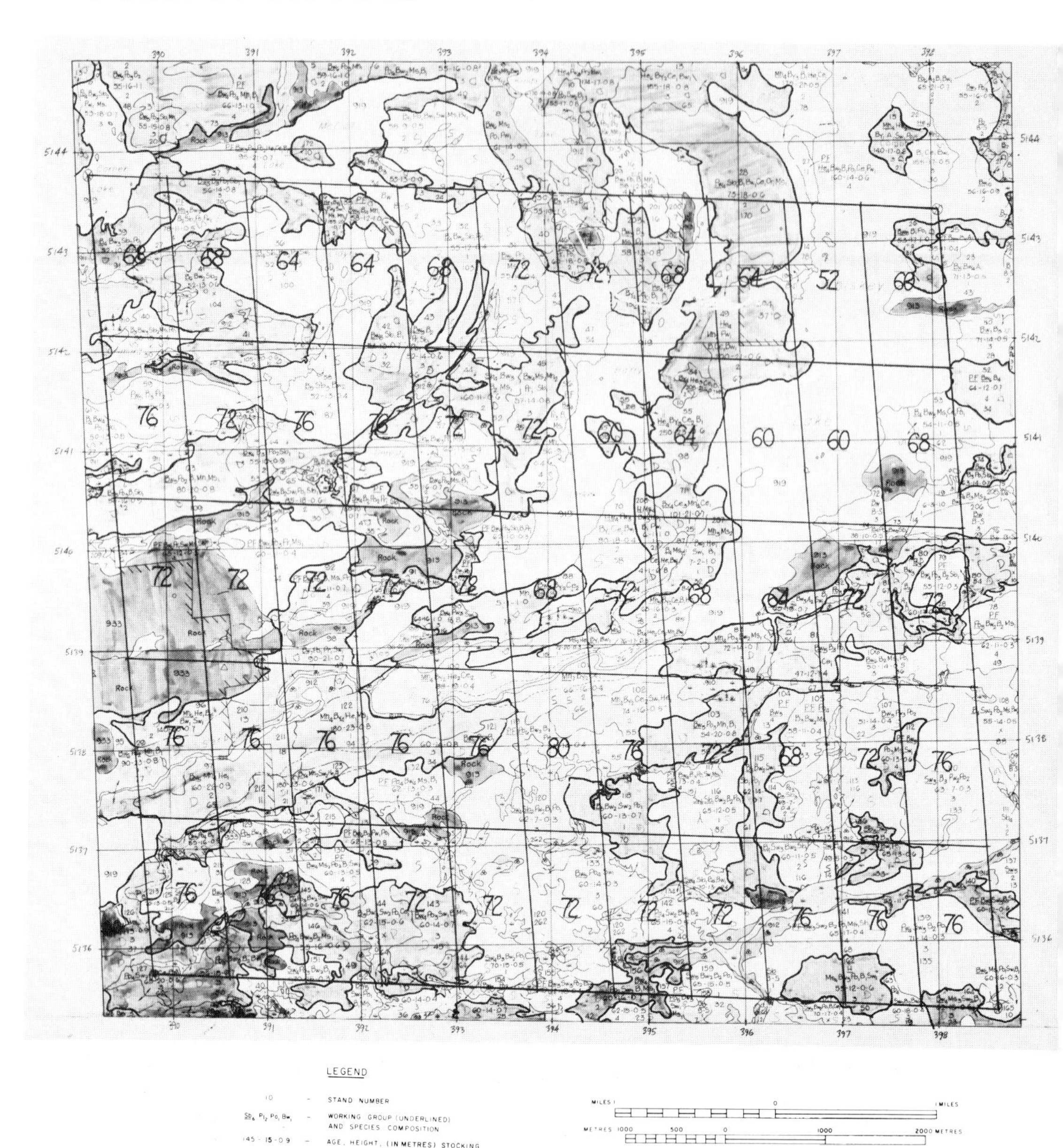

FIG.4 MNR Forest Inventory map of Gaiashk Township (1977) within the Serpent River Watershed, showing the superimposed GOES visible-band data grid.

was referenced to help in the analysis of a reflectance value. Table 1 lists each reflectance value analyzed and its corresponding average land-cover composition.

The land-cover for the Serpent River Watershed was quantified using Table 1 and a composite land-cover map. The latter was produced by overlaying the watershed boundary and a 1 km x 1 km grid onto the matrix of GOES visible-band data using the affine transformations. For each element of the 1 km x 1 km grid located in the watershed, the relative

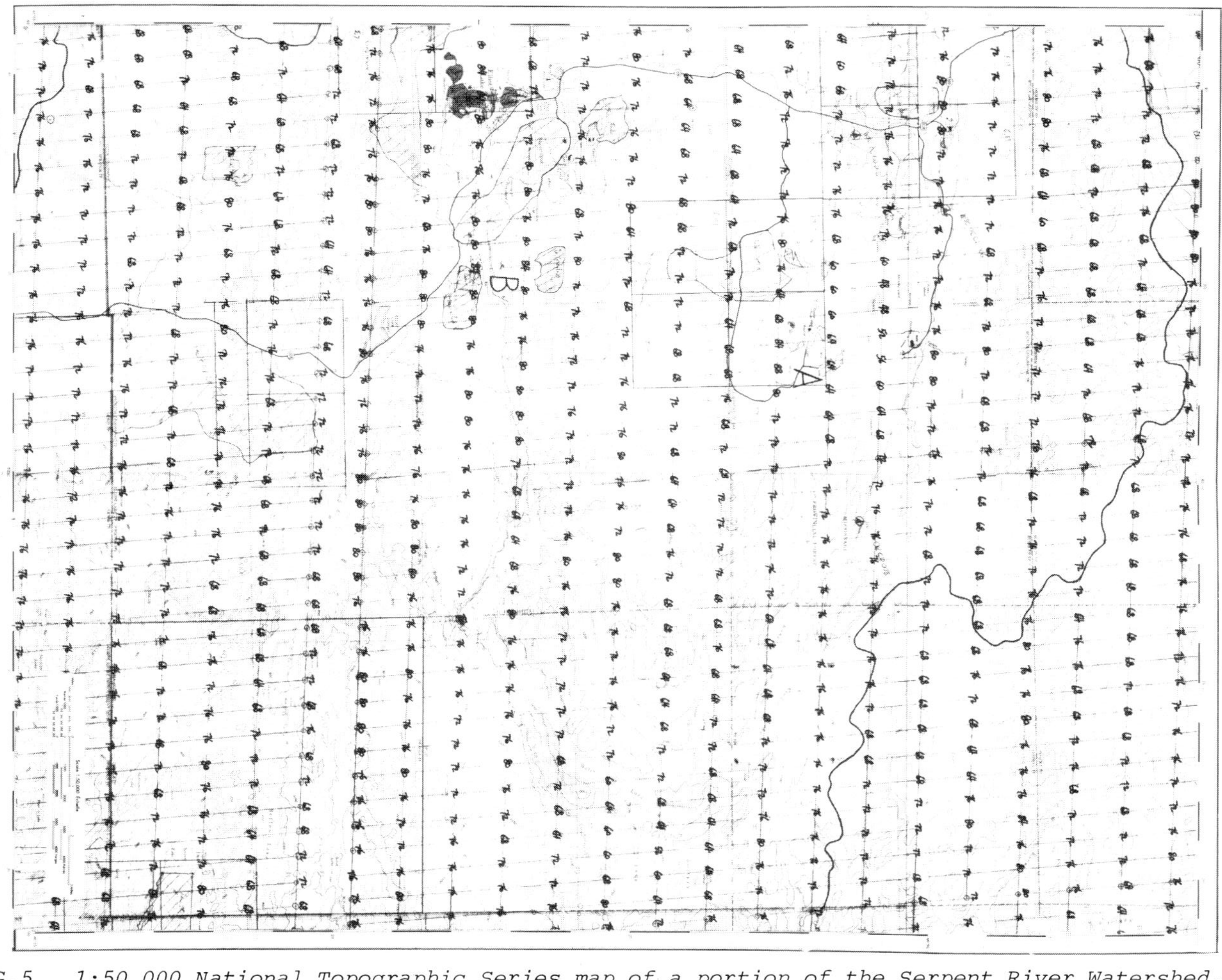

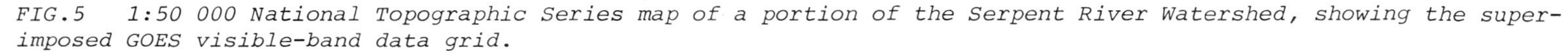

FIG.5 1:50 000 National Topographic Series map of a portion of the Serpent River Watershed, showing the superimposed GOES visible-band data grid.

percentages of land-cover were estimated on the basis of the average land-cover compositions (Table 1) corresponding to the pixels within that element (Figure 3). Total land-cover for the watershed was obtained by summing the contributions of each 1 km x 1 km element.

Table 1 -- Average land-cover compositions derived for GOES visible-band reflectance values.

GOES Reflectance Value	No. of Points	MEDIAN VALUES % Water	% Forest	% Urban/Barren	Average Land-Cover Composition
≤52	10	100	0	0	100% water
56	12	90-95	5-10	0	90% water, 10% forest
60	10	80	20	0	80% water, 20% forest
64	6	50	50	0	50% water, 50% forest
68	23	20-25	75-80	0	25% water, 75% forest
72	63	10	90	0	10% water, 90% forest
76	64	5	95	0	5% water, 95% forest
80	19	0	95	0-5	95% forest, 5% urban/barren
84, 88*	7	n/a	n/a	n/a	25% forest, 75% urban/barren

* Due to a varied mix of land-cover types, judgement was used to derive a representative composition.

Discussions and Conclusions

Accuracies of estimation of water-covered, forest-covered, and urban/barren areas by the GOES fractional method are well-documented by Harvey (1983) and Harvey and Solomon (1984). Based upon grid sizes ranging from 1 km x 1 km up to 4 km x 4 km, this technique compares favourably with conventional (1: 50 000-scale National Topographic Series maps) and Landsat techniques. As with both the conventional and Landsat methods, water and urban/barren classes were usually underestimated, while the forest class was usually overestimated. The range of error (based upon ground truth as shown in Figure 3) are the following:

	Size of Square Element											
	1 km x 1 km			2 km x 2 km			3 km x 3 km			4 km x 4 km		
	F	U/B	W	F	U/B	W	F	U/B	W	F	U/B	W
Mean error (%)	+7.8	-6.9	-0.9	+8.0	-6.0	-2.0	+6.3	-4.1	-2.2	+5.5	-3.1	-2.4
Standard Error of Estimate (%)	21.0	18.1	15.2	15.7	13.8	7.1	12.4	9.2	6.6	9.0	5.7	5.2

Note: F - Forest-covered area
U/B - Urban/barren area
W - Water-covered area

Since, in general, underestimation of water and urban areas and overestimation of forested areas lead to a underestimation of runoff, it may be assumed that the use of GOES will result in a slight underestimation of maximum runoff in most models. However, taking into account the error of measurement of maximum flows, which is in the order of 10-20%, the analysis of GOES digital data by the fractional method to obtain updated land-use land-cover information is acceptable for modelling a vast majority of rivers in Canada. The use of such data should not be expanded beyond about 55°N latitude, because for higher latitudes the distortion of the GOES pixels becomes too great to enable a reasonable application of the classification method. The application of the technique in areas of lower latitudes and located closer to the sub-satellite point may be expected to yield even more accurate results.

References

Goertz, H., 1982, Computer Processing of GOES Satellite Image Data, M.A.Sc. Project, Department of Civil Engineering, University of Waterloo, Canada.

Harvey, K.D., 1983, Hydrologic Modelling With Remotely-Sensed Land-Cover Input, M.A.Sc. Thesis, Department of Civil Engineering, University of Waterloo, Canada.

Harvey, K.D. and Solomon, S.I., 1984, Satellite Remotely-Sensed Land-Use Land-Cover Data for Hydrologic Modelling, Canadian Journal of Remote Sensing, Volume 10, No. 1, July, 1984.

Solomon, S.I. and Swain, J.B., 1981, Minicomputer-Oriented Software for Interpretation of Landsat and GOES Digital Data, Advances in Engineering Software, Volume 3.

Hydrologic Applications of Space Technology (Proceedings of the Cocoa Beach Workshop, Florida, August 1985). IAHS Publ. no. 160, 1986.

Application of satellite derived landcover data in estimating regional water potential

M. G. SRINIVAS
Centre of Studies in Resources Engineering,
Indian Institute of Technology, Bombay, India

Abstract

To assess regional water potential of approximately 915 Sq.kms. of area in the Central part of India, Landsat MSS data extracted from scene number 154-047, is digitally classified to obtain areal spread of land cover types. The rates of evapotranspiration and infiltration determined, respectively, from the Penman's relationship and sample field tests, are used to quantify the apportionment of rainfall to consumptive use and infiltration by taking the product of the respective rate and the area under each land cover type. The mean annual run-off is then estimated by deducting the losses from the total precipitation value arrived at by superposing the mean annual isohyetal chart over the area. The geohydrological features interpreted from the imagery are interpreted with field inventory data to determine the availability and distribution of the groundwater potential in the region. Thus, a viable scheme for computing the surface run-off and understanding the distribution of regional water potential is presented.

Introduction

The control the land cover details exercise on the natural apportionment of rainfall to consumptive use, surface and subsurface flows has been widely recognised. Large differences in vegetation type and cover and soil characteristics in otherwise similar watersheds can mean different peak flows and run-off from them (Onstad and Jamieson, 1976). Therefore, the general model of simulation of the response characteristics of a watershed for application to a specific case require proper identification and quantification of the physically significant parameters of the watershed. The distribution of forests, fields and waterbodies constitute some of the major parameters.

The general practice of delineating and quantifying the land cover details using readily available aerial photographs or survey maps usually provide adequate information but has the restriction of limited temporal validity. In the watersheds where rainfall constitute the only source of replenishment of the water potential, large fluctuations in time and space and even failure of rainfall, a commonly experienced phenomenon in India, create vast differences in the land cover details and hence results obtained by using data from aerial photographs may not be reliable. Further, developmental activities will be ever taking place causing changes in the landuse pattern. Hence the need for an alternative data source.

Of the various new types of data presently available for extracting land cover details, the Multi Spectral Scanner (MSS) imagery from Landsat satellites constitute a suitable source of data. The imagery is available for a scene at 16-day intervals in four band widths, two each in visible and near-infrared regions of the electro magnetic spectrum and can be analysed both digitally using the data on Computer Compatible Tapes (CCT) and visually using photographic prints.

Several studies have been reported in the past decade wherein Landsat MSS data is used for mapping land cover details (Ellefson et al, 1975, Cermak et al, 1979, Harvey and Solomon, 1984). There have also been significant number of studies using Landsat data to identify landcover parameters for hydrologic modelling including those for improving streamflow estimates (Rango et al, 1983, Allord and Scarpace, 1979). Estimating volume of run-off resulting from rainfall encompasses both atmospheric (precipitation) and land portion (evaporation, infiltration, transpiration) of the hydrologic cycle. A methodology which expresses the water potential utilised by the land cover units in terms of the rainfall can provide a convenient procedure for explaining quantitatively the land portion of the hydrologic cycle in a catchment. This paper describes such a methodology with particular reference to a test site of approximately 915 Sq.kms in area, in Central part of India.

Methodology of Approach to Run-off Estimation

It is convenient to consider the distribution of the rainfall on the land (P) to be composed of three components, namely, evapotranspiration or consumptive use (E_T), Infiltration (f) and Run-off (R), the last of which represent the available surface water potential for development. This enables expressing the run-off as

$$R = P - E_T - f \qquad (1)$$

The total rainfall is easily quantified by superposing the isohyetal chart over the area and taking the sum of the products of mean value of two isohyetes and the area enclosed between them.

For quantifying E_T, its daily rate in mm of water (U), is first determined using the Penman's equation given by Veihmeyer (1964) as,

$$U = (AH - 0.27E)/(A - 0.27) \qquad (2)$$

where,

A = Slope of the saturated vapour pressure curve of air at absolute temperature

$E = 0.35\ (e_a - e_d)(1 + 0.0001825\ u)$

$H = R_m\ (1 - \nu)(0.18+0.55S)-B(0.56-0.092\ \sqrt{e_d})\ (0.1+0.9S)$

e_a = Saturation vapour pressure at mean air temperature in mm of Hg

$e_d = e_a$ x relative humidity in percent

u = Mean wind velocity in m/sec.

R_m = Mean monthly extraterrestrial radiation in mm of water evaporated per day

ν = Estimated percentage of reflecting surface

S = Estimated ratio of actual duration of bright sunshine to maximum possible duration of bright sunshine

B = A coefficient dependent on temperature

The total of E_T is obtained by taking the product of U and the area covered by vegetation in the study area.

For quantifying the infiltration component, the rate of infiltration needs to be known for different land cover types. Infiltration is a complex phenomenon dependent on several factors such as, intensity and duration of rainfall, soil type, land slope. Hence, the actual value of infiltration rate is difficult to be determined from functional relationships only. Therefore, infiltration rates determined from field tests conducted for each of the physiographic units identified in the area, using single ring infiltrometer (Johnson, 1963) of flooding type, are adopted in this study. To arrive at total f, areas of physiographic units are multiplied by their respective infiltration rates and the duration of rainfall assumed based on the number of rainy days, one day maximum rainfall and the total precipitation. The sum of all such products represent the f component.

Having determined the quantitative estimates of P, E_T and F, the run-off component is arrived at using (1).

Study Area

The study area shown in Fig.1 is predominantly an upland region with a hill range in the direction of north-northwest and south-southeast. The land slopes down towards east, west and south from the hill range

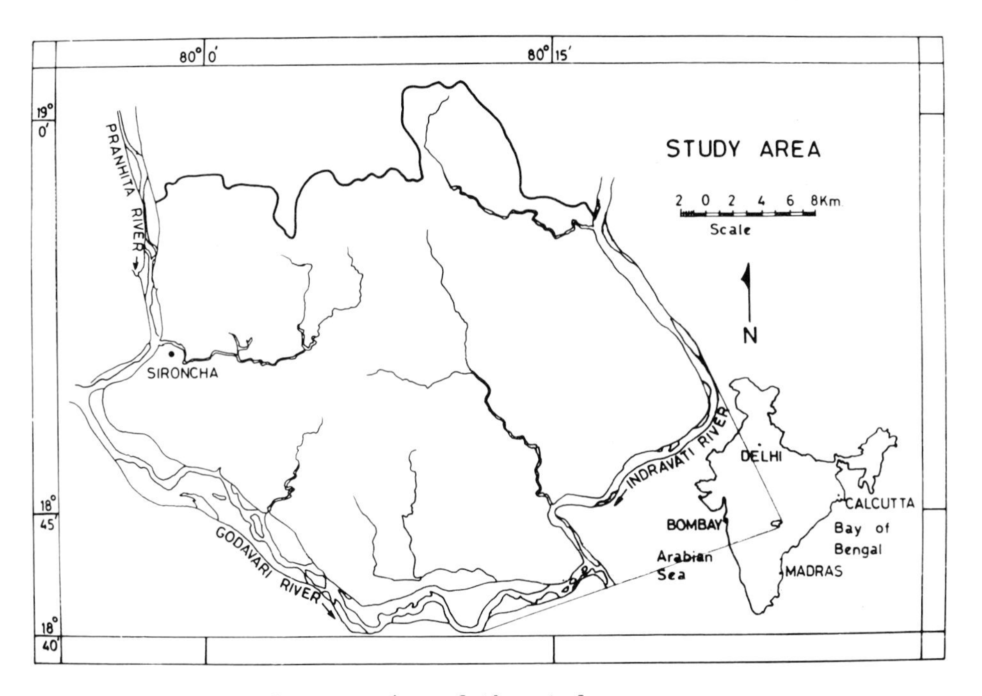

FIG.1 Location of the study area.

forming a gently undulating plain bordering the rivers. Tropical moist deciduous forest growth constitute a major land cover type in the region. The area falls in the upper right quadrant of the Landsat MSS scene number 154-047 of date 17.12.1972.

Results and Discussion

Drainage map of the study area prepared from the visual interpretation of 1:40,000 scale aerial photographs of 1969-70 is shown in Fig.2. A total of 19 sub-basins are delineated and the northern boundary of the study area follows the watershed line. A conspicuous drainage feature of the area is the absence of lakes and the seasonal nature of flow in the streams joining the main rivers. In Table 1 are listed areas of sub-basins measurd using a planimeter. It is observed that the total area draining into each of the three main streams is nearly the same.

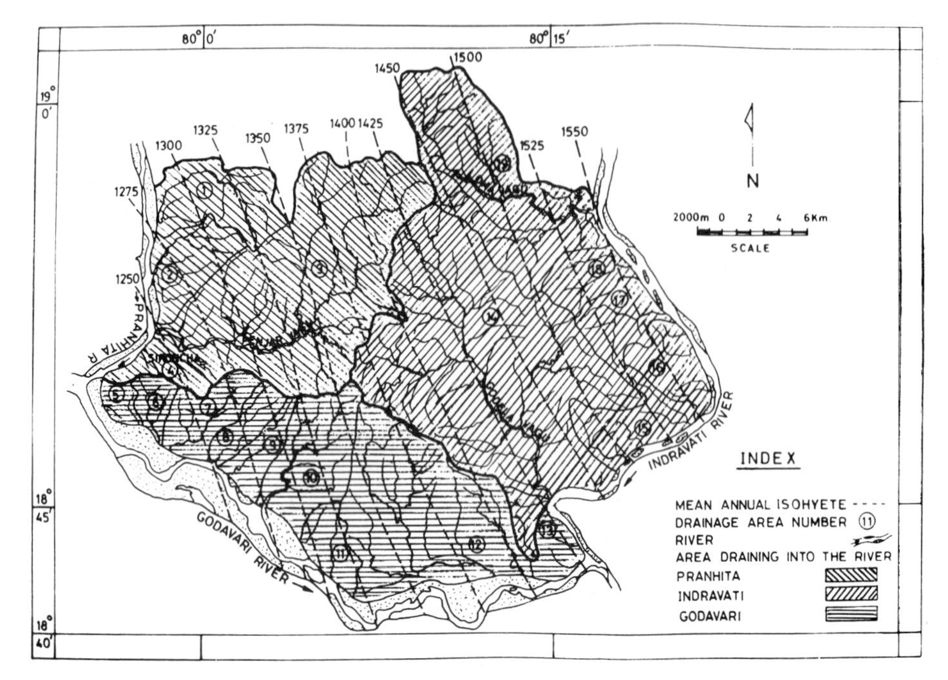

FIG.2 Drainage details with isohyetes.

TABLE 1 - Area of Sub-basins

Sub-basin No.	Area in Sq.kms.	Sub-basin No.	Area in Sq.kms.
1	37.220	11	16.412
2	26.447	12	111.927
3	173.012	13	16.920
4	9.990	14	210.790
5	10.271	15	26.678
6	9.566	16	19.980
7	22.734	17	22.273
8	12.732	18	17.680
9	13.843	19	108.580
10	45.293		
		Total area -	916.348

Total Precipitation (P)
The isohyetal map of the mean annual rainfall prepared from the data of meteorological stations (IMD, 1962) located in and around the study area, is shown superposed over the drainage map (Fig.2). The total precipitation in hectare metres due to the mean annual rainfall is calculated for each of the sub-basin as explained and are listed in Table 3.

Landcover Mapping
In view of the much greater dynamic range of reflectivity values for landcover units available on the Landsat MSS CCT data, landcover mapping was made based on digital method of pattern classification. A multivariate normal density function is assumed for each of the classes and the parameters of the function, namely, the mean vector

and the covariance matrix are determined based on maximum likelihood principle using training sets for each class. In the present case, four classes are chosen from aerial photographs namely, forest, cultivated land, open area and waterbody. Substituting the parameter values in the discriminant function for each pixel, decision on the class to which the pixel belong is made according to Baye's decision rule (Srinivas et al, 1982). Fig.3 shows a typical classified line printer output referring to the southwest part of the test site. Area in Sq.kms. covered by each landcover type was calculated and is shown in Table 2.

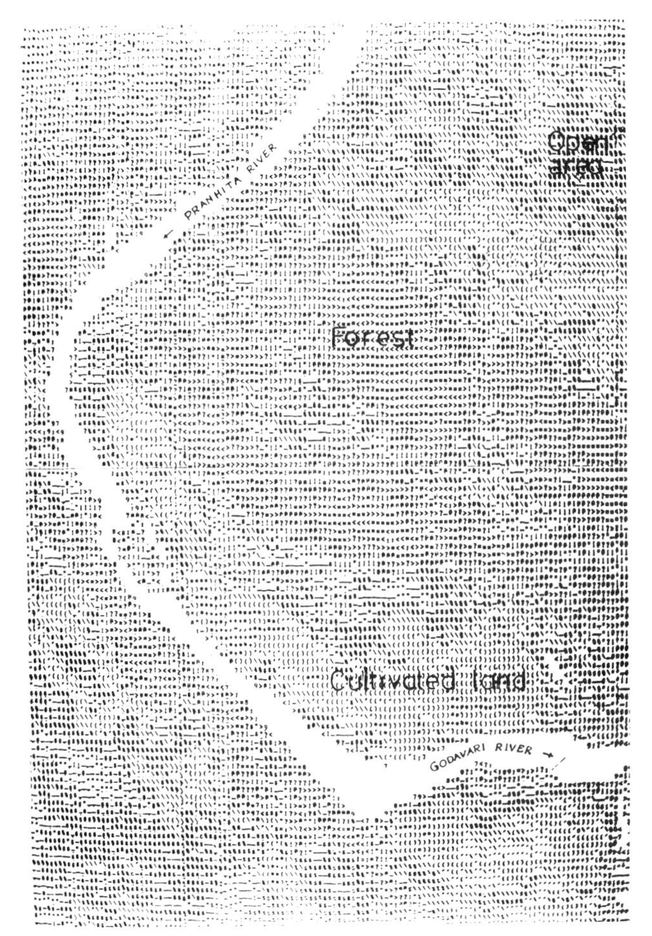

FIG.3 Landsat MSS landcover map.

Estimation of Total Evapotranspiration (E_T)
The evapotranspiration rate in mm of water per day (U) is determined by substituting for various parameters values taken from meteorological stations data (IMD, 1962). The values of the constants A and e_a are read from graphs of A vs temperature and e_a vs temperature (Veihmeyer, 1964). The percentage reflecting surface is assumed to be 0.2. Wherever the parameter values were available as weekly or monthly means only, value of U is assumed to be same for all the days of the corresponding week or month and monthly mean of U is determined. Fig.4 shows the variation of U over the months. Sum of

TABLE 2

Areas of Landcover Types

Landcover Type	Area in Sq.km.
Forests	465.910
Cultivated land	336.208
Open area	114.230
Waterbody (of main rivers excluded)	-

the products of monthly mean and the number of days in the respective months is taken as the total annual evapotranspiration rate and its value is 491.1 mm of water. The value of E_T is determined for each of the sub-basin by multiplying the sum of the areas of forests and cultivated land in each sub-basin by 491.1 and are shown in Table 3.

TABLE 3 - Values of P, E_T, f and run-off

Sub-basin Number	P in Ha.m.	E_T in Ha.m.	f in Ha.m.	Run-off in Ha.m.
1	4871.90	1827.90	636.38	2387.62
2	3380.20	1298.80	1233.29	848.11
3	22863.30	8496.60	4197.45	10165.25
4	1243.90	490.60	629.37	123.93
5	1258.20	504.30	647.08	106.82
6	1171.80	469.80	246.80	455.20
7	2847.70	1116.50	363.98	1367.22
8	1619.70	625.30	411.93	582.47
9	1764.40	679.80	533.62	550.98
10	5932.60	2223.90	1162.48	2546.22
11	2142.64	806.10	688.71	647.83
12	15236.50	5496.30	4667.34	5072.46
13	2389.05	830.90	563.48	894.67
14	30623.48	10548.20	2993.20	17082.08
15	3992.96	1310.10	373.76	2309.10
16	3087.91	980.20	252.50	1854.21
17	3418.20	1093.70	564.39	1760.11
18	2700.00	868.30	472.50	1359.20
19	16204.00	5332.40	1678.27	9193.83

For the whole test site area of 916.348 Sq.kms. the totals of P, E_T, f and run-off in hectare metres and percentagewise are given below.

Total precipitation	-	1,26,748.44 ha.m.	-	100%
Evapotranspiration	-	44,999.70 ha.m.	-	35.5%
Infiltration	-	22,436.56 ha.m.	-	17.7%
Run-off	-	59,312.18 ha.m.	-	46.8%

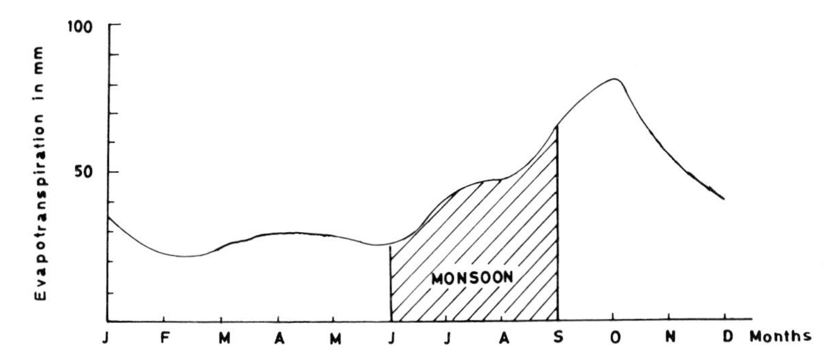

FIG.4 Monthly distribution of evapotranspiration.

Estimation of Total Infiltration (f)

Infiltration has a high initial rate and diminishes during continued rainfall to reach the permeability value in the limit. Hence, the duration and intensity of rainfall have greater influence on the infiltrating quantity and needs to be accounted. The study area experiences maximum rainfall during the period June-September called the monsoon period. The whole year is divided into three periods with respect to rainfall cycle - premonsoon, monsoon and remaining period. The effective monsoon has a mean date of June 20, for onset in the area, with a standard deviation of 9 days. For the period of first 3 weeks in June, only 50% of the rainfall is assumed to be infiltrating into the ground as the rainfall contributes mainly to the rise in the moisture content of the soil. For the period Sept. to May, the rainfall is generally isolated and scattered and hence is considered to completely infiltrate into the ground. During the monsoon period, 4th week of June to Sept., 30% of the rainfall is assumed to be of an intensity less than or equal to the average infiltration rate and of duration greater than or equal to the time required in a test for the infiltration rate to develop.

Infiltration tests were conducted in the field for each of the five physiographic units identified from aerial photointerpretation namely, hills and inselbergs (HI) of both sedimentary and granitic origin, sloping sedimentary and granitic pediplains (SSP and SGP), cultivated land (CL) and alluvial plain (AP). To account for the land slope on the infiltration rates, cosine of the land inclination to the horizontal is used as a multiplying factor and the inclinations taken for different units are HI - greater than 40°, SSP and GSP - 20° to 40°, CL - 10° to 20° and AP - less than 10°. Infiltration rates were determined from the infiltration vs time curves.

Total infiltration is arrived at by taking the product of the area of the physiographic unit (hectare), slope factor and rainfall (metre). f value obtained for each of the sub-basin is shown in Table 3.

Run-off(R)

The run-off component is obtained as the balance of rainfall left after accounting for evapotranspiration and infiltration from the total rainfall. The value of run-off calculated for each of the sub-basin is shown in Table 3.

Ground Water Potential

The underground water potential in a region is best analysed by interpreting a combination of information obtained from different sources.

Therefore, in the present case, the land cover details determined from Landsat data, drainage and hydro-geomorphological details mapped from aerial photographs and well inventory data recorded on the field were combined to develop a ground water occurrence map for the study area and is shown in Fig.5. The results are limited to unconfined zone. The value of yield potential for different units has been assigned by taking into consideration the total infiltration, variation

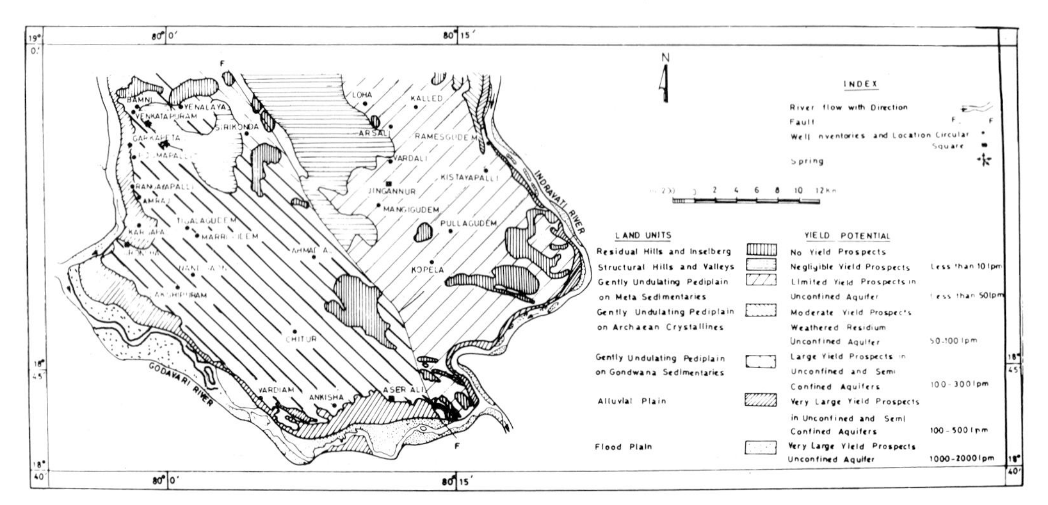

FIG.5 Groundwater potential distribution.

in the water level in the wells and the yield capacity attributed to the geological formation (Baweja, 1976) similar to those identified in the study area. The results show the richness of groundwater potential in the gently undulating gondwana sedimentaries and correlates well with the presence of cultivated lands in the southwest region of the test site.

Conclusions

The study has attempted to focus attention on the possibility of using satellite remotely sensed data for determining quantitative estimates of evapotranspiration, infiltration, total precipitation and runoff. The methodology presented, although simple, demonstrates the feasibility of runoff estimation based on valid principles. Extending the approach to monthly or weekly runoff estimation can lead to improving the runoff prediction. The precipitation values can also be input from satellite remote sensing sources. Implicit in the study is the greater scope for direct application of Landsat MSS data to surface water aspects than to groundwater potential aspects.

Acknowledgements

The study forms an extended work on the inhouse research programme of the Centre of Studies in Resources Engineering (CSRE), IIT, Bombay. Encouragement received from Prof.R.K. Katti, Head, CSRE for presenting the paper at the workshop is gratefully acknowledged.

References

Allord, G.J. and Scarpace, F.L., 1979, Improving Stream Flow Estimates Through the use of Landsat : Satellite Hydrology, M.Deutsch, D.R.

Wiesnet, A. Rango (Editors), American Water Resources Association, Proc. of V Annual W.T. Pecora Memorial Symposium on Remote Sensing, pp 284-291.

Baweja, B.K., 1976, Hydrological Map of India, Scale 1:5M, I Edition, Central Groundwater Board, Min. of Agriculture and Irrign., Govt. of India, pp 20.

Cermak, R.J., Feldman, A. and Webb, R.P., 1979, Hydrologic Landuse classification using Landsat, Satellite Hydrology, M.Deutsch, D.R. Wiesnet, A. Rango (Eds.), Am. Water Resources Assoc., Proc. of V. Ann. W.T. Pecora Memorial Symp. on Remote Sensing, pp 262-269.

Ellefson, R., Glados, L. and Wray, J.R., 1976, Computer Aided Mapping of Landuse, ERTS-1 A New Window on our Planet, R.S. Williams and W.D. Carter (Eds.), U.S. Geo. Survey, Prof. Paper 929, pp 234-242.

Harvey, K.D., Soloman, S.I., 1984, Satellite Remotely Sensed Landuse Landcover Data for Hydrologic Modelling, Canadian Jl.of Remote Sensing, Vol.10, no.1, pp 68-91.

Indian Meteorological Department (IMD), 1962, Climatological Tables Observatories in India, IMD, Poona, Govt. of India.

Johnson, A.I., 1963, A Field Method for Measurement of Infiltration, U.S. Geo. Survey Water Supply Paper 1544-F, U.S. Govt. Printing Office, Washington, pp.

Onstad, C.A., Jamieson, D.G., 1976, Modelling the Effect of Landuse Modifications on Run-off, Water Resources Research, V.6, no.5, pp 1287-1295.

Rango, A. Feldman, A., George, T.S. III and Ragan, R.M., 1983, Effective Use of Landsat Data in Hydrologic Models, Water Resources Bull., V.19, no.2, pp 165-174.

Srinivas, M.G., Marathe, G.T. and Ghosh, T.K., 1982, Interim Results on CCT Data Analysis for Water Resources Studies in Goa-Hubli Region, Progress Report, RSD II-Water Resources Engg., CSRE, IIT, Bombay, pp 26.

Veihmeyer, F.K., 1964, Evapotranspiration, Handbook of Applied Hydrology, Ven Te Chow (Ed.), McGraw Hill Book Co., New York, pp.11.23-11.33.

4 Snow hydrology

Hydrologic Applications of Space Technology (Proceedings of the Cocoa Beach Workshop, Florida, August 1985). IAHS Publ. no. 160, 1986.

The need for improved snow-cover monitoring techniques

A. RANGO
USDA Hydrology Laboratory, Agricultural Research Service, Beltsville, Maryland, 20705,USA
J. MARTINEC
Federal Institute for Snow and Avalanche Research, CH-7260 Weissfluhjoch/Davos, Switzerland

Abstract
Although satellite snow-cover extent has been shown to be an important input variable in the estimation of snowmelt runoff, the supply of this information unfortunately is not operational, and many problems remain to be solved. On small basins (< 1000 km^2), repetitive coverage in the visible and near infrared with a sufficient resolution must be increased to at least one observation per week. Although it is possible to automatically separate clouds from snow, clouds frequently obscure the snowpack and reliable microwave methods for observing the snow cover independent of the weather are needed. Manual production of snow-cover maps in regions with a homogeneous snowpack is relatively easy, however, this is not the case in regions of discontinuous snow cover, and simple digital analysis techniques have to be developed for widespread use. Additionally, the snow-cover data need to be available to users within 48 hours of acquisition to be useful for hydrological forecasting. Limited operational satellite snow mapping programs exist, but they must be expanded and upgraded to meet a variety of user needs.

Introduction
When earth resources satellites were launched in the early 1970's, images with snow immediately attracted attention because of the contrasting appearance with other surface features. In a short period of time many striking images of snow cover from both Landsat and the NOAA satellites were available for analysis. Snow-cover mapping techniques using photo-interpretation were developed, parallel with attempts to evaluate a variety of land cover and water features from satellites. Because it seemed relatively easy to manually map the snow-cover extent, it was erroneously assumed that the problem of mapping snow was solved, and research emphasis after several years was shifted to the digital classification of other surface features and the measurement of other snowpack properties. This initial conclusion was not justified because photointerpretive snow mapping is not adequate for many snow areas of the world, cloud cover obscures the snow frequently, repetitive observation cycles are not optimum, and systems for real time data delivery and analysis are not operational.

Importance of Snow Cover Information
The melting of seasonal snow cover is the source for a large portion of the streamflow generated in many mountain basins. From 50-90 percent of the annual total discharge can be produced by snowmelt in areas like the Rocky Mountains of the U.S.A., the Alps of Switzerland, and the Himalayan Mountains of Asia. Consequently, snow is a major factor in short term and seasonal discharge forecasts. The snow cover is not only important for the direct production of runoff, but it can also serve as a protective, insula-

ting blanket for the soil and agricultural crops. The snow that melts on agricultural lands is additionally important for crop growth through recharge of the soil moisture reservoir. In any approaches for calculating snowmelt, it is important that the methods used be applied to only that portion of the basin covered by snow.

On a larger scale, seasonal snow cover is also an important factor in the climate system. Snow cover can influence atmospheric general circulation by interacting with and modifying overlying air masses. The effects of snow cover can be manifested in storms tracking along snow boundaries, alterations of normal circulation patterns such as the monsoon, and unusually cold winter temperatures or delayed spring warming. The knowledge of snow cover distribution—extent, depth, and water equivalent—is vital for improving medium- and long-range weather forecasts and for perfecting general circulation models. Connected with this is the growing consensus of climate modellers that snow cover can play an instrumental role in the mechanism of climate change (Kukla, 1981). Snow has such influence because slight changes in average surface temperature of the Earth are greatly amplified by feedback between snow extent and global albedo.

Problems for Effective Snow Cover Mapping

Experience has shown that snow cover extent is one of the easier surface features to delineate with satellite data using manual or automated techniques. Despite this general conclusion there are several important problems that must be recognized and resolved when mapping snow cover. The following is a listing of a variety of factors to be considered when arriving at an accurate representation of areal snow cover:

1. clouds
2. vegetation cover
3. bare rock
4. mountain shadows
5. discontinuous snow cover
6. image quality and illumination levels

Once such problems have been considered, the requirements for an optimum snow cover mapping system include further that the snow cover should be monitored:

7. independently of weather conditions
8. with an adequate repeat period
9. with an adequate resolution
10. with data processing and delivery within 48 hours
11. using a simple and cost effective analysis system

In regard to progress, remote sensing analysts have devised ways to cope with the problems of vegetation cover, bare rock, and mountain shadows (Bowley, et al. 1981). Even the discrimination between clouds and snow is less of a problem now with the utilization of the 1.55–1.75μm spectral band on the Landsat Thematic Mapper (TM). However, with the high resolution satellite sensors of Landsat and NOAA it is still impossible to see through clouds to monitor the snow cover.

Another remaining problem is to adequately delineate discontinuous snow cover. In Figure 1 the various types of snow cover ablation are presented. Figures 1a and 1b are the types frequently encountered in the U.S.A. and represent contiguous snow cover retreat and a nearly contiguous snow cover

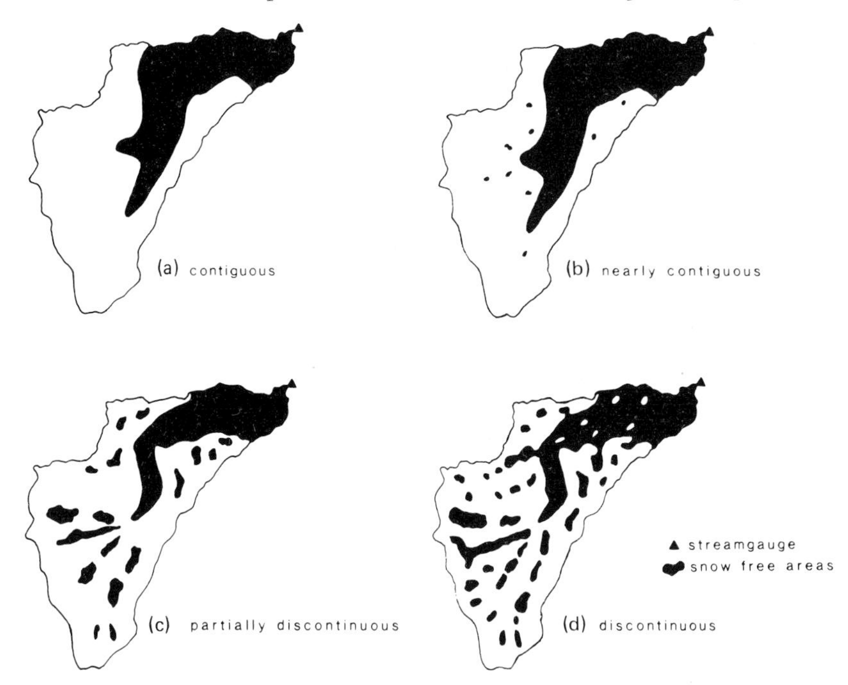

FIG.1 Various types of basin snow-cover ablation patterns observed depending on location.

retreat (with the appearance of only a few open areas), respectively. These two patterns are handled adequately using manual photointerpretation methods. In other areas of the world, such as Europe, however, ablation patterns shown in Figures 1c and 1d are more usual and not easily handled using photointerpretation because of the tedious mapping steps required. More often than not the use of photointerpretation in these discontinuous snow cover areas results in snow-covered area values that are too high. A digital analysis approach is required, however, only a few attemps have been made to develop systems to solve this problem (e.g., Anderson, 1982).

Improvements in resolution have progressed so that it is no longer a problem; unfortunately, parallel improvements in frequency of observation have not kept pace. As a result, even though current resolution is as good as 30 m (Landsat TM), effectively the best available useable resolution is only 1100 m (NOAA AVHRR), because the NOAA satellites have the only acceptable frequency of observation (daily). Data delivery on a routine basis within 48 hours is also not possible. Only in special instances can this time requirement be met. Simple digital systems for analysis of snow cover data are not yet available for general use. Much further development is required in each of these problem areas.

Future Trends in Snow Cover Mapping

Because there are many scientific problems still outstanding in snow mapping, research in several areas needs to be conducted. Primary among this research is the development and testing of microwave techniques for all-weather snow cover monitoring. It was shown by Rango, et al. (1979) that passive microwave techniques could be used to map snow cover extent on the large scale. However, for many basins the existing and near future passive microwave sensors in space possess resolutions (25-50 km) too crude to be useful. It remains to be seen if improved passive microwave resolution can be obtained through the use of large antennas and electrical scanning techniques.

The other logical approach is to develop and test shortwave (1-3 cm) active microwave sensors for all-weather snow mapping. The resolution associated with any such sensor (< 1 km) would easily be adequate for mountain basin snow mapping purposes. The real question is whether the data could be interpreted easily. The complexities of the backscattering process in rugged and diverse terrain may be a significant problem. Detailed comparison tests with visible snow maps in a variety of test areas are needed. According to Rott (1984) wet snow areas, which have low backscattering coefficients, can be clearly separated from most snow free surfaces in the X-band (2.4-3.75 cm), whereas dry snow cannot be detected because of minimal volume scattering. It must still be determined if dry snow can be distinguished from snow free areas in the K-band (0.7-2.4 cm) channels.

Of course research in the microwave region should not be pursued for the determination of mapping snow extent alone. As pointed out in several studies (e.g., Foster et al., 1984; Rott, 1983) the use of microwaves has great potential for measurement of other important snowpack properties, namely, snow water equivalent, depth, and wetness. The extraction of snow extent data would be only one valuable outcome of such a microwave research program.

We should also be developing simple digital analysis systems to take the place of manual techniques for extraction of snow cover extent data. Probably the most important reason is the suspected importance of discontinuous snow cover ablation patterns in a large number of basins around the world. When such patterns are encountered, the digital analysis approach is the only effective means of interpretation. But even in basins of contiguous snow cover retreat, there are important reasons to use digital mapping. The normal snow mapping problems associated with clouds, forest, bare rock, and shadows can be more easily handled with the automated approach. Additionally, when many basins and dates are being mapped the digital approach will be considerably faster and more accurate than manual interpretation.

Limited operational snow-cover products are available for certain areas of the world, but much work needs to be done to make the data available in flexible formats to satisfy different user needs. The existing NOAA National Weather Service satellite snow cover mapping services program is a case in point. Currently, very valuable snow maps are produced on a quasi-operational basis. Digital interactive analysis techniques are used to produce snow cover percentage maps at 1 km resolution for about 80 basins or subbasins in the western U.S.A. The methods are still being perfected to satisfy format and timeliness requirements of the users. Unfortunately, the program is in jeopardy because of inadequate financial resources. Requests for snow maps for almost 80 additional basins have been made (see Figure 2) and are unable to be satisfied. This is a pilot program that should be expanded into a full operational situation with routine or real-time data delivery within 48 hours.

Currently only NOAA polar orbiting satellites or the geostationary GOES satellite can be used for operational snow mapping because they possess operational frequencies of observation, namely, daily and half hourly, respectively. As a result, the best operational resolution is about 1 km which means that each elevation zone or basin subarea mapped has to exceed 200 km^2 (Rango, et al. 1985). This translates to a minimum basin size of about 1,000 km^2 assuming multiple elevation zones. To map the numerous important smaller basins, the frequency of observation of satellites like

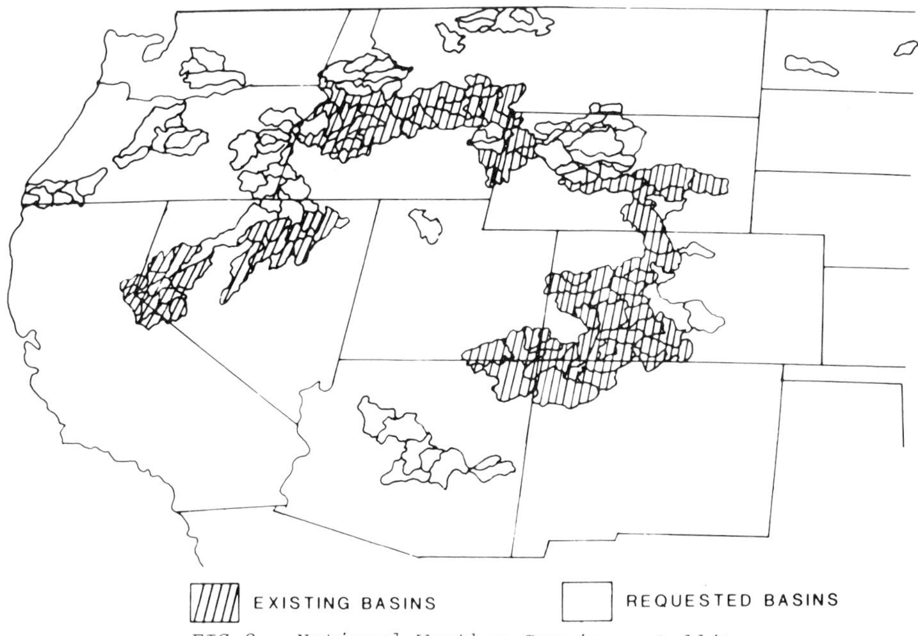

FIG.2 National Weather Service satellite snow-cover mapping basins in the USA for 1985.

Landsat has to be increased to at least weekly. Additionally, other routinely acquired important satellite data for snow mapping should be made available in operational formats. The 600 m resolution U.S. Air Force DMSP data are highly suitable for snow mapping purposes. In fact, Foster (1983) found that the sensor sensitivity on this satellite was such that reflected moonlight at night could be used to map snow cover thereby increasing the number of possible snow cover observations by 5 dates per month. These kinds of data should be made operationally available in both photographic and digital formats.

Emphasis must also be given to supplying data in remote, inaccessible regions where satellite snow cover extent data may constitute the longest continuous period of record. In these areas this may be the only type of data that can be used to produce forecasts of snowmelt runoff using either empirical techniques or deterministic models. In developed countries like the United States, the availability of the satellite snow cover data permits an incremental improvement in accuracy of forecasts over already existing conventional methods. In the developing countries, the satellite data, if it is available in real time, permits a major improvement in forecasting capability and water management decision making.

As the snow cover data become available regularly in real time, it will encourage the use of snowmelt runoff models. Some already exist that require the input of snow cover extent (e.g., Martinec, et al. 1983). When the availability of snow cover data is judged reliable, then more of the existing models will start to incorporate this real description of basin snow condition in preference to model simulated values. This is part of a trend towards the use of areal hydrological information instead of just point information.

Conclusions

1. Development of techniques for all-weather mapping of snow extent, particularly through clouds, is required before the availability of

snow cover data is judged reliable.

2. Development of simple computer based systems for automatic and rapid mapping of discontinuous snow cover using various types of remote sensing data is needed for use of the data worldwide.

3. High resolution satellite sensors do not provide repeat periods of observations that are operational. The satellite frequency of observation must at a minimum be weekly. Other pertinent satellite data should be made available for routine analysis.

4. Normal delivery of the satellite data must be reduced to 48 hours at a maximum.

5. Research on microwave observing techniques for determination of snow extent as well as snow water equivalent, depth, and wetness should be increased significantly.

6. Ongoing efforts to produce operational snow cover products should be expanded, and financial support for the programs should be increased to develop truly operational systems.

7. Collection, processing, and delivery of snow cover data for remote regions should be emphasized.

8. The utilization of the snow cover data in hydrological, as well as agricultural and climatological, models should be an ultimate goal of the snow mapping research effort.

References

Andersen, T., 1982, Operational Snow Mapping by Satellites: Hydrological Aspects of Alpine and High Mountain Areas (Proc. Exeter Symp., July 1982), IAHS Publ. no. 138, p. 149-154.

Bowley, C. J., Barnes, J. C., and Rango, A., 1981, Satellite Snow Mapping and Runoff Prediction Handbook: NASA Technical Paper 1829, Washington, D.C., 87 p.

Foster, J. L., 1983, Night-time Observations of Snow Using Visible Imagery: International Journal of Remote Sensing, v. 4, no. 4, p. 785-791.

Foster, J. L., Hall, D. K., Chang, A. T. C., and Rango, A., 1984, An Overview of Passive Microwave Snow Research and Results: Reviews of Geophysics and Space Physics, v. 22, no. 2, p. 195-208.

Kukla, G., 1981, Snow Covers and Climate: Glaciological Data, Report GD-11 (Snow Watch 1980), World Data Center A for Glaciology (Snow and Ice), Boulder, Colorado, p. 27-39.

Martinec, J., Rango, A., and Major, E., 1983, The Snowmelt-Runoff Model (SRM) User's Manual: NASA Reference Publication 1100, Washington, D.C., 118 pp.

Rango, A., Chang, A. T. C., and Foster, J. L., 1979, The Utilization of Spaceborne Microwave Radiometers for Monitoring Snowpack Properties: Nordic Hydrology, v. 10, p. 25-40.

Rango, A., Martinec, J., Foster, J., and Marks, D., 1985, Resolution in

Operational Remote Sensing of Snow Cover: Hydrological Applications of Remote Sensing and Remote Data Transmission (Proc. Hamburg Symp., August, 1983), IAHS Publ. no. 145.

Rott, H., 1983, Snow and Ice Monitoring by Microwave Techniques: Remote Sensing (Proc. Alpbach Summer School 27 July-5 August 1983), ESA SP-205, p. 75-86.

Rott, H., 1984, Synthetic Aperture Radar Capabilities for Snow and Glacier Monitoring: Adv. Space Res., v. 4, no. 11, p. 241-246.

Hydrologic Applications of Space Technology (Proceedings of the Cocoa Beach Workshop, Florida, August 1985). IAHS Publ. no. 160, 1986.

Determination of areal snow-water equivalent values using satellite imagery and aircraft gamma-ray spectrometry

RISTO KUITTINEN
Technical Research Centre of Finland,
Laboratory of Land Use, SF-02150 Espoo, Finland

Abstract

In 1983 and 1984 springtime areal snow-water equivalent values of Northern Finland were determined using enhanced digital NOAA - images and aircraft gamma-ray spectrometry.

Principal component analysis and histogram modificaton were used to process the most suitable images for snow detection and estimation of snow-water equivalent.

A gamma-ray spectrometer was installed in a Twin Otter aircraft and from a flight altitude of 60 m the snow-water equivalent values were measured twice during the melting season. The error of those measurements was 5-10 %.

When satellite images and gamma-ray spectrometry measurements are used together, the snowmelt process can be monitored. Satellite images give good information on the location of snow while gamma-ray techniques offer good possibilities for determining snow-water equivalent values.

1. Introduction

Snowmelt is a complex process dependent upon many things. This causes difficulties in forecasting snowmelt only on the basis of air temperature and precipitation observations. Real time measurements of snow cover help very much in forecasting the snowmelt. These measurements are very important for hydropower production and flood forecasts.

In Finland the length of snowmelt period is in general four weeks on an average. Thus fast measurements methods are needed if several snow cover measurements in large areas will be made and the results are used in forecasts.

For this reason a research and development project was carried out in Finland in 1981 - 1984. In this project fast processing methods were developed for polar-orbiting satellite imagery and aircraft gamma-ray spectrometry to determine the areal snow water equivalent values.

2. Processing weather satellite imagery for snow cover monitoring

The use of weather satellite images in snow cover monitoring has been studied for many years and it is operationally used in some countries. The problems of this method are well known: cloud cover, dense forests and slopes of mountains (NASA, 1979 and 1981).

Due to the northern location of Finland only polar-orbiting weather satellites can be used effectively in snow cover monitoring.

The study area was mainly Northern Finland, located to the north of the Arctic Circle. Forests are not dense in this area and snow could thus be detected also in forests. The area is mostly lowland and thus slopes do not cause any serious problems either.

The developed process for enchacing digital NOAA-images for visual interpretation of snow is the following:

1) Geometric correction of raw CCT-data by using the satellite orbit parameters (inclination and flight altitude).
2) Rectification of the geometric corrected image using maps and an affine transformation. Thus only small number of control points per image is needed.
3) Computing the first principal component (PC) of channels 1 and 5 of the NOAA-image. The covariance matrice is determined from a cloudless area containing different terrain types and phases of snowmelt.
4) Plotting the PC-images using a logarithmic function. The coefficients are determined so that snowless ground is black and totally snow-covered ground light gray or white.

Figure 1 shows how the direction of the first component of the PC-image is changing when snowmelt progresses. When the PC-images are determined from the same area this direction gives information on the phase of the snowmelt. The shape of the histogram of the PC-image changes at the same time. This phenomenon has been discussed by Merry (Merry et. al 1983) when Landsat data was concerned.

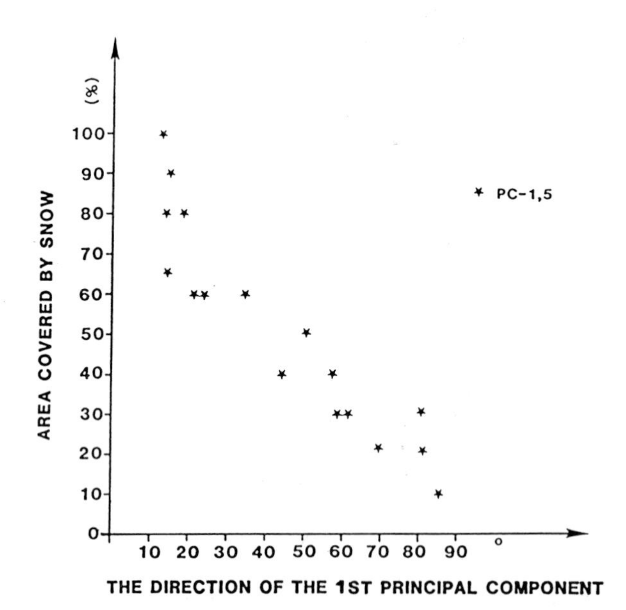

FIG.1 The correlation of the snow covered area and the direction of the first principal component of the NOAA/AVHRR image (channels 1 & 5).

Figure 2 shows how snow-water equivalent and the area of base spots on the ground are correlating during the melting period. Spots appear when snow-water equivalent is about 150 mm. This phenomenon gives a possibility to roughly estimate the snow-water equivalent using weather satellite images. This same phenomenon has been studied earlier by Dozier (Dozier et.al. 1981).

The problem of confusing clouds and snow in interpretation can be avoided in most cases in Finnish conditions because the tone, texture and pattern of the mainly forested terrain is different from that of clouds. The accuracy can be improved if snow is interpreted daily. The use of images taken in the morning also helps to discriminate between snow and clouds.

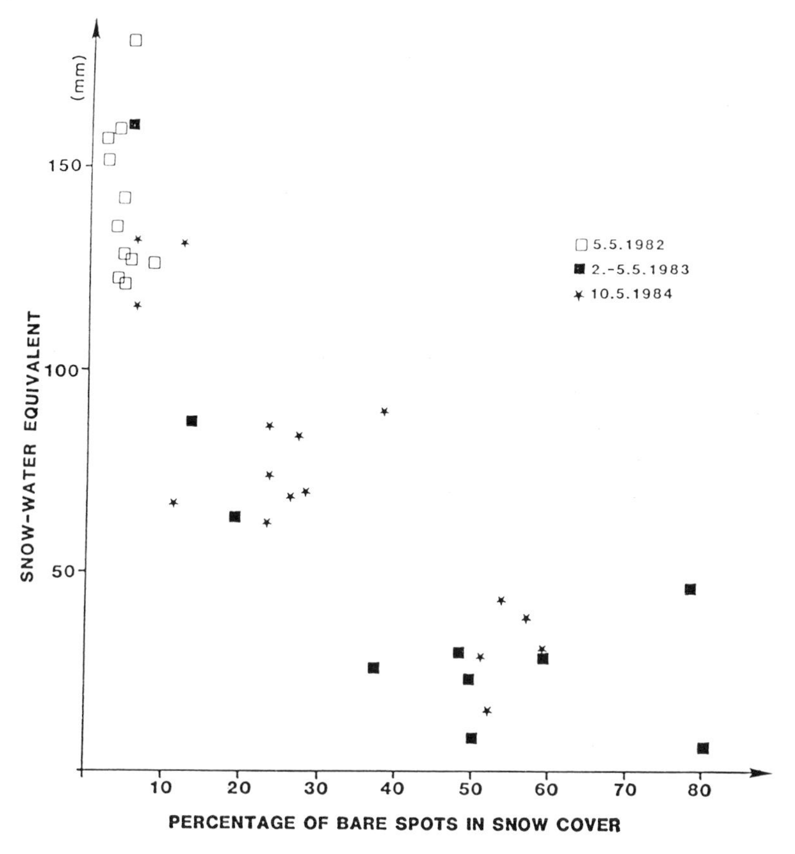

FIG.2 The correlation of snow-water equivalent and the percentage of bare spots in snow cover during melting period.

Figure 3 shows a partly cloudy image. In this case snow is partly melted.

3. Gamma-ray spectrometry for determining the snow-water equivalent

This method is based on the attenuation of gamma radiation by snow. The technique has been developed during the past twenty years. Operationally it is now used in Norway, USA, U.S.S.R and since this year also in Finland (WMO 1978), (KOHYNO, 1984). The main problems of gamma-method are the change of soil moisture in winter, calibration and areas where this technique cannot be used (swamps, wetlands).

The presumption of an operative gamma-method is that the results from measurements can be achieved within one or two days. This means that in large and sparsely populated areas only limited possibilities exist in use for correcting the effects of soil moisture changes in snow-water equivalent by making ground measurements.

So the measured values of snow-water equivalent are used in Finland without any exact soil moisture correction. One reason for this is that autumns are in general rainy and thus soil moisture does not change very much from one winter to another. Another reason is that by the gammma method one can measure during melting period also that water which lies on the

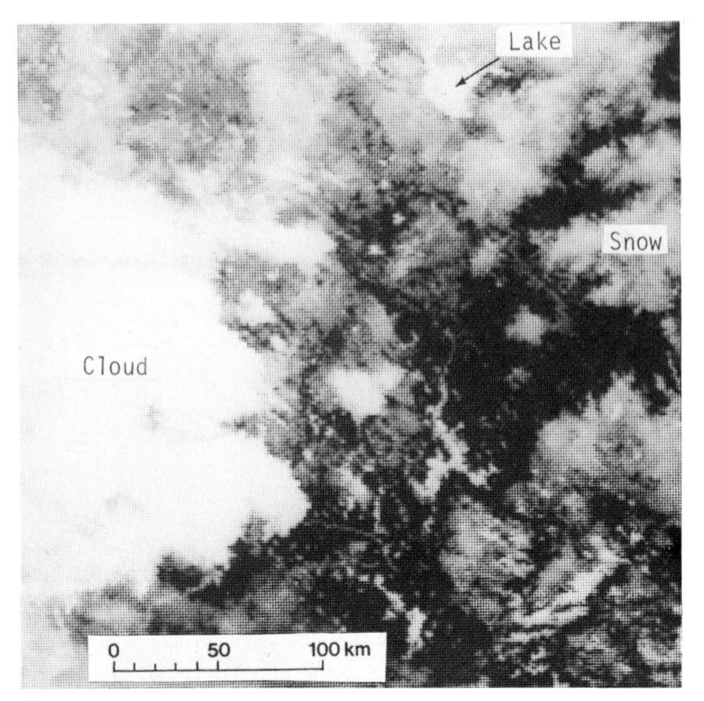

FIG.3 NOAA/AVHRR of 16th May 1984. Processed using principal component analysis.

ground and which cannot be measured by the gravimetric method. Figure 4 shows an example how snow-water equivalents measured by both methods correlated in measurements made in 1982 - 1984. We can see that in the latter part of the melting period (low snow-water equivalents) the gamma method gives larger snow-water equivalent values than the gravimetric method. This is caused by water on the ground which cannot be measured by the gravimetric method. It is possible that values measured by the gamma-method without any soil moisture correction are more useful than values measured by conventional methods.

The mean error of snow-water equivalent values measured by the gamma-method was in Finland 5-10 % of the measured snow-water equivalent. This error was determined from errors in navigation, background radiation measurement, flight altitude measurement, attenuation coefficient and the statistical nature of gamma radiation. The comparison with ground measurements cannot give right values for the error from the reasons mentioned above.

At the end of the project gamma radiation measurements of 450 km could be processed to snow-water equivalent values in eight hours after the landing of the aircraft.

4. Combining the information measured in satellite images and by gamma-ray techniques into areal snow-water equivalent values

No significant snowmelt exists in Northern Finland before the latter part of April. So for forecasting of springtime runoff the measurements at the end of April and in May are the most important ones. Prior to the snowmelt, ground measurements are today the most economical way to monitor the snow accumulation.

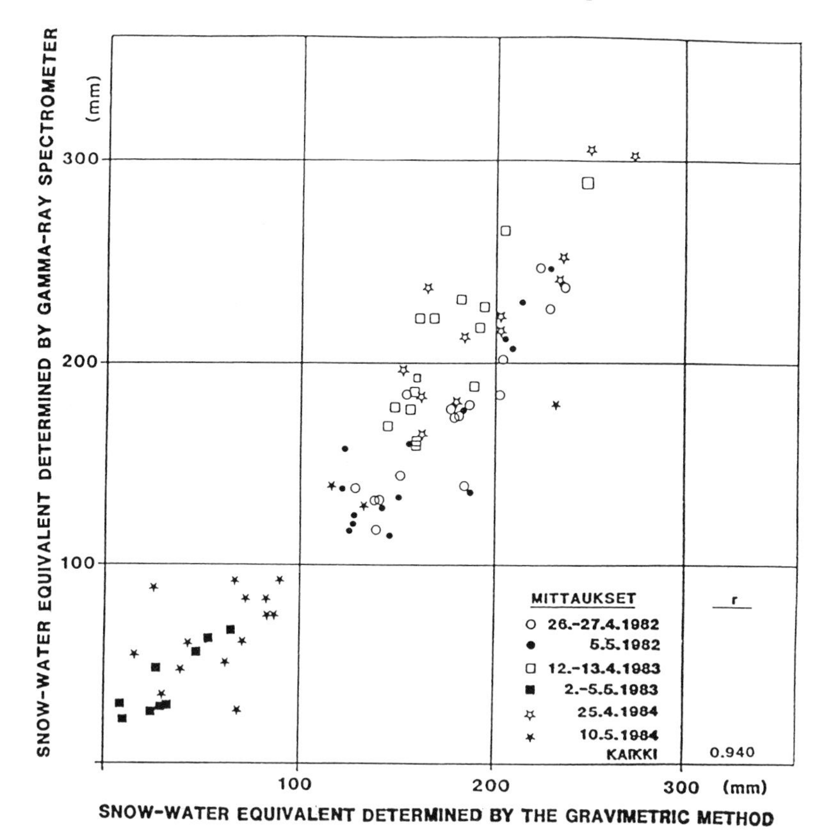

FIG.4 Snow-water equivalent determined by gamma-ray spectrometry and by the gravimetric method.

The cost of airborne gamma-ray spectrometry measurements of snow-water equivalent are so high that only 1-3 such measurements are possible during the snowmelt period. Weather satellites take images daily. So during the latter part of the snowmelt period it is possible to determine the snow covered area and roughly estimate the snow-water equivalent 2-3 times a week. Figure 5 and 6 show how the runoff and the values of the digital NOAA-images (channel 1) correlated during snowmelt in 1983 and 1984. The values of the NOAA-images represent forested areas and open areas. Darker tones mean also smaller snow-water equivalents.

The degree-day factor varies depending on the terrain type, slope etc. NOAA-images can be used in determining degree-day factor for smaller or larger basins, because land use, terrain types and canopy density can be interpreted using NOAA-data (Schneider et.al, 1981). In this stydy a wintertime and a summertime NOAA-image were used to interpret the density of forest canopy and terrain type in Northern Finland. After that it was determined for every interpreted class the degree-day factor. By using the percentages of different terrain types in the basins it was possible to determine degree-day factors for different basins. If representative temperature and wind information exist, this can help in snowmelt estimation. The use of satellite imagery in snowmelt process monitoring has been discussed by Thomsen (Thomsen 1980).

Figures 7 and 8 show the measured snow-water equivalents in 1983 and 1984. Only limited number of digital satellite images have been available besides the gamma-ray measurements.

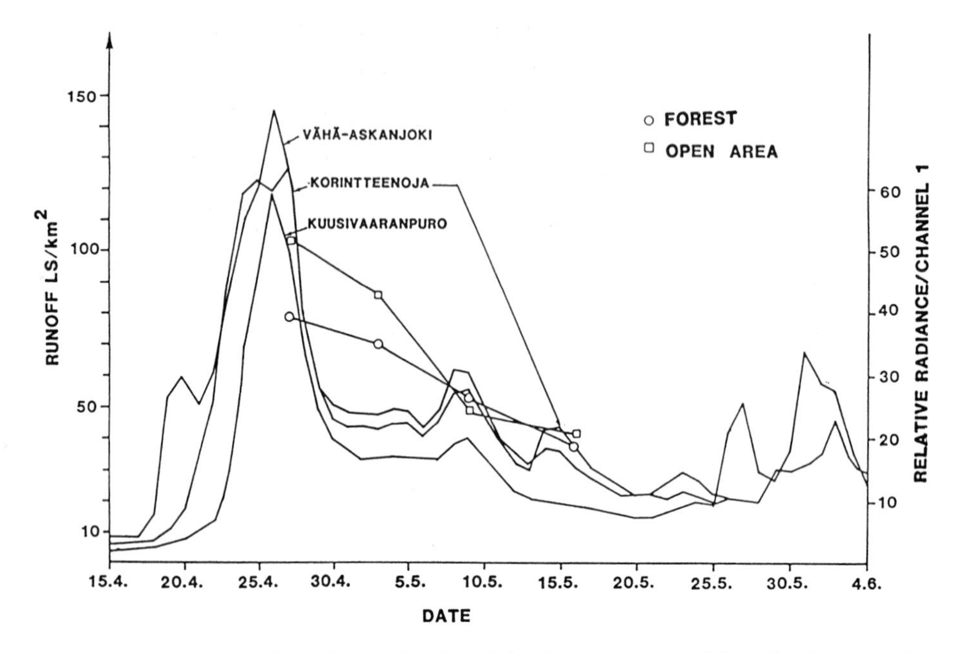

FIG.5 The relationship between runoff and the relative radiances measured by NOAA/AVHRR in 1983.

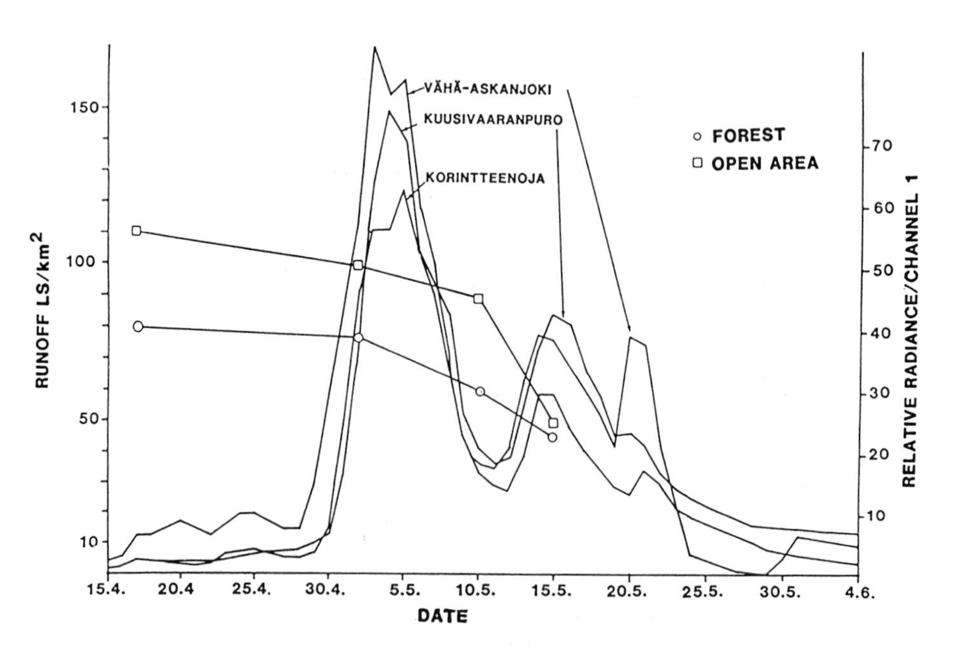

FIG.6 The relationship between runoff and the relative radiances measured by NOAA/AVHRR in 1984.

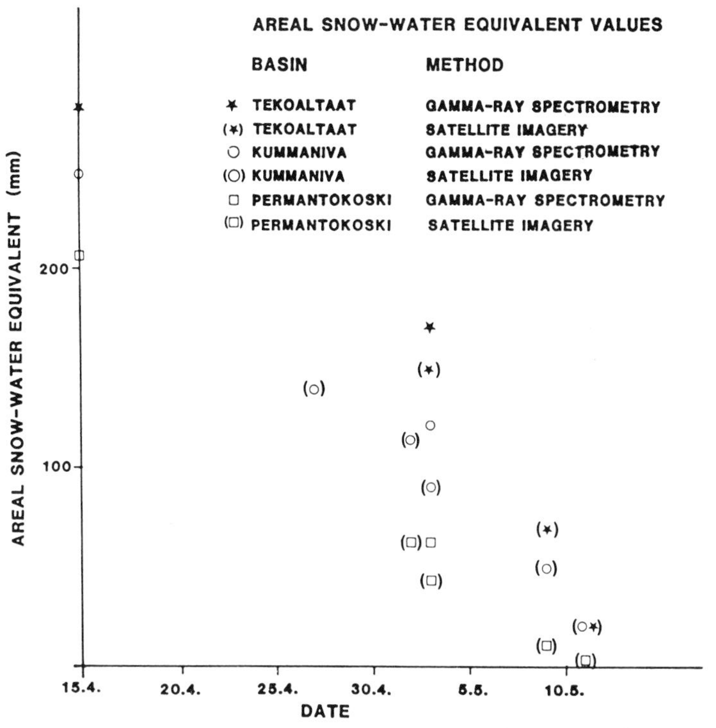

FIG.7 Measured areal snow-water equivalents in 1983 in some river basins in northern Finland.

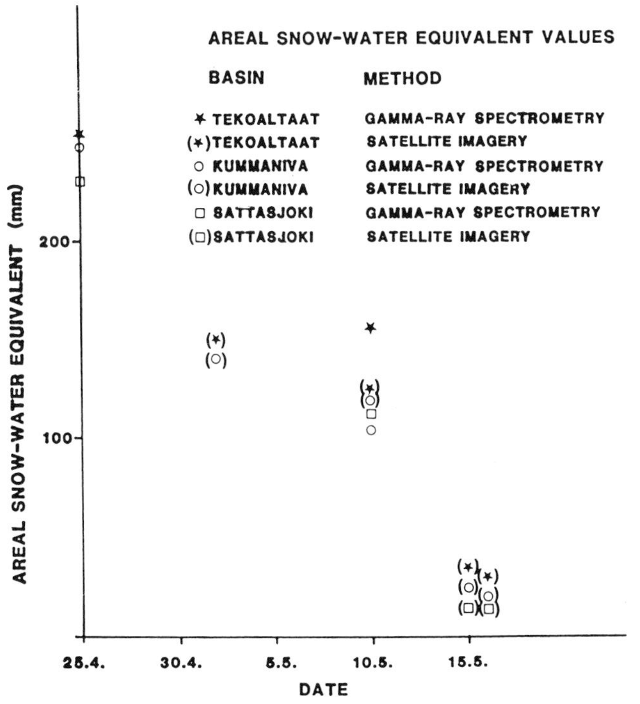

FIG.8 Measured areal snow-water equivalents in 1984 in some river basins in northern Finland.

Figure 9 shows an example how degree-day factor can be used together with these real time measurements in determining the areal snow-water equivalent. As can be noticed real time measurements have improved the accuracy of areal snow-water equivalent value; when snow has melted the discharge begins to decrease.

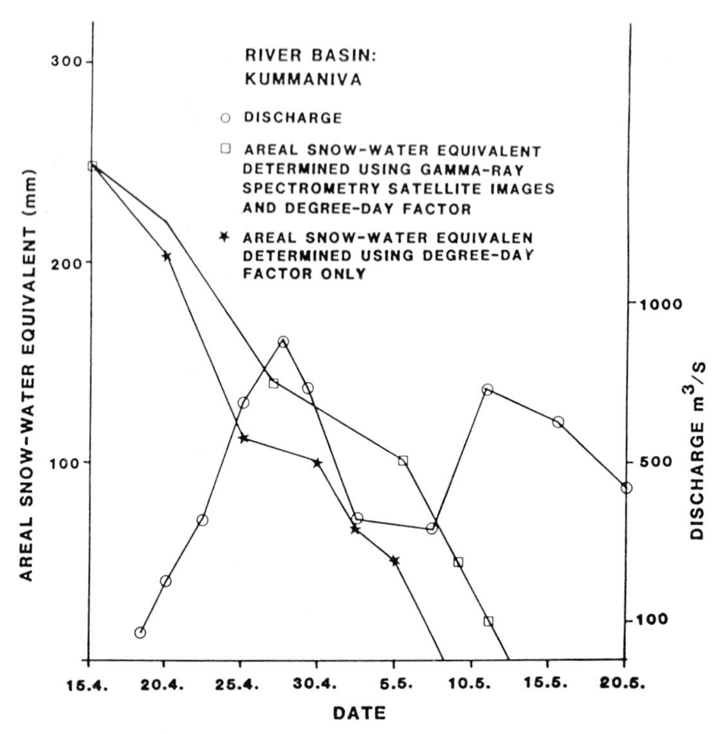

FIG.9 Areal snow-water equivalent and discharge in Kummaniva river basin in 1983.

5. Conclusions

Weather satellite imagery and airborme gamma-ray spectrometry offers a very effective method for monitoring the snow cover also in large river basins. Satellite images give in general good areal information on the snow cover and in the latter part of snowmelt also information on the snow-water equivalent. Gamma-ray spectrometry can be used to determine the snow-water equivalet in snowcourses. The representativeness of these courses can be checked using satellite imagery because satellite images show where and when snow has melted and what kind of forest and terrain exists in the river basin. The results presented in this paper are mainly based on measurements made in 1983 and 1984. To render the method more accurate, this study will be confirmed in the forthcoming years.

References

Application System Verification and Transfer Project. Volume VIII Satellite Snow Mapping and Runoff Prediction Handbook. NASA Technical Paper 1829. December 1981. USA.

Operational Applications of Satellite Snowcover Observations. NASA Conference Publication 2116. Sparks, Nevada, April 16-17, 1979. USA.

Workshop on Remote Sensing of Snow and Soil Moisture by Nuclear Techniques. WMO, IAHS and Norwegian National Committee for Hydrology. VOSS, April 23-27.1979 Norway.

Snötaxering med gammasfålningsteknik. Nordic Expert Meeting. NHP-rapport nr. 8. Koordineeringskommitteen för Hydrologi in Norden KOHNYO. Rovaniemi, October 9-10. 1984, Finland.

Dozier, Jeff et.al. 1981. Effect of Grain Size and Snowpack Water Equivalence on Visible and Near-Infrared Satellite observations of Snow. Water Reources Research, Vol. 17 No 4 pp. 1213-1221.

Merry C.J. et.al. 1983. The use of Landsat data for predicting snowmelt runoff in the upper Saint John River Basin. Proceedings of the 17th international symposium on remote sensing of environment. Ann Arbor Michigan, 9-13. May 1983. USA. pp. 519-533.

Schreider R.S et.al. 1981. Use of NOAA/AVHRR Visible and Near-Infrared Data for Land Remote Sensing. NOAA Technical Report NESS 84. USA.

Thomsen A.G, 1980. Spatial Simulation of Snow Processes. Nordic Hydrology Vol.11 pp. 273-284.

Hydrologic Applications of Space Technology (Proceedings of the Cocoa Beach Workshop, Florida, August 1985). IAHS Publ. no. 160, 1986.

Snow cover mapping for runoff simulations based on Landsat-MSS data in an alpine basin

M. F. BAUMGARTNER & K. SEIDEL
Institute for Communication Technology, Swiss Federal Institute of Technology, Zurich, Switzerland
H. HAEFNER & K. I. ITTEN
Remote Sensing Laboratories, Department of Geography, University of Zurich, Switzerland
J. MARTINEC
Federal Institute for Snow & Avalanche Research, Weissfluhjoch-Davos, Switzerland

Abstract

For the Martinec-Rango Snowmelt Runoff Model (SRM) a precise determination of the daily changes of the snow cover is the basic input variable. A method was developed for digital snow cover classification with Landsat-MSS data including an extrapolation for partly clouded scenes and areas with not available remote sensing data. The runoff simulations were tested in a large basin of the Swiss Alps (Rhine-Felsberg, 3249 km^2, 571-3614 m a.s.l.) regarding the heterogeneous topographic and climatic conditions.

Introduction and Objectives

The assessment and forecast of the quantities of surface runoff is a key objective for water management. In mountain areas the runoff in spring and summer is primarily affected by the changes of the seasonal snow cover.

Various tests have demonstrated that the Martinec-Rango Snowmelt Runoff Model (SRM; Martinec, 1980) is suited to forecast surface runoff under mountaineous conditions (Martinec, 1970 and 1975). The accuracy of the forecast depends especially on a measurement of the daily changes of the snow cover. An up-to-date, fast and exact recording of these changes is only possible by remote sensing techniques (Haefner, 1980; Itten, 1980).

Therefore, it is the purpose of this paper to outline a method to map and determine the snow cover in a large basin by Landsat-MSS data. The satellite images have been processed digitally using an interactive image processing system (Besse, 1981; Egeli, 1983).

Special attention has to be given to the difficult and variable topographical and climatical conditions in the Alps. Serious problems were the often occuring clouds and not recorded data, which complicate the determination of the snow cover. Even less suited images have to be considered, in order to get enough remote sensing information to monitor the varying snow cover during a melting period. The areas with 'missing data' have to be estimated using an extrapolation technique, based on a digital terrain model.

The different climatological conditions in the basin and the frequent changes of rain- and snowfall during the melting period complicate the application of the SRM and have to be respected for discharge simulation. A solution is presented to overcome these obstacles for a rather large catchment area in the Swiss Alps and results are presented.

Study Site

The test site 'Felsberg' is located in the eastern part of the Swiss Alps (Fig. 1) and includes the four Rhine-tributaries 'Vorderrhein', 'Hinterrhein', 'Landwasser' and 'Albula'. Its size is 3249 km^2, the basin relief 3043 m (lowest point: stream gauge 'Felsberg', 571 m a.s.l., highest point: 'Toedi', 3614 m a.s.l.). The ice covered area (glaciers) totals 3% at the end of the hydrological year (September 30th).

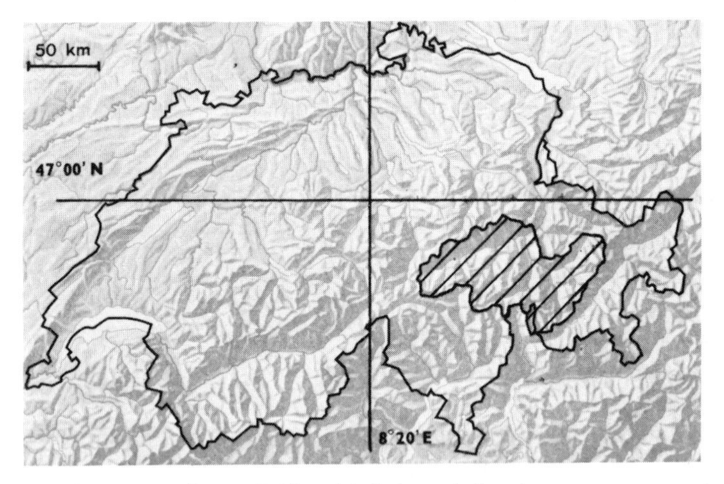

FIG.1 Location of the 'Felsberg' basin:
area of Switzerland: 41,293 km^2
area of 'Felsberg' basin (shaded area): 3,249 km^2

The basin can be divided into three different climatological regions. The western part ('Vorderrhein') has a significant higher amount of precipitation than the eastern part ('Landwasser' and 'Albula'). The southern part ('Hinterrhein') is influenced by the climate of the South Alps, i.e. very high precipitations for a short time during summer and autumn, compared to the more evenly distributed precipitations in the northern part of the Alps. This differences can be explained by differently oriented mountain chains and the influence of the westerly winds. The water regime in spring and summer depends mainly on snowmelt, in summer and autumn on rainfall.

In many valleys of the Alps the runoff is controlled by reservoirs for hydroelectric power generation. This raises a serious problem in the comparison of the measured with the calculated runoff on a daily basis. The recorded (actual) daily minima and maxima and weekly variations reflect the needs for electricity and does not show the natural runoff.

Snow Cover Determination by Satellite Data

For the determination of the changing snow cover during the snowmelt period Landsat-MSS digital recordings were used. Important procedures for the processing of the satellite images are:

- Preprocessing, as a geometric transformation of the images to a basic coordinate system and resampling to a unique pixelsize
- Determination of an adequate classification scheme and training samples for a supervised classification
- Snow cover classification
- Superimposition of all data into a multivariate data set
- Extrapolation to estimate the snow cover for areas with not available data

- Problem Spots of Snow Cover Determination

Due to the increase of the solar irradiance in spring and summer clouds develop in the late morning (Rott, 1978). The Landsat-MSS sensors (Tab. 1) are recording the radiation reflected from the clouds and therefore the earth surface is invisible. In addition the spectral bands do not allow an automated separation between snow and clouds. In a false color representation a different-

Tab. 1: Landsat-MSS characteristics

	Landsat 1-3	Landsat 4,5
Altitude	920 km	705 km
Period	102 min	99 min
Frame area	185*185 km^2	185*185 km^2
Resolution	56*79 m^2	56*79 m^2
Repetition rate	18 days	16 days
Band 4	0.5-0.6 um	0.5-0.6 um
Band 5	0.6-0.7 um	0.6-0.7 um
Band 6	0.7-0.8 um	0.7-0.8 um
Band 7	0.8-1.1 um	0.8-1.1 um

iation becomes possible, based on the cloud forms and the cloud shadows. For every image a digital cloud mask was produced by visual inspections on a interactive image processing system. Together with missing frame segments (not available remote sensing data) a special procedure was established: an extrapolation technique, based on elevation, aspect and slope for each pixel, allows an estimation of the snow coverage in the unknown parts (Seidel, 1983). This and the request for the snow coverage in different elevation zones lead to the use of a Digital Terrain Model (DTM) as a suitable auxiliary information source for the processing of satellite data.

Because of the repetition rate of Landsat (Tab. 1) and the often by heavyly cloud coverage obscured scenes, a sufficient number of images during a snowmelt season is very seldom recorded. Considering even less suitable scenes, for the snowmelt period 1982 sufficient data were available. The following dates with frame numbers 209/027 and 209/028 have been used:

(1)	25-MAR82:	1.4% cloudcover/18.8% not available
(2)	18-MAY82:	15.1% cloudcover/13.1% not available
(3)	5-JUN82:	20.9% cloudcover/ 2.1% not available
(4)	11-JUL82:	0.9% cloudcover/ 3.4% not available
(5)	29-JUL82:	10.9/0.2% cloudcover/ 3.4% not available

It was necessary to compensate in (1) for missing lines by doubling the neighboring lines and in (3) for misregistered lines and channels. The frame (209/027) of scenes (4) and (5) did only cover a part of the basin. They were digitally mosaiced with the southwards adjacent frames (209/028).

The cloud coverage on the record of July 29th has been reduced by a pixelwise comparison with the record of July 11th, i.e. in each doubtful case the picture element in (5) has been assigned to the category of the corresponding element in (4). This procedure is not possible as soon as new snowfall has changed the situation in the mean time.

- Digital Terrain Model and Basin Perimeter

The DTM is used for the extrapolation process mentioned above. For the test site 'Felsberg' the DTM was interpolated from the (250*250) m^2 grid into a raster size of (100*100) m^2 applying the Akima method (Akima, 1974), which is based on a bicubic interpolation.

In order to determine the contribution to the total snow coverage from 'obscured' and 'not available' areas we used a method published earlier (Seidel, 1983). We devided the continuum of elevation-aspect-slope values into 205 classes:

- 5 elevation zones (560-1100, 1100-1600, 1600-2100, 2100-2600, 2600-3600 m a.s.l.)
- 8 aspect classes (N, NE, E, SE, S, SW, W, NW, N)
- 5 slope classes (<0-15, 16-22, 23-28, 29-36, $37-90^{o}$)
- 1 class for flat terrain

The basin boundary has been digitized from the National Topographic Map 1:50'000.

- Preprocessing

The Landsat-MSS digital products were received in UTM coordinates. They were transformed to the coordinate system of the National Topographic Map (based on a conform, Special-UTM projection) to facilitate the comparison of the different data sets (satellite images, DTM, masks). With the standard reference point approach, the Landsat images and the map were registered by an affine backward transformation (Steiner, 1977). At the same time a nearest neighbor resampling from 56*79 m^2 MSS resolution to the common raster size of (100*100) m^2 was carried out.

- Classification

The different Landsat-MSS scenes have been analysed with respect to snow cover. During a supervised classification process each picture element was assigned to one of the following categories: 'snow free', 'transition zone' and 'snow covered'. For the different scenes we had to use different classification schemes due to recording conditions: illumination, atmospheric conditions, areal extent of snow, reflectivity of the snow surface. The accuracy of the classification increases with the number of classes. For the most complex situation we had to consider a detailed list of classes:

- Water
- Forest (conifereous)
- Crop fields
- Meadow
- Pasture
- Wet grassland (wet and long grass from the previous year, beneath the transition zone, watered by the melting snow)
- Transition zone (snow patches, approx. 50 % snow covered)
- Dark snow (less reflecting snow due to soiling or debris)
- Snow (in shadow)
- Snow (in sun)

For the supervised classification, training samples for each of these classes have been selected. Experience and familiarity with the terrain is necessary to delineate representative samples. Special attention is recommended during the time of maximum snowmelt. Uncarefully selected training samples cause serious misclassifications.

In parallel to the complexity of the set of training samples an appropriate expensive classification procedure was found to be adequate ranging from Parallelepiped Discriminant (PPD), Minimum Distance, Mahalanobis Distance and Maximum Likelihood analyses. In addition, a reduction of the variables using Principal Components as well as Fisher's Linear Discriminant Vectors (Fisher, 1936) was carried out. Best classification results were always obtained using two MSS channels (band 5/band 7). Finally in the classified images, the detailed classes were condensed into the above mentioned main categories: 'snow free', 'transition zone' and 'snow covered'.

A pictorial representation is given in Fig. 2. Until now, the areas marked as 'clouds' or 'not available' were disregarded and have to be related to the three main categories with a method outlined in the following.

- Snow Cover Extrapolation

The classified Landsat-MSS images and the DTM classes are superimposed into a multivariate data set. As mentioned above, the region can be subdivided into 205 classes using a DTM. Each class is characterised by defined ranges of elevation, aspect and slope. Under the assumption that for each class a unique relative snow coverage is given we assigned to all cloud covered picture elements the same relative snow coverage as detected for the same class in the cloudfree portion. Finally, the snow

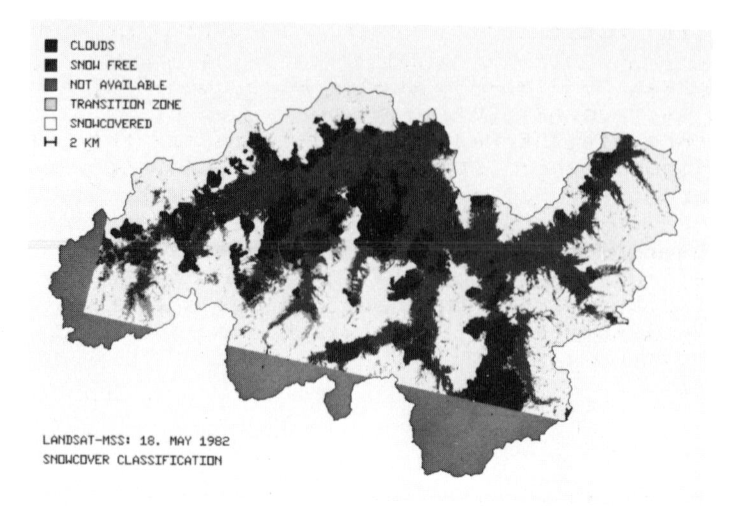

FIG.2 Classification result of a partly cloud covered scene.

coverage is summed up for each elevation zone separately, as demanded by the SRM. The contribution of the transition zone was weighted with 50 %. From these values the depletion curves have been constructed (Fig. 3), representing the relative snow coverage for each elevation zone during the snowmelt period in 1982.

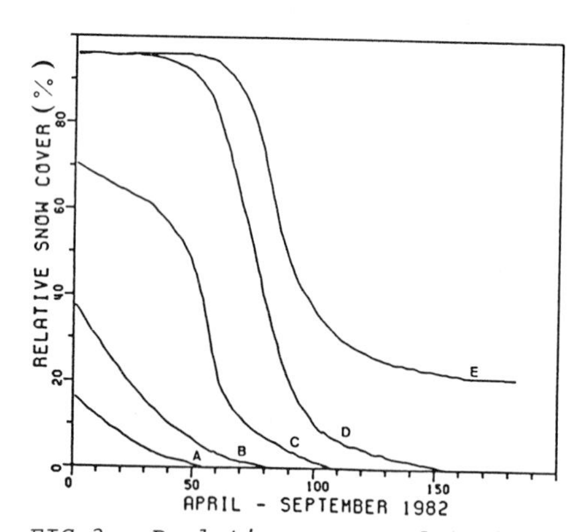

FIG.3 Depletion curves for five elevation zones A to E.

The Martinec-Rango Snowmelt Runoff Model

The SRM-Model is designed to simulate or forecast the daily discharge in mountain basins, resulting mainly from snowmelt but also from precipitation (Martinec, 1983).

Climatological variables, such as daily air temperature, precipitation and snow coverage are required. The values were taken from the records of one or more base stations. The discharge was measured at the stream gauge 'Felsberg' and has been used to

estimate the overall accuracy of the simulated runoff. The discharge is heavily influenced by the hydroelectric power generation so that the daily, weekly or seasonal runoff does not show the natural discharge.
In addition, basin dependent parameters are required to specify the global hydrological and topographical properties. With reference to the 'Dischma' Valley (Martinec, 1970) the above mentioned five elevation zones were selected. For the test site 'Felsberg' the recession coefficient was derived from the known coefficient of the 'Dischma' Valley (Martinec, 1963).

Based on the snow cover measurements a snowmelt runoff simulation with the SRM was carried out for the period April 1st to September 30th, 1982.

Simulations and Results

Daily air temperature and precipitation are necessary input variables for the SRM. In order to get representative values for the rather large 'Felsberg'-basin we used the arithmetic means of 7 base stations located within the catchment area: Alveneu (1175 m a.s.l.), Arosa (1847 m a.s.l.), Chur (586 m a.s.l.), Davos (1590 m a.s.l.), Disentis (1180 m a.s.l.), Hinterrhein (1619 m a.s.l.), Weissfluhjoch (2667 m a.s.l.).

We found the resulting discharge curve from this 'synthetic base station' very similar to the curve based on the 'Disentis' temperature and precipitation records. That will say for further computations the 'Disentis' values are representative for the 'Felsberg'-basin. In Fig. 4 the simulated and measured discharge curves are presented for comparison.

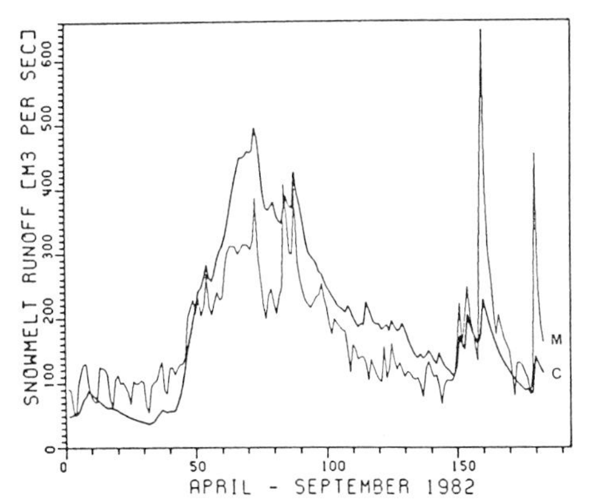

FIG.4 Simulated (C) and measured (M) discharge:
runoff M: 2778 × 10^6 m^3
runoff C: 2937 × 10^6 m^3
relative difference: 5.7%

In view of the operation of reservoirs the daily simulated flows do not always agree with the measured discharge. The simulated seasonal runoff volume, however, does not deviate very much from the measured volume.

It has to be emphasized that during the simulation with the

SRM no 'updating' was carried out, i.e. the measured discharge was at no time used to correct the deviation.

Conclusions

With the applied procedures it is possible to determine the changing snow cover with Landsat-MSS data even in a large alpine basin. Furthermore methods have been developed to estimate the snow coverage for partly clouded areas. The runoff can be simulated with the SRM if enough suitable satellite images during the snowmelt period are available. To this effect it is necessary to test a possible data complementation by NOAA-AVHRR imagery.

Acknowledgement

Many thanks to Dr. A. Rango and E. Major for making available the SRM computer program for this study.

References

Akima, H., 1974, A Method of Bivariate Interpolation and Smooth Surface Fitting Based on Local Procedures, Commun. Ass. Comput. Mach., Vol. 17, No. 1, pp. 18-2Ø, 26-31.

Besse, L., Seidel, K., Kuebler, O., 1981, Large Scale Multipurpose Interactive Image Processing Facility at ETH Zuerich, Design and Digital Image Processing Systems, James L. Mannos, Editor, Proc. SPIE 3Ø1, pp. 154-161.

Egeli, E., Gerig, G., Klein, F., Kuebler,O., 1983, A Hardware and Software Optimized Program System for Interactive Image Processing, Architecture and Algorithms for Digital Image Processing, Andre Oosterlinck, Per-Eric Danielsson, Editors, Proc. SPIE 435, pp. 134-138.

Fisher, R.A., 1936, The Use of Multiple Measurements in Taxonomic Problems, Annals of Eugenics 7, Part II, pp. 179-188.

Haefner, H., 198Ø, Snow surveys from Earth Resources Satellites in the Swiss Alps - A Review on Six Years' Research, Remote Sensing Series, Department of Geography, University of Zurich, pp. 1-65.

Itten, K.I., 198Ø, Snow Mapping from Spaceplatforms, in: SALOMONSON V.V. + BHAVSAR P.D. (Edit.): The Contribution of Space Observations to Water Resources Management, COSPAR Symp., Bangalore, India.

Martinec, J., 1963, Seasonal Forecasts of Discharge for Operation of Reservoirs (In Czech, English Abstract), Prace a Studie VUV Praha-Podbaba, Vol. 11Ø, p. 27.

Martinec, J., 197Ø, Study of Snowmelt Runoff Process in two Representative Watersheds with Different Elevation Range, Symp. on the Results of Research on Representative and Experimental Basins, Wellington, IAHS Publ. No. 96, pp. 29-39.

Martinec, J., 1975, New Methods in Snowmelt Runoff Studies in Representative Basins, In: The Hydrological Characteristics of River Basins, Proc. of the Tokyo Symp., IAHS Publ. No. 117, pp. 99-1Ø7.

Martinec, J., 198Ø, Snowmelt-Runoff Forecasts Based on Automatic Temperature Measurements, Proceedings at the Oxford Symposium, IAHS Publ. No. 129, pp. 239-246.
Martinec, J., Rango, A., Major, E., 1983, The Snowmelt Runoff Model (SRM) User's Manual, NASA Reference Publication 11ØØ, Washington, D.C., 11Ø pp.
Rott, H., 1978, Zur Schneekartierung in alpinen Einzugsgebieten aus Satellitenbildern, Zeitschrift fuer Gletscherkunde und Glaziologie, Bd. 14, H. 1, pp. 81-93.
Seidel, K., Ade, F., Lichtenegger, J., 1983, Augmenting LANDSAT MSS Data with Topographic Information for Enhanced Registration and Classification, IEEE Transactions on Geoscience and Remote Sensing, Vol. GE-21, No. 3, pp. 252-258.
Steiner, D., Kirby, M.E., 1977, Geometrical Referencing of Landsat Images by Affine Transformation and Overlaying of Map Data, Photogrammetria, Vol. 33, pp. 41-75.

Hydrologic Applications of Space Technology (Proceedings of the Cocoa Beach Workshop, Florida, August 1985). IAHS Publ. no. 160, 1986.

Remote sensing of snowpack properties by microwave radiometry

A. T. C. CHANG
Hydrological Sciences Branch,
NASA/Goddard Space Flight Center,
Greenbelt,
Maryland, USA

Abstract
The ever increasing demand for water throughout the world imposes a challenging problem for water resources managers. A conservative estimate of future needs indicates an increase of 3-5 times the present demand by the year of 2000. By then a lack of adequate water supply has been postulated to be the major resource problem of this country. Since snow represents an important source of water supply, improved knowledge of the snow water storage over large regions should improve the estimate of spring runoff and better management of the water resources. Microwave measurements have the capability to penetrate the snowpack and respond to variations in subsurface properties. It provides the only means to sense the snow depth or water equivalent information under nearly all weather conditions.

Microwave radiation emitted from the ground beneath a snowpack is attenuated and scattered by snow crystals. The effect of scattering is proportional to the size of snow crystals which is dependent on the age of snow. The emitted radiation measured by radiometers is used to infer the internal snowpack properties. Observations from spaceborne radiometers have been used for areas with uniform snow cover such as the Great Plains of the U.S. with some success. One of the challenging aspects in retrieving snow parameters is to understand the inhomogeneity of the snowpack caused by the different phases of metamorphism of the snow. This process normally produces vertical variations in the snow density and ice layers. By using multifrequency techniques, it may be possible to infer the internal structure of the snowpack due to different weather conditions, as well as the snow depth.

Introduction

The use of remotely-acquired microwave data, in conjunction with essential ground measurements, will most likely lead to improved information extraction regarding snowpack properties beyond that available by conventional techniques. Landsat visible and near-infrared data have recently come into near operational use for performing snowcovered area measurements (Rango, 1975; 1978). However, Landsat data acquisition is hampered by cloudcover, sometimes at critical times when a snowpack is ripe. Furthermore, information on water equivalent, free water content, and other snowpack properties germane to accurate runoff predictions is not currently obtainable using Landsat data alone because only surface and very near-surface reflectances are detected.

Microwaves are mostly unaffected by clouds and can penetrate through various snow depths depending on the wavelength. Hence, microwave sensors are potentially capable of determining the internal snowpack properties such assnow depth and snow water equivalent (Hall et al., 1978; Rango, et al., 1979). However, operational use of remotely-collected microwave data for snowpack analysis is not imminent because of complexities involved in the data analysis. Snowpack and soil properties are highly variable and their effects on microwave emission are still being explored. Nevertheless, much work is being done to develop passive microwave techniques (Edgerton, et al., 1973; Schmugge et al., 1974; Chang et al., 1976; Kong et al., 1979; Chang and Shiue, 1980; Matzler et al., 1980 and Stiles and Ulaby, 1980) for analysis of snowpack properties.

Microwave Emission from Snow

Microwave emission from a layer of snow over ground medium consists of two parts: (1) emission by the snow volume and (2) emission by the underlying ground. Both contributions are governed by the transmission and the reflection properties of the air-snow and snow-ground interfaces and by the absorption and scattering properties of the snow layer.

A snowpack is a dielectric medium which can be described either as a collection of scatterers distributed within a lossy dielectric or as a continuous random medium with a large dielectric variation. The real part of the dielectric constant of snow will be between that of air (ε = 1.0) and that of ice (ε = 3.15) and can be estimated as a function of density by using dielectric mixing formulae. For a snow density of 500 Kg/m^3 will yield a dielectric constant of 2. The resulting emissivity for a smooth surface would be approximately 0.98, and a T_B very close to the physical temperature should be observed. Indeed, this is approximately observed for long wavelengths. For shorter wavelengths, volume scattering by the individual ice grain reduces the T_B by scattering some of the radiation out of the sensor's field of view. This has the effect of introducing some of the cold sky brightness temperature into the radiometer field of view, thus reducing the observed T_B.

Snowpack temperature usually is quite close to its melting point. When any solid is near its melting point, its molecules have a greater amount of mobility and can change quickly in response to changing external conditions. When snow is melting, its structure and its electromagnetic behavior changes markly (Chang and Gloersen, 1975). The grain size changes rapidly following slight wetting. The effective dielectric constant of the wet snow increases due to the high dielectric constant of water in the microwave region. This change provides an opportunity to detect the wetness of snow using microwave techniques.

In order to understand the electromagnetic wave interaction with snowpack quantitatively, radiative transfer models have been used. The radiative transfer equation generally serves as the starting point for model calculations. By assuming a spherical shape snow crystal, Mie scattering theory can be used to account for the scattered energy distributions. Figure 1 shows the relationship between microwave brightness and snow water equivalent for different frequencies based on the radiative transfer calculations. The brightness decreases as the snow water equivalent increases. The 37 GHz brightness decreases much more rapidly than the longer wavelength brightness due to the more pronounced scattering effect. By using the radiative transfer models, microwave brightness emerging from a snowpack can be estimated. Based on the knowledge gained using this technique, snow parameter retrieval algorithms can be developed.

Observational Results

There have been several different experiments designed to measure the microwave brightness temperature as a function of snow depth or water equivalent. The first truck-mounted radiometer experiment was conducted on a site in the northern part of the Sierra Nevada Range near Truckee, CA by Edgerton, et al. (1973). They reported a smooth and pronounced reduction

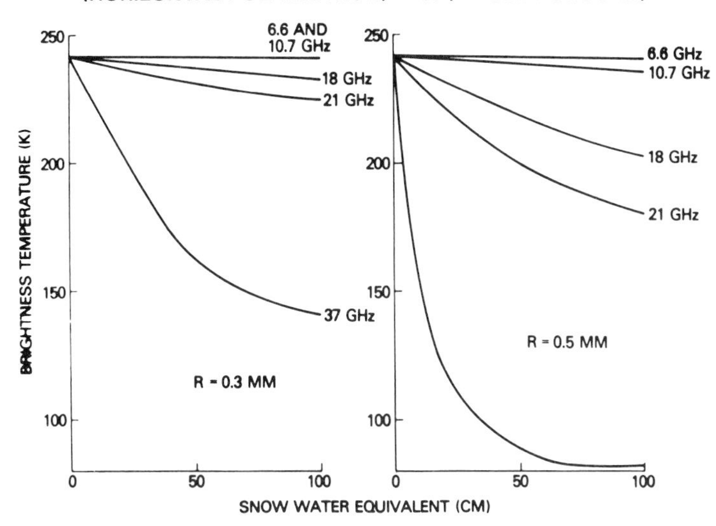

FIG.1 Calculated brightness temperature as a function of snow water equivalent.

of 37 GHz brightness temperature during the snow accumulation period. These results indicate that microwave brightness temperatures may be used to measure the water equivalent of a snowpack. Recently, several groups have been involved in microwave snowpack characterization experiments using ground-based systems (Stiles and Ulaby, 1980, Hofer and Matzler, 1980, and Chang et al., 1979).

During the winters of 1976, 1977 and 1980, several aircraft missions took place in the Colorado Rockies for snowpack studies. Steamboat Springs, Rabbit Ears Pass and Walden, CO, were the major study sites. The radiometers on board the aircraft include a four channel Multi-Frequency Microwave Radiometer (MFMR) and a Passive Microwave Imaging System (PMIS). Coordinated with these flights, extensive ground truth information was gathered. Snow density, water equivalent, depth, wetness, approximate grain size, layer classification and soil condition were measured by the ground truth teams. For the purpose of this study the data were averaged over the entire flight line for better comparison with the large microwave radiometer footprint obtained from airborne sensors. The 37 GHz brightness is used to predict the SWE while the 10.7 GHz brightness is used to determine the underlying soil conditions.

Some preliminary results derived from the Nimbus-7 Scanning Multichannel Microwave Radiometer (SMMR) also show the potential of microwave instrument in sensing snowpack properties (Chang et al., 1981). SMMR is five frequency, dual polarization microwave radiometer which measures the upwelling microwave radiation at 6.6, 10.7, 18.0, 21.0, and 37.0 GHz while scanning 25° to either side of the spacecraft with a constant incidence angle of approximately 50° with respect to the Earth's surface. The spatial resolution varies from 25 km for the 37 GHz to 150 km for the 6.6 GHz. Detailed descriptions of this instrument can be found in Gloersen and Barath (1977).

The study areas chosen were (1) central Russia and (2) the high plains of Canada (Foster et al., 1980). The vegetation, topography, climate and latitude of these two areas are similar. The generally flat terrain of these areas, which is sometimes broken by hills is covered with various grasses. Both of these two areas experience very cold winters with snow possibly covering the ground from December to March.

Due to limited available snow course data, it is rather difficult to compile SWE data in a timely fashion for comparison with the satellite measurements. SWE is calculated by multiplying the snow depth and the snow density. Snow depth information was obtained from meteorological stations, whereas the snow density was assumed to be 0.3 g/cm^3 for all the calculations (variations from this assumed density could account for some of the scatter observed in the data). Figure 2 shows the 37 GHz vertical polarization brightness temperature versus the snow depth for the Canadian and Russian test sites as compared with the calculated results. The figure shows that most of the data points fall in the range of mean radius of 0.3 to 0.5 mm. These results provide us more

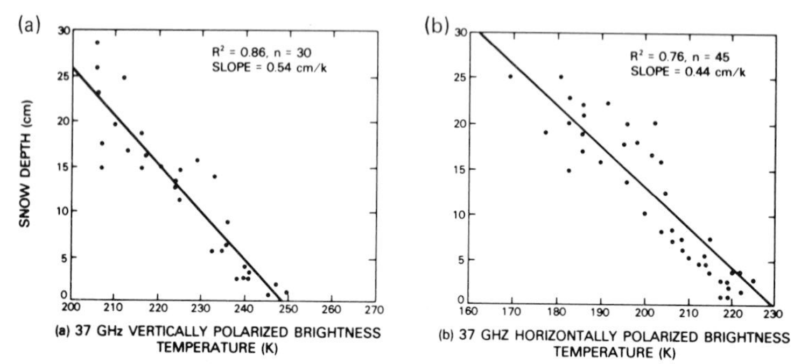

FIG.2 Snow depth vs. microwave brightness at 37 GHz from satellite for (a) Canadian High Plain and (b) Central Russia.

confidence in the assumed mean radius (0.35 mm) used in this study. The time period of the SMMR data used is February 15 to 21, 1979. During this time period the snow depth variation across the study areas is quite limited (from 1 to 30 cm). Although the footprint of each brightness measurement represents a rather large area (25 km x 25 km), the effect of snow cover can still be observed. Figure 3 shows the scattering of SMMR 37 GHz brightness temperature versus snow depth for the Russian test site. The linear regression technique gives a R^2 of 0.75 for the T_B and snow depth. The data display considerable scatter, which is probably due to the inhomogeneity within each footprint and the assumptions used in this study. The theoretically calculated brightness curve fits well with observations and can be utilized to infer the snow depth or SWE from microwave brightness temperature measured by spaceborne sensors. No attempt has been made in this study to relate the polarization factor to the freeze/thaw soil condition determination, because there are no reliable surface observations for comparison.

One of the challenging aspects in retrieving snow parameters is to understand the inhomogeneity of the snowpack caused by the different phases of metamorphism of the snow. This process normally produces vertical variations in the snow density and ice layers. A series of field experiments over a period of five winters were taken place in Colorado and Vermont by the NASA/Goddard group. Multifrequency radiometers with frequencies between 5 and 37 GHz were used to measure the brightness temperature of snow. The results of these experiments reconfirm that snowpack parameters such as snow water equivalent, snow wetness can be related to brightness variations. The volume scattering dominates the 37 GHz brightness, while interference effect is more pronounced in the 5 GHz observations. Preliminary results from the 1983 winter experiment

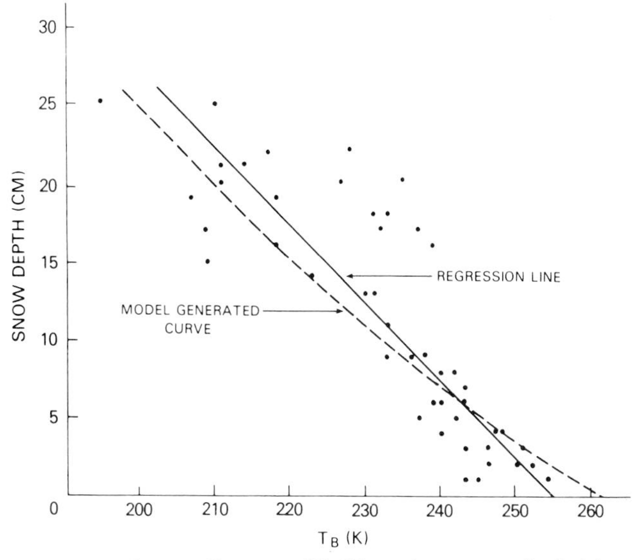

FIG.3 Nimbus-7 SMMR 37 GHz microwave brightness temperature vs. snow depth for Central Russia.

indicate that brightness measured at different incidence angles could reveal the interference effect between ice layers (Figure 4). This effect is clearly displayed at the 10.7 GHz observations. However, at 37 GHz the interference is not very distinguishable due to strong scattering of snow crystals. By using multifrequency techniques, it is possible to

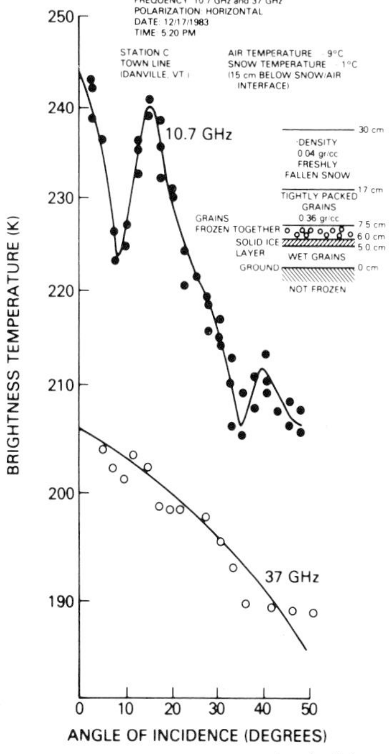

FIG.4 Microwave brightness for snowpack with embedded ice layers.

study the age and evolution of the snowpack due to different weather conditions, as well as the snow depth. This is important in extending our understanding on the interaction of snow covered surface with the Earth climate system.

Summary

The microwave radiometer observations can be utilized to infer the snow water equivalent under dry snow conditions. The results from a scattering model match well with the experimental results. The capability of the 37 GHz radiometer has been demonstrated by using data collected by ground experiments, aircraft and spacecraft measurements. For deeper snowpacks, a wavelength longer than 0.8 cm is required to infer the snowpack information.

Due to the strong dependence of the emerging brightness temperature on the mean crystal radius, it is necessary to characterize the crystal sizes within the snowpack carefully. In addition, crystal size distribution should be monitored and documented in order to account for the different types of snow metamorphism found in different snow sites.

By using multifrequency observations, one could obtain some structure information within a snowpack. This information at present is difficult if not impossible to obtain without digging a snowpit, which is both tedious and time consuming. However, further experiments are required before this technique can be used for remote sensing.

At present, the poor sensor resolution from satellite observations limits the use of satellite data to large homogeneous regions such as the high plains. Even this coarsely derived information could be valulable for runoff prediction purposes for the time period right before the rapid spring melt in these test sites. In these areas, snow also provides the necessary insulation for the underlying vegetation such as winter wheat. Satellite derived information on snow depth could be the key to early detection of winter kill. This information will greatly enhance the accuracy of overall crop yield prediction. As satellite spatial resolution improves with future generations of microwave radiometers, applications should be found in other areas such as intermountain valleys and large mountain plateaus. Then the capabilities of microwave radiometry will become more directly applicable to seasonal and short term runoff forecasting.

References

Chang, A. T. C. and J. C. Shiue (1980), "A Comparative Study of Microwave Radiometer Observations Over Snowfields with Radiative Transfer Model Calculations," Remote Sensing of Environment, 10, p. 215-229.

Chang, A. T. C., J. L. Foster, D. K. Hall, A. Rango and B. K. Hartline (1981), "Snow Water Equivalent Determination by Microwave Radiometry," NASA TM 82074.

Chang, T. C. and P. Gloersen (1975), "Microwave Emission from Dry and Wet Snow," in Operational Applications of Satellite Snowcover Observations, NASA SP-391, Washington, D.C., p. 399-407.

Chang, T. C., P. Gloersen, T. Schmugge, T. T. Wilheit and H. J. Zwally (1976), "Microwave Emission from Snow and Glacier Ice," Journal Glaciology, V. 16, No. 74, p. 23-39.

Edgerton, A. T., F. Ruskey, D. Williams, A. Stogryn, G. Poe, D. Meeks and O. Russell (1973), "Microwave Emission Characteristics of Natural Materials and the Environment," Final Technical Report 9016R-8, Microwave Systems, Aerojet-General Corporation, Azusa, California.

Foster, J. L., A. Rango, D. K. Hall, A. T. C. Chang, L. J. Allison and B. C. Diesen (1980), "Snowpack Monitoring in North America and Eurasia using Passive Microwave Satellite Data," Remote Sensing of Environment,

10, p. 285-298.

Gloersen, P. and F. T. Barath (1977), "A Scanning Multichannel Microwave Radiometer for Nimbus-G and Seasat-A," IEEE Journal of Oceanic Engineering, Vol. OE-2, p. 172-178.

Hall, D. K., A. Chang, J. L. Foster, A. Rango and T. Schmugge (1978), "Passive Microwave Studies of Snowpack Properties," Proceedings of the 46th Annual Western Snow Conference, Otter Rock, OR, p. 33-39.

Kong, J. A., R. Shin, J. C. Shiue and L. Tsang (1979), "Theory and Experiment for Passive Microwave Remote Sensing of Snowpacks," Journal of Geophysical Research, 84, p. 5669-5673.

Matzler, C., E. Schanda, R. Hofer and W. Good (1980), "Microwave Signatures of the Natural Snow Cover at Weissfluhjoch," NASA CP-2153, p. 203-223, available from NTIS, Springfield, Virginia.

Rango, A. (ed.) (1975), "Operational Applications of Satellite Snowcover Observations," NASA SP-391, Washington, D.C., 430 p.

Rango, A. (1978), "Pilot tests of satellite snowcover/runoff forecasting systems," Proceedings of the 46th Annual Western Snow Conference, Otter Rock, Oregon, p. 7-14.

Rango, A., A. T. C. Chang and J. L. Foster (1979), "The Utilization of Spaceborne Microwave Radiometers for Monitoring Snowpack Properties," Nordic Hydrology, 10, p. 25-40.

Schmugge, T. T., T. Wilheit, P. Gloersen, M. F. Meier, D. Frank and I. Dirmhirn (1974), "Microwave Signatures of Snow and Fresh Water Ice," in Advanced Concepts and Techniques in the Study of Snow and Ice Resources, National Academy of Sciences, Washington, D.C., p. 551-562.

Stiles, W. H. and F. T. Ulaby (1980), "Microwave Remote Sensing of Snowpacks," NASA Contractor Report No. 3263, 404 p., available from NTIS, Springfield, Virginia.

Hydrologic Applications of Space Technology (Proceedings of the Cocoa Beach Workshop, Florida, August 1985). IAHS Publ. no. 160, 1986.

Mapping of snow-cover parameters by a spaceborne microwave radiometer

MARTTI HALLIKAINEN, PETRI JOLMA & MARTTI TIURI
Helsinki University of Technology, Radio Laboratory, SF-02150 Espoo, Finland
RISTO KUITTINEN
Technical Research Centre of Finland, Laboratory of Land Use, SF-02100 Espoo, Finland

Abstract
Spaceborne microwave radiometers can monitor snow-cover parameters on a global basis with a practically all-weather viewing capability. Algorithms to retrieve the water equivalent of snow cover have been developed. In areas with mixed surface types (forests, farmland, etc.) the retrieval accuracy is improved by including the surface type effects in the algorithm. Based on the microwave response to snow water equivalent, three distinct categories can be observed: early and mid-winter, spring (melt-freeze period), and melting period. Substantial differences in the response may occur between consecutive winters.

Introduction
Snow is important to hydrology, agriculture, weather, and climate. In order to increase the accuracy of forecasts in these fields, high-quality snow information is needed. It has been concluded that this need may be met best in the future using remote-sensing techniques in combination with conventional snow-surveying methods (Rango and Hartline, 1982).

Microwave remote sensing has some advantages that make it particularly useful for snow mapping. The first advantage of using microwaves instead of optical or infrared waves is their capability to penetrate dry snow. This offers a chance to measure the depth and water equivalent of dry snow cover. The second advantage relates to the capability of microwaves to penetrate clouds. There are several atmospheric transmission "windows" in the visible, infrared, and microwave regions available for satellite observations of ground. Only microwaves can be used under cloudy conditions. Cloud attenuation in the microwave region, especially in the lower frequency range, is orders of magnitude smaller than the attenuation in the visible and infrared regions. This is important for snow mapping which requires successive observations in order to monitor the changes in the snow depth and water equivalent.

Microwave brightness temperature of snow-covered terrain
A microwave radiometer is a very sensitive receiver that is used to measure the intensity of microwave radiation emitted by natural targets. The microwave range is part of the electromagnetic spectrum, covering frequencies between 1 GHz (wavelength 30 cm) and 300 GHz (wavelength 1 mm). The intensity of the natural microwave emission depends on several parameters, including the temperature, electrical properties, and surface roughness of the target. Additional important parameters related to the radiometer and its antenna are the viewing angle, frequency, and polarization (orientation of the electric field).

The intensity of the radiation is expressed as the brightness temperature of the target. The brightness temperature (denoted by T_B and expressed in kelvins) is related to the physical temperature of the target T, by

$$T_B = \varepsilon T \quad ; \qquad 0 < \varepsilon < 1 \tag{1}$$

where ε is the emissivity of the target.

Figures 1 to 3 illustrate the effects of liquid water content, measurement frequency, and polarization to the brightness temperature of snow-covered terrain (Abdelrazik, 1984; Hallikainen, 1984). At frequencies above 15 GHz, the brightness temperature for dry snow decreases with increasing snow depth (water equivalent) and increasing grain size, whereas the brightness temperature for wet snow is practically independent of the snow depth.

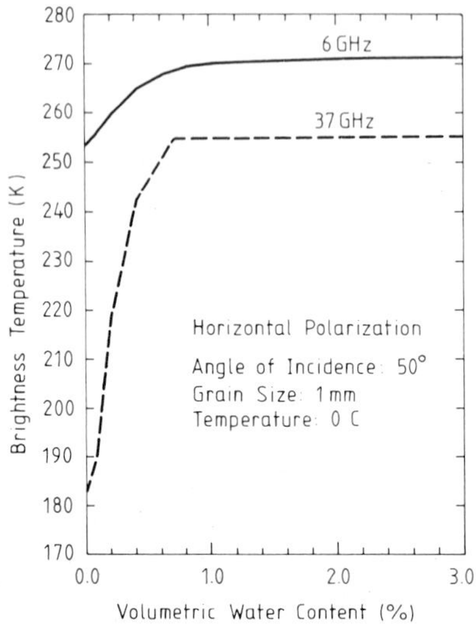

FIG.1 Calculated brightness temperature of snow-covered terrain as a function of water content. Thickness of snow cover is 50cm (Abdelrazik, 1984).

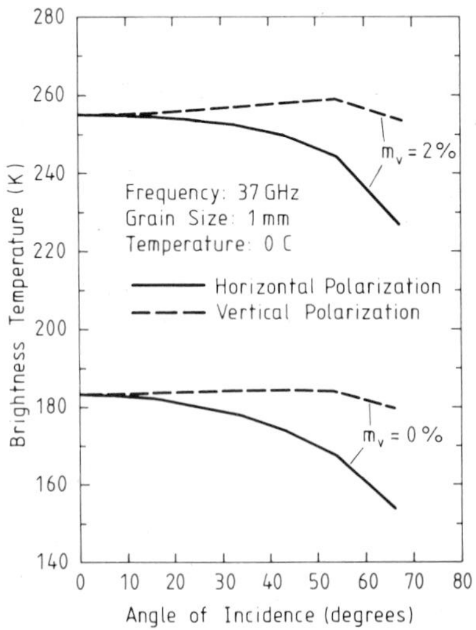

FIG.2 Calculated brightness temperature of snow-covered terrain for volumetric water contents of 0% and 2%. Thickness of snow cover is 50cm (Abdelrazik, 1984).

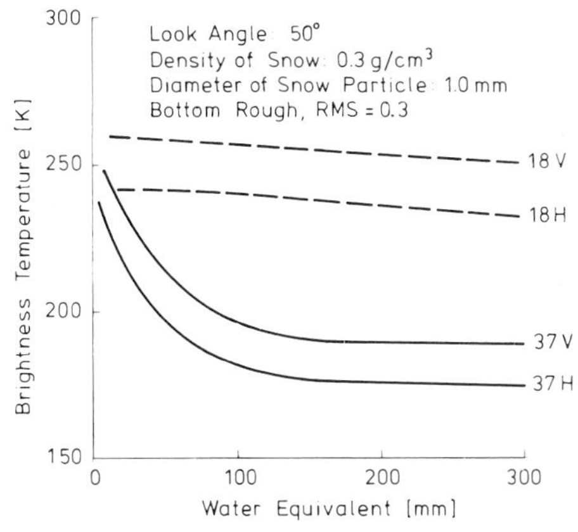

FIG.3 Calculated brightness temperature of dry snow-covered terrain at 18 GHz and 37 GHz. Horizontal and vertical polarization are denoted by H and V, respectively (Hallikainen, 1984).

Consequently, melt-freeze cycles of snow cover in the spring appear as alternating low (dry snow at night) and high (wet snow by day) brightness temperatures. The capability of microwave radiometry to discriminate wet snow from bare soil depends on the soil and vegetation type, the liquid water content of soil, etc.

A major source of spaceborne microwave radiometer data is Nimbus-7. The Nimbus-7 satellite carries a Scanning Multichannel Microwave Radiometer (SMMR) that is used to map the brightness temperature of Earth. The frequencies are 6.6, 10.7, 18.0, 21.0, and 37.0 GHz. At each frequency, both horizontally and vertically polarized microwave radiation are measured. The conical scan covers a swath width of 780 km with a local incidence angle of 50°. The surface resolution varies from 151 x 97 km^2 at 6.6 GHz to 27 x 18 km^2 at 37 GHz.

Water equivalent algorithms

Several different algorithms to retrieve the water equivalent from Nimbus-7 SMMR data have been tested previously (Künzi et al, 1982). Using the difference between the brightness temperatures at 18 GHz and 37 GHz for horizontal polarization (T_{18H} - T_{37H}), snow maps for Winter 1978-79 have been produced on a global basis (Künzi et al, 1982). The algorithm employs the average response to snow water equivalent and it can be expected to work with satisfactory accuracy in homogeneous areas where a single surface type (farmland etc.) dominates.

In areas with mixed surface types, the retrieval accuracy can be improved by accounting for the major land-cover categories. Hence the general form of the retrieval algorithm is

$$\Delta T(W_{eq}) = \sum_i f_i \ \Delta T_i(W_{eq}) \quad . \qquad (2)$$

In Eq. (2), W_{eq} is the water equivalent of snow cover and f_i is the fraction of surface type i within the resolution cell. ΔT is observed by the satellite and it may be either the brightness temperature at a single frequency or a mathematical expression including brightness temperatures at different frequencies. ΔT_i is a similar quantity for surface type i. Eq. (2) states that the total response to water equivalent within each resolution cell can be expressed as a summation of responses from various surface types.

Hallikainen (1984) defined ΔT by using the brightness temperature difference between 18 GHz and 37 GHz (horizontal polarization), compared to the corresponding value before the first snowfall:

$$\Delta T(W_{eq}) = [T_{18H}(W_{eq}) - T_{37H}(W_{eq})] - [T_{18H}(W_{eq}=0)] - T_{37H}(W_{eq}=0)] \quad . \quad (3)$$

In order to use the algorithm in Eq. (2), the ΔT response to water equivalent for each surface type, ΔT_i, must be derived. In Finland, Nimbus-7 SMMR CELL data (resolution 60 x 60 km^2) for Winter 1978-79 were employed to derive the ΔT response to snow water equivalent for major surface types. The derivation was performed by minimizing the error between the satellite-derived (Eq. (2)) and manually measured water equivalent values in Finland. The land-cover categories were forests, farmland, bogs, and water (ice-covered lakes and rivers).

An example of the results is given in Figure 4. The ΔT response to the water equivalent is highest for ice-covered areas and lowest for forests. This is due to the masking of microwave emission from ground by trees. As predicted by the theory, the responses slightly saturate around W_{eq} = 100 mm (Hallikainen, 1984).

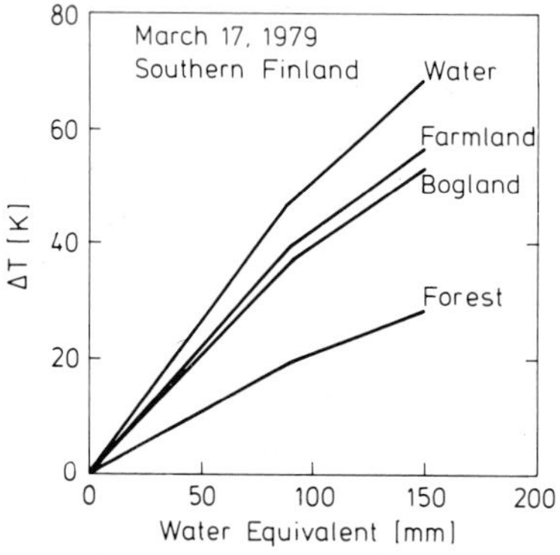

FIG.4 Optimized ΔT response (Eq. (3)) to snow water equivalent for major surface types in Southern Finland (March 17, 1979).

Using the responses shown in Figure 4 along with the results for Central and Northern Finland (three sets of responses are needed), a linear correlation coefficient of R = 0.76 between the satellite-derived and the manually measured values was obtained for March 17, Figure 5. This is a substantial improvement from R = 0.21, obtained by neglecting the effect of surface types and using the average response. For February 15-21, 1979, similar results have been reported by Hallikainen (1984).

Variations in the microwave response to water equivalent

Nimbus-7 SMMR TCT data (resolution 0.5 degrees latitude x 0.5 degrees longitude) for Winters 1980-81 and 1981-82 were used to observe both short-term and long-term variations in the microwave signatures of snow-covered terrain. Nighttime data averaged over 6-day periods were employed.

The water equivalent values were divided into 25-mm ranges. Consequently, range 1 was from 0 to 25 mm, range 2 from 25 to 50 mm etc. An average ΔT response for each water equivalent range in Southern Finland was then observed. The number of 6-day periods considered was 14 for Winter 1980-81 and 13 for Winter 1981-82. For both winters, only the last period is for wet snow.

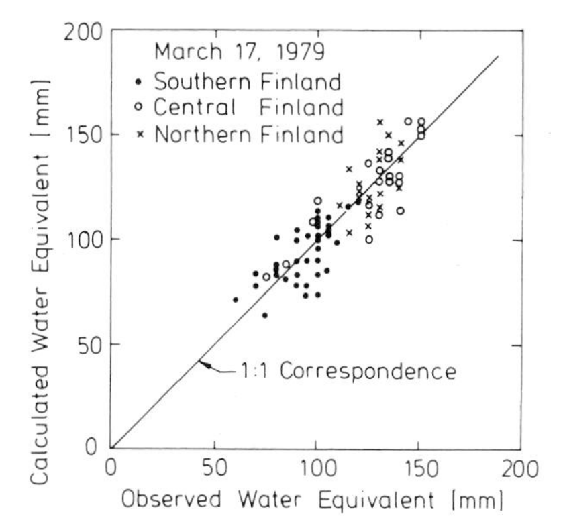

FIG.5 Comparison of satellite-derived and observed water equivalent values in Finland. Linear correlation coefficient R = 0.76 (March 17, 1979).

The results are shown in Figure 6. Ideally, all the responses for dry snow should form a single curve. The spread of the responses is a measure of the algorithm's sensitivity to different snow conditions.

Comparison between the results for Winters 1980-81 and 1981-82 shows that the absolute level of the ΔT response is substantially lower for 1980-81 than for 1981-82. This is obviously caused by the differences between the snow conditions for the two winters. In 1980-81 the snow depth was considerably above the average. Frequent snowfalls kept the average grain

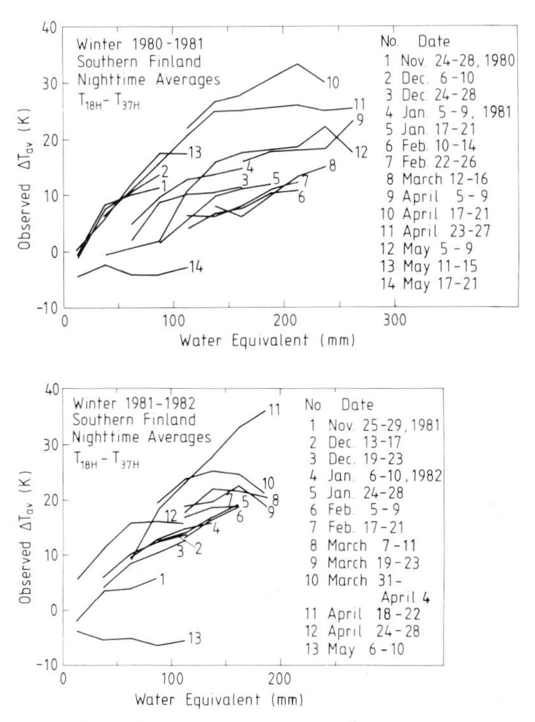

FIG.6 Observed average ΔT response (Eq. (3)) to snow water equivalent in Southern Finland for winters 1980-1981 and 1981-1982.

size small in the topmost snow layers. In 1981-82 fewer snowfalls occurred, making the surface layer to go through several melt-freeze cycles. This obviously resulted in increased grain size and high response.

Conclusions

Spaceborne microwave radiometers can provide information on snow-cover parameters on a global basis. Using a simple algorithm, the water equivalent of dry snow can be retrieved from radiometer data with satisfactory accuracy if a single surface type (farmland etc.) dominates in the measurement area. In the case of mixed surface types (farmland, forests, etc.), the contribution from each land-cover category has to be considered separately in the algorithm. Three distinct response classes exist: early and mid-winter, spring (after melt-freeze cycles), and melting period (wet snow). Variations in the snow conditions from winter to winter may change the response for each class.

References

Hallikainen, M., 1984, Retrieval of snow water equivalent from Nimbus-7 SMMR data: Effect of land-cover categories and weather conditions: IEEE J. Oceanic Engineering, Vol. OE-9, pp. 372-376.

Künzi, K., Patil, S., Rott, H., 1982, Snow-cover parameters retrieved from Nimbus-7 scanning multichannel microwave radiometer (SMMR) data; IEEE Trans. on Geoscience and Remote Sensing, Vol. GE-20, pp. 452-467.

Rango, A., Hartline, B., Eds., 1982, Plan of Research for Snowpack Properties Remote Sensing - $(PRS)^2$; Recommendations of the Snowpack Properties Working Group: Greenbelt, MD, NASA Goddard Space Flight Center.

Abdelrazik, M., 1984, The dielectric behavior of snow in the 3- to 37-GHz range. PhD Thesis, University of Kansas.

Hydrologic Applications of Space Technology (Proceedings of the Cocoa Beach Workshop, Florida, August 1985). IAHS Publ. no. 160, 1986.

Prospects of microwave remote sensing for snow hydrology

HELMUT ROTT
Institute of Meteorology & Geophysics,
University of Innsbruck, Austria

Abstract
Emission and backscattering characteristics of snow-covered terrain in the microwave region are briefly reviewed. The capabilities of past and present spaceborne microwave sensors in regard to snow cover monitoring are summarized. An outlook is given on the capabilities of microwave sensors on future satellites in respect to snow hydrology. Specifications are provided for an optimum microwave system for snow cover monitoring based on a multichannel imaging microwave radiometer and on a synthetic aperture radar system.

Introduction
Efficient monitoring of the snow cover is possible by use of satellite remote sensing methods, which are able to provide improved temporal and spatial coverage. For operational use in hydrology microwave techniques are very promising because microwaves are able to penetrate clouds and therefore to provide data on the snow cover in regular time intervals. Another advantage is the possibility to detect the depth and water equivalent of dry snow because of the penetration capability.

However, while visible and infrared satellite data on the snow cover are in regular use for modelling and forecasting snowmelt runoff, the applications of microwave data in snow hydrology are still very limited. This is partly due to the experimental character of the relevant satellite missions and partly due to the system specifications which have not been optimum for snow applications. Recognizing the needs for improved snow cover monitoring in hydrology and water management, the capabilities of previous and present satellite microwave systems are reviewed and possibilities for improvements are discussed in this paper.

The snow cover parameters of main interest for hydrology are the areal extent, the water equivalent, and the liquid water content (or at least qualitative information on the melting condition). The requirements of spatial resolution and temporal repetition rate cover a wide range depending on basin size and type and on the application (Herschy et al., 1985). Typical repetition rates are between 1 and 7 days, typical numbers for the spatial resolution are between 100 m and 1 km.

Microwave Interaction with Snow
A simplified illustration of microwave emission and scattering processes from snow covered ground is shown in Figure 1, neglecting atmospheric effects and multiple scattering. The measured brightness temperature may include contributions from the snow layer and from the underlying ground. The radiation emitted or reflected at the soil surface is absorbed and scattered in the snowpack in dependence of the wavelength and of the dielectric properties. A radar beam incident on snow covered terrain is scattered at the air/snow boundary, in the snow volume, and at the snow/ground boundary.

For the interpretation of microwave emission and scattering it is essential to consider the magnitude of the different contributions which is

dependent on the transmittance of the snowpack decribed by the penetration depth δ_p. For a uniform medium δ_p is related to the extinction coefficient k_e by: $\delta_p = 1/k_e$
where k_e is given by the absorption coefficient k_a and the scattering coefficient k_s: $k_e = k_a + k_s$.

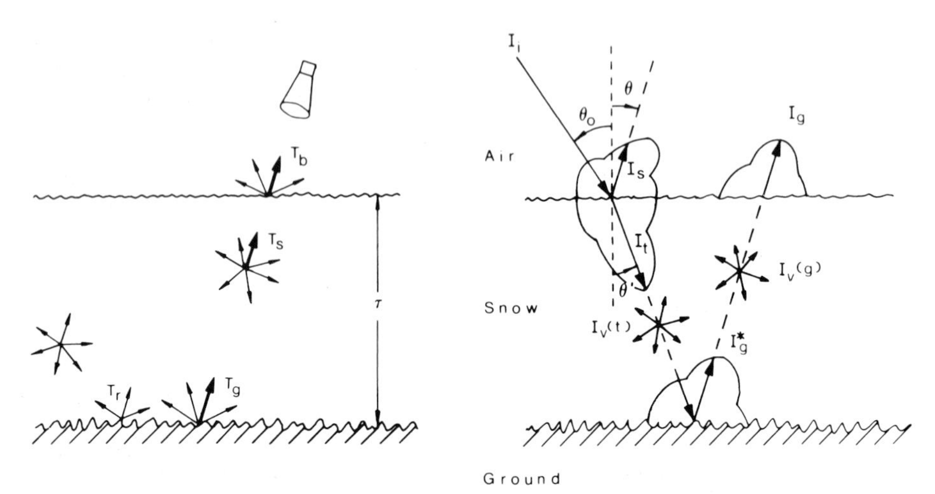

FIG.1 Simplified illustration of emission and backscattering from snow-covered ground.

T_b - brightness temperature of the snow-ground medium.

T_g - emission at the ground surface.

T_r - reflection at the ground surface.

T_s - emission due to volume scattering.

τ - optical thickness of the snow layer.

Scattering contributions:
I_s - from the air/snow interface.

$I_v(t)$ - volume scattering of the transmitted beam.

I_g^* - from the snow/ground interface.

$I_v(g)$ - volume scattering of I_g^*.

I_g - I_g^* after transmission through the snowpack.

In case of wet snow the simplification $k_e \approx k_a$ is possible at microwave frequencies because the absorption losses are significantly larger than the scattering losses. Due to the high dielectric losses δ_p of wet snow is in the order of one wavelength only so that the soil contribution is of no relevance. This results in the following typical signatures of wet snow:

- The brightness temperature is comparatively high because wet snow radiates almost like a black body.
- The backscattering coefficient is low (apart from angles near specular reflection).

For dry snow the penetration depth is 2 to 3 orders of magnitude larger than for wet snow. At 40 GHz ($\lambda = 0.75$ cm) δ_p is less than 1 m, at 10 GHz ($\lambda = 3.0$ cm) δ_p is about 10 m. δ_p is reduced by layering and inhomogeneities in the snowpack. Backscattering from a dry snowpack is insignificantly in the L- to X-band range (< 11 GHz) where existing airborne and spaceborne SAR systems are operating. The contribution from the ground surface is dominating in the backscattering signal. Volume scattering effects are strongly increasing with frequency and at frequencies $\gtrsim 15$ to 20 GHz backscattering and emission from a dry snow volume are significant.

For mapping of snow-covered areas the discrimination against snow-free surfaces is of importance. This is illustrated in the Figures 2 and 3 showing typical microwave emission and backscattering signatures of snow-covered and snow-free ground at incidence angles $\theta = 50°$ in dependence of frequency. The variability of natural targets may result in considerable scattering around the plotted curves.

Considering the emission, dry soil and wet snow show little variation with the frequency and reveal similar brightness temperatures T_b. For wet soil the T_b-values are significantly lower and show an increase with frequency. For dry snow T_b is decreasing with increasing frequency; the decrease depends on the thickness and density of the scattering snow layer and on the size of the scattering particles. The frequency-dependence of T_b, which is derived from measurements at two or more frequencies $\gtrsim 15$ GHz, enables clear discrimination of dry snow and can be related to the water equivalent of the snow layer.

The backscattering coefficient σ^o shows an increase with frequency

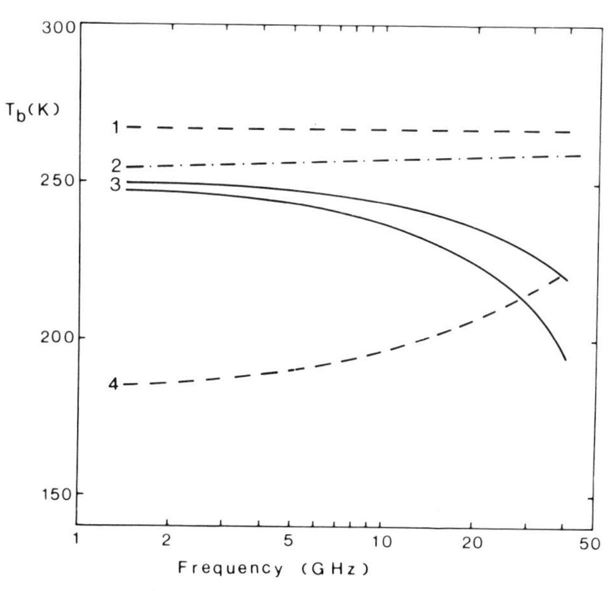

FIG.2 Typical values of the brightness temperatures at horizontal polarization and at an incidence angle of 50° for: (1) dry soil, (2) wet snow, (3) dry snow of different depth, (4) very wet soil.

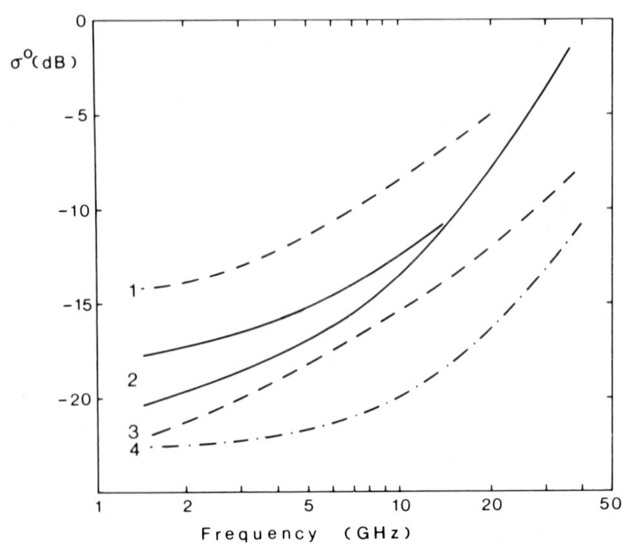

FIG.3 Typical values of the backscattering coefficient σ° at 50° incidence angle (parallel polarizations) for: (1) rough soil surfaces, (2) dry snow including different soil contributions, (3) smooth soil, (4) wet snow.

for snow covered as well as for snow-free ground. Bare soil surfaces cover a wide range of σ°-values, depending on surface roughness and wetness. For frequencies ≤ 10 GHz backscattering from soil covered with dry snow is clearly dominated from the soil contribution. At higher frequencies the increase of σ° is stronger for dry snow than for other targets. This might offer a possibility for dry snow mapping, but presently not sufficient experimental data are available on this problem. For σ° of wet snow considerable variability is found according to wetness, grain size, and surface roughness (Mätzler and Schanda, 1984), but σ° is usually lower than for most other surfaces with the exception of water and swamps. The discrimination between wet snow and snow-free ground is optimum in the 8 to 15 GHz range and at incidence angles ≳ 25°, at low frequencies smooth soil and wet snow surfaces may reveal similar σ°-values.

Snow Mapping with Spaceborne Microwave Sensors

Several active and passive microwave sensors with capabilities for snow and ice mapping have been operating on board of satellites. The active sensors (synthetic aperture radar, SAR, systems) operated on Seasat (from July to October 1978) and on Space Shuttle Flights (Shuttle Imaging Radar-A, -B). The technical characteristcs of these systems were far from the optimum for snow applications. The sensors operated in the L-band at 1.28 GHz (23.5 cm wavelength) in hh polarizations. The image resulotion was 25 m (4 looks) for Seasat and 40 m (6 looks) for SIR-A. For SIR-B the azimuth resolution was 25 m (4 looks), while the range resolution varied between 17 m and 58 m in dependence of the antenna look angle. Main differences in the SAR images resulted from the antenna look angle: 20° (off nadir) for Seasat SAR, 47° for SIR-A and selectable between 15° and 60° for SIR-B.

A considerable number of scenes on glaciers has been acquired by the spaceborne SAR systems. Investigations of these data clearly demonstrated the significance for glaciological applications; some information of relevance for seasonal snow cover mapping was also obtained (Rott, 1984a, b). The wet snow surfaces on the glaciers revealed low backscattering values, but for a variety of snow-free surfaces (e.g. meadows, alluvial deposits, soil) similar values were observed. This shows that L-band frequencies are not suitable for snow mapping even in case of wet snow; dry snow cover is transparent at these frequencies. Information for the selection of the antenna look angle could also be derived. For application in mountain areas look angles around 50 degrees are favourable, strong geometric distortions limit the usefulness of SAR data at low incidence angles. More relevant information for the definition of a snow monitoring system was gained from an airborne SAR experiment mentioned in the next paragraph.

The passive microwave imagers which have been operating on satellites revealed better capabilities for snow mapping than the radar systems. The best sensor for snow mapping hitherto has been the Scanning Multichannel Microwave Radiometer (SMMR) which was launched on Nimbus-7 in October 1978 and is still operating in 1985. As for any passive microwave system, a major drawback of SMMR is the limited spatial resolution which is determined by the antenna aperture. SMMR operates at five frequencies (6.6, 10.7, 18.0, 21.0, 37.0 GHz) in horizontal and vertical polarization and covers a swath of 780 km under an earth incidence angle of about 50°; for full global coverage 3 days of SMMR operation are required. For snow mapping the 18 GHz and 37 GHz channels are utilized, for which standard data (brightness temperatures) are produced for 60 x 60 km^2 cells (18 GHz) and 30 x 30 km^2 cells (37 GHz). This resolution is adequate for large scale climatology and for snow mapping in large drainage basins ($\gtrsim 10^5$ km^2).

Algorithms have been developed for mapping the areal extent and the water equivalent of dry snow. The onset of snowmelt and melting-refreezing snow can also be detected (Künzi et al., 1982). An empirical relation was derived between the SMMR brightness temperatures (the differences between the 18 GHz and 37 GHz channels) and snow water equivalent for test sites in Canada, Finland, and Southern Russia. The algorithm for the determination of the snow water equivalent was improved by Hallikainen (1984) who investigated the effects of major surface types in Finland on the brightness temperature of snow-covered areas. Forests, for example, mask partly the microwave emission from ground and snow so that different coefficients are used for the calculation of snow water equivalent from the SMMR data. An improvement for water equivalent determination can also be expected by including information on grain size, because microwave emission is dependent also on the size of the scattering particles. In the different investigations linear correlation coefficients of about $R^2 \approx 0.75$ were found between SMMR-derived and observed water equivalent. The SMMR algorithm can be applied only for water equivalent values $\lesssim$ 150 mm, because of the limited penetration depth at 37 GHz.

Definition of a Snow Cover Monitoring System

The specification of a microwave system for snow cover monitoring was based on the following sources:

- the analyses of spaceborne microwave data from active and passive sensors (summarized in the previous paragraph),
- emission and backscatter measurements reported in the literature,
- an airborne SAR experiment on snow mapping,
- simulations of SAR image products.

Systematic measurements on microwave emission and scattering from snow have been reported from the Institute of Applied Physics of the University of Berne (Mätzler et al., 1980; Mätzler et al., 1982; Mätzler and Schanda, 1984) and from the University of Kansas Research Center (Stiles and Ulaby, 1980; Ulaby and Stiles, 1980a, b). However, only few backscatter measurements have been carried out at higher microwave frequencies (K-band). Detailed passive microwave measurements on snow have been reported also from the Helsinki Technical University (Tiuri and Schultz, 1980).

While the conclusions from the spaceborne SAR experiments regarding snow hydrology were rather limited, an airborne experiment over an Alpine test site could provide more relevant data. During the European SAR-580 Experiment,conducted in June and July 1981 by the European Space Agency and by the Joint Research Centre of the European Communities, partly snow covered test sites in the Swiss (Mätzler and Schanda, 1984) and Austrian Alps (Rott, 1984a; Rott and Domik, 1984) were surveyed with an airborne SAR operating in the X- (at 9.4 GHz) and L-bands (at 1.3 GHz) resp. in the X- and C- (at 5.3 GHz) bands . The experiments showed very clearly that melting snow cover can be mapped with X-band and C-band SAR. For parallel polarizations (hh or vv) discrimination of snow is possible at surface incidence angles between about 25 and 80 degrees (from the normal to the surface), while at cross polarizations snow mapping is possible also at angles < 25°. However, due to the high power requirements the use of cross polarizations may not be practicable for spaceborne systems.

Detailed specifications of a spaceborne SAR system for snow mapping were elaborated in a study for the European Space Agency (Rott et al., 1985). The study included a review of theory and experiments on backscattering from snow, the analysis of airborne and spaceborne SAR data, and a simulation task. The simulations considered effects of the antenna look angle, spatial resolution, and signal to noise ratio. The investigations resulted in the definition of a SAR sensor for wet snow cover monitoring:

Frequency	X-band	
Polarizations	hh or vv	
Incidence angle	40 to 50 degrees	(off nadir)
Spatial resolution	15 to 20 m, 1 look	
Range of °	-25 dB to 0 dB	
Radiometric resolution	3 dB for 15 m x 15 m	(at -25 dB)
Radiometric accuracy	1 dB (mean)	
Image localisation	200 m	
Swath width	~ 300 km	
Data turnaround	6 h - 24 h	

The simulations clearly indicated that spatial resolutions of at least 20 m are required in complex terrain because for snow mapping averaging over a number of pixels is necessary to reduce the speckle effect. Due to the required repetition rate for snow mapping, which is in the order of a few days, significant improvements over present SAR capabilities in regard to areal coverage are required. Even with two spacecrafts the temporal requirements cannot be met in case of narrow swath radars. Therefore wide swath systems would be necessary, where high resolution images can be selected for subareas in order to reduce the data rate.

Compared to radar systems, microwave radiometers have the advantage of wide areal coverage and significantly lower data rates. However, for hydrological applications major improvements of spatial resolution over existing spaceborne radiometers are required.

For passive microwave remote sensing of snow an imaging radiometer of the SMMR-type with constant earth incidence angle of about 50° and swath width of about 1000 km appears useful. The radiometer should include at least the following frequencies, dual polarization would be useful:

one frequency in the 15 to 20 GHz range,
one freqency in the 35 to 40 GHz range,
one frequency at about 90 GHz.

Improved determination of snow water equivalent and information on the metamorphic state can be expected if 3 frequencies below 40 GHz (at about 15 GHz, 25 GHz, 38 GHz) are employed. The 90 GHz frequency is of interest for mapping snow extent because better spatial resolution can be achieved than at lower frequencies. However, dense clouds and precipitation mask the surface signals in this channel, while at frequencies 40 GHz snow mapping is possible under almost all weather conditions.

Spatial resolutions of at least 10 km should be achieved in the 20 to 40 GHz range, and 5 km for the 90 GHz channel. These requirements appear realistic when the present sensors are considered. Further improvements are highly desirable and should be possible by the development of aperture synthesis techniques.

Snow Monitoring Capabilities of Future Spaceborne Microwave Systems

During the next decade microwave remote sensing will gain a leading position withing earth observation. A variety of active and passive microwave systems are planned, but the prospects for hydrological applications are not too optimistic.

Apart from short-term missions on Space Shuttle Flights the launch of SAR systems is planned for 1989 and 1990 on the following satellites: the ESA Remote Sensing Satellite (ERS-1), the Japanese Earth Observation Satellite (J-ERS-1), and the Canadian RADARSAT.

The specifications of the SAR systems of ERS-1 (Joyce et al., 1984) and J-ERS-1 (Fukai et al., 1984) are not favorable for snow mapping. The ERS-1 SAR is designed for ocean and sea ice applications and will operate in the C-band (at 5.3 GHz), the swath width will be 80 km and the incidence angle at the swath's center will be 23° off nadir. At this angle ambiguities exist in the radar return of wet snow and other surfaces; moreover, the use in hilly and mountainous areas will be restricted due to strong geometric distortions. Also the foreseen radiometric sensitivity of -18 dB may not be sufficient for the low return signal of wet snow.

The SAR system of J-ERS-1 will operate in the L-band which according to the backscattering properties is not useful for snow mapping. The swath width will be 75 km, the incidence angle 33°.

RADARSAT will be dedicated to ice mapping, coastal zone surveys, and various land applications. The system has not yet been finally approved; it will operate in the C-band, provide a spatial resolution of 25 m and should be able to provide images within a ground range distance of about 500 km (20° to about 45° incidence angle). Because of the wide coverage this system could be of interest for snow cover monitoring.

Regarding the passive microwave systems the prospects for snow monitoring are better. The main restrictions of these sensors result from the spatial resolution; the data dissemmination problem has also to be solved.

In 1986 a scanning microwave radiometer, the Special Sensor Microwave/Imager (SSM/I) will be launched on the US Air Force DMSP satellite, a similar system is foreseen for the US-Navy N-ROSS (Navy Remote Sensing System) in 1989. The 19.35, 37 and 85.5 GHz channels of SSM/I are of interest for snow mapping, the spatial resolutions of the channels will be approximately 50 km, 25 km, and 15 km respectively. The swath width of 1400 km provides twice daily coverage at higher latitudes, so that the system is of considerable interest for large scale snow mapping. However, since DMSP and N-ROSS are military satellites, it is unlikely that hydrological users in various countries can rely on these data for operational programmes.

A real operational passive microwave system, the advanced microwave sounder unit (AMSU) is planned for the next generation of the NOAA satellites to be in operation after about 1990 (Staelin, 1984). Though AMSU is designed for atmospheric sounding, some of the channels are also of interest for earth surface observations. AMSU will probably consist of two sub-systems: AMSU-A with 15 channels between 23 and 90 GHz and about 50 km footprint size and AMSU-B with 5 channels between 90 GHz and 183 GHz and about 15 km footprint size. For snow mapping two channels below 40 GHz and a window channel at about 90 GHz could be applied. The improved resolution of the AMSU-B 90 GHz channel is of interest for snow mapping, however, the final decision on the incorporation of AMSU-B in the NOAA system has not yet been made.

Conclusions

Microwave sensors offer unique capabilities for snow cover monitoring. However, the technical and operational characteristics of existing and planned microwave systems up to the early 1990's are aiming at other applications and the prospects for use in snow hydrology are not promising. Moreover, for the operational use long-term continuity of data acquisition and fast data delivery are of vital importance.

In view of the potential of satellite systems for monitoring not only the snow cover, but also other hydrological elements, a satellite system dedicated to hydrology and water management would be highly desirable (Herschy et al., 1985). For such a system a multispectral imaging microwave radiometer is certainly a prime candidate, which can be used for monitoring extent and water equivalent of dry snow, precipitation, cloud liquid water content, and soil moisture. The spatial resolution of the sensor should be at least in the order of 5 to 10 km, and further improvements are desirable.

SAR systems would be required for supplementing the radiometers for wet snow cover mapping and for applications in complex terrain where the spatial resolution of passive sensors may not be sufficient. The capabilities of SAR for wet snow monitoring are known, the possibilities for dry snow mapping are only speculative and certainly major changes of existing SAR systems, in particular in regard to the sensing frequencies, would be required. But also a system for mapping the wet snow cover with sufficient temporal and spatial resolution could be valuable, because for snowmelt runoff the boundaries of the snow areas during the melting season are of high interest and these should be detectable with X-band SAR.

References

Fukai, M., et al., 1984, Some test results of synthetic aperture radar transmitter and receiver: Proc. IGARSS'84, ESA SP-215, p.821-825.

Hallikainen, M.T., 1984, Retrieval of snow water equivalent from Nimbus-7 SMMR data: effect of land-cover categories and weather conditions: IEEE J. of Oceanic Eng., Vol. OE-9(5), p.372-376.

Herschy, R.W., Barrett, E.C. Roozekrans, J.N., 1985, Remote Sensing in Hydrology and Water Management: Final Report, EARSeL WG10, European Space Agency, Paris, 225 p.

Joyce, H., Cox, R.P., Sawyer, F.G., 1984, The active microwave instrument for ERS-1, Proc. IGARSS'89, ESA SP-215, p.835-840.

Künzi, K., Patil, S., Rott, H., 1982, Snow cover parameters retrieved from Nimbus-7 Scanning Multichannel Microwave radiometer (SMMR) data, IEEE Trans. Geosc. Rem. Sens., Vo. GE-20, p.452-467.

Mätzler, C., Schanda, E., Hofer, R., Good, W., 1980, Microwave signatures of the natural snow cover at Weissfluhjoch. Microwave Rem. Sens. of Snowpack Properties, NASA Conf. Publ. 2153, p.147-167.

Mätzler, C., Schanda, E., Good, W., 1982, Towards the definition of optimum sensor specifications for microwave remote sensing of snow. IEEE Trans. Geosc. Rem. Sens., GE-20, p.57-66.

Mätzler, C., Schanda, E., 1984, Snow mapping with active microwave sensors. Int. J. Remote Sens., 5(2), p.409-422.

Rott, H., 1984a, The analysis of backscattering properties from SAR data of mountain regions, IEEE J. of Oceanic Eng., Special Issue on Microwave Signatures of the Sea, Sea Ice, and Snow, Vol. OE-9(5), p.347-355.

Rott, H., 1984b, Synthetic aperture radar capabilities for snow and glacier monitoring, Advances in Space Research, 4(11), p.241-246.

Rott, H., Domik G., 1984, The SAR experiment on snow and glaciers at the Austrian test site, Final Report of the European SAR-580 Campaign, JRC, Ispra, Italy, in press.

Rott, H., Domik, G., Mätzler, C., Miller, H., 1985, Study on use and characteristics of SAR for land snow and ice applications, Final Report to ESA, Mitteilungen des Instituts für Meteorologie und Geophysik, Universität Innsbruck, Nr.1 (1985).

Staelin, D.H., 1984, Passive microwave remote sensing of the atmosphere, Proc. IGARSS'84, ESA SP-215, p.413-415.

Stiles, W.H., Ulaby, F.T., 1980, Radar observations of snowpacks. Microwave Remote Sensing of Snowpack Properties, NASA Conf. Publ. 2153, p.131-146.

Ulaby, F.T., Stiles, W.H., 1980a, The active and passive microwave response to snow paramters, 2, water equivalent of dry snow, J. Geophys. Res., 85(Gl), p.1045-1049.

Ulaby, F.T., Stiles, W.H., 1980b, Microwave radiometer observations of snowpacks, Microwave Remote Sensing of Snowpack Properties, NASA Conf. Publ. 2153, p.187-201.

Tiuri, M., Schultz, H., 1980, Theoretical and experimental studies of microwave radiation from a natural snow field, Microwave Remote Sensing of Snowpack Properties, NASA Conf. Publ. 2153, p.225-234.

Hydrologic Applications of Space Technology (Proceedings of the Cocoa Beach Workshop, Florida, August 1985). IAHS Publ. no. 160, 1986.

Snow fork for field determination of the density and wetness profiles of a snow pack

MARTTI TIURI & ARI SIHVOLA
Helsinki University of Technology,
Radio Laboratory, SF-02150 Espoo, Finland

Abstract
A radiowave sensor (a snow fork) for determining the density and wetness profiles of a snow pack with a single measurement has been developed. The snow fork is based on the measurement of the dielectric properties (real and imaginary part) of snow around 1 GHz. Due to the open structure of the resonator the measurement is non-destructive. Automatic measuring equipment guarantees instantaneous measurement results that can be recorded in the field.

Introduction
In snow studies and in remote sensing applications it is important to know the dependence between the dielectric properties of snow and its density and wetness. Instruments for measuring the dielectric properties of snow in the field have been developed after Ambach /1/ first suggested a method to measure the wetness of snow through its dielectric properties. With these methods, the real part of the permittivity of wet snow must be measured and, by weighing, the density of snow. From these the wetness of snow can be calculated.

In this paper an instrument for field studies of snow packs will be presented which measures non-destructively both the real part and the imaginary part of the complex permittivity of snow at the same time. From these two values both the density and wetness of snow can be determined. This eliminates the need of a separate density measurement.

Previous field measurement systems
The snow sensors developed in Austria /2/ operate at relatively low frequencies ($f < 100$ MHz). They use air gap condensers as dielectric sensors and alternating current bridges (a Twin-T-bridge or a Wien-Robinson-bridge) as sensor electronics. The condensers consist of 7 stainless-steel plates, 10×10 cm^2, 1.5 mm in thickness, and a spacing of 2.1 cm. The sensor electronics have been optimized for different operating frequencies, and, after completed tuning, the dielectric constant can be calculated through a simple formula /2/.

The Swiss snow research group has developed two snow sensors appropriate to usage in the field, namely a quarter-wavelength coaxial resonator and a "saw" resonator /2/, /3/, /4/. The coaxial resonator penetrates partly in the snow the penetration depth being adjustable. The sensor therefore only measures the properties of the uppermost layer of the snow cover. The desired dielectric properties result as a solution of a transcendental equation. The saw resonator is specially suitable for hard materials. It is a parallel-wire resonator and the wire line consists of the real saw blade and its mirror image. Both sensors operate at the 1 GHz region.

The dependence between the dielectric properties and the density and the wetness
The present snow sensor is based on the simultaneous measurement of both the real part and the imaginary part of the dielectric constant of snow.

Latest studies of the dielectric properties of snow show that the knowledge of these allows both the density and the wetness to be determined /5/, /6/. The imaginary part of the dielectric constant is directly related to the wetness and the real part is dependent on the density and wetness.

From the reported results and from the additional measurements made by the Finnish snow research group the following formulas explaining the dielectric properties of snow have been discovered /5/:

$$\varepsilon_d' = 1 + 1{,}7\rho_d + 0{,}7\rho_d^2 \qquad (1)$$

$$\Delta\varepsilon_s' = \varepsilon_s' - \varepsilon_d' = (0{,}10\ W + 0{,}80\ W^2)\varepsilon_w' \qquad (2)$$

$$\varepsilon_s'' = (0{,}10\ W + 0{,}80\ W^2)\varepsilon_w'' \qquad (3)$$

where

ε_d' is the real part of the permittivity of dry snow
ε_s' is the real part of the permittivity of snow
ε_s'' is the imaginary part of the permittivity of snow
ρ_d is the "dry density" of snow relative to the density of water (the density of snow when all liquid water in it is replaced by air)
ρ_s is the density of wet snow relative to the density of water
W is the wetness by volume
$\rho_d = \rho_s - W$
$\varepsilon_w = \varepsilon_w' - j\varepsilon_w''$ is the complex permittivity of water ($\varepsilon_w = 88 - j9{,}8$ at 1 GHz)

The effect of liquid water on the complex permittivity of wet snow is equal for both the real part and the imaginary part. The formulas (1), (2), and (3) are frequency-independent (i.e. $\Delta\varepsilon_s'$ and ε_s'' follow the frequency-dependence of water) in the microwave range where ice is dispersionless.

Figure 1 illustrates the dielectric properties of snow as a function of

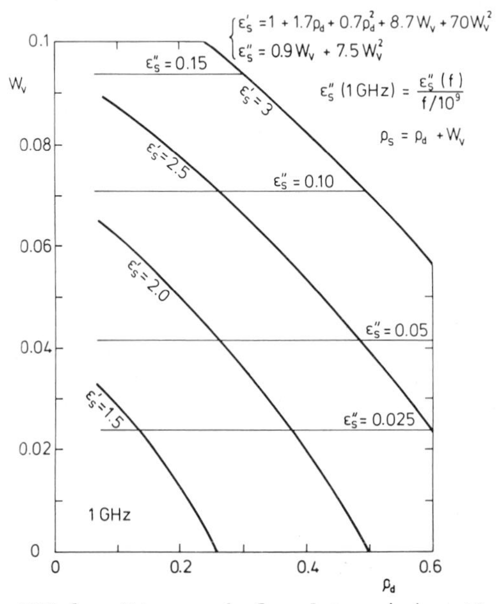

FIG.1 Nomograph for determining the wetness and density of snow from its complex dielectric constant at 1 GHz.

its dry density and wetness at 1 GHz according to the formulas above. The permittivity at other frequencies in the frequency range 1 MHz ... 4 GHz can be accurately calculated knowing that the real part is constant and the loss tangent increases linearly with frequency /5/.

Snow fork

Mechanical design

The snow sensor developed at the Radio Laboratory, Helsinki University of Technology, consists of a resonator that can be pushed into snow or any other porous, granular, or liquid material which is to be measured. The resonator is a parallel-wire transmission-line resonator that is open-circuited at the one end and short-circuited at the other one according to Figure 2.

The purpose of the resonator is to find out the complex permittivity of the material under measurement. This is achieved by measuring the change in the resonance curve of the resonator when it is pushed into snow. When the sensor is put into snow the real part of the permittivity of snow lowers the resonant frequency and the imaginary part broadens the resonance curve also increasing the attenuation at the resonant frequency.

The length of the wires of the resonator is about a quarter of the wave-length in the resonance. A resonant frequency in air around 1 GHz makes the dimensions of the resonator suitable.

High-frequency power is fed in and out through rigid coaxial cables and coupling loops. The cables are coated and supported by a glass fiber pipe which forms a solid stock. The coupling loops are protected by epoxy plastic.

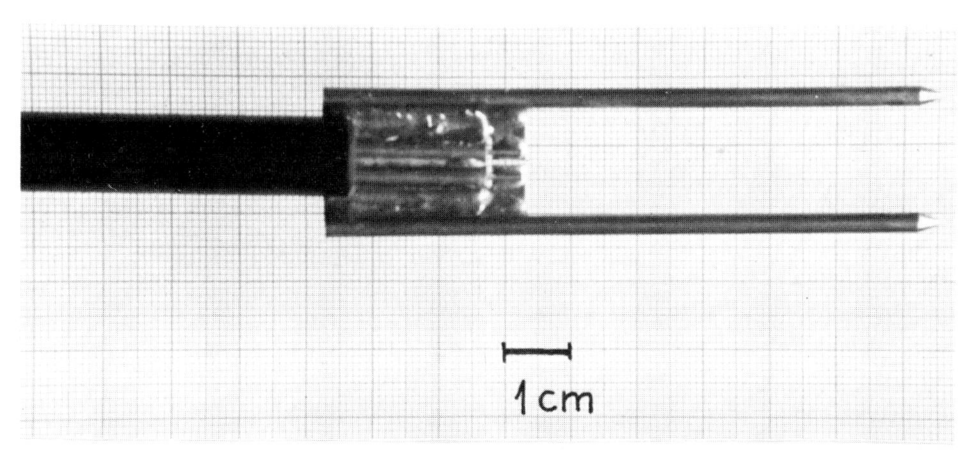

FIG.2 The snow fork.

The wires are made of stainless steel and they are sharpened at the end which makes the structure easy to push into snowpack even through a possible crust. However, the wires are thin enough so that the measurement operation does not deform snow and change the density considerably. This property, the absence of destructiveness, means a great advantage compared to other measurement systems.

Electrical design

If the resonant frequency of the resonator in air is f_a and f_s when put in snow the real part of the permittivity of snow is

$$\varepsilon_s' = \left(\frac{f_a}{f_s}\right)^2 . \qquad (4)$$

The calculation of the imaginary part ε_s'' or the loss factor $\tan\delta_s = \varepsilon_s''/\varepsilon_s'$ is more complicated. Owing to the open structure the resonator has radiation losses which broaden the resonance curve and lower the quality factor. Unloaded Q-values of sensors described in this paper are between 40 and 70. The smaller the separation between the wires is, the higher is the Q-value.

When Δf_a is the 3-dB bandwidth of the resonance curve in air, the inverse of the loaded quality factor is

$$\frac{1}{Q_{L_a}} = \frac{\Delta f_a}{f_a} \; . \tag{5}$$

When the resonator is pushed in to snow the dielectric losses of snow broaden the resonance curve. If in the snow the loaded quality factor is Q_{L_s} and the 3 dB bandwidth is Δf_s

$$\frac{1}{Q_{L_s}} = \frac{\Delta f_s}{f_s} = \frac{1}{Q_{L_\varepsilon}} + \frac{1}{Q_s} \tag{6}$$

where Q_{L_ε} is the loaded quality factor of the resonator in a lossless material with the same real part of the permittivity as the snow and Q_s is the dielectric quality factor of the snow ($1/Q_s = \tan\delta_s$, loss factor of the snow).

The loaded quality factor Q_{L_ε} depends on the frequency. It has to be calibrated by measuring $1/Q_{L_\varepsilon} = \Delta f_\varepsilon / f_\varepsilon$ when the sensor os surrounded by different lossless materials (or such materials whose losses are precisely known).

Hence when the loaded quality factor in snow is measured the loss factor of snow can be calculated:

$$\frac{\varepsilon_s''}{\varepsilon_s'} = \tan\delta_s = \frac{\Delta f_s}{f_s} - \frac{1}{Q_{L_\varepsilon}} = \frac{\Delta f_s - \Delta f_\varepsilon}{f_s} \tag{7}$$

Figure 3 shows the relation between the values of ε_s' and ε_s'' and the values of f_s and Δf_s for a sensor that has a resonant frequency of 844 MHz in air.

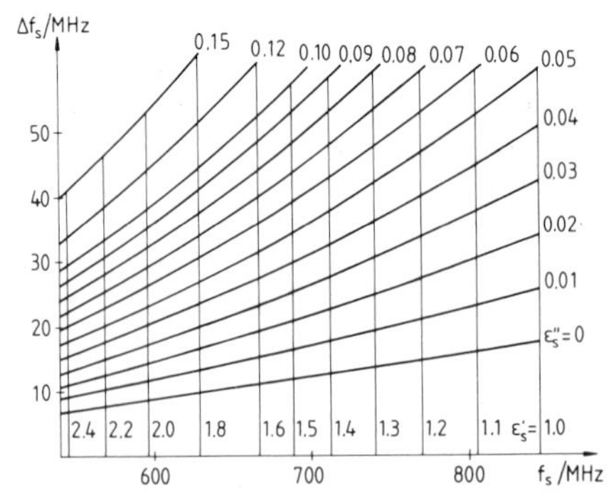

FIG.3 The permittivity curves of a fork with air resonance at 844 MHz.

The complete measuring system

In order to have real-time results of the permittivity of snow the measurement is automatized. The system consists of a voltage controlled oscillator and electronics for calculating the resonant frequency, the attenuation, the 3-dB bandwidth, and the real part of the permittivity. These values and information about the depth of the sensor in the snowpack are recorded on the tape in the field using a lightweight instrumentation recorder. The whole system is portable weighing around 2 kg.

Figure 4 shows a measured density and wetness profile.

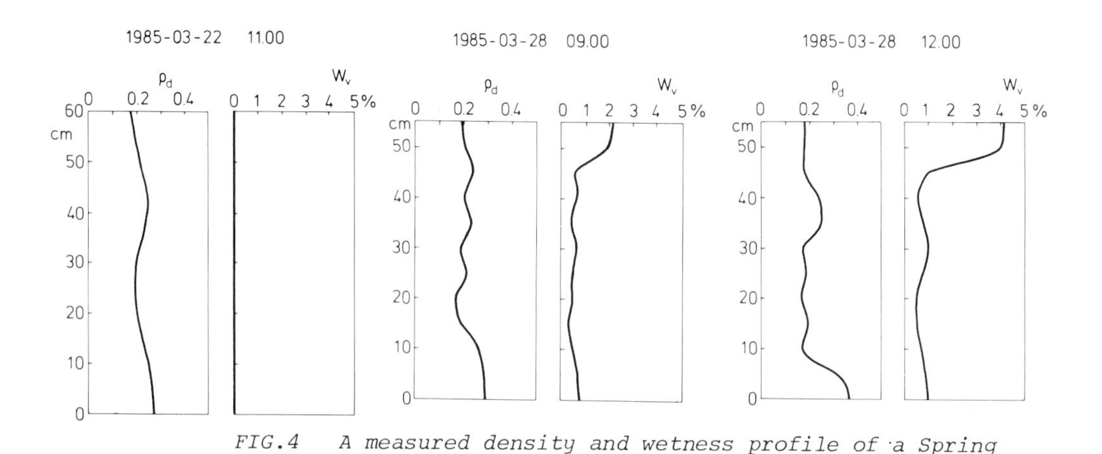

FIG.4 A measured density and wetness profile of a Spring snowpack.

Accuracy of the measurement

One source of error in measuring compressible materials with the fork is that the spikes, though thin, press the material to be measured and increase the density of the material in the neighbourhood of the spikes. However, the magnitude of this error can be estimated by solving the potential problem of the parallel-wire TEM-line. The relative error in measuring the real part of the dielectric constant can be shown to be 1,5 - 3 % depending on its absolute value.

In measuring dielectric materials with the snow fork the accuracy for the resonant frequency can be approximated to be ± 5 MHz, that for the bandwidth of the resonance peak ± 5 percent, and that for the attenuation ± 1 dB. This leads to 1.5% - error in ε_S' for snow with the relative density 0.5, and 3% - error in the density estimation calculated through the dielectric measurement. The relative accuracy in wetness determination will be about 10 percent when the wetness is around 0.01 and less than 5 percent when the wetness is 0.05 or more.

The method assumes that the snow to be measured is relatively clean (has a pH-value close to seven). If the snow is dirty its losses increase and the measurement gives too high values for the wetness. A correction can be made if the pH-value is known /5/.

References

1. W.Ambach, W.Bitterlich, F.Howorka: Ein Gerät zur Bestimmung des freien Wassergehaltes in der Schneedecke durch dielektrische Messung. Acta Physica Austriaca, Band XX, Heft 1-4, 1965.
2. A.Denoth, A.Foglar, P.Weiland, Ch.Mätzler, H.Aebischer, M.Tiuri, A.Sihvola: A comparative study of instruments for measuring the liquid water content of snow. Journal of Applied Physics, Vol. 56, No. 7, p. 2154-2160, 1984.

3. H.Aebischer: Methoden zur Messung der Schneefeuchtigkeit mit Hilfe von Mikrowellen. Lizentiatarbeit, Universität Bern, Institut für Angewandte Physik, 1983.
4. H.Aebisher, Ch.Mätzler: A microwave sensor for the measurement of the liquid water content on the surface of the snow cover. 13th European Microwave Conference, Nürnberg, Microwave Exhibitions and Publishers Ltd, Kent, England, 1983.
5. M. Tiuri, A. Sihvola, E. Nyfors, M. Hallikainen: The complex dielectric constant of snow at microwave frequencies. IEEE Journal of Oceanic Engineering, Vol OE-9, No 5, p. 377-382, 1984.
6. M.Tiuri, A.Sihvola, E.Nyfors: Microwave sensor for snowpack wetness and density profile measurement. 12th European Microwave Conference, Helsinki, Microwave Exhibitions and Publishers Ltd, Kent, England, 1982.

5 Miscellaneous applications

Hydrologic Applications of Space Technology (Proceedings of the Cocoa Beach Workshop, Florida, August 1985). IAHS Publ. no. 160, 1986.

Monitoring suspended sediments with remote sensing techniques

JERRY C. RITCHIE
USDA-ARS Hydrology Laboratory, Beltsville, Maryland 20705, USA
FRANK R. SCHIEBE
USDA-ARS Water Quality & Watershed Research Laboratory, Durant, Oklahoma 74702, USA

Abstract

Suspended sediments are a major factor affecting water quality of agricultural impoundments. Research was undertaken to develop remote sensing techniques which could be used to monitor suspended sediments in these impoundments. Research on the remote sensing of high concentrations (greater than 50 mg l^{-1}) of suspended sediments in surface waters of an agricultural impoundment was carried out by 1) making laboratory measurements under carefully controlled conditions using a large optical tank facility where sediment collected from Lake Chicot had been resuspended; 2) making in situ measurements using a hand-held spectroradiometer over the surface of the Lake Chicot; and 3) using data obtained from 33 Landsat MSS scenes of Lake Chicot.

The laboratory and hand-held radiometer measurements showed that radiance or reflectance in the near infrared region, 700 to 900 nm, is significantly related to suspended sediments over a wide range of concentrations. The analysis of Landsat showed that MSS bands 5 and 6 radiance or reflectance were best correlated with suspended sediments.

These studies under three different conditions have shown that it should be possible to develop a technique to monitor suspended sediments in agricultural and other water bodies using remote sensing technology. With such a technique, a conservation agency could better plan land conservation practices to improve water quality of those impoundments where the suspended sediments problem are greatest.

Introduction

Suspended sediments are a major problem around the world. These suspended sediments affect water quality in lakes and reservoirs (Cooper et al. 1984; Ritchie 1972) and can be used as an indicator of erosion problems in the watershed.

Many studies have shown that suspended materials can be detected using remote sensing techniques. However, most of these studies have been in marine waters, estuaries, and large lakes where suspended sediments are usually less than 50 mg l^{-1}. In agricultural impoundments suspended sediment concentrations are usually greater than 50 mg l^{-1}, especially in those watersheds having significant erosion problems. Conservation agencies need techniques which can be used to monitor vast areas quickly to locate those reservoirs that have significant suspended sediment problems. With such a technique a conservation agency would be better able to locate and to concentrate their efforts on those watersheds having the most significant erosion problems.

The purpose of this study was to evaluate remote sensing techniques for monitoring suspended sediment concentrations that are typical (greater than 50 mg l^{-1}) of agricultural impoundments. Studies were made in the laboratory, in situ with a portable spectroradiometer, and with Landsat multispectral scanner (MSS) images. This paper discusses the results of these three studies.

Study Area

Lake Chicot, a large natural lake in southeastern Arkansas, was chosen as the study site. The lake was formed in an old cutoff channel of the Mississippi River. Levee construction along the Mississippi River and channel improvement in the watershed has increased the watershed size from approximately 100 km^2 to 930 km^2.

Land use change from native forest and wetlands to agriculture has resulted in increased erosion potential and sediment delivery to the lake. The suspended sediments in Lake Chicot has reduced the biological productivity (Cooper et al. 1984) and the "aesthetic" value of the lake. These factors have combined to reduce the recreational use of the lake and brought complaints from the local people. The U. S. Army Corps of Engineers has undertaken a program to improve the water quality in the lake (Price et al. 1984).

A summary of 6 years of physical, chemical, and biological data on Lake Chicot has been published (Nix and Schiebe 1984). This history of limnological data, as well as the "visible" suspended sediment problems make this lake an ideal study site. Lake Chicot (Fig. 1) is divided into a north and south basin by a causeway and road. The south basin receives runoff from approximately 900 km^2 mostly row crop (cotton and soybeans)

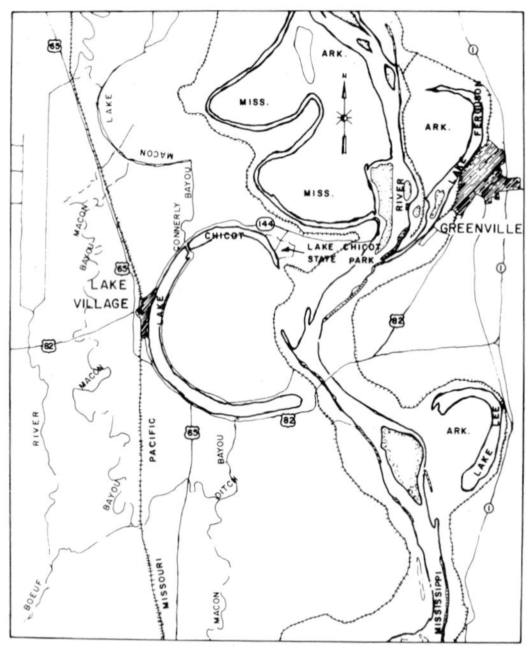

FIG.1 Map of Lake Chicot, Arkansas.

watershed. The north basin receives only ephermial runoff from its smaller watershed. The south basin has higher total and suspended sediments than the north basin (Fig. 2). The lake is 0.8 km wide and 25 km long; thus it can be easily found on Landsat MSS scenes and even NOAA Advanced Very High Resolution Radiometer (AVHRR) scenes.

Although Lake Chicot is larger than typical agricultural reservoirs,

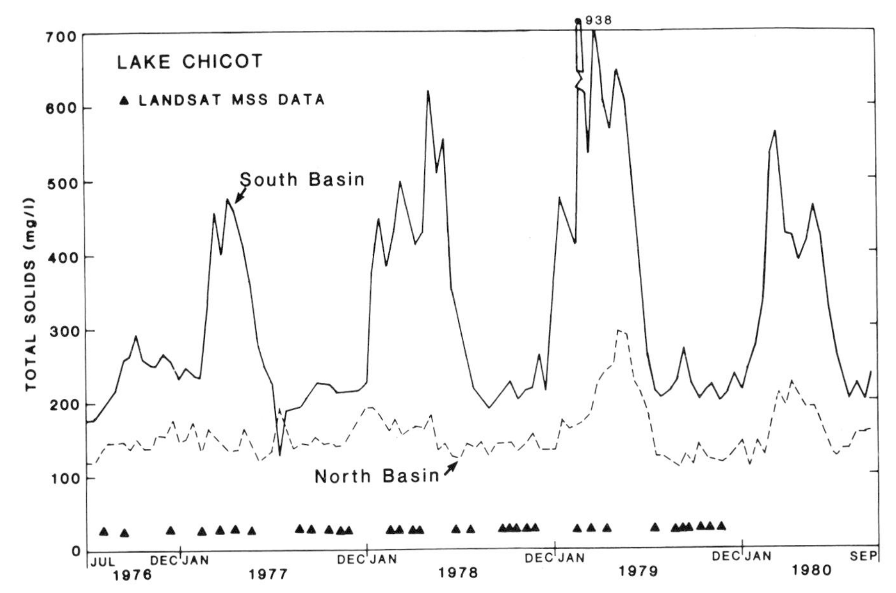

FIG.2 Concentration of total solids in the north and south basins of Lake Chicot. Solid triangles show dates of Landsat MSS images analysed.

its suspended sediment concentrations (Fig. 2) are typical of the suspended sediment concentrations in impoundments that have erosion problems on their watersheds. Thus, Lake Chicot provided a good research site for studying high suspended sediment concentrations in the surface water of a lake.

Methods and Materials

Sediment samples were collected from Lake Chicot and taken to the National Aeronautic and Space Administration's (NASA) Marine Upwelled Spectral Signature Laboratory (MUSSL) at the Langley Research Center in Hampton, Virginia. The sediments were resuspended in a 11,600 liter tank which is illuminated by a 32,280 $\ell m\ m^{-2}$ artificial light source. Radiance was measured above the water surface in the tank with a scanning spectroradiometer. Suspended sediment concentrations from 0 to 700 mg l^{-1} were used in the experiment. Water samples from the tank were tested for total sediments, suspended sediments, dissolved organic carbon, total organic carbon, particulate organic carbon, chlorophyll, iron, copper, sediment mineralogy and particle size distribution. Spectral radiance measurements were made from 400 to 1000 nanometers (nm). More detailed discussion of the MUSSL facility and research techniques are given by Whitlock (1977), Witte et al. (1979) and Freidman et al. (1980).

In situ measurements of the upwelled radiance and incident radiation spectra were made at 20 to 50 cm above the water surface on Lake Chicot using a portable spectroradiometer from a small boat. The portable spectroradiometer was equipped with a teflon diffusing screen and a 2.95 meter fiber optical conduit. Upwelled radiance was measured normal to the surface and incident radiation was measured at 180° from the lake surface. Measurements were made on cloud free days and over water whose depth was at least 3 times secchi depth. The spectroradiometer was calibrated before and after each day of use. Measurements were made at 25 nm intervals from 400 to 1500 nm. The data were expressed in microwatts per square centimeter per namometer ($\mu W\ cm^{-2} nm^{-1}$). Reflectance was calculated as the ratio of upwelled radiance to incident radiation.

Thirty-three Landsat MSS scenes of Lake Chicot (path 025 row 037) between July 1976 and November 1979 (Fig. 2) were analyzed. Film negatives of the 4 MSS bands were purchased for the 33 scenes. Computer compatible tapes (CCT) were purchased for 10 of the 33 scenes.

Digital values for the 33 Landsat film negatives were determined by densiotometer analysis as described in the Landsat User's Guide (USGS 1979). Digital data were extracted from the 10 Landsat CCT's and used to verify the densiotometer measurements from the same ten images. The two data set were highly correlated ($r^2 = 0.98$). The regression equation from this comparison was used to produce a consistent data set from the 33 scenes.

The Landsat digital data were converted to radiance in milliwatts per square centimeter per steradian ($mW\ cm^{-2}\ sr^{-1}$) and reflectance (Robinove 1982, Richardson et al. 1980, Richardson 1982) so that the data would be the same for the 4-year period, since scenes from Landsat 1, 2, and 3 were used. The Landsat scenes were sampled in the north and south basin to produce 63 observations of MSS data. More details of the Landsat analyses is given in Ritchie et al. (1985).

Water samples for the in situ and Landsat studies were made by collecting two grab samples of the upper 2 cm of the water column on each sampling date. Total, dissolved, and suspended sediment concentration were measured on each sample. Secchi depth was measured at each collection site. Particle size analysis was made on selected samples. More details on field measurements and laboratory techniques are given in Ritchie et al. (1976, 1983) and Nix and Schiebe (1984).

Results and Discussion

Laboratory Studies

Upwelled radiance measurements made over the MUSSL tank with resuspended Lake Chicot sediments showed that reflectance (Fig. 3) changed little for

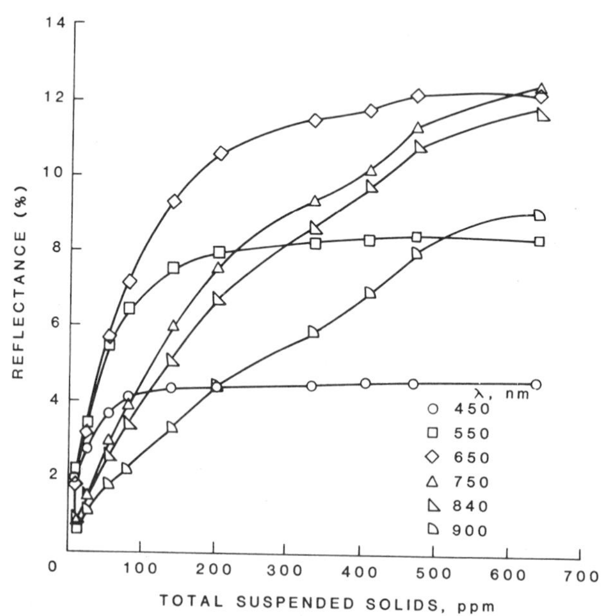

FIG.3 Laboratory measurements of reflectance as a function of total suspended solids at different wavelengths (adapted from Whitlock et al., 1981).

wavelengths between 400 and 600 nm when suspended sediments were greater than 100 mg l^{-1}. At suspended sediment concentrations less than 100 mg l^{-1} there was separation of signal at those wavelengths. For wavelengths between 600 and 900 nm, there was good separation of the radiance and reflectance signals for all suspended sediment concentrations (5 to 690 mg l^{-1}) used in the tank. Both the upwelled radiance and reflectance were a linear function of total and suspended sediments over the range of concentrations used for wavelengths between 650 and 900 nm (Whitlock et al. 1981). The good signal discrimination in these laboratory studies between 650 and 900 nm would indicate that an algorithm to estimate high concentrations suspended sediments from remote sensing data could be developed. Atmospheric transmission losses due to adsorption at wavelengths greater than 900 nm would probably limit using the higher wavelengths. The laboratory studies indicated that other factors influence the measured radiance; however, suspended sediments clearly dominated the radiance response. Thus, the laboratory studies indicate that an algorithm to estimate suspended sediments could be developed from radiance or reflectance data.

In Situ Studies

A portable spectroradiometer was used to make in situ measurements of the upwelled radiance from the surface of Lake Chicot between July 1976 and December 1977. These studies showed that the intensity and spectral distribution of radiance varied with the suspended sediment concentration (Fig. 4). As suspended sediment increased, the difference in radiance changed, especially between 600 and 900 nm. At the lower wavelengths the change in radiance with increased suspended sediments was small. There was also a shift in the spectral distribution of radiance toward the red wavelengths. Above 900 nm no significant patterns in intensity or spectral distribution was found.

Analyses of the radiance or reflectance data by wavelength showed that at wavelengths below 600 nm the radiance or reflectance data tended to saturate when suspended sediments were between 50 and 100 mg l^{-1} and especially at concentrations greater than 100 mg l^{-1}. However, the saturation did not occur as fast or as strongly as had been seen in the laboratory studies. Good signal separation in both radiance and reflectance was found between 600 and 900 nm for different suspended sediment concentrations. The response curve at 800 nm (Figs. 5 and 6) appeared to be nearly linear for the range of suspended sediments measured.

Even though the response curves were not linear over all wavelengths, linear regression analysis gave the best fits for the relationship between total or suspended sediments and radiance or reflectance at all wavelengths. Statistically significant correlation coefficients (r) between total solids or suspended sediments and radiance or reflectance were found between 450 and 900 nm (Figs. 7 and 8) with the best correlations between 700 and 900 nm. Suspended sediments had 2 to 5 percent higher correlation coefficients than total solids with radiance or reflectance between 600 and 900 nm.

Correcting the data for Fresnel reflectance due to sun angle improved the correlation coefficients by 2 to 4 percent. Reflectance data corrected for sun angle had an r value of 0.96 for suspended sediments at 725, 750 and 800 nm. Thus, the calculated equations would account for 92 percent of the variability.

The analyses of the in situ radiance and reflectance data found that a linear regression of suspended sediment and radiance or reflectance could be used effectively to estimate suspended sediments with concentrations up to 500 mg l^{-1}. Thus, as with the laboratory, the study showed that

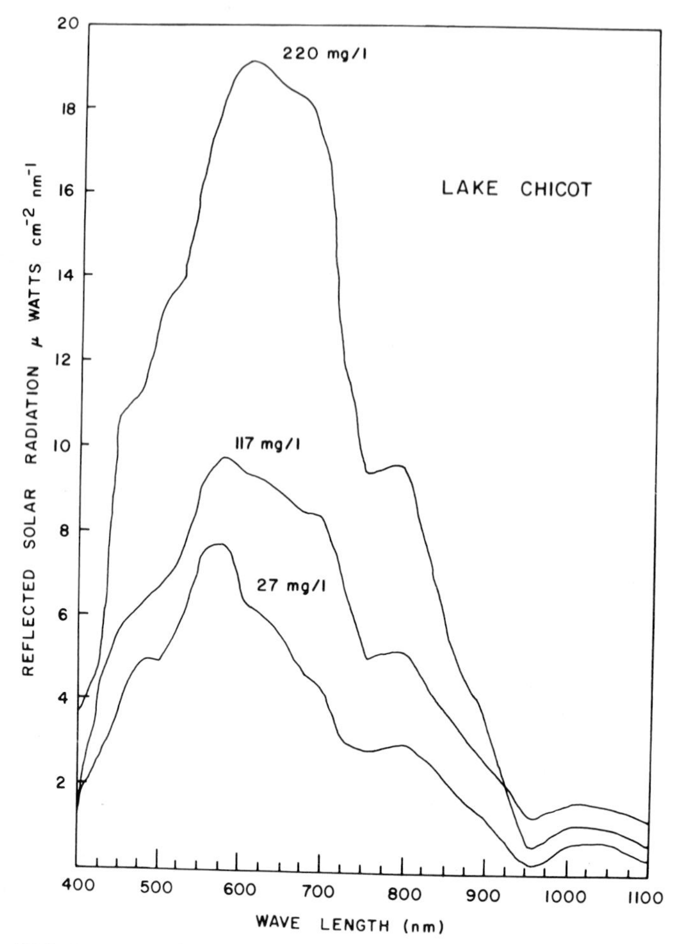

FIG.4 In situ measurements of radiance as a function of wavelengths for different concentrations of suspended sediments.

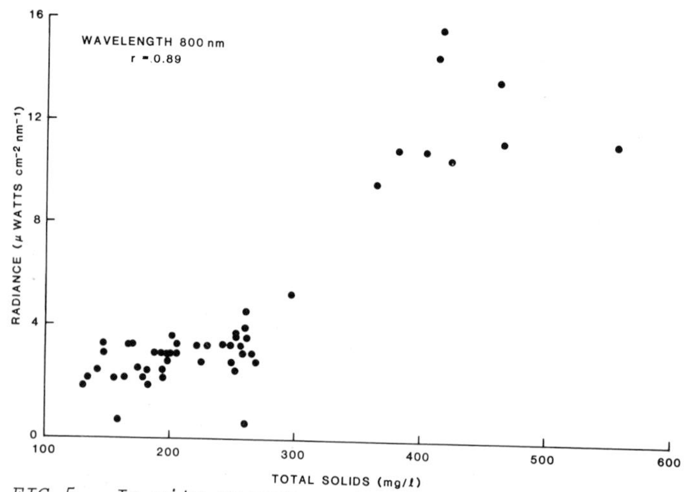

FIG.5 In situ measurements of radiance for different concentrations of total solids.

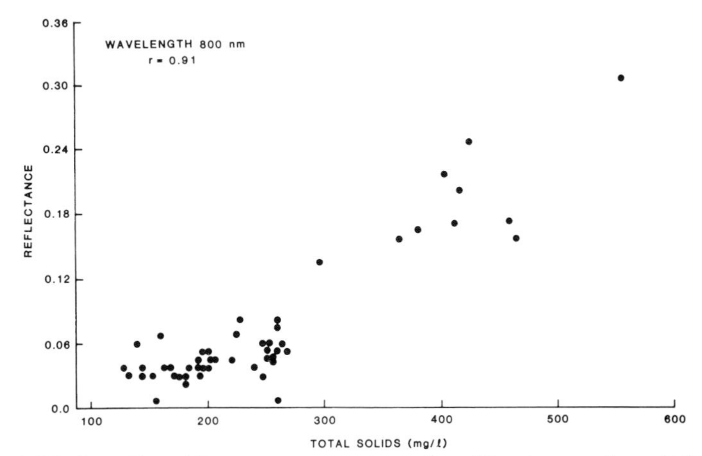

FIG.6 In situ measurements of reflectance for different concentrations of total solids.

it should be possible to develop an algorithm to estimate total or suspended sediments from remotely sensed data.

Landsat MSS Studies

Having found in laboratory and in situ studies that suspended sediments were related to radiance and reflectance, in the third part of this study we analyzed 33 Landsat MSS images to determine if similar relationships could be found in the MSS data.

Other studies have shown that suspended sediment patterns can be observed with Landsat MSS images. Quantifications of these patterns would provide useful information for lake management. LeCroy (1982) examined 20 Landsat images of Lake Chicot covering the period between 1972 and 1979 and concluded that Landsat imagery "provided an insight

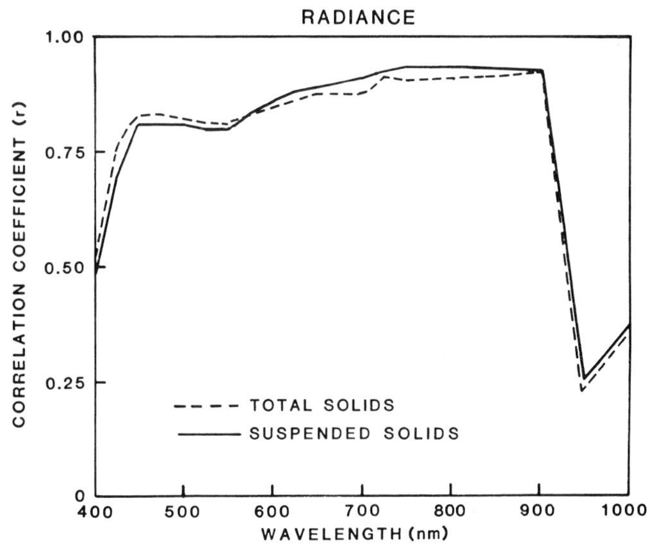

FIG.7 Plot of correlation coefficients (r) for the linear relationship between total or suspended solids and radiance.

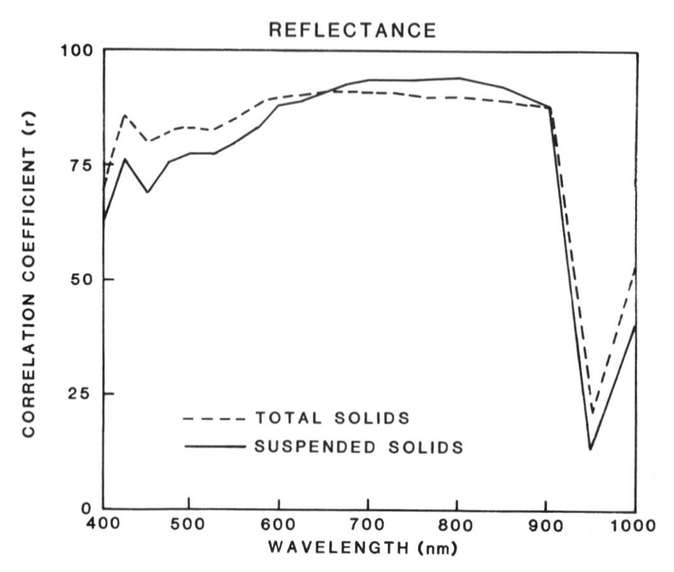

FIG.8 Plot of correlation coefficients (r) for the linear relationship between total and suspended solids and reflectance.

into the distribution, possible origin and seasonal variability of the turbidity of the lake." He also found that "distinct sediment patterns only appear on band 7 when suspended sediments are greater than 100 ppm; and, in addition, the upwelled signals are exponential in nature, resulting in a saturation of band 5..."

We analyzed 33 Landsat MSS images of Lake Chicot for the period between July 1976 and November 1979. Sampling the images in the north and south basin gave a total of 63 observations of MSS data and associated ground data. Suspended sediments ranged from 1 to 828 mg l^{-1} and total sediments ranged from 117 to 908 mg l^{-1} so that there was a wide range of sediment concentrations for comparison with the MSS data.

MSS band 5 and 6 radiance and reflectance were found to have the highest correlation to suspended or total sediments in the surface water (Table 1) Correlation with radiance was equal for these two bands. Reflectance in MSS band 6 had a better correlation for both total and suspended sediments. Logarithmic transformations and other nonlinear analysis did not improve the correlation coefficients.

These analysis of Landsat MSS data support the laboratory and in situ studies in indicating that wavelengths between 600 and 800 nm would be best for estimating suspended sediments.

Multiple regressions with reflectance data from the four MSS bands with total or suspended sediments did not give significantly different correlation coefficients using 1, 2, 3 or 4 bands of data (Table 2). Multiple regressions with radiance did provide significantly improved correlation coefficients when using two bands. Adding the third and fourth MSS bands did not significantly improve the correlation coefficients over that obtained from only 2 bands.

A simple regression using MSS band 6 reflectance data had correlation coefficients that were not significantly lower than the multiple regression. For this set of data, the MSS band 6 reflectance data would provide estimates of total or suspended sediments that were as good as any of the multiple regressions.

Table 1. Correlation coefficients (r) for the linear regression between MSS response and total and suspended solids. All r values are significant at the 5 percent level of probability

MSS Band	Total Solids	Suspended Solids
Radiance		
4	0.48	0.51
5	0.65	0.68
6	0.64	0.69
7	0.51	0.57
Reflectance		
4	0.51	0.52
5	0.65	0.68
6	0.73	0.78
7	0.57	0.63

Table 2. Multiple regression correlation coefficients (r) for the relationship between radiance and reflectance for the MSS and total and suspended solids.

MSS Band(s)	Total Solids	Suspended Solids
Radiance		
1 band	0.65 (5)*	0.69 (6)
2 bands	0.73 (4,5)	0.76 (4,5)
3 bands	0.76 (4,5,6)	0.80 (4,5,6)
4 bands	0.76 (4,5,6,7)	0.81 (4,5,6,7)
Reflectance		
1 band	0.73 (6)	0.78 (6)
2 bands	0.73 (4,6)	0.79 (4,6)
3 bands	0.75 (4,5,6)	0.83 (4,5,6)
4 bands	0.76 (4,5,6,7)	0.83 (4,5,6,7)

*Number in paranthesis is the MSS band(s) that gave the best multiple correlation.

Conclusions

This series of studies using laboratory, in situ, and Landsat measurements of radiance and reflectance for suspended sediments in surface water of Lake Chicot has shown that measurements made between 600 and 900 nm were the best for estimating suspended sediments concentrations (greater than 100 mg l^{-1}) that are typical of those concentrations found in agricultural impoundment with erosion problems in their watersheds. The studies showed that the radiance tended to become saturated at lower wavelengths as suspended sediment concentration increased. The lower correlation coefficients for the Landsat MSS data were probably due to the atmospheric scattering of light. Further research is needed to develop a simple technique to correct the MSS data for atmospheric scattering.

These studies show that it should be possible to develop a remote sensing technique using satellite data to estimate suspended sediments in agricultural impoundments. Such a technique would help conservation agencies determine those watersheds with significant erosion problems and thus to target their efforts on the critical areas.

References

Cooper, C. M., E. J. Bacon and J. C. Ritchie, 1984, Biological cycles in Lake Chicot, Arkansas: p. 49-61. IN J. F. Nix and F. R. Schiebe (eds), Limnological studies of Lake Chicot, Arkansas: Quachita Baptist University, Arkadelphia, Arkansas.

Friedman, E., L. Poole, A. Cherdak, and W. Houghton, 1980, Absorption coefficient instruments for turbid natural water: Applied Optics, v. 19, p. 1688-1693.

LeCroy, S. R., 1982, Determination of turbidity patterns in Lake Chicot from Landsat MSS imagery: NASA Contract Report 165870.

Nix, J. F. and F. R. Schiebe (eds), 1984, Limnological studies of Lake Chicot, Arkansas: Quachita Baptist University, Arkadelphia, Arkansas.

Price, R., F. Schiebe and H. Stefan, 1984, Management strategy for Lake Chicot: p. 135-146. IN J. F. Nix and F. R. Schiebe (eds), Limnological studies of Lake Chicot, Arkansas: Quachita Baptist University, Arkadelphia, Arkansas.

Richardson, A. J., 1982, Relating Landsat digital count values to ground reflectance for optically thin atmospheric conditions: Applied Optics, v. 21, p. 457-464.

Richardson, A. J., D. E. Escobar, H. W. Gausman, and J. A. Everitt, 1980, Comparison of Landsat-2 and field spectrometer reflectance of South Texas rangeland communities: Proceedings Sixth Symposium Machine Processing of Remotely Sensed Data, LARS, Purdue University, West Lafayette, Indiana, p. 88-97.

Ritchie, J. C., 1972, Sediment, fish and fish habitat: J. Soil and Water Conservation, v. 27, p. 124-125.

Ritchie, J. C., F. R. Schiebe, and C. M. Cooper, 1983, Spectral measurements of surface suspended matter in an oxbow lake in the Lower Mississippi valley: J. Freshwater Ecology, v. 2, p. 175-181.

Ritchie, J. C., F. R. Schiebe and C. M. Cooper, 1985, Landsat studies of surface water of Lake Chicot, Arkansas: Technical Papers of the 51st Annual Meeting of the American Society of Photogrammetry, p 492-498.

Ritchie, J. C., F. R. Schiebe and J. R. McHenry, 1976, Remote sensing of suspended sediments in surface water: Photogrammetric Engineering and Remote Sensing, v. 42, p. 1539-1545.

Robinove, C. J., 1982, Computation with physical values from Landsat digital data: Photogrammetric Engineering and Remote Sensing, v. 48, p. 781-784.

U. S. Geological Survey, 1979, Landsat User's Handbook (revised): USGS, Washington, D.C.

Whitlock, C. H., 1977, Fundamental analysis of the linear multiple regression technique for quantification of water quality parameters from remote sensing data. NASA TM X-74600, National Technical Information Service, Springfield, Virginia, p. 176.

Whitlock, C. H., W. G. Witte, T. A. Talany, W. D. Morris, J. W. Usry, and L. R. Poole, 1981, Research for reliable quantification of water sediment concentration from multispectral scanner remote sensing data: USDA/NASA AgRISTARS Report CP-Z1-04078 (JSC-17134).

Witte, W. G., J. W. Usry, C. H. Whitlock, and E. A. Gurganus, 1979, Spectral measurements of ocean-dumped wastes tested in marine upwelled spectral signature laboratory: NASA TP 1480, National Technical Information Service, Springfield, Virginia, p. 31.

Hydrologic Applications of Space Technology (Proceedings of the Cocoa Beach Workshop, Florida, August 1985). IAHS Publ. no. 160, 1986.

Verification of Lake Aswan High Dam sediment model by Landsat imagery

MOSTAFA M. SOLIMAN
Faculty of Engineering, Ain Shams University, Cairo, Egypt
A. M. ZAKI
SESA Institute, Ministry of Irrigation, Cairo, Egypt

Abstract
After the construction of the High Dam of Aswan, Egypt, the river Nile carries each year a big amount of silt which deposits in the Dam lake. A mathematical model was set to study the rate of advance of this silt. The results obtained from the model was checked by some recorded data from the lake.

Another attempt is presented in this paper to verify the rate of silt advance using Landsat's Imagery produced by the Remote Sensing Center.

Introduction

The natural process of obtaining equilibrium between sediment transport is complicated by various factors, such as variability of discharges, variation in total run off from year to year, and periodic changes in the volume of sediment transport, with the mode of transport differing from one state to another. It is therefore difficult to attempt a complete representation of the phenomena occurring in nature.

The effort presented in this respect, is for a simplified model (Soliman and others 1985) to respond to a given solution more or less like the process in nature.

Model Formulation:

A numerical model is established taking into consideration the following:

$$C_s = C_a U_a^m \qquad (1)$$

Where, C_s = sediment concentration (mg/kg)

C_a = mean annual sediment rate at reservoir inlet (92×10^6 m^3/year)

U_a = average velocity (m/sec)

m = a constant found to be 1.366 for Aswan Dam

Therefore the suspended sediment discharge at the inlet section $Q_{s,o}$ can be given as,

$$Q_{s,o} = C_{s,o} Q_{w,o} \qquad (2)$$

Where $C_{s,o}$ is the suspended sediment concentration at the inlet station.

$Q_{w,o}$ = is the discharge

Thru substitution Eq. (2) becomes

$$Q_{S,o} = (C_a)_o (U_a^{m})_o \cdot Q_{w,o}$$

At any section the velocity U_i is

$$U_i = \frac{Q_{w,i}}{b_i h_i}$$

Where b_i is the channel width at station i with a distance

l_i from the reservoir inlet

h_i is the water depth

and hence forth at inlet station.

$$Q_{s,o} = (C_a)_o \frac{Q^{m+1}_{w,o}}{b_o^{m} \cdot h_o^{m}}$$

The following simple differential equation for sediment deposition rate over a small reach dx may be given as follows:

$$\frac{\partial z}{\partial t} = - \frac{1}{b} \frac{\partial Qs}{\partial x} \quad \ldots\ldots\ldots\ldots\ldots\ldots (3)$$

Where z is the bed elevation and t is time. If the water level is assumed to be constant for a certain reach therefore.

$$\Delta z = -\Delta h$$

and therefore Eq. 3 becomes

$$\frac{\partial h}{\partial t} = \frac{Q_{s,o}\, b_o^{m} \cdot h_o^{m}}{b} \frac{\partial (1/bh)^m}{\partial x} \quad \ldots\ldots\ldots\ldots (4)$$

Initial and Boundary conditions:

a) Initial conditions:

z (x,t = 0) initial bed elevation is given such that

h (x,t =0) = water level (x) - z (x,t =0)

b) Boundary conditions:

Equilibrium conditions at inlet station exist at,

z (x=o,t) = constant = Z_o

h (X-o,t) = Constant = h_o

using the finite difference techniques Eq (4) becomes

$$\frac{h_{i+1} - h_i}{\Delta t} = \frac{Q_{s,o} \cdot b_o^{m} \cdot h_o^{m}}{b_i \Delta_x} \frac{(1/b_{i+1} \cdot h_{i+1}^{m}) - (1/b_i \cdot h_i)^m)}{} \quad \ldots\ldots\ldots\ldots\ldots (5)$$

A computer program was set to calculate the advance rate of sediment deposition on the reservoir bed considering the maximum reservoir length as 488 km, t = 0.1 year and x=1 km.

Fig. (1) shows the output of the model study compared with the existed bed level. A result which could be refined in order to get a better agreement.

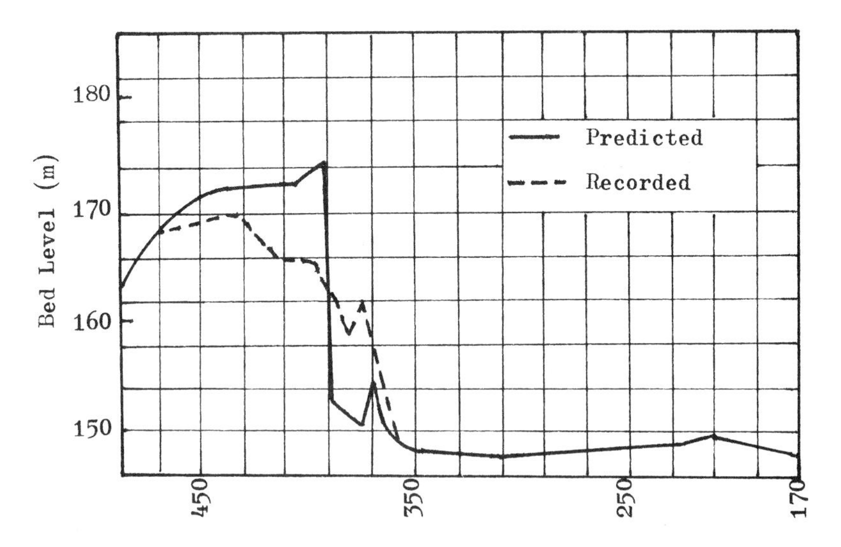

FIG.1 Predicted and recorded bed level.

Fig. (2) shows the occurrence of siltation of lake Nasser reservoir using Landsat's Digital Imagery (Smith 1978). It shows clearly the use of this achievement to verify the model study.

Conclusion:

A simplified model was set to estimate the rate of advance of sediment deposition in Aswan High Dam Reservoir. A check was first verified by some records and later by using Landsat's Digital Imagery. A result which could be considered as encouraging.

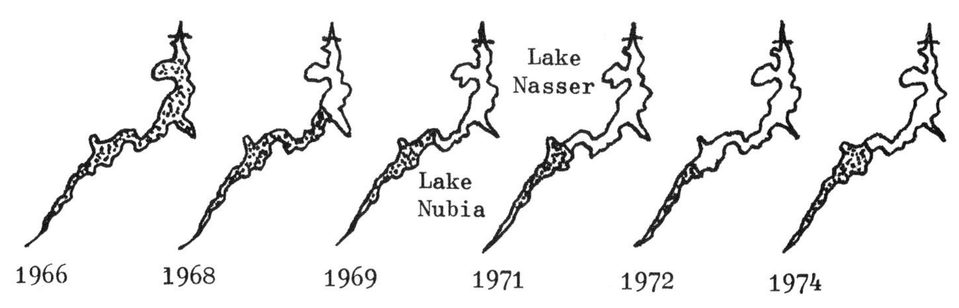

Illustration of areas covered by flood-turbid waters in some selected years.

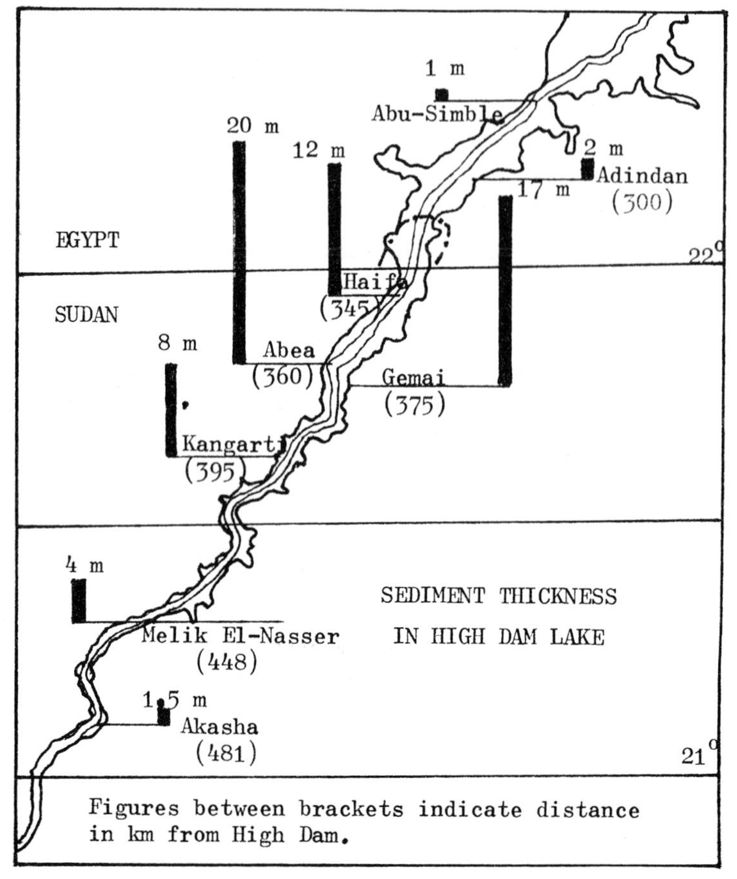

FIG.2 Distribution of siltation in the Aswan High Dam Reservoir.

References:

Soliman, M.M., Salah S.S., and Makary, A.Z., 1985, A Reservoir Sedimentation Modeling Process for Aswan High Dam Reservoir: Faculty of Engineering Ain Shams University.

Smith, Scot E., 1978, Assessment of Surface Area, Siltation, and Plant Production of Lake Nasser Reservoir Using Landsat's Digital Imagery: presented at ISEE of Hydraulic Engineering Works, Tennessee, 12-13 Sept.

Hydrologic Applications of Space Technology (Proceedings of the Cocoa Beach Workshop, Florida, August 1985). IAHS Publ. no. 160, 1986.

Visual interpretation of standard satellite images for the design of water resources schemes

T. R. E. CHIDLEY
University of Aston, Birmingham, UK
R. S. DRAYTON
University College, Cardiff, UK

Abstract

Visual interpretation of standard Landsat images was assessed as a practical method for use in water resources. Conclusions were drawn, regarding its value in the production of hydrologic maps and the evaluation of parameters used in water resource models. The study area was a temperate-maritime area of Britain, with a wide variety of topography and land-use. Results were assessed by comparison with Ordnance Survey maps at a variety of scales. The problem of making an objective evaluation of mapping accuracy is discussed. Subjectively it appeared that neither summer nor winter imagery provided a reliable map of the drainage network. Nevertheless, estimates of catchment area and stream frequency made from the imagery performed well in an important British flood model, and it is concluded that simple regression models based on these variables would be adequate for regional studies. The technique is particularly appropriate to reconnaissance work in the Third World.

Introduction

Many water resources techniques are based on the use of empirical formulae which reflect the climate, topography and land-use of an area. The use of these formulae often results in streamflow estimates with large standard errors, even with reliable input parameters. Satellite imagery provides a source of data, which would be useful where mapping is non-existent or of poor quality. This situation is most likely to arise in the Third World, so the purpose of this study was to evaluate techniques appropriate to those regions i.e. techniques which are cheap, simple and not requiring sophisticated equipment. Our decision was to evaluate the visual interpretation of standard Landsat photoproducts which could be ordered directly from National Points of Contact.

A considerable amount of work had been done on the use of Landsat with models having land-cover as a major variable, such as the SCS, HEC and STORM models. (For a review see Rango et al 1983). However, little work had been done on models based on the morphology of catchments. The principle morphological characteristics are frequently found to be catchment area and drainage density, and the key to both of these is a good map of the drainage network. Hence the primary objective of the study was to assess the reliability of visual interpretation as a method for mapping drainage networks. Moving on from there, we hoped to assess the significance of the extra error incurred when using those maps in conjunction with morphological models of streamflow.

Earlier attempts to map drainage features from Landsat imagery had met with a surprising degree of success (Fowler et al 1977, Killpack and McCoy 1981, Rango et al 1975, Ashworth, Chidley and Collins, 1984). Catchment areas had been evaluated consistently well, but drainage density was found to vary with relief, date and cover. However, no work had been done on European basins, and no attempt had been made to evaluate the usefulness of the data in models.

Method

The study area included 8 catchments lying in and around the South Wales coalfield. Four of the rivers are steep, deeply incised, with urban development on the valley floor, forestry on the valley sides, and open moorland on the interfluves. Two rivers are moderately incised, with mixed agriculture on the valley floor and with moorland above, while the remaining two rivers lie on the flat, highly developed agricultural area of the coastal plain. The climate is westerly maritime, with rainfall varying from 930mm on the coastal plain to 2400mm at the highest altitude of 890m.

Extracts of Landsat scene 219/24 were purchased as photoprints at a nominal scale of 1:250,000 in Band 7 (near infrared). A summer scene (August 1980) and a snow-covered winter scene (January 1982) were used.

The drainage network was drawn directly onto a clear acetate overlay. Features were identified positively as rivers if they possessed dark tone, were linear, had the typical irregularities of a river and "fitted" the topography. Streams were identified with "high confidence" as extending from or joining sections of positively identified streams, or where a distinct valley was identified (this being a high rainfall area). Streams were mapped with "low confidence" as dark-toned irregular lineaments possibly extending from positively identified streams, where there was little topographic evidence. Catchment boundaries were mapped primarily on the basis of the drainage network, but using interpretations of the topography.

Catchment areas and stream frequencies were measured for the 8 catchments and compared with values estimated from 1:250,000 maps, 1:50,000 maps and with "accepted" values given in the UK Flood Studies Report (NERC 1975) which were derived from 1:25,000 maps.

Discussion of results

Figures 1 to 3 show maps of the drainage network as interpreted from the imagery and from the 1:250,000 map. Tables 1 and 2 give values for the catchment areas and stream frequencies estimated from those maps, and the accepted values from the UK Flood Studies Report (NERC 1975).

The summer image provided a generally low level of detail, missing several major rivers and the majority of low-order streams. Most detail

Table 1 Estimates of catchment area made from UK Flood Studies Report, O.S. 1:250,000 map and Landsat imagery (km^2)

Station	FSR	1:250000 Map	Summer Landsat	Winter Landsat
Honddu	62.2	60.2	18.8	63.5
Afon Lwyd	98.1	91.8	120.6	97.3
Usk	184.0	186.3	278.1	200.0
Cynon	109.0	104.4	56.3	98.5
Taff	455.0	444.8	398.8	458.1
Ogmore	158.0	154.5	146.9	137.9
Neath	191.0	188.1	192.5	137.5
Ewenny	62.9	60.6	-	-

Table 2 Estimates of stream frequency made from UK Flood Studies Report, O.S. 1:50,000 and 1:250,000 maps and from Landsat imagery (junctions/km^2)

Station	FSR	1:50,000 Map	1:250,000 Map	Summer Landsat	Winter Landsat
Honddu	1.01	0.47	0.080	0.05	0.457
Afon Lwyd	1.17	0.77	0.020	0.083	0.329
Usk	1.67	0.22	0.108	0.104	0.330
Cynon	2.33	0.72	0.037	0.178	0.264
Taff	2.17	0.78	0.068	0.138	0.220
Ogmore	2.63	0.99	0.082	0.204	0.370
Neath	2.59	0.87	0.136	0.062	0.109
Ewenny	1.41	0.83	0.079	-	-

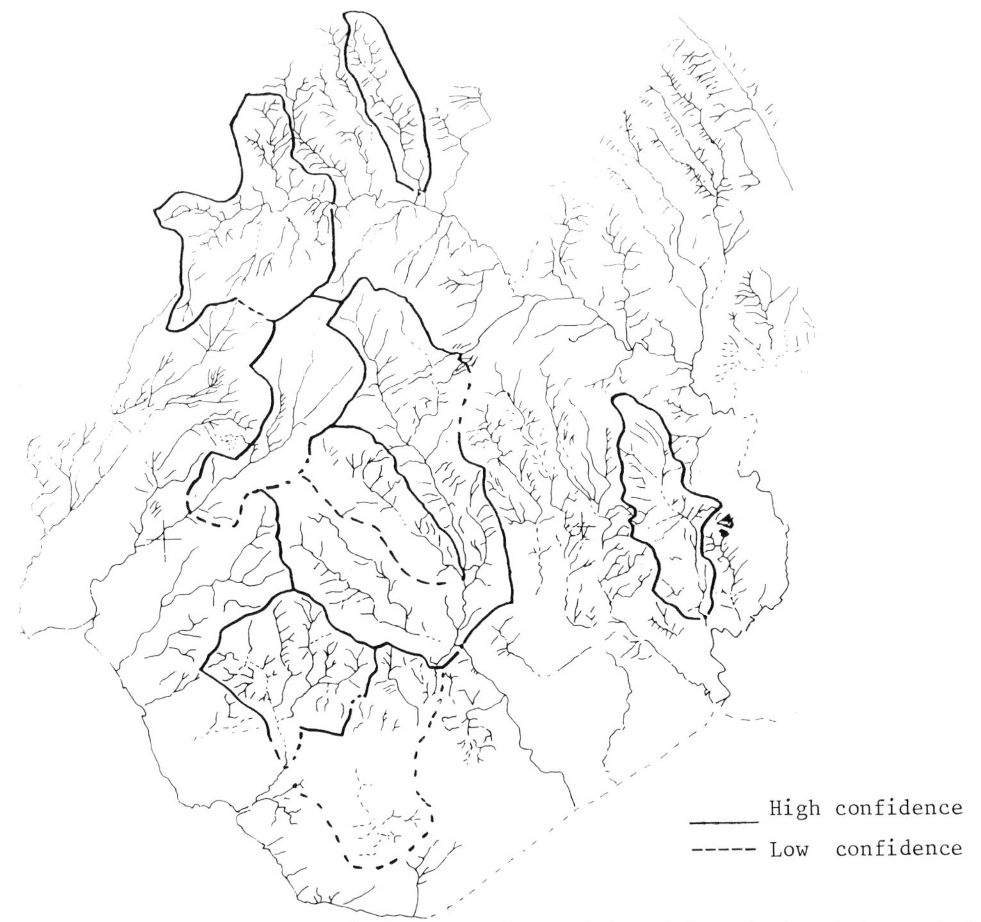

FIG.1 Drainage network & catchment boundaries interpreted from Landsat Band 7 (Winter 1982).

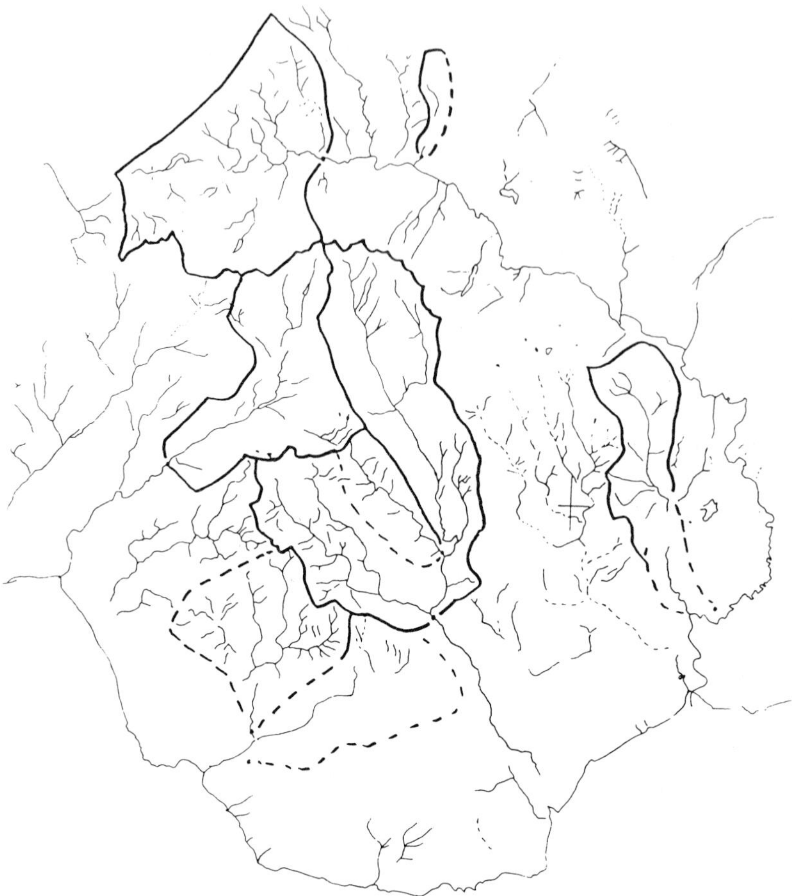

FIG.2 Drainage network & catchment boundaries interpreted from Landsat Band 7 (Summer 1980).

was lost in the agricultural areas, which have a very textured appearance due to the pattern of small fields. Larger rivers were obscured by riverine forestry and urban development. The winter image gave much more detail, but the increased definition was mainly due to the low sun angle. The enhancement due to shading depended on the orientation of valleys, and did not apply consistently.

The resolution offered by Landsat was insufficient to positively identify streams throughout their length. Therefore the definition of the network depended on a subjective interpretation using contextual evidence. This led to many errors in connecting sub-catchments to the main streams.

Quantitative evaluation of the mapping was found to be difficult. Measures of one-to-one correspondence may be very misleading, especially in areas which are rich in head-capture, where streams may be positioned correctly, but connected wrongly (Fig. 4). Comparison of lower order streams with 1:250,000 maps may also be misleading, because the inclusion of streams on those maps may not be according to objective criteria (Ordnance Survey 1985).

The success of the interpretations in mapping the basic structure of the network was judged by comparing only main rivers i.e. those above first order which discharge at the coast. The winter image showed 68% of the length of main rivers correctly, and the summer image showed 61% (Fig. 5).

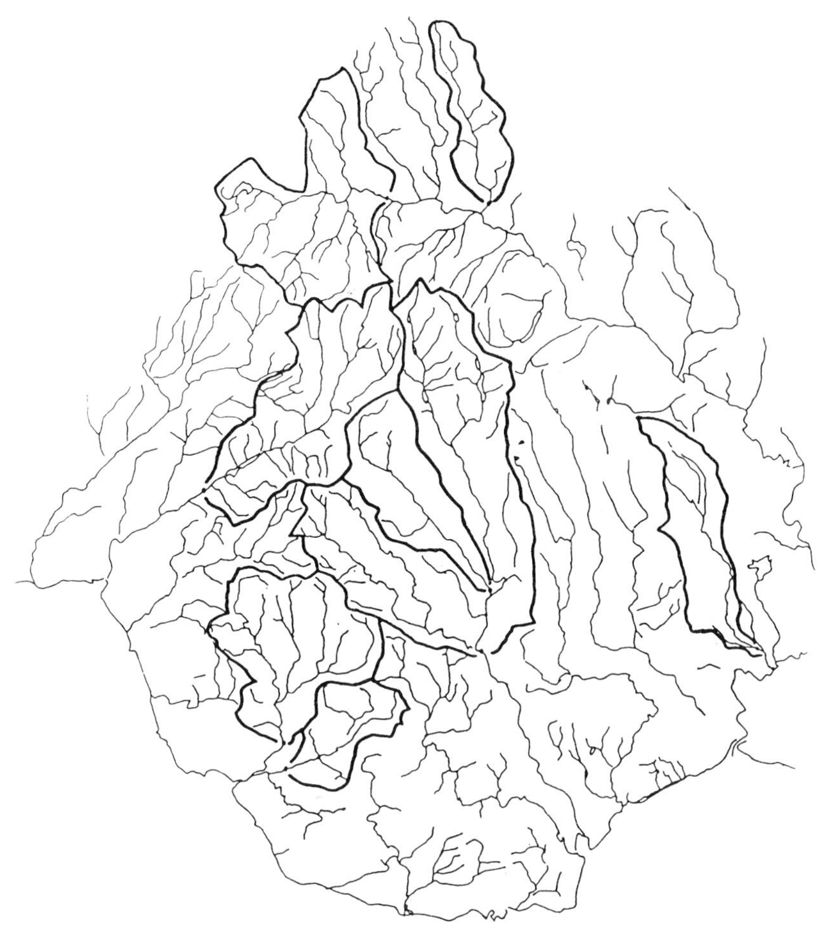

FIG.3 Drainage network & catchment boundaries interpreted from 1:250,000 map.

Two of the largest rivers in the area were not detected. Although they were deeply incised (250m to 300m relief) they were obscured by forestry and urban areas in the valley floors.

Values of catchment area were generally of the same order as values from maps, with the winter image giving generally better estimates. In individual catchments errors of up to 70% were found, and one catchment boundary (in the mixed-farming area) could not be defined at all. These results are significantly worse than those given by Rango (1975) and Killpack and McCoy (1981).

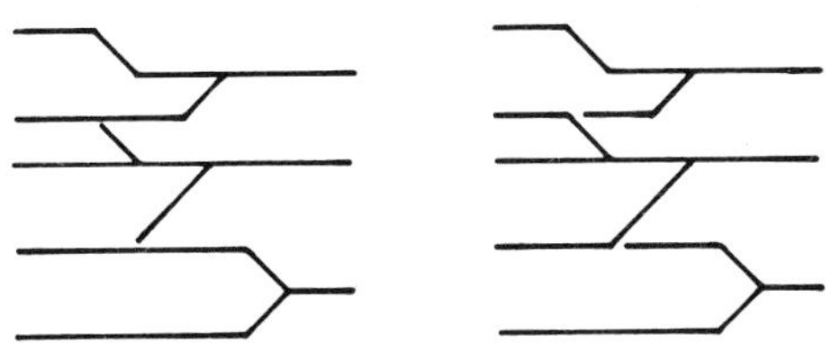

FIG.4 Example of good correspondence of channel locations, but poor correspondence of junctions.

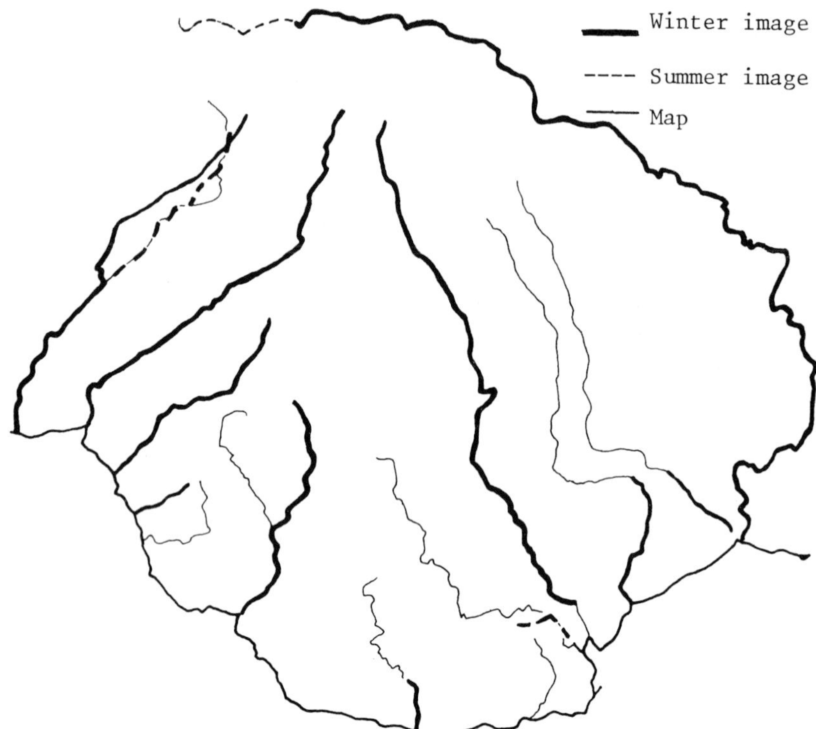

FIG.5 Main rivers on 1:250,000 map shown correctly in Landsat interpretation.

Values of stream frequency were of a similar order to values from 1:250,000 maps but very much lower than the accepted values from 1:25,000 maps. Nevertheless they could be useful in numerical models if they correlate well. Scatter diagrams are shown in Fig. 6, where it can be seen that the summer image gives a reasonable correlation (r^2 = 0.62), but the winter image gives no correlation at all, probably due to the inconsistent enhancement of sun shading. It is interesting to note that the subjectivity involved in drawing maps of 1:50,000 and 1:250,000 scale has also given rise to very poor correlation with the 1:25,000 accepted values (r^2 = 0.26 and 0.11 respectively).

The next step was to see how these parameter estimates would perform in a morphological model. The model chosen was a regional flood estimator from the UK Flood Studies Report (NERC 1975), which is a type gaining favour world-wide. This gives the mean annual flood as :

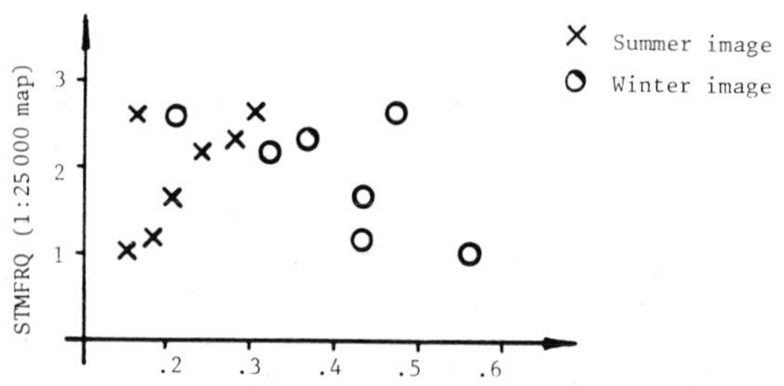

FIG.6 Comparison of steam frequency (j/km²).

$$Q = 0.0213\ AREA^{.94}\ STMFRQ^{.27}\ SOIL^{1.23}\ RSMD^{1.03}\ (1 + LAKE)^{-.85}\ S1085^{.16}$$

Values of recorded mean annual flood for the study catchments have been plotted in Fig. 7 against values estimated from this model. In the first case the values of catchment area (AREA) and stream frequency (STMFRQ) were estimated from the Landsat imagery. In the second case the accepted values in the Flood Studies Report were used. In both cases the values of the other variables (soil type, soil moisture, lake attenuation and stream slope) were taken from the Flood Studies Report. It can be seen that the estimates using values from the winter image are not significantly different from those using accepted values. This lack of sensitivity may be explained by the small contribution which area makes to the variance of flood magnitude in this 7-parameter model.

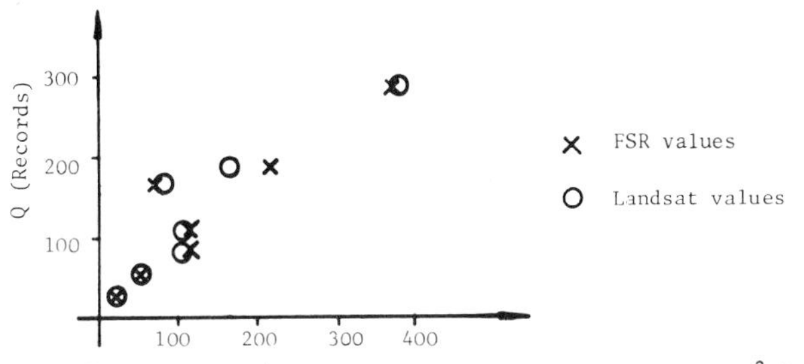

FIG.7 Comparison of mean annual flood (m^3/s).

A simpler approach to flood estimation would be to use regression models based on parameters from Landsat images alone. Regressing catchment area and stream frequency on mean annual flood for the seven study catchments, a correlation coefficient of 0.82 was found. This indicates that within hydrologically homogeneous regions it would be possible to construct useful hydrologic models based on Landsat topographic data alone.

Preliminary investigations using simulated SPOT data (Chidley and Drayton 1985) indicate that the improved resolution of SPOT will enable drainage mapping with greatly improved reliability at scales around 1:50,000.

Conclusions

In contrast to earlier work, drainage networks could not be mapped reliably using standard Landsat photoproducts. Unreliability was related more to land-cover than to relief. Nevertheless, main rivers could be mapped with reasonable confidence, and catchment areas and stream frequencies could be estimated to an accuracy appropriate to simple hydrological models. Subjectivity is an important issue and is being investigated further.

References

Ashworth, M., Chidley, T.R.E. and Collins, W.G., 1984, Visual analysis of digital images for studies in water resources, ISPRS, Rio de Janeiro, Brazil.

Chidley, T.R.E. and Drayton, R.S., 1985, Application of SPOT Imagery in Water Resources: Proc. NRSC 1984 SPOT Simulation Campaign, in print.

Fowler, T.R., Castruccio, P.A., Loats, H.L., 1977, The application of remote sensing to the development and formulation of hydrologic planning models: Final report NASA CR - 150236.

Killpack, D.P. and McCoy, R.M., 1981, An application of Landsat derived

data to a regional hydrologic model: Remote Sens. Quart. 3(2) 27-33.
Natural Environment Research Council, 1975, Flood Studies Report, Swindon.
Ordnance Survey, 1985, Personal communication.
Rango, A., Foster, J., Salomonson, V.V., 1975, Extraction and utilization of space acquired physiographic data for water resources development: Water Res. Bull. 11(6), 1245-1255.
Rango, A., Feldman, A., George, T.S., Ragan, R.M., 1983, Effective use of Landsat data in hydrological models: Water Res. Bull. 19(2), 165-174.

Hydrologic Applications of Space Technology (Proceedings of the Cocoa Beach Workshop, Florida, August 1985). IAHS Publ. no. 160, 1986.

Remote sensing technology applications — the Kenya experience

JUSTUS I. MWANJE
Department of Geography, University of Nairobi, Nairobi, Kenya

Abstract
The Republic of Kenya is situated in the Eastern Region of the continent of Africa. It is a land of diversity with regard to climate, terrain and ecological conditions. With a rapidly growing population, now at 20 million, and an annual growth rate of 4%, the need for urgent applications of remote sensing technology in Kenya is growing so as to deal with the pressure on land. The techniques are used to speed up the collection of resources data as the base for planning development.

Remote sensing technology has been applied in Kenya since the mid 1970's. However, the application of aerial photographs for mapping dates back to three decades. To the present the application of remote sensing techniques to the evaluation of hydrological resources is still very limited and not as extensive as in land use mapping. However, there are significant indications that the applications of remote sensing to hydrological studies in Kenya will increase very fast in the next decade.

The growth of remote sensing in Kenya was put into motion by the events which led to the formation of the African Remote Sensing Council in the mid 1970's. This paper traces this development and analyzes the current state of the application art and/or science of remote sensing technology in Kenya. Considered here, are the major programs which include governmental and non-governmental agencies that use the technology. Governmental agencies include the Kenya Rangeland Ecological Monitoring Unit (KREMU), the Central Bureau of Statistics (CBS), National Agricultural Laboratories (NAL), and the Survey of Kenya (SK). The non-governmental agencies include the Regional Remote Sensing Facility and the Global Environment Monitoring System (GEMS).

Emphasis is placed on the need for the training and development of skilled manpower especially in the fields of photography and satellite image interpretation. Presently, the leading training institution in Kenya, which unfortunately is hampered with shortage of equipment and personnel, is the University of Nairobi, one of the three National Universities in the country. To some extent the Regional Remote Sensing Facility provides training. Other training opportunities organized and provided locally are sponsored by international agencies (e.g. FAO, ESA, etc.) and institutions (e.g. ITC).

Trends in the growth of the technology are elucidated and proposals for the establishment of a National Remote Sensing Centre are presented. Such a centre would manage the proposed LANDSAT Ground Receiving Station proposed for construction in Nairobi. Also it would be responsible for the collection, storage and dissemination of data received by the station; conduct research; guide the government on all aspects of the management of natural resources; promote sub-regional, regional and international co-operation; to launch resource surveys; and other aspects of the application of remote sensing technology.

The paper makes recommendations on various aspects for facilitation of the application of remote sensing technology. It is observed that the potential for application of remote sensing technology in Kenya is tremendous. Thus there is need for design and development of relevant programmes for the natural resources scenario of Kenya with an emphasis on utilization of water resources, land use, forestry and food production systems. Equally, there is need to promote co-operation at all levels aimed at obtaining the necessary technological and financial aid from international bodies, if Kenya, like other developing countries has to maximize from the experience of developed nations, especially in the field of remote sensing applications, in order to improve the welfare of her peoples.

Introduction

The Republic of Kenya covers an area of 582,646 sq. Kms. of which 11,230 sq. Km (1.93%) is water. The country is characterized by a highly diversified terrain, climate and ecological conditions endowed with a wide range of niches, resource use opportunities, practices and challenges. Kenya has a human population of nearly 20 million people (with a growth rate of about 4%). Nearly 60% of this population is youth. Agricultural potential, defined as the ability of the land to support rainfed agriculture, is limited because nearly 2/3 of the total land surface of the Republic is classified as low potential (Table I). This vast area constitutes the arid and semi-arid regions which accommodates 10% of the people, 50% of the cattle, 55% of the sheep, 75% of the goats, and all the camels in the Republic. Recent opening-up of irrigable settlement schemes has resulted in immigration of more people into the low potential areas.

Hence the major primary resource in Kenya is the dry lands characterized with a very small arid zone. Although the inhabitants of these areas are fairly well adapted to its harsh environment, the new immigrants are not. Therefore, this calls for utilization of new technologies such as remote sensing approaches in order to develop scientific knowledge necessary for the development of these areas.

The other important resource is water, a scarce and vital resource in Kenya's dry lands, as elsewhere in the third world. The demand for water in rural and urban areas of Kenya is estimated at 4.2 million m^3 per year

Table 1.---AGRICULTURAL LAND POTENTIAL IN KENYA

Land Category (Potential)	Rainfall Range	Area (hectare)	% Total
High	>889 mm 980 mm (Coast Province)	6,785,000	11.9
Medium	Coast Prov. (762-1016 mm) Eastern Prov. (635-899 mm) Nyanza/Rift Valley Prov. (762-889 mm)	3,157,000	5.6
Low	635-762 mm	42,105,000	74.0
All Others	---	4.867,000	8.6
Total		56,914,000	100

Source: Statistical Abstracts, Republic of Kenya, 1970, and Other Sources.

and irrigation demand is expected to rise to nearly tenfold by 1990. The major river catchment and drainage areas in Kenya include the Suam-Turkwel (43,898 Km^2), the Kerio (18,130 Km^2), the Ewaso Ng'iro (205,000 Km^2), the Athi (70,000 Km^2) and the upper Tana-Thiba (19,658 Km^2) (Fig. I). Most rivers in western and Nyanza Provinces drain their waters into Lake Victoria, an international water mass shared among Kenya, Uganda and Tanzania. It is important to note the problem of floods affecting mainly the Lake Victoria Basin and parts of Narok District in the South West part of the country. Recent reports indicate extensive destruction of property by this calamity. Its control has become a national priority leading to the establishment of a permanent technical committee under the auspices of the Ministry of Water Development to conduct studies and make recommendations that would enhance development of resources in the affected areas.

Although the Government of Kenya requires constant supply of information regarding its natural resources for purposes of economic development, only a limited effort is underway to collect it, by any means, including remote sensing. It is well known that the applications of remote sensing are developing very quickly The information gathered through satellites, visual and digital data processing, computerized geo-base information systems, simulation modelling and automated cartography, have opened new avenues for natural resource assessment. So far, the application of remote sensing in Kenya by various government ministries and other agencies has been on an ad hoc basis with little or no co-ordination. However, the establishment of the Kenya Rangeland Ecological Monitoring Unit (KREMU), now in the new Ministry of Planning and National Development, has to some extent, introduced an orderly application of remote sensing techniques to national data inventory for resource use planning.

The State of Remote Sensing Technology in Kenya

Satellite based remote sensing, because it relies on the recording of electromagnetic energy rather than the more limited photography is a fast advancing technology which has quickly moved into digital information acquisition and processing, and the exciting possibility of automated mapping systems. With the fast advances registered by other airborne and orbital remote sensing techniques, it is possible to have real time digital processing of data acquired on resources of the earth's surface with increased accuracy. The introduction of new systems with thematic mapping capability (e.g. LANDSAT-D) and high ground-resolution systems (E.g. SPOT) should enhance this goal. Hence, Kenya cannot ignore this advancement in remote sensing technology provided suitable for rapid resource data inventory. Thus, the relevance of remote sensing to our national resource development is unquestionable.

Nevertheless, the present level of applications of remotely sensed data in Kenya, like in most developing nations, is well below its potential, yet we fall within the food deficit region, Africa South of the Sahara. Data so far used in Kenya is acquired from the U.S.A. In recent times, the establishment, in Kenya, of the Regional Remote Sensing Facility, a joint project of the Regional Centre for Services in Surveying and Mapping, and the United States Agency for International Development (USAID) has tended to speed the utilization of LANDSAT data, supplemented with aircraft photography, usually commissioned by the Survey of Kenya, a government department of the Ministry of Lands and Settlement and other agencies.

In the last decade, the work done using remote sensing technology has offered the country tremendous opportunities for mapping and assessment of location, state and dynamics of natural resources. In particular, there is a growing need for natural resource information. As already mentioned, Kenya possesses extensive and diversified resources and is prone to

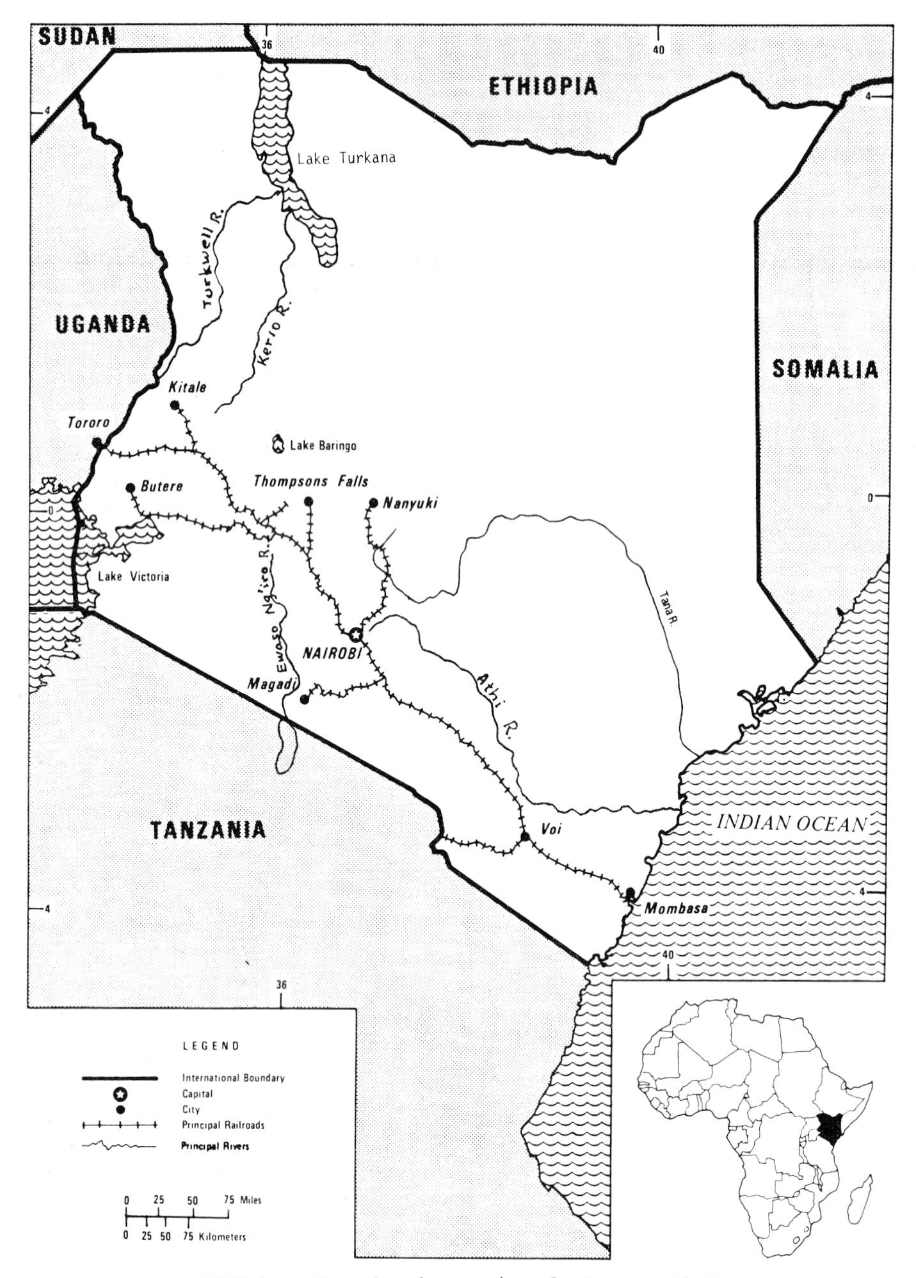

FIG.1 Map showing major features of Kenya.

ecological disturbances such as droughts, floods, etc., which can be easily recorded by satellites and the resulting data be analyzed for effective management. The vast rangelands, river stages and inland lakes can easily be mapped by LANDSAT satellite for quick establishment of resource development priorities. Examples of such priorities include: harnessing of the irrigation potential of the Kano Plains of the Lake Victoria Basin, and the Lower Tana Plains in the Coast Province; the protection of wildlife ecosystems such as the Amboseli and Tsavo National Parks; rangeland improvement in the North-Eastern Province; and monitoring of flood hazards.

The availability of remote sensing data in Kenya is matched with very low utilization, hence it is not easy to obtain information, for example, on long-term effects of weather dynamics on the utilization of natural resources such as rangeland biomass. Data on weather can easily be derived from meteorological satellites while that on rangeland biomass from LANDSAT. There are reasons for this low utilization of remote sensing data, and they include:

(1) Lack of adequate and constant supply of remote sensing specialists for employment in applications agencies. This problem is aggrevated by the inability of the government and other public corporations to retain skilled remote sensing professionals who tend to be lured by better prospects offered by private industry, where some may never utilize their knowledge fully.

(2) Lack of coordination among government agencies which may find remote sensing technology useful to their application, hence the result is duplication of data utilization leading to diffusion of scarce financial and personnel resources. However, to some degree, this problem has been minimized by the formation, in 1976, of the National Committee on the Application of Satellite and Space Technology (COASST) under the auspices of the National Council for Science and Technology. Unfortunately, this committee lacks executive powers protected by the law so as to ensure proper use of remote sensing data in the country.

(3) Non-availability of sufficient and advanced training facilities in the country resulting in the prevalence of rudimentary interpretation techniques.

(4) Lack of a ground receiving station for remote sensing data. Such a facility could provide a multiplier-effect on growth of professionals and techniques as well as enhance demand for remote sensing applications as the latter could be effectively used to obtain repetitive, synoptic, spatial and temporal data on natural resources which could be effectively put into national economic and social development plans.

Remote Sensing Programs in Kenya

Despite the fact that Kenya became aware of the potential of using remote sensing data in the early 1970's, it was not until the beginning of the last decade that serious thought was focused in this direction. The United Nations Economic Commission for Africa (ECA) took the lead by putting remote sensing on the agenda of the meeting of the Council of African Ministers of Economic Planning, held in Nairobi in 1975. This action resulted in Resolution 280/X11 which documented the agreement by African Ministers to establish the African Remote Sensing Council, to enable member states to share the technology by focusing attention on manpower training, technology transfer, and international co-operation in the peaceful uses of Outer Space, with the view to adoption and sharing of the benefits of remote sensing by earth satellites to all countries in the region.

In 1976, an intergovernmental meeting under the auspices of ECA considered a report by experts and hence resolved that in addition to the creation of an African Remote Sensing Council (which took root in 1978 with headquarters in Bamako, Mali), the following should be planned and achieved:

(1) The establishment of three ground receiving stations to be located at Ouagadougou (Upper Volta) Kinshasa (Zaire) and Nairobi (Kenya).

(2) The establishment of five training and user assistance centres to be located at Ouagadougou, Kinshasa, Nairobi, Cairo (Egypt) and Ile-Ife (Nigeria).

The African Remote Sensing Council, which was officially approved after a ratification of its constitution by ten African countries at a meeting in

Ouagadougou, Upper Volta, during September 1979, had the following objectives:

(1) To keep member countries abreast of relevant scientific activities and development in remote sensing.

(2) To encourage greater interest and African participation of remote sensing and related technologies to development problems.

(3) To avoid duplication of remote sensing facilities.

To ensure that these objectives are achieved, two regional management committees of the African Remote Sensing Council were formed. These are: the West Africa Regional Remote Sensing Management Committee (WARMCOM) and the East Africa Regional Remote Sensing Management Committee (EARMCOM). In addition, these committees ensure that the regional remote sensing facilities are managed economically and efficiently.

As a result of the creation of the afore-analyzed awareness, the following remote sensing programs have been established in Kenya:

(1) Regional Remote Sensing Facility. Situated at Ruaraka in Nairobi, this facility was funded initially by the U.S. Agency for International Development (USAID). The facility is the remote sensing division of the Mapping Centre. It provides advice, services (e.g. training resource managers), and support for users (e.g. providing subsidized consultancy for investigators) in the Eastern Africa Region. The main source of imagery for the facility is EROS Data Center, Sioux Falls, South Dakota, U.S.A. Hence, the facility provides copies of satellite images from an extensive library of photographic transparencies and can create scaled enlargements, map overlays and photographically enhanced images using a Super Chromega Camera F, a Wing-Lynch Photographic Processor, a Chromega D Camera, Photo Processor, Light tables and a Karzl Reflecting Projector. There is also equipment for image interpretation. The facility also contributes significantly to natural resource development projects in the region.

(2) Kenya Rangeland Ecological Monitoring Unit (KREMU). KREMU is a project funded by the Canadian International Development Agency (CIDA)-through a bilateral agreement between the government of Canada and Kenya. Initially, the Unit belonged to the Ministry of Wildlife and Tourism, then moved to the Ministry of Environment and Natural Resources and later moved to the Ministry of Finance and Economic Planning. At present, the Unit belongs to the newly created Ministry of Planning and National Development. The Unit has three light aircrafts and a fleet of Landrover vehicles which are used to collect data under the widened mandate for land use mapping, forest cover mapping and related aspects, and ecological monitoring of Kenya's rangelands. The data is collected on a 5x5 Km. grid network covering nearly 500,000 Km^2 of the country's land surface. The data is stored in a computerized geographical information system and later retrieved for resource analyses.

In recent times KREMU established a remote sensing section which has embarked on analysis of LANDSAT Satellite imagery for resource use mapping. The scale of images used is 1:500,000 hence each image shows an area of 50 x 52 Km. The survey has been supplemented by aerial photography in places where the images are obscured by cloud cover. Digital analysis has been accomplished on computers in CANADA and FRANCE under bilateral agreements. Projects covered by this ongoing exercise include production of a Land Use Map of Kenya, Crop Detection and Monitoring, Forest Mapping (analogue and partially digital) and Wildlife Habitat Maps. Other applications of remote sensing techniques include the use of airborne digital radiometers (green machines) to estimate biomass (in rangeland areas) and maize yield forecasting (in high potential areas).

(3) Central Bureau of Statistics (CBS). This is a department of the Ministry of Finance. Its establishment in 1974 was initially funded by the

U.S. Agency for International Development (USAID). Its main objective is to inventory statistics of importance to national development planning e.g. population census, economic surveys, crop yield surveys, etc. In 1979, the bureau used LANDSAT imagery for establishing land use boundaries and related these to human population densities in facilitating enumeration procedures for that year's census. The operational remote sensing equipment found at the bureau include an overhead projector, a colour additive viewer, and a zoom transfer scope.

(4) National Agricultural Laboratories (NAL). This is a department of the Ministry of Agriculture and Livestock Development. At these laboratories is located the Kenya Soil Survey Unit, which has extensively used photo-interpretation techniques to produce soil maps at the scale 1:250,000. LANDSAT imagery has been used for exploratory surveys of Kenya Soils.

(5) Survey of Kenya (SK). Again, this is a department of the Government of Kenya in the Ministry of Lands and Settlement, whose main function is to produce standard and other types of maps required by the state and other user agencies. LANDSAT imagery is mainly used to update the 1:250,000 maps.

(6) University of Nairobi. The University of Nairobi is the most established of the three National Universities of Kenya. It is the only University that has departments offering some remote sensing courses. These departments include Geography, and Surveying and Photogrammetry. The former offers a course on Air-Photo Interpretation (2nd year science undergraduates) and Advanced Environmental Remote Sensing (3rd year science undergraduates). The latter offers an optional course on Remote Sensing and Photo-Interpretation (3rd year undergraduates). None of the departments provide postgraduate training in Remote Sensing. Both departments suffer lack of training equipment. This is one area where technical assistance from donor agencies would be welcome.

Other training programs have been mounted in Kenya by reputable international institutions and agencies (e.g. European Space Agency, International Institute for Aerial Survey and Earth Sciences (ITC), etc.). Such training is organized in the form of seminars and workshops.

(7) Global Environmental Monitoring System (GEMS). Ecological monitoring activities within the renewable resource network of the United Nations Environmental Programme (UNEP), located at Gigiri in Nairobi, are carried out by GEMS. The latter's methodology, developed in East Africa, aims t creating an understanding of the dynamics of the rapidly evolving ecosystems of arid regions. Data is therefore collected at three levels: (i) Ground surveys for biomass productivity and sociological determinants' data. For large areas, it is costly. (ii) Low-level systematic reconnaissance flights to collect information on seasonal abundance and distribution of the human and large mammal components of the system. (iii) Satellite imagery (mainly LANDSAT) for mapping of geomorphic features as well as of the seasonal changes in biomass productivity.

It should be mentioned here that a similar data collection system is used at KREMU, hence this may lead to duplication at national level of the applications of remote sensing technology.

(8) Regional Remote Sensing Receiving Station. Through the African Remote Sensing Council, Kenya successfully bid for the location of remote sensing receiving station within its borders capable of tracking both LANDSAT (American) and SPOT (French) satellites. Encouraging feasibility studies sponsored by the French government were completed in 1984. It is suggested that although the facility would provide services to East, Central and South African governments, it be considered as a Kenyan project and financed in that respect. The reason for this is the prevalence of unpredictable geo-political climate among some countries in the region

which might not urger well for a regional joint venture. Further, it is hoped that actual handling of data on natural resources from neighboring countries will not pose any politics other than scientific implications. As mentioned earlier, if the Kenyan station takes-off, it should be possible to establish similar projects at Kinshasa (Zaire) and Ouagadougou (Ivory Coast) as proposed by the African Remote Sensing Council under the auspices of the UNECA. So far, the Canadian government has shown interest in funding the Ouagadougou station while NASA indicated willingness, in principle, to assist Kinshasa. However, nothing significant seems to have happened in both cases.

The proposed station in Kenya would be more suitable as it would reduce overlap with any future station at Quagadougou and covers the Red Sea coasts of Sudan, Ethiopia, and Somalia as opposed to a station at Kinshasa. The parts that could be covered by a station at the latter location would be taken care of by the South African station. However, such stations would require permission from the USA and France for access to their respective satellites.

It should be mentioned that the Italian government has established a Telemetry Station at San Marco, near Malindi in Kenya. In September 1973, the Italian Centre Richerche Aerospaziali of the University of Rome began discussions with the government of Kenya on the possibility of converting the San Marco Station into a LANDSAT receiving station. However, considering the costs involved, it would appear that the advantages of an international tracking, receiving and data processing station located at Nairobi would override those of having a limited range receiving station at San Marco. However, the picture may change when the Italian government provides a more attractive proposal. But the results of such action remains to be seen as the proposed Nairobi station seems to be more attractive given the existing efficient and up-to-date infrastructure, in addition to the proximity of user community.

At the Meteorological department, Dagoretti in Nairobi, are equipments that track and receive weather pictures from geostationary weather satellites. However, with the establishment of the proposed remote sensing receiving station and its possible link to the existing systems in Nairobi, it should become feasible to engage in sophisticated data manipulations. This would enable resource use planners to study and monitor such hazards like droughts and floods which are prevalent in some parts of the region.

Hydrological Applications of Remote Sensing Technology in Kenya

In Kenya, like in most developing countries, the identification, evaluation and monitoring of water resources is of vital importance. The application of satellite data in hydrology should include ground water exploration, flood damage estimation and monitoring, water quality analysis, surface water inventory, irrigation monitoring, the detection and mapping of wetland areas, and the mapping of some coastal features and reefs for assessment of marine resources. Proper use of remote sensing data should always result in a rational planning, development and management of hydrological resources.

Of significant economic importance in Kenya are the fresh water lakes. Some of these lakes, namely Victoria and Naivasha are plagued with the problem of floating islands. The latter consisting primarily of papyrus vegetation, drift into harbours (e.g. Kisumu on Lake Victoria) causing problems to steamer traffic and disrupting intake of water at supply stations, required for domestic and industrial consumption. Sometimes they destroy fishing gear, a serious problem on Lake Jipe on Kenya-Tanzania border near Mt. Kilimanjaro, and also on Lake Victoria.

The use of LANDSAT data gathered by the Multi-Spectral Scanner at selected intervals have assisted in showing the trans-migration of floating islands in Lake Naivasha. Thus, by plotting the distribution of vegetation over the surface of Lake Naivasha on selected dates (i.e. January 9th, 18th, and 27th and February 14th and 23rd of 1979) a record of the mobility of the floating islands of vegetation was compiled. However, no velocity modelling was done, although the synoptic view of the vegetation distribution and pattern at five points over a period of 45 days was revealed. The satellite data also revealed that the floating islands have some internal structure. Hence, this application provides a capability for monitoring the movement of floating islands on Kenyan lakes and elsewhere, a useful achievement for management of fresh water bodies.

A part from this preliminary study, little else has been accomplished on hydrological resources of Kenya. However, new projects are underway and they include the study of flood problem in the Lake Victoria Basin, and the study of seasonal variation of near-surface moisture in Lambwe Valley Ecosystem and its impact on the population dynamics of tsetse flies which are vectors of the African human trypanosomiasis (sleeping sickness) disease. It is hoped that other studies will make extensive use of remote sensing data in order to develop appropriate flood and disease control strategies respectively.

National Goals for the Application of Remote Sensing Technology in Kenya.

In the consideration of the remote sensing applications in Kenya the progress made so far is small but impressive. The national goal is to achieve high technological advancement in the adoption and application of remote sensing techniques. The present lack of co-ordination among agencies using remotely sensed data has been the demise of the technology. It is therefore hoped that the government of Kenya will soon establish a National Remote Sensing Centre under the Science and Technology (Amendment) Act, No. 7 of 1979, (date of Assent 10th May, 1979) Part IV, Paragraph 12 (2), "Establishment of Research Institutes." Feasibility studies have been completed on this aspect.

The functions of the Centre should include the following:

(1) To manage the LANDSAT receiving station and provide satellite data to national and other users at a price.
(2) To observe and ensure standardization of reception and utilization of satellite data.
(3) To obtain permission from relevant organizations and governments for tracking and receiving data from their respective satellites.
(4) To carry out surveys and provide technical knowledge in remote sensing research and applications.
(5) To conduct solid research on issues which could provide new knowledge on the nature and scope of environment and natural resource, and advice decision makers accordingly.
(6) To provide consultancy services and airborne survey facilities to user agencies.
(7) To promote sub-regional, regional and international (multi-lateral) co-operation on all aspects of remote sensing and outer space technologies, and allied sciences.

Trends, Conclusions and Recommendations

The status of remote sensing technology in Kenya has been considered. It has been established that increasing utilization of this relatively new technology resulted from the events which led to the formation of the African Remote Sensing Council in the 1970's. The possibilities and applicability of the airborne remote sensing technique are now on a firm foundation. However, the major problems facing the application of this technology include cloud cover interference on satellite imagery taken during same period of the year, lack of a LANDSAT receiving station in the region, shortage of trained and skilled manpower and lack of applications' co-ordination at National level.

Remote sensing technology is dynamic and therefore its adoption and use in Kenya and elsewhere will present new challenges such as keeping abreast with new ideas and new aspects of the technology which improve and grow more sophisticated very fast. There will be need for dedicated scientists to man this rapidly changing technology in order to utilize it fully for national development. We know that decision making in the field of development is an intertwined matrix of political moves and technical decisions promoted by exogeneous influences such as economic change (e.g. market dynamics) or natural events (e.g. flood disasters, disease epidemics, etc.). However, with more information derived from satellites, current political decision "games" on these aspects may become a thing of the past as the truth must prevail on resources utilization.

Every government needs information to be run properly. On the other hand, technology has its impact on society. Hence, society should decide whether it must also have an impact on the way technology is presented. Reshaping technology (i.e. making it appropriate) may be the main issue in national development strategy. Therefore, new perspectives in decision making will result when most policy designers become more and more aware of the power of information acquired from space. Kenya, like most developing countries of the world, is therefore at a cross-road with regard to the mapping of its technological path into the future.

Following these considerations, some recommendations expected to have an impact on the use of remote sensing technology in Kenya are made. They include:

(1) Action must be taken to establish a fully-fledged National Remote Sensing Centre.
(2) A LANDSAT receiving station should be built in Nairobi.
(3) Strengthening of the incorporation of remote sensing techniques in existing range of data collecting systems so that data utilization becomes an interaction and collaboration between the decision maker,the planner, the data collection groups and the implementing and monitoring organizations and/or agencies.
(4) Implementation of extensive and intensive personnel training programmes in all aspects of remote sensing technology.
(5) Promotion of sub-regional, regional and multi-lateral co-operation in all aspects of the adoption, absorption and application of remote sensing technology which must become a national priority.
(6) Decision makers, planners and personnel in various fields of the economy, should be made fully aware of the knowledge, potentials and limitations of remote sensing techniques through seminars, conferences and other training programmes (or forums) by national (e.g. Universities, Survey Departments, National Remote Sensing Centre, etc.), regional (e.g. Universities, Specialized Institutions, Regional Remote Sensing Facilities, etc.) and international bodies (e.g. FAO, ESA, etc.), in order to improve resources perception, hence evolve effective policy in the use of such resources.
(7) Kenyan scientists should become members of the proposed African Remote Sensing Society.

It can be seen that the establishment of a LANDSAT remote sensing receiving station in Kenya and the implementation of the foregoing measures should certainly have a marked impact on the growth of remote sensing applications. The potential is tremendous.

It is well known that remote sensing technology is yet to be perfected.

Hence, Kenya, like most other developing nations of the World will need more assistance from donor agencies before it can stand on its own in this area of technological development. However, it must be emphasized that goals and means should not be mixed up with each other and, of course, man is not created to serve technology but use it to improve on the quality of human life.

References

Agatsiva, J.L. and Mwendwa, H., 1982, Land Use Mapping of Kenya Using Remote Sensing Techniques: KREMU Technical Report Series, No. 72.

Croze, H., 1983, Remote Sensing of Natural Resources in Eastern Africa Ecological Monitoring of Rangeland. Training Programme Material, Regional Remote Sensing Facility, Nairobi, Kenya.

Dudal, R., 1982, Natural Resources for Self Reliance: ITC Journal, 1982-1, 60-62.

Gaudet, J.J. and Falconer, A., 1983, Remote Sensing for Tropical Freshwater Bodies: The Problem of Floating Islands on Lake Naivasha: Training Programme Material, Regional Remote Sensing Facility, Nairobi, Kenya.

Gwynne, M.D., 1975, Satellite Remote Sensing in Kenya--An Assessment of the Present Situation With Recommendations for the Future: UNDP/FAO Habitat Utilization Project, KEN 73/005, Nairobi, Kenya.

Kenya, 1979, The Science and Technology (Amendment) Act, No. 7 of 1979 (Date of Assent 10th May, 1979), Part IV, Para. 12(2)-Establishment of Research Institutes."

Kenya, 1981a, Kenya National Remote Sensing Program: A Proposal, Prepared by Dr. Charles K. Paul, USAID, Washington, D.C., for the National Council of Science and Technology, Nairobi, Kenya.

Kenya, 1981b, Kenya Position Paper on the Report of the ECA Technical Mission on Remote Sensing in Africa.

Kenya, 1981c, Water Resources and Hydrology Series. Several Issues, Ministry of Water Development, Republic of Kenya.

Mosonyi, E., Lindner, A., and Francke, F., 1984, Modelling Techniques in the Planning of Irrigation Systems: Journal of Applied Geography and Development, Vol. 12, 94-108.

Mwanje, J.I., 1981, Rapid Forage Inventory of Kenya Rangelands by Double Sampling for Regression Estimation: A Feasibility Study Using An Airborne Digital Radiometer: MSC. Thesis, University of British Columbia, CANADA. Also published as: KREMU Technical Report Series, No. 75.

Mwanje, J.I., and Ottichilo, W.K., 1982, Identification of the Range of Information Requirements for Decision Making on Which Remote Sensing May Have an Impact: Proceedings of the Fourth International Seminar Remote Sensing - Decision - Making, p. 119-205.

Odingo, R.S., (Ed.), 1976, Kamburu/Gtaru Ecological Survey, Final Report on a Trans-Disciplinary Ecological Study of the KAMBURU/GTARU Hydroelectic Dam Area on the Tana River Basin in Eastern Kenya. Published - University of Nairobi, Kenya.

Odingo, R.S., 1982, Land Evaluation, Land Use and Development in Developing Countries; the Potential Contribution of Remote Sensing: Proceedings of the Tokyo Geographical Society - UNU Workshop on Land Use and Land Evaluation, Tokyo 1981.

Odingo, R.S., 1983, Report on Interregional Strengthening of Remote Sensing Applications Technology in Africa South of the Sahara: Submitted to the FAO, December 1983.

Ojany, F.F., 1983, Strategies for Developing the Resources of the Arid and Semi-arid Overview: The Kenyan Geographer (Special Issue), Vol. 5, Nos. 1 and 1, 1-6.

Ongweny, G.S., 1983, Development of Water Resources: The Kenyan Geographer (Special Issue), Vol. 5, Nos. 1 and 2, 36-46.

UNECA,1974, Report on the ECA Technical Mission on Remote Sensing in Africa: February - March 1976.

United States, National Academy of Sciences, 1977, Resource Sensing from Space, Prospects for Developing Countries: Washington, D.C., National Academy of Sciences.

Hydrologic Applications of Space Technology (Proceedings of the Cocoa Beach Workshop, Florida, August 1985). IAHS Publ. no. 160, 1986.

Hydrologic applications of remote sensing in China

YANG JICHENG
Remote Sensing Applications Center, Ministry of Water Resources and Electric Power, Beijing, China

Abstract

There are a lot of big rivers, lakes, and reservoirs in China. Remote sensing has been widely used for hydrology. Uses include the following: (1) study of sediment deposition and flood regulation capacity in Dong Ting Lake--the second largest freshwater lake in China; (2) study of estuary, intertidal habitat deposition and river courses variation in the Yellow River, Yangtze River, and Pearl River; (3) rapid mapping of flooded areas (monitoring of flood); (4) study of the Three Gorge Reservoir of the Yangtze River; and (5) study of temperature traverse of cooling water at electric power plants.

General

China is a country with many mountains. Plateaus and mountainous areas cover 59 percent, hilly areas 10 percent, plains 12 percent, and basins 19 percent of the total territory. The whole country has an area of 9.6 million square kilometers. The topography of the country is of high altitude in the western part, low altitude in eastern part. One hundred million hectares of cultivated lands are concentrated in the three main plains of the country--the Northeast Plain, the North China Plain, and the Middle and Lower Yangtze River Plain--and the Pearl River Delta as well as some island plains.

China's climate is strongly influenced by monsoon. It is wet in summer and dry in winter. Annual mean precipitation decreases from 1500-2000 mm and more in the southeast region to 200 mm and less in the northwest region. In the deserts of Xingjiang there is often no rainfall during the whole year. The annual mean precipitation of the whole country is about 630 mm, most of which is concentrated in four months only. The precipitation varies from year to year as well.

China has a large number of rivers. Among which the Yangtze River, Yellow River, Huai River, Hai River, Pearl River, Liao River, Heilong River, Songhua River, Yaluzangbu River, Lancang River, and Nu River are the longer ones. Moreover, there are some inland rivers in the arid areas in the northwest. These inland rivers originate in the snow covered mountainous areas, so the runoff often disappears and they become seasonal rivers. And there are some rivers flowing out of our national boundary in the southwest, northeast and northwest of the country (Table 1.).

In summer and autumn the wet currents from the Pacific Ocean and Indian Ocean bring about abundant rain, while in winter and spring the dry and cold currents from the central part of European-Asian Continent and the Mongolian Plateau bring about less rain. The coastal areas in the eastern and southern parts of China are humid in climate and rich in rainfall, while the northwestern inland areas are dry in climate and with less rainfall, because of interception of the monsoon penetration by mountains. This is the basic climatic difference between the south and the north, the former is rich in water and the latter is poor in water. This difference in climate is a

Table 1.--The main rivers of China

River	Length (km)	Catchment Area (10^3 sq km)	Annual Runoff (10^9 cu m)
Yangtze	6,300	1808.5	921
Yellow	5,460	752.4	47
Heilong	3,101	886.9	(119)
Lancang	2,354	164.8	69
Pearl	2,210	442.6	307
Talimu	2,179	198.0	
Yaluzanbu	2,057	240.5	138
Nu	2,013	134.9	64
Songhua	1,956	545.6	76
Liao	1,390	219.0	22
Hai	1,090	264.6	23
Huai	1,000	296.1	39

main factor for the uneven distribution of water resources either in space or in time.

The amount of water resources is very unevenly distributed from region to region. If classified according to annual mean precipitation, China can be divided into five different regions, i.e. more rain, humid, semihumid, semiarid, and arid. The distribution of surface runoff in China is basically similar to that of precipitation, but with an even higher degree.

Table 2.--Regions classified according to precipitation and runoff in China

Serial No.	Classified according to precipitation	Annual mean precipitation (m m)	Annual mean runoff depth (m m)	Classified according to runoff
I	more rain	>1600	>900	abundant water
II	humid	800-1600	200-900	more water
III	semi-humid	400- 800	50-200	intermediate
IV	semi-arid	200- 400	10- 50	less water
V	arid	< 200	< 10	arid

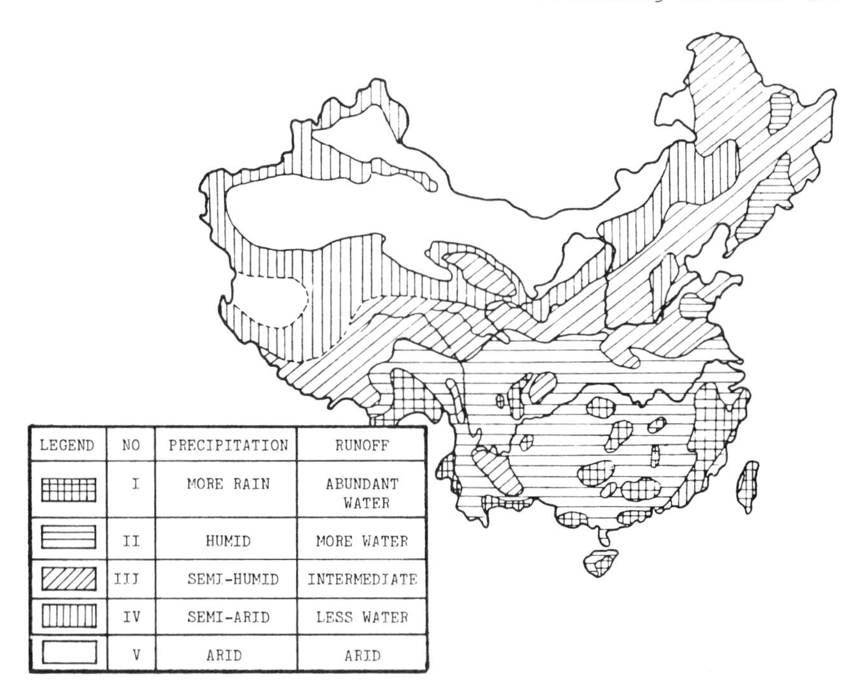

FIG.1 Map showing the regional classification of precipitation and runoff in China.

The criteria for these classifications are given in Table 2, and the sketch map of classifications is shown in Figure 1.

Remote Sensing Applications

Remote sensing has been widely used for water resources, hydropower and electric power studies, such as the analysis of water resources; mapping of surface water; measurement of water quality and pollution; study of soil moisture and evapotranspiration; measurement of snow cover; rapid mapping of flooded areas; study of engineering geology; study of lake, estuary, intertidal habitat deposition and river course variation; study of temperature traverse of cooling water at electric power plants; and study of ground water. Chinese scientists of water resources, hydropower and electric power are fully aware of the urgency of finding solutions for the above problems and of the necessity of employing the newest and most satisfactory techniques. Recently multispectral imagery, IR color imagery, thermal infrared imagery, and SLAR imagery have been used to analyze some of these problems and have gained some achievements. The hydrologic applications of remote sensing are emphasized in this paper.

Study of sediment deposition and flood regulation capacity in Dong Ting Lake.--Using digital image processing system, mosaiced, rectified and ratio enhanced maps have been made of Dong Ting Lake--the second largest freshwater lake in China. Different optical processing images have been made by the optical equipment, 20 different times CCT's were used, and much ground truth data were collected. Investigations are being made on the volume of this lake and the land use, at different seasons. Studies are carried out on the flood regulation capacity. More than 30 software packages have been developed for this subject, which will provide new data for water resources planning and exploitation. The study of sediment deposition show that the sediment of Dong Ting Lake mainly comes from Yangtze River, and another four big rivers flowing into Dong Ting Lake are relatively clean.

Study of estuary, intertidal habitat deposit and river course variation in the Yellow River, Yangtze River, and Pearl River.--Air photos of the estuaries of the Pearl River and the Yellow River were taken by multispectral and color infrared scanning. Supervised classification of these photos was done by the digital image processing system. Using air photos and landsat images, the water depth of seashore at Pearl River was classified. There are six different kinds from 0.5 m to 5.0 m. The classified maps are very useful to select places for reclamation, navigation and cultivation. In the estuary of the Yangtze River and Yellow River, the sediment deposition and the sand bar were displayed very distinctly (Plate 4).

Rapid mapping of flooded areas and flood hazard (monitoring of flood).--Investigations have been made on the flooded areas and flood hazard at the San Jiang Plain, Northeastern China, in September 1981 by landsat imagery and on Hefei Region in Anhui Province in 1984 by Polar Orbit Meteorology Satellite NOAA-7 imagery.

Data are processed by photoprocess and digital image processing methods with ground data to divide the extent of inundation and flood hazard.

The methods that were used are false color image, density slicing, information extraction and classification (Plates 5 and 6).

Study of the Three Gorge Reservoir of the Yangtze River.--For the biggest dam for hydropower in China, the inundation of the reservoir was investigated by different schemes. Color infrared airphotos were obtained at 1:30,000 scale and enlarged to 1:10,000, 1:5,000, and 1:3,000. The backwater curves were calculated and located to color infrared airphoto.

Study of temperature traverse of cooling water at electric power plants.---The Dou He, Da Gang, Wang Ting electric power plants have gained some achievements by thermal infrared image which have been processed by density slicing method (Plate 7).

Hydrologic Applications of Space Technology (Proceedings of the Cocoa Beach Workshop, Florida, August 1985). IAHS Publ. no. 160, 1986.

Hydrological data collection, interpretation and analysis in Greenland

THORKILD THOMSEN
Greenland technical Organization
Hauser Plads 20, DK 1127 Copenhagen K, Denmark
HENRIK HOJMARK THOMSEN
The Geological Survey of Greenland,
Oster Voldgade 10, DK 1350 Copenhagen K,
Denmark

Abstract
Hydro-glaciological investigations are carried out in Greenland to investigate the hydrological conditions for hydropower plants.

Data for hydrological model simulations are collected from 41 automatic stations designed to work under the rigorous conditions of arctic climate. The automatic stations are supplemented by manual measurements of temperature, rainfall, snow distribution, runoff and ablation.

The data are subjected to parameter analysis to provide input for the model simulation. In this data interpretation satellite information is useful to describe air temperature and snow distribution and delineate drainage basins on the Inland Ice.

Data interpretation is resource consuming, but the level at which data can be interpretated is high. The two step process of data interpretation and data analysis simulation makes it possible to describe a hydrological system on the basis of only a few years of measurements.

Introduction
Hydro-glaciological investigations are carried out in Greenland by Greenlands technical Organization (GTO) and the Geological Survey of Greenland (GGU), both state agencies under the Ministry of Greenland. The objective is to investigate the hydrological conditions for the establishment of hydropower plants. There are no hydropower plants in Greenland today, but investigations are carried out in twenty basins (Fig. 1). The first power plant is expected to be projected in 1987, and four other plants to be put into operation before the year 2000.

The investigations cover a description of the hydro-glaciological regimes and procurement of the hydrological basis, based on long time-series of the essential parameters such as runoff, precipitation, ablation and temperature for the dimensioning of hydropower plants.

Data from automatic hydro-meteorological stations are used for the hydrological calculations. The automatic stations are supplemented by manual measurements of temperature, rainfall, snow distribution, simultaneous runoff measurements in subdrainage basins (synchron measurements) and ablation measurements on local glaciers and the Inland Ice.

The collected data are subjected to a data parameter analysis. Satellite information is included in this data interpretation. The data parameter analysis is followed by model simulation - the final data analysis. The two step processing of data provides more degrees of freedom for the determination of uncertain parts and a better possibility of interpreting the results.

Automatic data collection

Since 1977 a network of 41 stations has been established in the relevant basins making registrations every three hours.

The criterion of a data registration system in Greenland is that it works under extreme climatic conditions. Wind velocities can be as high as 80 m/sec. (300 km/hour) and temperatures have been measured as low as -54 degrees celsius. This entailes special internal reference measurements and the possibility of transmission of data through communication satellites. At present the ARGOS system is used. Satellite transmission is made in order to monitor the stations and to optimize time for manual measurements of temperature and precipitation, and the time for station inspection.

The stations developed by GTO have been built to fulfil this objective and is thus an expensive but reliable system. The hydrological data system developed to-day offers a reliability of return data from Greenland of 90-95%, depending on the transducer group considered.

The data registration system has been built up around a data logger of the DATEL type, meeting certain military specifications, including being operative at temperatures of -40 degrees celsius for certain circuits.

The data logger has 64 channels and data cassette collection medium. The energy supply is 12 V DC, the logger being however, operative from approximately 10 to 14,5 V DC. "Battery lowflag" is however set on tape when the nominal 12 V voltage drops to 11 V. The system continues however, within specifications until the voltage drops to 10 V from the 12 V nominal voltage supply. The current required is typically 80 mA when taping, and typically 500 μA during stand-by. The registration interval is pre-set and may be varied from continous registration to a 30-hour interval. At each registration time is stated to the nearest second. All registrations are stored on tape with a 36-bit clock in BCD code and channel values of 14 bits in binary code. The resolution on single values is, however, 12 bits at 32 channels and 8 bits at the other 32 channels.

Four different station types have been developed, measuring a varying number of parameters. In our daily terminology these stations are limniloggers, climate stations, ice-windload stations, and hydro-climatic calibration stations. A few commercial water gauges are also used.

At the hydro-climatic calibration stations more detailed temperature and radiation measurements are made. This is done in order to set up a general energy model for snow and ice melting and calculate water balance in a well-defined arctic precipitation drainage basin when adequate measuring series become available. This will allow work to be focused on evaporation values in an arctic precipitation basin using the water balance and radiation measurements. This can then

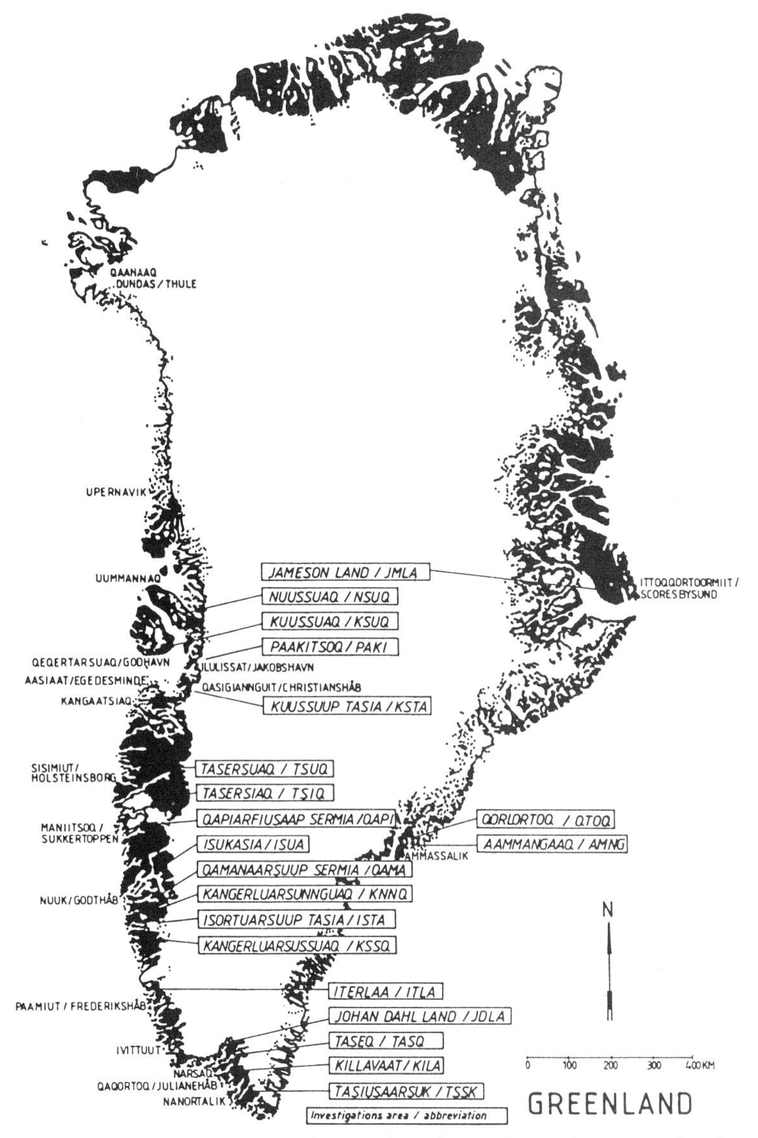

FIG.1 Hydrological investigation sites in Greenland.

be extrapolated to other areas in West Greenland. The measurements will also be used to control the single parameters, precipitation gauges, wind velocities etc.

Table 1 shows the various single parameters measured. Different parameters are measured at the four stationtypes. Reference readings of the internal voltage supply for the logger and transducers are measured simultanously with the climatic parameters.

Comparison between automatic and manual sampled data shows good agreement (Braithwaite, 1983). There were earlier problems with the measurement of precipitation, but this was partly solved by mechanical adjustment of the Belfort precipitation gauge mechanism.

With the tape and energy consumption stated, the stations

Table 1: Transducer data

PARAMETER	TRANSDUCER TYPE	PRECISION/TOLERANCE[1]	MEASURING RANGE BIT RESOLUTION	
Temperature in water and rock	GI type Pt 100	< +/- 0,2°C	-15,5-+15,5°C	0,12°C
Temperature in air, surface	GI type Pt 100	< +/- 0,7°C	-56,0-+31,0°C	0,34°C
Wind Velocity	Aanderaa with Hall generator and F/V converter	+/- 1-2 %	0-100 m/s	0,02 m/s
Wind Velocity	Schiltknecht 655	+/- 5 %	0-90 m/s	0,02 m/s
Wind Direction	Aanderaa	± 2-5°	0-360°	1°
Precipitation gauge	Belfort type 5915X	Unknown	0-300 mm	0,1 mm
		Unknown	0-600 mm	0,15 mm
Air Pressure (abs.)	YSI type:			
	21,8 - 28,5 "Hg	± 1 - 2 mb	725,6-977,7mb	0,06 mb
	24,5 - 29,5 "Hg	± 1 - 2 mb	820,2-1008,3mb	0,05 mb
	27,0 - 31,5 "Hg	± 1 - 2 mb	905,8-1075,1mb	0,04 mb
	28,0 - 32,0 "Hg	± 1 - 2 mb	940,7-1091,2mb	0,04 mb
Air Humidity	Lambrecht 800L100	± 2,5 %	0 - 100 %	0,4 %
Water Level	H&B 15122-2	± 0,1-0,2 %	0 - 10 m Vs	2,4 mm
Short-Wave[2] Radiation	Kipp & Zonen CM5 & CM7 0,3-2,8 μm	< 2 - 3 %	0-1395 W/m²	5,5 W/m²
		< 2 - 3 %	0-1047 W/m²	4,1 W/m²
Long-Wave[2] Radiation	Epply PIR 4-50 μm	< 2 - 3 %	0-698 W/m²	2,7 W/m²
Dynamometers	PIAB - ZK	± 1 - 3 kg	0-130 kg	0,03 kg
	PIAB - K	± 1 - 4 kg	0-250 kg	0,06 kg
Ground Current	Blank Conductor	± 0,5-1,0 % at DC	1-100 %	0,4 %

[1] = Tolerance Values stated in relation to max. reading, typically appr. 40-50% of interval stated.

[2] = Radiation Scale IPS 1956.

are capable of measuring all parameters every three hours from one to three years, depending on the particular station type. In practice each station registers all measurements every three hours, corresponding to a total of 3.2 million values per year.

Data interpretation

Air temperature. To evalue the temperature distribution in a specified area a radiation temperature map is produced from NOAA data (channel 4), (Thingvad and Søgaard, 1984). An example of temperature distribution from Jameson Land in East Greenland is shown in Fig. 2.

The temperature data can be used as distributed information or an area integrated unit. The various temperature gradients on the ground surface can be used to evalue local temperature to the extent permitted by the pixel size. The radiation temperatures are usually too low due to the diminution effect of the atmosphere.

Various methods are being tried to use data from the auto-

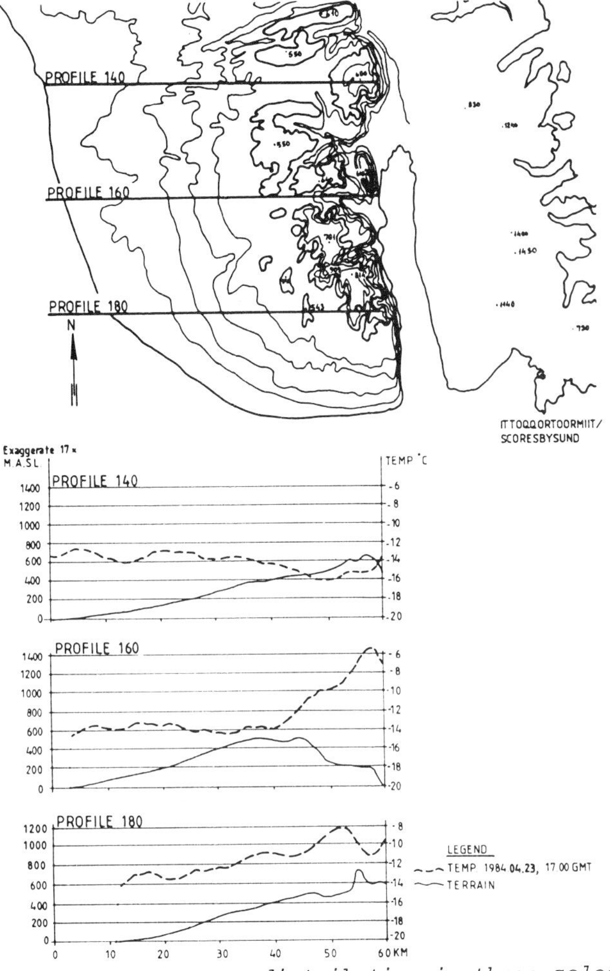

FIG.2 Temperature distribution in three selected profiles across Jameson Land. Radiation temperature based on NOAA data channel 4.

matic stations for calibration to a ground truth temperature.

Precipitation - time-series analyses. Modelling of seasonal hydrological time-series often requires the identification of periodic functions of its base parameters.

As long a time-series as possible is observed in the frequency spectrum based on a Fourier transformation. The explaining variance of the single terms in the cosine/sine series will indicate any repetitive interval. On the basis of the calculated autocorrelation function for the Fourier transformed time-series, a time lag will be found iteratively. The time lag established with the largest autocorrelation function coefficient can then be related in terms of time to the calibration and simulation periods.

The main data of such a Fourier transformation of the precipitation figures for the town Nuuk are presented in Table 2.

Table 2: Main data for Fourier transformation of annual precipitation f(t) at Nuuk based on the 62 years, 1922 to 1984.

$$f(t)=\frac{a_0}{2}+\sum_{k=1}^{\infty}\left(a_k\cos\frac{2\pi tk}{T}+b_k\sin\frac{2\pi tk}{T}\right),\ T = \text{period of } f(t)$$

$$f(t)=616+49\cos\frac{2\pi t}{62}-160\sin\frac{2\pi t}{62}-34\cos\frac{4\pi t}{62}-15\sin\frac{4\pi t}{62}+\ldots$$

and $\frac{a_0}{2}=\bar{x}$ (annual average precipitation)

The first harmonic accounts for 38% of the total variance the second harmonic accounts for 2%, etc.

(To fit a periodic function of Fourier form to the annual precipitation, several terms are used).

Snow and ablation. Satellite information is used to determine the snow distribution and the snow melting. The data were analysed specifically with respect to the distribution of snow cover during the melting season (Søgaard, in press). The snow distribution is applied either distributed or area integrated. Additionally a relative snow distribution is worked out on the basis of ground observations throughout several winters. This relative distribution is used to distribute the precipitation in the basin over the years simulated.

To describe the routing of the meltwater during the snow melt period, snow cover depletion curves for several seasons are worked out (Fig. 3). The melting starts rather late and heavy melting occurs in the beginning of June. Within the basin, however, rather different snow melting patterns exist. This has been investigated by combining the satellite data with a geographical high resolution elevation model (Søgaard,

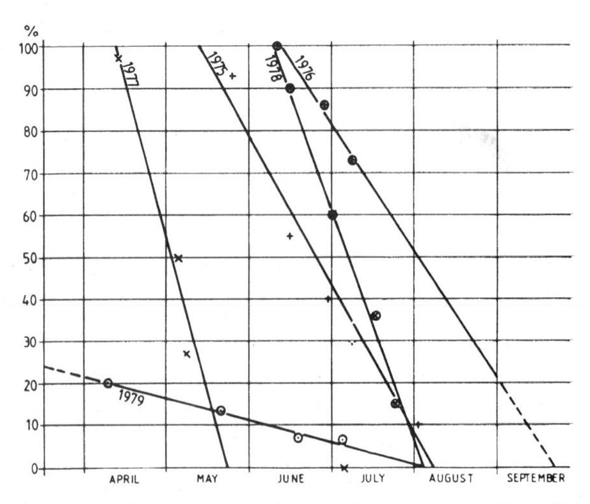

FIG.3 Snow cover depletion curves for Kangerluarsunnguaq near Nuuk, based on NOAA data.

in prep). The temperature distribution used for determination of the melting of the snow pack is found by the parameter analysis of the air temperature. The gradient of the relative snow distribution also expresses the time constant for the routing in the near surface water magazines as an average. The ablation from local glaciers and the Inland Ice is calculated from temperature data. The ablation is determined by manual measurements twice a year (Thomsen, 1984) and are used for calibration. 100% melting is determined by the degree-dayfactor. The degree-dayfactor is then determined iteratively until the best conformity is reached (Fig. 4).

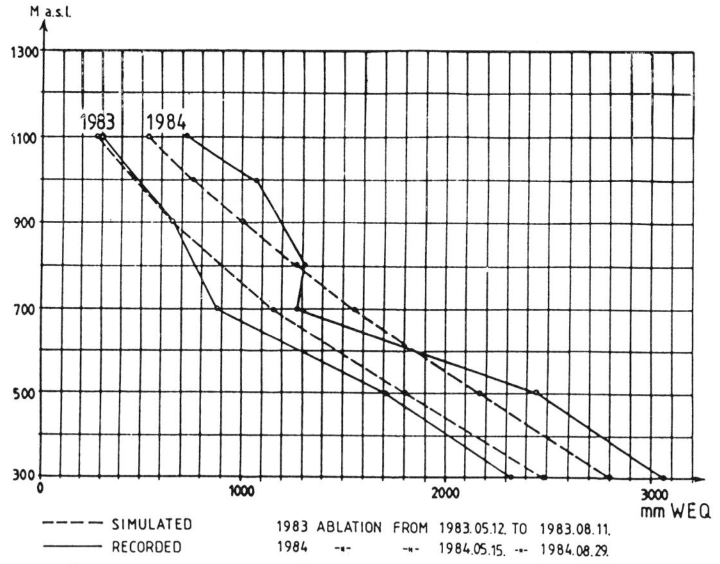

FIG.4 Recorded and simulated ablation at Paakitsup Akuliarusersua.

Drainage basins on the Inland Ice. A large part of the runoff from several of the drainage basins is meltwater from the Inland Ice.

The Inland Ice offers special problems in delineating individual drainage basins, especially at higher altitudes where topographic information is limited. Furthermore the surface drainage basins inferred from maps may not reflect the actual hydrological basins, due to the influence of the subglacial topography on routing the water flowing in and beneath the ice.

Digital Landsat data have been used for detecting surface features on the Inland Ice related to ice and meltwater drainage (Thomsen, 1983). Krimmel and Meier (1975) show Landsat scenes taken under conditions of low sun-angle to be very suitable to accentuate subtle topographic surface features on glaciers reflecting the subglacial topography. For this purpose digital Landsat data (MSS) recorded late in the melt season under low sun-angle conditions were chosen. Contrast stretching based on the frequency distribution of the grey tone values in the images has been used to increase the ability to detect surface features on the ice. Each band was stretched separately. Band 7 (0.8-1.1 μm) was assigned to the red gun, band 5 (0.6-0.7μm) to the green gun and band 4 (0.5-0.6μm) to the blue gun to form false colour images.

The false colour Landsat images have a great ability to detect flowline patterns and supra-glacial streams which can be related to ice and meltwater drainage. Furthermore, the character of the subglacial terrain is clearly depicted through shadow patterns, giving the ice surface a plastic appearance. An example of the ability of Landsat data to detect surface features on the Inland Ice is given in Fig.5.

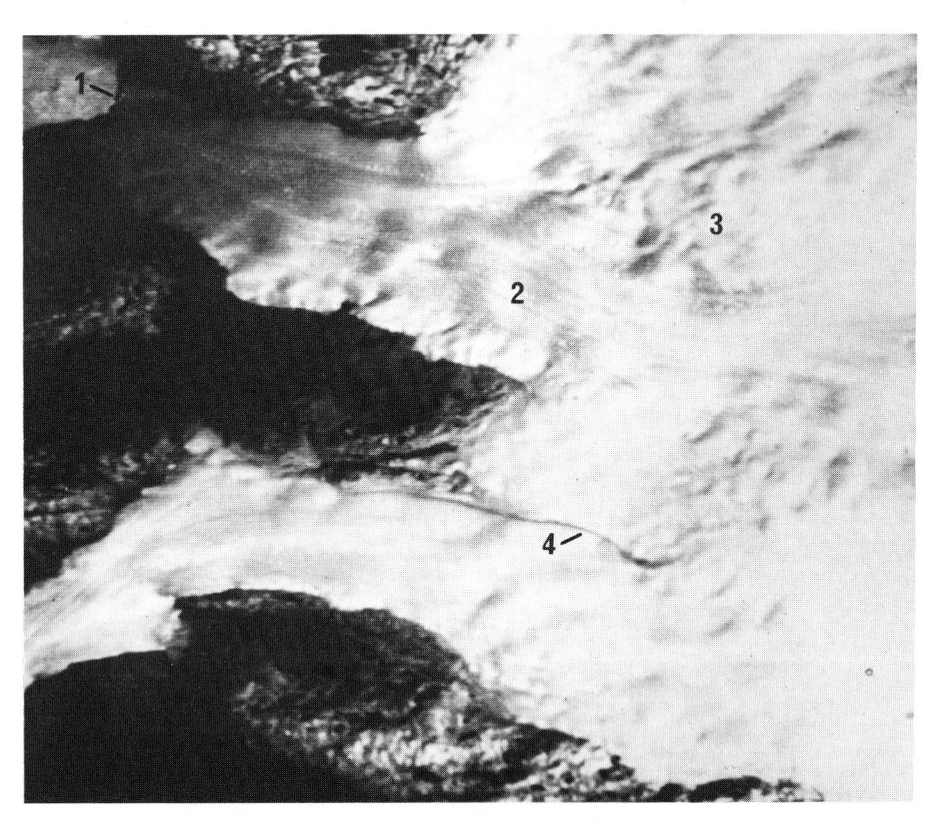

FIG.5 Marginal part of the Inland Ice east of Nuuk. Contrast enhanced Landsat 2 scene, acquired 23 September 1979.
1. Glacier margin ending in fjord.
2. Flowlines.
3. Shadow patterns from subtle topographic surface features reflecting a subglacial ridge complex.
4. Medial moraine.

This information, together with existing topographic information, is used for a preliminary delineation of drainage basins on the Inland Ice as input for the subsequent model simulation. More exact data on the subglacial topography are necessary for further model simulations. For this purpose a radio echo-sounding programme has been started. In this connection the Landsat data serve as a important basis for location of study areas and for planning the tracks of the radio echo-sounding survey.

Other parameter analysis. Determination of other necessary parameters such as time constants for routing, magazine capacities, rain/snow change temperatures, precipitation corrections, runoff relations etc. are found by mearurements in the particular drainage basins and map studies.

Data analysis

Data from the parameter analysis on temperature, precipitation, ablation and delineation of drainage basins are used as input for the Arctic Hydrological Routing, AHR model, describing the hydrological regime in Greenland. This AHR model described in Thomsen and Jørgensen (1984), is based on principles for routing through a linear reservoir, using input from the data parameter interpretation. The exact determination of parameters makes it possible to give a more accurate determination of other parameters which cannot be determined unambiguously. The result of such a model calibration after two years of measurements is shown in Fig. 6. This result is to be verified during 1985 when there will be five years of measurements available. Results should then provide the data for dimensioning the hydropower plant at Kangerluarsunnguaq near Nuuk.

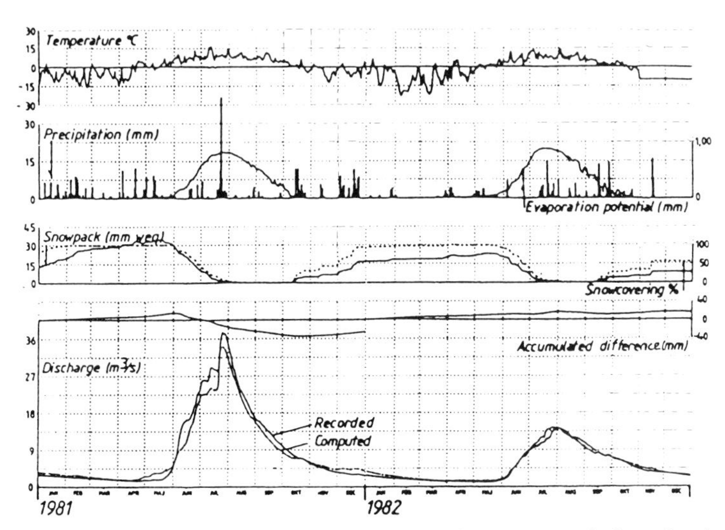

FIG.6 Comparison between streamflow recorded and simulated simulated calculated using the AHR model at Kangerluarsunnguaq near Nuuk.

Conclusion

Description of a hydrological system is possible on the basis of only a few years of measurements followed by a data parameter analysis in which satellite information forms an essential part.

Satellite information is useful to describe air temperature and relative snow distribution and for the delineation of drainage basins on the Inland Ice.

Parameter analyses are resource consuming in both manual work and EDP time. However the level of information at which the few years of data can be interpreted is so high that it is possible at an early stage to set out the dimensioning hydrological basis for hydropower plants.

Improved satellite information in the forthcoming years is expected to give better interpretation possibilities and understanding of the hydro-glaciological processes in arctic areas.

Acknowledgements

The satellite data has been analysed on the image processing equipment DK. IDIMS at the Technical University of Denmark. For the preparatin of NOAA data we would like to acknowledge H. Søgaard, Geographical Institute, University of Copenhagen.

The work has been supported by EEC's European fund for Regional Development. H. Højmark Thomsen publishes with the permission of the Director of the Geological Survey of Greenland.

References

Braithwaite, R.J., 1983, Comparisons between automatic and manual climate stations at Qamanârssûp sermia. Grønlands geol. Unders. Gletscher-hydrol. Meddr., no. 83/5, 17 p.

Krimmel, R.M. and Meier, M.F., 1975, Glacier applications of ERTS images. Journal of Glaciology. v. 15, no. 73, p. 391-402

Søgaard, H., 1985, Snow mapping in Greenland based on multi-temporal satellite data. In: Hydrological Applications of Remote Sensing and Remote Daya Transmission (Proc. Hamburg Symp., August 1983), 383-393. IAHS Publ.no.145.

Søgaard, H., in prep., Variation in surface temperature and albedo in Greenlandic testbasin.

Thingvad, N. and Søgaard, H., 1984, Sneforholdene i Jameson Land. Grønlands tekniske Organisation. Internal Report, 41p.

Thomsen, H.H., 1983, Glaciological applications of Landsat images in connection with hydropower investigations in West Greenland. Proceedings of the EARSel/ESA Symposium on Remote Sensing Applications for Environmental Studies. European Space Agency, Spec. Publ. 188, p. 133-136.

Thomsen, H.H., 1984, Mass balance measurements at the margin of the Inland Ice near Jakobshavn, West Greenland. Polarforschung, v. 54, no. 1, p. 37-41.

Thomsen, T. and Jørgensen, G.H., 1984, Hydrological Data-Model Work in Greenland. Nordic Hydrology, 15, p. 39-56.

Hydrologic Applications of Space Technology (Proceedings of the Cocoa Beach Workshop, Florida, August 1985). IAHS Publ. no. 160, 1986.

NRSA experience in hydrologic applications of space technology during the last decade

A. S. RAMAMOORTHI
National Remote Sensing Agency,
Hyderabad 500 037, India

Abstract

Since 1975 the National Remote Sensing Agency (NRSA) has been the premier organization in India carrying out operational applications of both satellite and aerial remote sensing technology. With facilities like the earth station for regular acquisition of Landsat and Metsat data, sophisticated interactive computer systems for analyzing the data, aircraft for aerial multispectral and photographic surveys, laboratories for generating photo-outputs, etc., several remote sensing projects have been carried out in NRSA. Of these, projects related to the hydrologic applications of space technology form a large number. In this paper the experience gained during the last decade in executing projects in the following fields in hydrology is described (1) mapping of rivers frequently changing their courses and causing bank erosion problems, (2) mapping and monitoring surface water storages for assessing water availability, (3) mapping of inundated areas of rivers flooding vast areas and in delineating flood prone areas, (4) mapping snow-covered areas for forecasting snowmelt runoffs, (5) mapping command areas under irrigation projects, (6) mapping potential zones of ground water, (7) mapping and monitoring watershed features that affect the runoff from precipitation, and (8) in mapping water pollution.

The paper also briefly deals with the hydrologic application projects that will be carried out under the Indian Remote Sensing Satellite Utilization Program.

Introduction

Bounded by the Himalayas in the north, India stretches about 3218 km (2000 mi) southwards and tapers off into the Indian Ocean with the Arabian Sea in the West and the Bay of Bengal in the East, measuring about 2977 km (1850 mi) West to East. In area, India is the seventh largest country in the World. The accurate assessment and judicious management of the usable water and land resources are of great importance to a developing country like India. Having appreciated the potential of remote sensing technology as a tool for optimum planning and management at the level of the Nation, State and even small areas, the Government of India established the National Remote Sensing Agency (NRSA) in 1975 with facilities for satellite data collection, interpretation and analysis, product generation and data utilization. The NRSA Earth Station since the end of 1979 is acquiring Landsat and meteorological satellite data; it will receive SPOT data as well as data from the Indian Remote Sensing Satellite (IRS) to be launched in 1986 and data from the Indian Stretched Rohini Satellite Series (SROSS) satellite also to be launched in 1986. The hydrologic applications using satellite and aerial multispectral scanner data that have been carried out during the last decade in NRSA are briefly dealt with in the following paragraphs.

Mapping of rivers frequently changing their courses and causing bank erosion problems

Most of the rainfall in India occurs during the monsoon season of June to

September when some rivers like Kosi, Gandak, etc. form new channels in their lower reaches every year and cause considerable bank-erosion, breach of embankments or destruction of spurs. For instance, Kosi is well-known for its potential for changing courses. From its original course it had shifted from east to west a distance of about 112 km (70 mi) in a period of 130 years. So in 1963 it was controlled by a barrage and confined to flow within 8 km to 16 km (5 to 10 mi) width between two flood embankments, about 160 km (100 mi) long on either side. But still the Kosi and its spill channels go on continuously changing their courses, eroding the spurs and threatening the safety of the embankments at many places. Ground surveys of the river by conventional methods done every year after the floods, were beset with difficulties and were time consuming; hence required data for executing erosion protection works in time was not forthcoming. It was in these circumstances that for the first time an aerial multispectral scanner survey of Kosi was done in January 1978 from an altitude of about 2900 m (9500 ft). The visicorder outputs generated, particularly the 0.815 micron channel, gave an overall continuous picture of the river configuration and clearly indicated the vulnerable portions of the embankments and the spurs where the river was concentrating it attack. The output products were available within a few weeks time for the engineers to plan anti-erosion works. Such aerial multispectral scanner surveys have been carried out in respect of Gandak, Ganga, and Brahmaputra rivers also.

From Landsat imageries on 1:250,000 scale also, it is possible to study this aspect of river behavior though not in great detail because of the coarse resolution. During the year 1984, the spot where the Kosi breached its eastern embankment in September and the course it took thereafter could be mapped from Landsat imageries of the nearest dates of satellite over-pass. Similarly, the bank erosion that has been taking place in some of the vulnerable reaches in the course of Brahmaputra river has been mapped using multidate satellite imageries.

Mapping and monitoring surface-water storage for assessing water availability and for planning reservoir regulation and regional integrated water--resources utilization

Regular and timely information on the quantity of water available in storage reservoirs and tanks in a river basin is required for judicious utilization for irrigation, hydropower development etc. Though it is not possible to know the depths of water from satellite imageries, it has been found that even by visual interpretation from enlarged imageries one could map the extent of waterspread areas of major reservoirs like Krishnarajasagar, Tungabhadra, Bhakra, etc., to a high degree of accuracy. The hundreds of large tanks in the States of Tamil Nadu, Karnataka and Andhra Pradesh are clearly seen in satellite imageries and hence they can be inventoried and their waterspread monitored.

Mapping of inundated areas of rivers flooding vast areas and delineating flood prone areas so that flood control and flood management works could be undertaken

It is estimated that about 40 million hectares is the area liable to floods in India. Every year vast areas are flooded consequent to high stages in the rivers Brahmaputra, Ganga, Kosi, etc. Mapping of inundated areas by ground survey methods is an arduous time-consuming task. Although an aerial survey could be done, it is costly, depends on weather and has limited coverage. Though of a coarser resolution and dependent on cloud free conditions over the area of interest, satellite digital data, false color and black and white imageries have proved to be very useful in mapping flooded area of Sahibi River, Kosi, Ganga, etc. Improved contrast between land and water boundaries can be obtained by band-ratioing and contrast stretching techniques. It has been observed that there was not much difference between the area of flood inundation as delineated from satellite data and as delineated by aerial photo-mosaics and ground data in the case of Sahibi flood of 1977.

Mapping snowcover areas for forecasting snowmelt runoff

The snow-covered watersheds in the Himalayas are very large, varying from about 5,200 sq km (2000 sq mi) to about 52,000 sq km (20,000 sq mi) and they are at very high altitudes. Since NOAA data is available daily and covers a large part of the Himalayas unlike Landsat, NOAA data has been used in snow-cover area (SCA) mapping and forecasting seasonal snowmelt runoff of Sutlej since 1980 even though it is of coarser resolution compared to Landsat. It has been found that with SCA obtained from NOAA satellite data it is possible to predict seasonal snowmelt runoff within ten percent more or less than the actual runoff, as in the case of the Sutlej river. For monthly or fortnightly runoff forecasting, much data and methodology to predict the western disturbances are required.

Mapping command areas under irrigation projects to determine the efficient use of water

Irrigated areas under large tanks and reservoirs are distinctly seen in false color composites of satellite data and hence can be delineated and measured. However, experience in mapping crops in the command area of Krishnarajasagara and Rajasthan canal has shown that under Indian agricultural conditions, one requires multidate aerial multispectral scanner (MSS) and ground-truth data, in addition to multidate satellite data. Aerial MSS has been found to furnish information on the crop species, crop acreage, crop growth stage, etc.

Mapping potential zones of ground water for planning conjunctive use of surface and ground water for irrigation

Satellite data has been found to be very useful for mapping zones of potential ground water. From satellite imageries information required on the geology, geomorphology, drainage density, soils, land cover/land use is obtained and from a coordinated study of this information, zones of potential ground water have been indicated in the southern part of Tamil Nadu, parts of Karnataka, Madhya Pradesh, Uttar Pradesh, Bundelkhand region, etc.

Mapping and monitoring the watershed features that affect the runoff from precipitation

Besides rainfall, land cover/land use is one of the important factors that affects the quantity of runoff from a basin. From both digital analysis of satellite data and visual interpretation of imageries, one can map or detect changes in the pattern of hydrologic land cover/land use (forest land, agricultural land, barren land, settlement, wet lands, water bodies, etc.) in a river basin fairly accurately. Hence, many such projects have been carried out covering a large part of the river basins in the country.

Mapping parameters affecting water pollution so that corrective steps could be undertaken

Remote sensing techniques have been used in water quality studies also, though in an experimental mode. For example, an aerial survey made of the Godavari river near Rajamundry affected by the effluent from a nearby paper mill showed the quality of water because of variations in reflectance due to depth, suspended sediments, pollutants and/or biological activities. It is felt that monitoring water quality and pollution of rivers using satellite technology is a challenging task requiring much more research and development work.

Hydrologic application projects that will be carried out under the Indian Remote Sensing Satellite Utilization Program

Under the program for utilization of the data from the Indian Remote Sensing Satellite that will be launched in 1986, it is proposed to carry out 16 projects covering various disciplines. Among these are some of the hydrological applications like flood mapping, ground-water studies, snow mapping, water-quality mapping and watershed characterization. For these five themes, suitable sites have been selected and preliminary work is in progress.

Hydrologic Applications of Space Technology (Proceedings of the Cocoa Beach Workshop, Florida, August 1985). IAHS Publ. no. 160, 1986.

Space technology and prediction of the availability of flood water in the Niger River

JEAN-MARIE GRÉGOIRE & HANS-GUNTER KOHL
Joint Research Centre of the European Communities, 21020 - Ispra (Varese), Italy

Abstract

In the framework of the "JOLIBA Project", the Joint Research Centre (J.R.C.) of the European Communities investigates the potentialities of space technics for crop production forecasting (millet, sorghum and rice) in West Africa. The fact that rice culture along the Niger is actually conditionned by flood water availability put in evidence the importance of the hydrological objective.

It soon appears that the main problem was not the setting of a flood prediction model but the collect and the availability of hydro-meteorological information to be introduced in existing models; collect having to be done in a short time over a large area not always easily accessible.

Under such conditions, space technics can provide input at least in two domains:

- transmission/reception of hydro-meteorological data measured and collected on the ground by data-collecting-platforms (DCP); telecommunication technics;
- dynamic description of ground surface characters on the river catchment (vegetation cover, free surface water areas, swamps ..) in order to monitor natural indicators of both rainfall and river water; remote sensing technics.

The present research activity aims to integrate the two technics mentioned, data transmission and remote sensing, to a river flood prediction methodology.

To do so, a test-site has been choosen in the Milo catchment, one of the five tributaries which form the hydrographic network of the Upper Niger in Guinea.

Field studies made it possible to identify some landscape units which can be indicators of the hydrological dynamic of both the river and the catchment basin to which they belong.

A clustering of the 199 basins, present in the study area, has been performed according to drainage and retention potentialities. Seven categories of basin were individualized for the monitoring of surface features.

The transmission segment of the system will use the DCP function of the Meteosat satellite and allows the connection to national and regional nets in West Africa. Results of this research work will be very usefull for more operational activities, such as the "Hydro Niger" project, or for regional center such as "AGRHYMET" in Niamey.

Monitoring of land surface characters, on satellite imagery, and collect in almost real time of hydro-meteorological data, would allow prediction of flood characteristics on the upper Niger catchment.

The "theoretic" flood will then be used as input for propagation model, such as the one established by O.R.S.T.O.M. (Office de la Recherche Scientifique et Technique Outre-Mer), to predict the flood water availability downstream, with special regard to the internal delta of the Niger river in Mali.

1. Introduction

The work presented here is part of the so called "JOLIBA Project" dealing with the definition of space technics potentialities for crops production forecasting in West Africa (Berg, 1984).

This project is funded by the European Developing Fund (E.D.F.) of the Commission of the European Communities in Brussels. The technical aspects are under the responsability of the Joint Research Centre (J.R.C.) of the E.C.

Among the crops present in West Africa, rice is particularly important for food policy, mainly along the Niger river and its tributaries. The fact that rice cultivation is actually conditionned by flood water availability put in evidence the importance of river flood prediction.

Prediction methodology covers at least two different aspects. The first one is the setting of models to establish relationships between rainfalls and water levels in the river, and to forecast the flood propagation characteristics.

The second one is the collect of hydro-meteorological information to be introduced in models, collect having to be done in a short time over a large area not always easily accessible.

Under such conditions, space technics can provide input at least in two domains:

- transmission/reception of data measured and collected on the ground; telecommunication technics;
- dynamic description of ground surface characters on the river catchment; remote sensing technics.

The work presented below is a proposal for integration of the two technics mentioned, data transmission and remote sensing, for the Niger river flood prediction.

The telecommunication segment is based on the use of automatic data-collecting-platforms (DCP) for measurement and transmission of rainfalls and water levels through the METEOSAT DCP function.

The remote sensing segment is based on the monitoring of three land-surface features:

- areas affected by bush fires;
- density and vigor of the vegetation cover;
- hydrological status of indicator pools and swampy areas.

The methodological aspect, which has been developped on a test-site located in the Upper basin of the Niger river in Guinea, is described here.

A proposal for operational use is presented, according to a typical hydrological year of the Niger river.

2. Study area

The Niger river, 4200 km long, runs through five countries of West Africa: Guinea, Mali, Niger, Benin and Nigeria.

The hydrographic network of the so called Upper Basin (ORSTOM, 1970), in Guinea (Fig. 1), is formed by the High Niger itself and four tributaries: Niandan, Mafou, Milo and Tinkisso. The study area (36000 km^2) covers part of the upper basin, the catchments of high Niger, Niandan, Mafou and Milo.

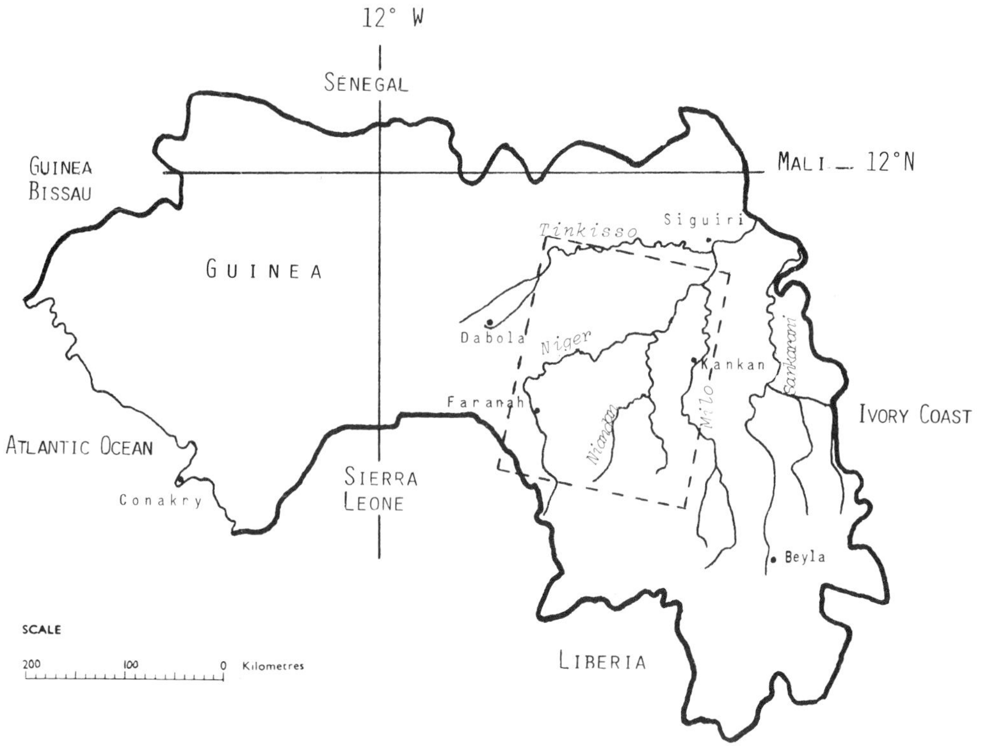

FIG.1 Hydrographic network of the Upper Niger, in Guinea.
--------- Study area

Tributaries of the right bank of the Niger, Niandan, Mafou and Milo flow generally South-North below the high plateaux North East of Macenta, and cross the contact area between the granite outcrops (to the South West) and the schist regions (to the North East). There are also important dolerite outcrops which mark the Southern limit of the "Niandan-Banie" chain (Goloubinow, 1950).

The passage from the granite area to the schist area is accompanied by a fairly sharp change in the type and density of the vegetation cover. There is a transition from light forest to a mosaic of Savanna with scrub which has many areas of very sparce plant cover. If one looks in detail, the geographical distribution of vegetation types is highly correlated with the morpho-pedology and the land-use (Grégoire, 1983).

3. Data and methodology

The methodology, which has been developped for the prediction of the Niger river flood, is based on the monitoring of surface features which are indicators of the rainfall/surface flow relationship.

Having operationality in mind, the monitoring has to be performed on a limited geographical space in order to reduce data treatment operations. To do so, the limits of the 199 catchments present in the study area have been digitalised and registered with topographic map at 1/200000^{e} scale and geometrically corrected Landsat-MSS imagery mosaic.

On this set of data (see Table 1), geomorphological and radiometrically derived parameters (see Table 2) were choosen and quantified in order to allow a clustering of the 199 basins according to their drainage and retention potentialities.

TABLE 1

Cartographic data	Topographic map-IGN-1/200000e Sheets Kankan, Farana, Kérouané and Kissidougou
Satellite imagery	Landsat-3MSS; path 215-row 53; 03/05/1975 02/28/1976 12/02/1982 path 215-row 52; 09/27/1982 12/08/1982

TABLE 2

Geomorphological parameters	Stream order Mean length of 1st order segments Drainage density Maximum basin relief
Radiometrically derived parameters	Extent of bush fires State of the vegetation cover Extent of free water in indicator pools

Seven categories of basin were individualized for the monitoring of the following surface features which are indicators of the rainfall/surface flow relationship:

- extent of bush fires;
- state of the vegetation cover;
- extent of free water in indicator pools;
- state of swampy areas.

Such features should allow on one hand to describe and quantify the effect of rainfall on the environment, and on the other hand to forecast the effect of the resulting environmental conditions on the future rainfall/surface flow relationship; in other words to forecast the waterheight in the main drainage system.

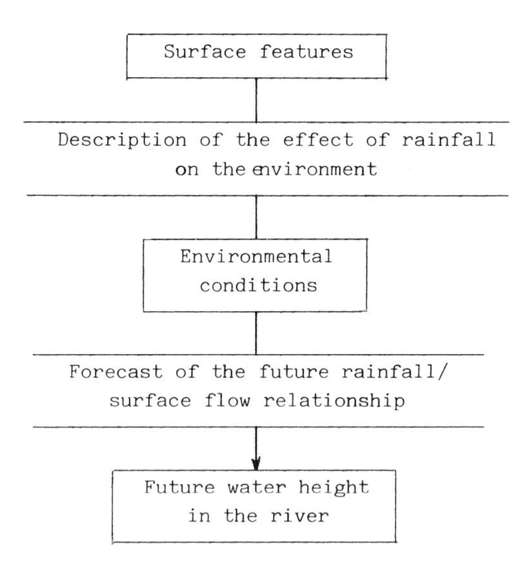

Proposal for operationality

Figure 2 presents the way in which the rainfall/surface flow relationship could be monitored, according to a typical hydrological year of the Niger river. In other words, such a proposal indicates when the surface features, described before, should be observed and which type of output they could give in a river flood prediction system.

Conclusions and perspectives

We have seen that space technics could provide an efficient tool for hydrological forecasting.

According to the Niger river specificity, surface features have been individualized for the monitoring of the rainfall/surface flow relationship.

For operational purposes, such a monitoring should be done on a limited geographical space: seven categories of basin were defined according to their drainage and retention potentialities.

We shall now apply the methodology, described above, to:

- the treatment of a complete hydrological year, if satellite imagery is available;
- the choice of judicious geographical location for data-collecting-platforms; a DCP network, for the collect of hydro-meteorological information, is in fact essential for flood forecasting on the Niger catchment.

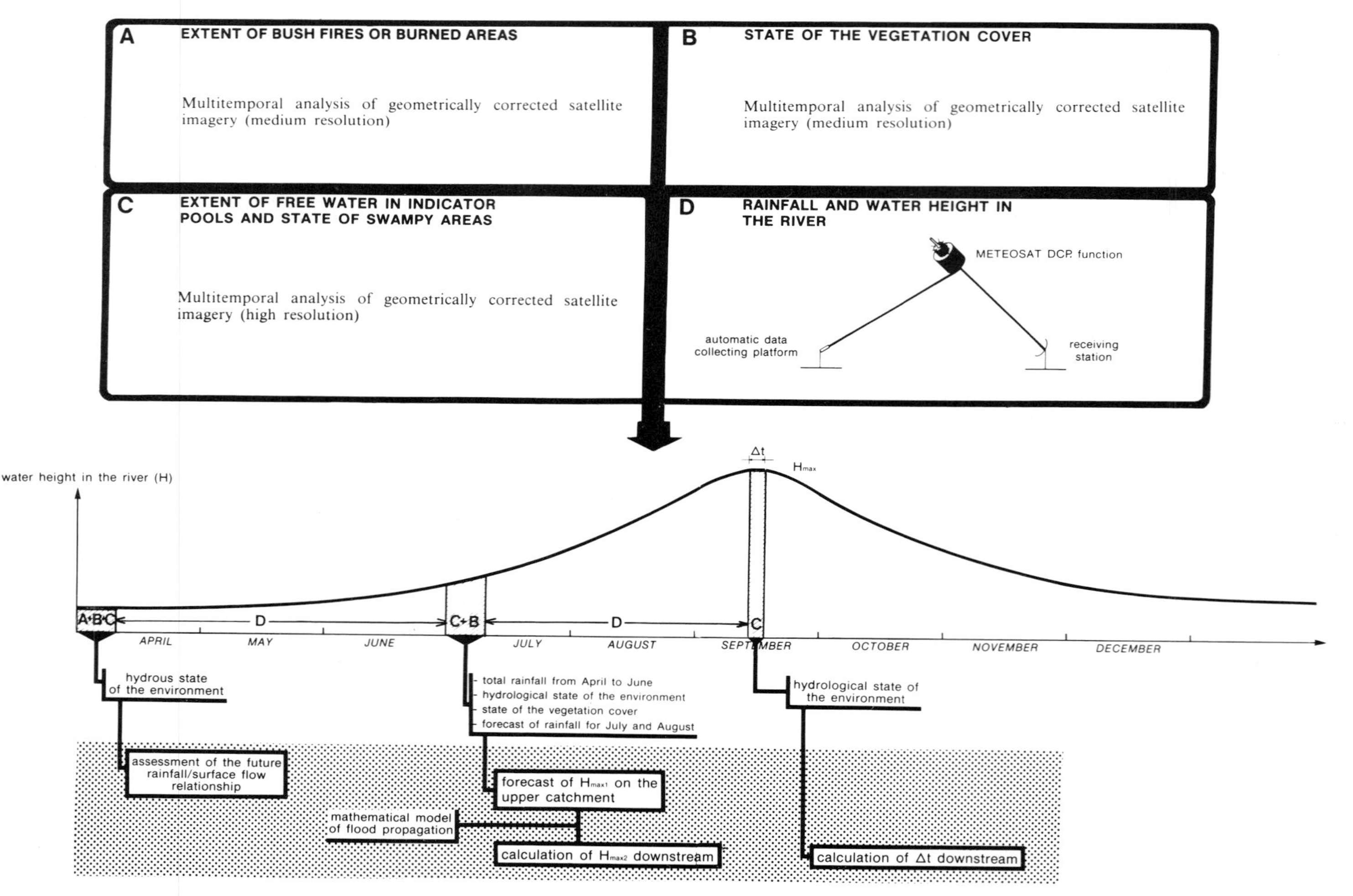

FIG.2 *Remote sensing & telecommunication technics as input for a pediction system of the Niger River flood (expected results).*

References

Berg, A., 1984, Le Projet Joliba en Afrique de l'Ouest: Le Courrier n° 84, March-April 1984, p. 70-72.

Orstom, 1970, Monographie hydrologique du Bassin du Niger. Première partie: Le Niger supérieur et le Bani. May 1970, p. 117.

Goloubinow, R., 1950, Notice explicative sur la feuille Kankan Est (n° NC. 29 NO-E. 26). Grande Imprimerie Africaine. Dakar, p. 28.

Grégoire, J.-M., 1983, Prediction of the availability of flood water in the Niger basin: use of indicator reservoirs. Technical Note n° 1.04.10.83.30/EFD. Joint Research Centre. June 1983, p. 4.

6 Modeling and forecasting

Hydrologic Applications of Space Technology (Proceedings of the Cocoa Beach Workshop, Florida, August 1985). IAHS Publ. no. 160, 1986.

Satellite data as input for long-term and short-term hydrological models

G. A. SCHULTZ
Ruhr-University Bochum
Bochum, F.R.Germany

Abstract
Design and operation of water resources management projects very often suffer from inadequate hydrological data. Remote sensing (RS) data can be of great value as input into hydrological models computing the relevant data for design and operation purposes. Often, however, the resolution in time and space of the RS data is not in agreement with the model input requirements. After a brief discussion of time scales of hydrologic processes, mathematical models are discussed relevant for dynamic hydrological purposes. The potential of various types of RS data as input for these hydrologic models is evaluated. In order to give some information on the question: "which RS system and which type of RS data (spectral bands) is relevant for which hydrologic problem?" three water resources problems are discussed along with case studies as examples. The first example deals with a long-term hydrological model for the design of water supply systems using IR data from a polar-orbiting satellite as input. The second example shows potential application of IR data from a geo-stationary satellite as input into a hydrometeorological model to be used for the design of flood protection measures. In the third example a real-time flood forecasting model is presented which uses radar rainfall measurements as input. This input could, however, be replaced by appropriate satellite data, if available.

Introduction

The recent availability of Remote Sensing (RS) data, particularly satellite imagery will have two major effects on hydrological modeling:

- RS information in form of electromagnetic data from various spectral bands has to be manipulated such that it can be used as input for hydrological models (model input problem)
- this new type of model input fields requires significant changes of the structure of existing hydrologic models or even the development of completely new model types (model structure problem).

The problem of the influence of RS data sources on the structure of hydrologic models was dealt with by the author elsewhere (Schultz, 1985). Therefore the emphasis of this paper lies on RS data as model input.

In this context the important question arises: which RS system and which data (spectral bands) are relevant for which hydrological problem? Since this question is particularly relevant for design and operation of water resources systems, the paper deals mainly with potential RS input into the corresponding highly dynamic hydrological models.

Time Scale in Hydrologic Processes

Before the problem of the choice of an adequate RS system for input data and a corresponding hydrological model can be discussed, it is necessary to say a few words about hydrological time scales relevant for different hydrologic processes.

It is obvious that e.g. a flash flood is a highly dynamic process of short duration (hours) and high variability within the duration of an event (e.g. minutes). On the other hand melting of a glacier or ground water flow represent a process of infinite duration and low variability in time (months). From these extreme examples it can be concluded that two time constants are relevant in hydrologic processes:

- total duration of the process
- time intervals within the duration depending on the process' time variability.

Mathematical modeling of hydrologic processes incorporates adequate choice of the two relevant time parameters. In terms of mathematical statistics the hydrologic process is described by the population statistics (infinite time series or infinite number of events). Since our knowledge of these processes is, however, always based on finite samples (measurements) and since the amount of work for describing the process is limited, we always have to base our description and modeling of such processes on finite time series or finite numbers of events (sample statistics) and on time intervals as long as possible.

Particularly in the field of water resources systems design and management it is necessary to find a compromize between:

- desired high accuracy of results (requiring long time series (duration) and short time intervals (variability) and
- low costs (requiring shorter time series and longer time intervals).

Very often such compromize cannot be found due to the inadequacy of the available hydrological data. In such cases the water project may become a failure.

Hydrologic Models for Water Resources Management Problems

Modern planning techniques (e.g. operations research methods) for design and operation of water resources systems require a thorough knowledge of the relevant hydrologic processes which determine the economic, ecological and social efficiency of such water projects. Since also the planning costs are of major importance, it is necessary to find methods (e.g. mathematical hydrological models) which lead to the above mentioned compromize between required high accuracy and low costs.

Usually conventional hydrologic models are fed with input data from classical observation networks. This fact implies an interdependence between model structure and input data formats. Although remote sensing (RS) data sources can never replace conventional hydrologic observation networks, RS data have two distinct advantages:

- RS platforms provide data with high resolution in space (instead of conventional point measurements)
- RS data can be obtained for areas for which no measurements exist (e.g. in remote areas).

Therefore RS data, particularly satellite data can be most helpful for design and operation purposes, if they are used in combination with ground truth. Disadvantages of satellite data are unfavourable combinations of resolution in time and space. Satellites providing data with high resolution in space (e.g. Landsat (~28 m), Spot) have a low resolution in time (18 days) while those providing a high resolution in time (Meteosat (1/2 h), Goes, GMS) produce data of low resolution in space (~5 km).

If, for the solution of a water resources management problem, the use of RS data becomes indispensible because of the inadequacy of observed data (ground truth), the following questions become relevant:

- what is the relevant time scale (different for various design problems and for operation)?
- which satellite system can provide data with adequate resolution in time and space?
- which spectral channel (or combination of channels) is relevant for the specific hydrologic process?
- which type of hydrologic model can be used or has to be developed?

Particularly the last two questions cannot yet be answered satisfactorily for most cases. The knowledge which spectral channels (or channel combinations) give information relevant for which hydrological process, is by no means adequate. Furthermore, most of the existing hydrologic models are suitable only for conventional input data and cannot be used for RS information. New models of a different mathematical structure have to be developed (Schultz, 1985). The few models available at present amenable for RS input are still in their infancy.

Potential of Remote Sensing Data as Input to Dynamic Hydrological Models

The following discussion will be limited to dynamic hydrological models (high variability in time) which are of the highest relevance to design and operation of water resources systems. Consideration will be given to the problem of time scale and the necessary compromize between required accuracy and costs (1st section of this paper) as well as to the problems of selection of an appropriate hydrological model in connection with the choice of an adequate RS system (2nd section). The three most important problems in the field of (quantitative) water resources management will be discussed in view of potential use of RS model input data:

- design of water supply systems (e.g. for municipal and industrial supply, irrigation, hydropower, navigation, low flow augmentation)
- design of flood protection measures
- operation of water resources systems (e.g. multi-purpose, multi-unit reservoir systems).

The first problem requires hydrological data of long duration (many years) and a not too fine (e.g. months) resolution in time. This means, a long-term model is needed with a long time series of monthly data as model input.

The second problem requires short-term data (flood hydrographs) but many time-independent events and a high resolution in time (e.g. 10 minutes).

The third problem requires short-term forecasts in real-time with high resolution in time.

Table 1 gives more information on these 3 water resources management tasks and the relevant data requirements, potential RS data sources as well as hydrologic models applicable. The given RS data sources as well as the hydrologic models in Table 1 are meant as examples only.They are given here only because they have been used by the author's team. It is, of course, possible that other RS data sources and other - hopefully better - hydrological models can be used or developed.

The last column of Table 1 mentions one example for each of the three discussed water resources management tasks which will be discussed in the following three sections.

Long-term Hydrologic Model for Design of Water Supply Systems

The problem

The design of a water supply reservoir system (e.g. based on a large dam) requires a long time series of river flow data in order to evaluate the water supply reliability. These data are very often not available. Only for a short planning period (1-3 years) an observation network is usually installed yielding hydrological data not allowing a reliability evaluation.

Objective

The short time series of observed (ground) data shall be extended with the aid of satellite data which are available for many years in the past (e.g. NOAA for ~12 years).

Time Scale

Required is a long time series (many years). The relevant time interval

Water Resources Management Tasks	Data Requirements			Potential Remote Sensing Data Source (as example)	Hydrological Model (as example)	Example Given
	Length of Time Series	Time Intervals	Data Source (Conventional)			
Design of water supply systems	Long-term (continuous for many years)	Months	Observed or generated runoff data	IR data from polar orbiting satellites (e.g. NOAA, TIROS N)	Transfer function in convolution integral (theory of linear systems)	River systems in Southern France
Design of flood protection measures	Short-term (extreme events of many years)	Hours, days, 10 minutes (urban systems)	Observed or extrapolated runoff data	IR data from geostationary satellites (e.G. GOES, METEOSAT, GMS)	Rainfall model plus rainfall-runoff model of distributed or lumped system type (e.g. unit hydrograph)	General
Operation of water resources systems	Short-term	10 minutes (urban), hours, days	Observed in real-time + forecast rainfall + runoff	Ground based weather radar, IR data from geostationary satellites	Rainfall model + rainfall-runoff model (distributed system type)	River system in Southern Germany

TABLE 1 Potential use of remote sensing information for water resources management tasks

Δt = 1 month is an acceptable compromize (accuracy vs. costs) for river runoff data.

RS Input Data
Since a long-term data series is required, NOAA data seem appropriate although this polar orbiting satellite produces only 2 images per day. Only information from one spectral channel was chosen, i.e. infrared. These infrared (IR) data had to be manipulated in order to become usable as model input. Therefore an input variable B(T) was developed (T being cloud top temperature) which uses the two IR images per day and the three coldest "grey steps" of the grey scale contained in the images.

$$B(T) = 0.5 \sum_{k=1}^{2} \sum_{i=1}^{3} B(T_i)_{k,l}^{a_i} \qquad (1)$$

where:

$B(T_i)_{k,l}$ = fractional cloud cover index of IR density range i (i=1,2,3) on image k (k=1,2) of day l (NOAA produces 2 images per day) valid for the river catchment area.

l = number of day

a_i = weighting coefficient of the i'th density range (i=1,2,3)

B(T) can be interpreted as a mean daily temperature weighted cloud cover index computed for the whole river catchment area.

Hydrologic Model
Following the theory of linear systems the model applies a transfer function h_k which transforms the input B(T) into an output q_l (representing a daily indicator of runoff). The required monthly runoff then is just the sum of q_l for all days of the month. The transformation of model input into output is done with the aid of the well known convolution integral containing B(T) as input and h_k as transfer function in an appropriate way (Strübing and Schultz, 1985, Schultz, 1985, Strübing 1984).

Results
The model was applied for river catchments in southern France. Figure 1 shows an example of the model performance. The model was calibrated with simultaneous ground truth and satellite imagery of the year 1977.

Short-term Model for Design of Flood Protection Measures

The problem
Flood protection structures (e.g. flood retention reservoirs, levees) have to be designed such that they can resist floods of rather high recurrence intervals (e.g. the hundred years flood HQ_{100}). Very often no flow data and no rainfall data relevant for the project area are available. Many flood events should, however, be known in order to establish a probability distribution of floods (flood frequency analysis).

Objective
The missing flood runoff data shall be computed with the aid of a rainfall-runoff model. Satellite imagery shall be used in order to determine the flood producing rainfalls over the relevant catchment area.

Time Scale
Only single flood events are of interest. Total flood duration is usually

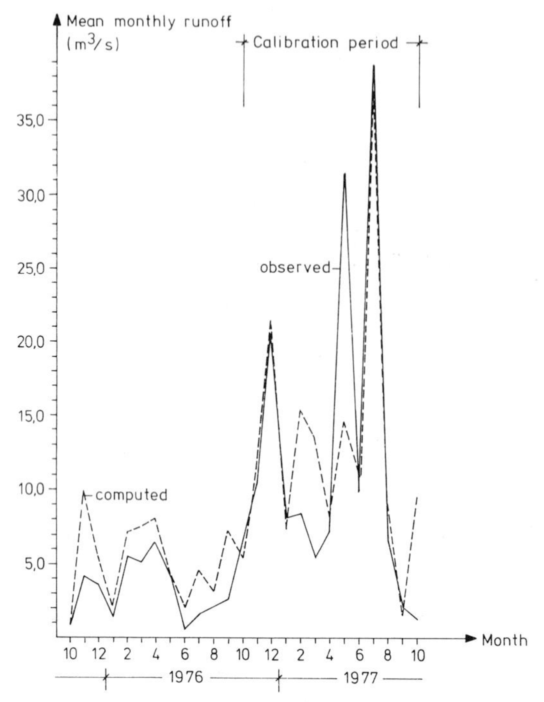

FIG.1 Monthly runoff values based on IR satellite imagery (Save River, France).

not more than hours (small basin) up to days (large catchments). Variability of rainfall is high: time intervals should be short, e.g. $\Delta t = 1/2$ hour.

RS Input Data
Suitable data for rainfall estimation are among others 1/2 hour IR images, e.g. from GOES, GMS or Meteosat satellites (geostationary). Figure 2 shows a comparison between IR information obtained from Meteosat (Fig. 2a) and simultaneous observed ground truth (i.e. isohyets constructed with the aid of rain gauge measurements) for the same area in southern Germany (Fig. 2b).

Hydrologic Model
The short-term hydrologic model transforming satellite data into a flood hydrograph consists of two consecutive partial models:

a) rainfall model transforming the satellite information into rainfall data

b) runoff model transforming this rainfall into a flow hydrograph

For a) various models are in use (Barrett and Martin, 1981) such as cloud indexing methods, life history methods, bi-spectral, cloud model and micro-wave methods.

For b) classical hydrological black-box models can be used (e.g. unit hydrograph) or - if the rainfall is estimated with high resolution in space - also distributed type models can be applied. An example of such a model will be given in the next chapter.

Results
Although it would be possible

- to compute a series of flood producing hyetographs for a river catchment area from satellite imagery

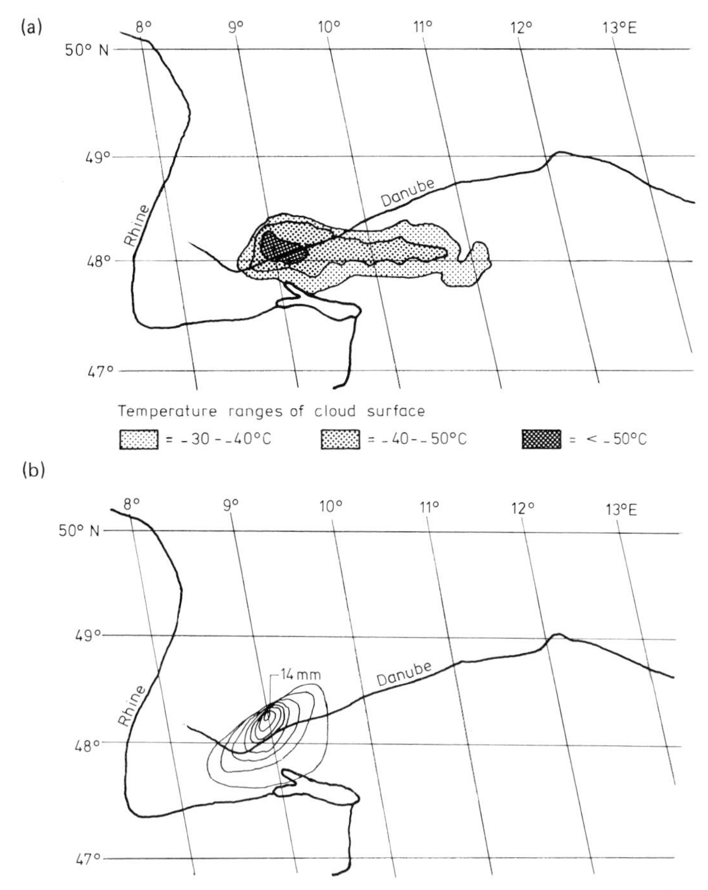

FIG.2 Comparison between IR satellite information and simultaneous isohyets (ground truth) in Southern Germany.

(a) Convective cell derived from METEOSAT IR image 16.55 h GMT, 6th August, 1978.

(b) Isohyetal map based on rain gauges, 16.45 - 17.15 h GMT, 6th August, 1978.

- to use these hyetographs as input into rainfall-runoff models
- to use the resulting flood hydrographs as basis for the computation of a flood probability distribution function

the author does not know of a successful application of this integrated technique yet.

Short-term Hydrologic Model for Operation of a Water Resources System

The problem

Water resources systems (e.g. dams for water supply, irrigation etc. or for flood protection) have to be operated in real-time. Particularly for highly dynamic processes, e.g. flood events, it is necessary to have a real-time forecast of the event (flood hydrograph) to be expected in the near future. The longer the lead-time of the forecast the more valuable it is for systems operation.

Objective

In order to have available a flood forecast as early as possible the computation of the forecast shall be based on RS data estimating the flood producing rainfall.

In order to extend the lead-time of the flood forecast even further, also a rainfall forecasting model shall be applied.

Time Scale

Since floods are usually of short duration with high intensity, the total duration will be days; time intervals should be between 10 minutes (urban areas) and hours (medium size catchments). Important is further the fact that the forecast must become available in real time, i.e. between observation of input data and issue of the forecast an almost zero time delay is required.

RS Input Data

RS data of high relevance for flood forecasting in real time are radar rainfall measurements. Area rainfall data with very high resolution in time (≥ 1 rainfall intensity measurement/minute) and space (~ few hundred meters (distance) and 1° angle) can be obtained from a weather radar (Attmannspacher, Riedl, 1979). Also data from satellite imagery could be used similarily as indicated in the previous example. The RS data handling would be similar to the handling of the radar data. This example will deal with radar data as model input since this technique is already operational (Klatt, Schultz, 1985). In the example discussed here, data obtained from a C-band weather radar were used.

Hydrologic Model

The mathematical model consists of three partial models:

a) model transforming the observed radar echo into rainfall

b) deterministic model transforming the rainfall into a runoff hydrograph (rainfall-runoff model)

c) stochastic model for real-time rainfall forecasting

The model under a) is working on the basis of the classical Z-R relationship (Attmannspacher, Riedl, 1979). The model under b) is a linear distributed system model described elsewhere (Klatt, Schultz, 1985, Klatt, 1983). The model under c) is a stochastic model which is based on conditional probabilities for various rainfall types. On the condition of how long and how much it has been raining until the time of forecast, the amount and duration of rainfall until the end of the precipitation event is forecast. Also rainfall forecasting models with the aid of satellite imagery seem possible.

Results

Flood forecasts with the above mentioned model (without the rainfall forecasting part of the model) made at a time after the end of rainfall yielded good results in a river basin in southern Germany (Fig. 3). If, however, the forecast has to be made during the storm, the rainfall forecasting routine has to be used which renders the results usually less accurate (Klatt, Schultz, 1985, Schultz, 1985, Klatt 1983).

Summary and Conclusions

For purposes of design and operation of water resources systems often conventional hydrological data are inadequate. In such cases remote sensing data are of great value for the estimation of the relevant hydrological data. The data requirements are, however, very different as far as the time scale is concerned. Since the time resolution of satellite information is specified by the system, problems arise which satellite system's data to

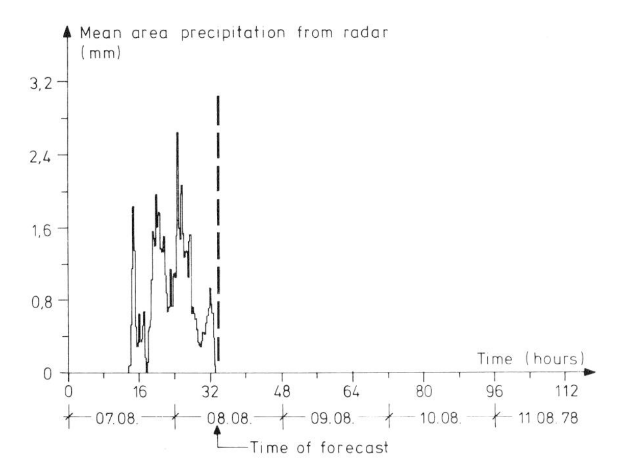

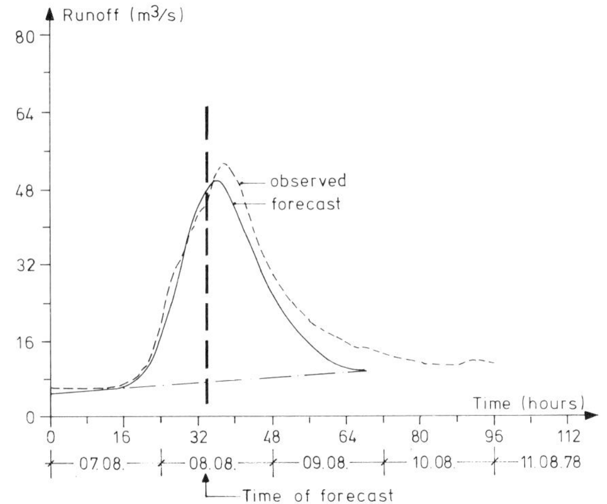

FIG.3 Real-time flood forecast based on radar rainfall measurements (Gauge Lauben, Günz River).

use for which water resources management problem. Furthermore the available hydrological models are usually not suitable for RS input data.

After general discussion of these problems three examples are given showing the potential use of RS data as input for hydrological models for three of the most important problems in water resources management.

In conclusion the following statements can be made:

1. Not only for the determination of river catchment characteristics but also for dynamic hydrological processes RS data can serve as model input.

2. Knowledge on which spectral bands are relevant for which hydrological processes is not well developed yet.

3. Hydrologic models are normally not suitable for RS input. They have to be modified or new models must be developed.

4. Recent research efforts show first approaches for the use of dynamic RS data as input to hydrologic models.

5. New RS information from new satellite systems in combination with improved or new hydrologic models will provide us in future with improved and promising applications of RS data for solving water resources management problems.

References

Attmannspacher, W., and Riedl, J., 1979, Radar Area Precipitation Measurements as Basic Data for Hydrological Purposes: Proceedings Symposium/ Workshop on Digital Radar Reflectivity Processing, Edmonton, Canada.

Barrett, E.C. and Martin, D.W., 1981, The Use of Satellite Data in Rainfall Monitoring: Academic Press, London, 340 p.

Klatt, P., 1983, Vorhersage von Hochwasser aus radargemessenem und prognostiziertem Niederschlag: Schriftenreihe Hydrologie und Wasserwirtschaft, No. 3 (Ed. G.A. Schultz), Ruhr-University Bochum, 155 p.

Klatt, P. and Schultz, G.A., 1985, Flood Forecasting on the Basis of Radar Rainfall Measurements and Rainfall Forecasting: IAHS Publication, No. 145.

Schultz, G.A., 1985, How does Remote Sensing Influence the Structure of Hydrologic Models: Proceedings IVth International Hydrology Symposium, Fort Collins, 1985.

Strübing, G., 1984, Satellitendaten als Basis der Bestimmung von monatlichen Abflüssen für wasserwirtschaftliche Planungen: Schriftenreihe Hydrologie und Wasserwirtschaft, No. 1 (Ed. G.A. Schultz), Ruhr-University Bochum, 163 p.

Strübing, G., and Schultz, G.A., 1985, Estimation of Monthly River Runoff Data on the Basis of Satellite Imagery: IAHS Publication, No. 145.

Hydrologic Applications of Space Technology (Proceedings of the Cocoa Beach Workshop, Florida, August 1985). IAHS Publ. no. 160, 1986.

Development of a modular hydrological forecasting model based on remotely sensed data, for interactive utilization on a microcomputer

J. P. FORTIN & J. P. VILLENEUVE
INRS-Eau, Université du Québec, Sainte-Foy, Québec, Canada
A. GUILBOT
Laboratoire d'Hydrologie Mathématique, Université des Sciences et Techniques du Languedoc, Montpellier, France
B. SEGUIN
Station de Bioclimatologie, INRA, Avignon, France

Abstract

Following the previous development and application of hydrological simulation models characterized by physiographic, state, input and output variables spatially distributed according to a square grid information system, and, as such, suitable to the assimilation of remotely sensed data, the authors are now developing a forecasting model. This new model has a modular structure for more flexibility. Moreover, it will be implemented on a microcomputer as a users' friendly interactive package.

The initial version of the model will be divided into nine modules: PHYSIOGRAPHY, PRECIPITATION (including snow accumulation and melt), HYDROLOGY (both production and routing functions), EVAPOTRANSPIRATION, FORECAST, OPTIMIZATION, INPUT, OUTPUT and MAIN. The model is again based on a square grid information system whose grid size vary according to basin characteristics and size. It is conceived so as to make a maximum use of remotely sensed data both for the description of the physiographic and land-use characteristics of the basin, and for the input variables, mostly meteorological in nature, without relying necessarily on those for the daily preparation of forecasts. A description of each module is included, as well as of the functioning of the complete model.

A few examples of spatially distributed variables similar to those that will be used or produced by the new forecasting model are also shown. These variables, which may already be used or produced by the CEQUEAU model, include land-use data derived from LANDSAT-MSS imagery, precipitation from radar, snow cover distribution from satellite data and model simulation, and finally, actual evapotranspiration from satellite data.

Operational use of the model is finally discussed.

Introduction

Development of deterministic hydrological models has really started in the mid sixties with the Stanford model (Crawford and Linsley, 1964 and 1966). This model has been followed by many others, all of them based on available data, that is conventional maps and data observed at meteorological and streamflow stations (Cormary, 1969; Girard et al., 1971 and 1972; Anderson, 1973; U.S. Army Corps of Engineering, 1975; ...).

In the next decade, remote sensing began to be applied for land-use determination, flood-plain delineation, snow cover mapping and other studies with potential application to hydrological modelling (Robinove,

1969; Rango, 1975; Séguin, 1980). Studies in which use of remote sensing was combined in some way or the other with that of hydrological models is more recent (Fortin et al., 1979 and 1983; Bowley et al., 1981; Martinec, 1982; ...). In the main time, other models were developed, but not really geared to use that type of data. Peck et al. (1981) write that "the most obvious conclusion of the study is that most hydrologic models in their present configuration do not have a significant potential for using remotely sensed observations (...). Hydrologic modeling can be improved through the development of a new generation of models or subroutines for existing models which recognize the characteristics of the new remote sensing capabilities".

Among the previous generation of models are those developed at INRS-Eau. These models are characterized by physiographic, input, output and state variables spatially distributed according to a square grid information system (Girard et al., 1972; Girard et al., 1980; Morin et al., 1981; Villeneuve and Isabel, 1984). As such, they are more than others, suited to the assimilation of remotely sensed data, as will be shown by examples in the second part of this paper.

In agreement with Peck's conclusions, the authors want to go one step further in developing a new forecasting model. This model will be of the distributed type and based as much as possible on remotely sensed data, without relying necessarily on those for the daily preparation of forecasts. Moreover, it will be implemented on a microcomputer as a user's friendly interactive package.

General structure of the model

For more flexibility and ease of development, the model will be divided into modules, each of them being devoted to a specific task. These modules are: PHYSIOGRAPHY, PRECIPITATION (including snow accumulation and melt), HYDROLOGY (both production and routing functions), EVAPOTRANSPIRATION, FORECAST, OPTIMIZATION, INPUT, OUTPUT and MAIN.

All modules will share a common data base. The grid size will be allowed to vary from module to module, depending on the spatial accuracy of available data (PRECIPITATION and EVAPOTRANSPIRATION) or basin characteristics (HYDROLOGY). The separation of the model into modules will also permit the independant development and replacement of each module. In practice, the only constraints on a particular module will be the type and format of input variables necessary for the module itself as well as the type and format of the output variables necessary for other modules.

For the first version of the model, a time step of 3 or 6 hours is considered. The objective is however to use a time step varying with hydrological events.

The INPUT module

The objective of the INPUT module will be on-line retrieval and quality control of conventional meteorological and hydrological data as well as remote sensing data from satellite and meteorological radar stations. The INPUT module will next make that information available in proper format to the PRECIPITATION, EVAPOTRANSPIRATION and OUTPUT modules (figure 1).

The PHYSIOGRAPHY module

All variables related to basin characteristics, for instance terrain elevation and slope, drainage information and land-use, will be handled by the PHYSIOGRAPHY module. An off-line procedure, will first permit to prepare the data bank containing all pertinent information on the basin

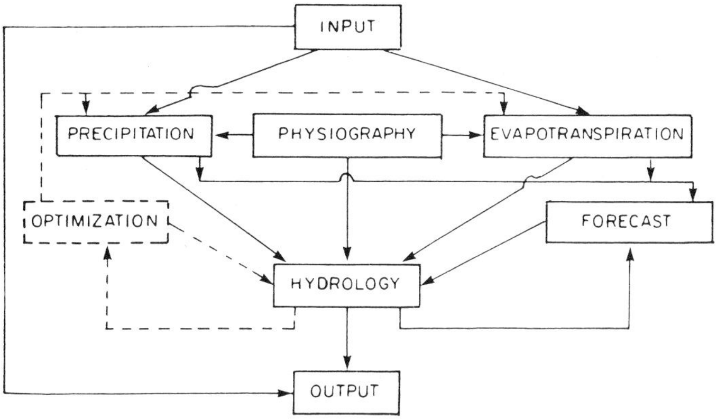

FIG.1 Flow information in the model.

for later use in the model. Actual plans are to use a grid size of 4 x 4 km, but that size will be allowed to change (1, 2, 4, 8, ..., km) to suit basin characteristics and size. Hopefully, all that information will come from remote sensing. A procedure is being developed to use SPOT data to obtain all necessary data on basin topography. Land-use and soil data will be extracted from SPOT, TM or MSS data. Furthermore, remote sensing will permit the preparation of seasonal data banks if necessary. Once this is done, the next step will be to use an interactive procedure to restructure the original data bank according to hydrological contributing areas, as will be explained later on.

The objective of the PHYSIOGRAPHY module is to feed the PRECIPITATION, EVAPOTRANSPIRATION and HYDROLOGY modules with the relevant data.

The PRECIPITATION module

If radar data are available, the PRECIPITATION module, using information on the radar location, the size of the radar pixels (from the INPUT module) and the location and shape of the basin, as furnished by the PHYSIOGRAPHY module, prepares the precipitation map calibrated with raingauge data (figure 2, grid A). When only standard raingauge data are available, that information is spatially interpolated (Thiessen polygons or weights according distance) to get the precipitation map. Information on air temperature and terrain elevation is used to determine whether rain or snow falls on a particular grid cell.

The PRECIPITATION module includes a sub-module for snow accumulation and melt (figure 2, grid B). That sub-module is based on a modified snowmelt-index method in which the various processes are simulated as a function of basin characteristics, as furnished by the original or restructured data bank of the PHYSIOGRAPHIC module. Snow will thus melt faster in south facing slopes than on slopes oriented to the north. Land-use is also taken into account. At any time step, a map of snow cover on the basin (snow depth and snow water equivalent) will be available for display, output or updating purposes. Rainfall estimation from integrated satellite, radar and raingauge data, when operational, will be introduced in the model in much the same way as radar data.

The EVAPOTRANSPIRATION module

Actual evapotranspiration will be obtained on each grid cell or contributing area (figure 2, grid C) through the use of various estimation methods

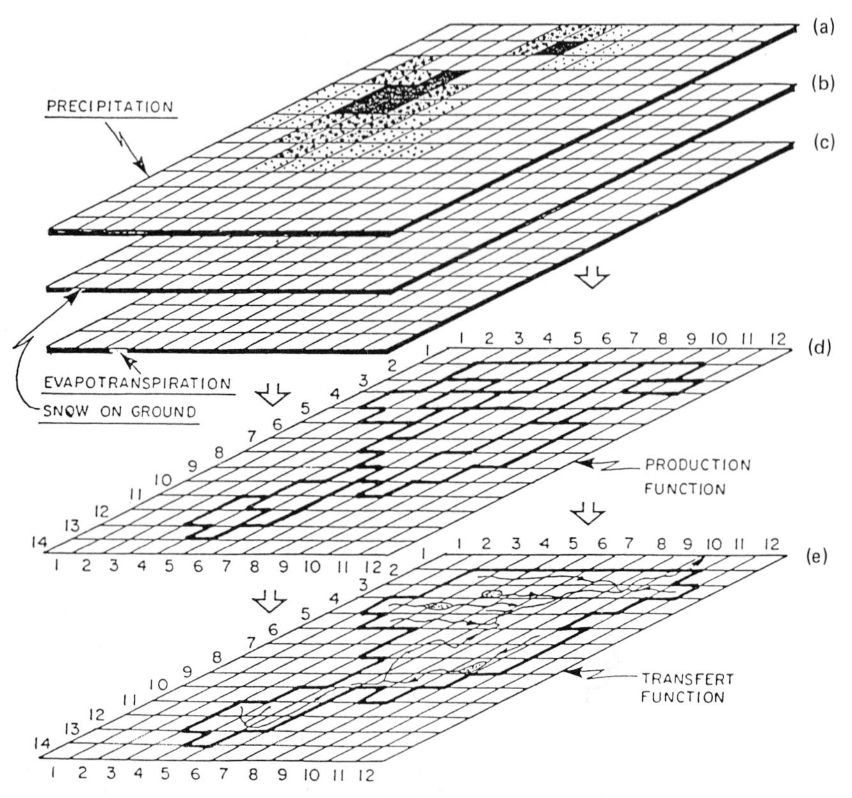

FIG.2 Spatial structure.

depending on data availability. A method in which the spatial distribution of net radiation and surface temperature will be evaluated by remote sensing will be favored, however (Séguin, 1980; Séguin and Itier, 1983). This should allow more representative evaluation of actual evapotranspiration to be made, because the method will take land-use into account. As a second choice, Penman type equations will be used to determine potential evapotranspiration from which actual evapotranspiration will be estimated, using information on the soil water budget, as simulated by the HYDROLOGY module. Finally, if only air temperature is available on the basin, less accurate methods, like that of Thornthwaite, will be used to estimate potential evapotranspiration.

The HYDROLOGY module

This module is divided into two sub-modules, namely PRODUCTION and TRANSFERT.

As far as the PRODUCTION function is concerned, the basin is divided into contributing areas determined by aggregation of grid cells as a function of land-use, soil-type, topography and drainage pattern (figure 2, grid D). This has the advantage of requiring less computations than if a water budget was estimated for all grid cells, while retaining relatively homogeneous areas. At the same time, the contributing areas being based on a square grid information system, addressing and mapping is facilitated. The function assumes hydrological processes leading to the "production" of water for routing in streams, can be simulated by reservoirs, the upper one being relatively shallow in order that its water budget be eventually compared to data on soil moisture obtained by microwave or gamma ray sensors. Identical values can be given to reservoir parameters for all contributing areas, but variation of these parameters, infiltration for instance, according to land-use, soil-type and topography are expected. Water from the contributing areas is routed through a number of reaches in the drainage network by the TRANSFERT function (figure 2, grid E). It has been defined so as computation time is minimal. A modified kinematic wave equation in which the spatial and time increments can be varied, is solved by an explicite four point finite difference method. Reservoir and lake routing are considered special cases of river routing. As seen in figure 2 (grid E), the reaches are tied to the original grid mesh, so that the coordinates of their end points can be easily determined. Characteristics of each of the reaches are estimated from data provided by the PHYSIOGRAPHY module.

The OPTIMIZATION module

Usually, distributed parameters models are so complicated and time consuming that automatic calibration of their parameters is almost prohibited. They are subjectively ajusted by trials and errors and sensitivity analysis is discarded. Automatic calibration of model parameters can be done however, if the model is properly structured (Villeneuve and Isabel, 1984). A model structure similar to that suggested by these authors is used here, except for the routing function, which is more flexible than the previous one. It is thus believed that it will be possible to calibrate the model in an automatic fashion, with the use of a multi-algorithm procedure, as suggested by Cormary and Guilbot (1971) and Villeneuve and Isabel (1984), beginning with the Monte-Carlo method, followed by the SIMPLEX and conjuguate gradient methods. A sensitivity analysis will also be done in order to find out what parameters have the greatest effect on flow simulation.

The FORECAST module

No model is perfect and so are the input data, whether they come from conventional and remote sensing observations or forecasted variables. Errors are also associated with streamflow measurements. Since the objective of a forecasting procedure is to give the best streamflow estimation at any particular time and place, the information given to the model up to the previous time step has to be updated with the latest observations. The actual target is short term forecasting, that is one or two days ahead, because of limitation in forecasted variables, but a medium or long term forecasting mode is also planned. An autoregressive model, whose parameters will be defined by Kalman filtering, will likely be applied to input and output variables. The optimal memory length of that autoregressive model will have to be determined. The possibility of updating the state variables will also be looked at. The whole procedure is in the evaluating stage for the moment.

The OUTPUT module

Essentially, the OUTPUT module will display any requested result or input variable (such as radar data). Tables and graphics will be available, as well as maps. On-site printers and plotters will be used, but remote transmission of information is planned. The module will be programmed so as to meet the specifications of as much output devices as possible.

The MAIN module

The MAIN module is the link between the user and the other modules. The global structure of the model is programmed in this module. It is also through that module, that the model can be runned in a interactive or batch mode on a microcomputer.

Examples of spatially distributed variables

The idea of developing a new distributed model based on remote sensing came partly from the experience gained with the CEQUEAU model (Morin et al., 1981). A certain number of studies have been undertaken to use remotely sensed data with that model. A few examples will be presented in this paper.

Estimation of land-use data

In the CEQUEAU model, the number of land-use classes is limited to (a) forested areas, (b) unforested areas, (c) swamps and (d) water. The percentage of each class on each grid cell (figure 3 and table 1) is first determined and used later on in different sections of the model. For instance, snowmelt is computed separately for forested and unforested areas. These percentages are usually estimated from topographic maps.

To test the potential of remotely sensed data for the determination of class occupation on a grid cell basis, a study was undertaken on the Yamaska river, south-east of Montréal. Only the information pertaining to the sub-basin corresponding to streamflow station 030302 is shown here (figure 3). A first data bank was prepared, using percentages obtained from 1:250 000 maps (table 1). Landsat MSS imagery was then used and gave

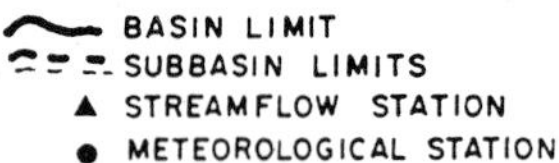

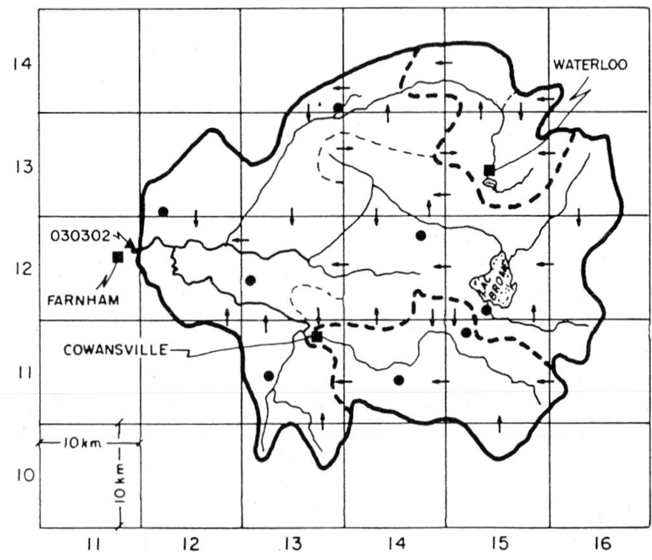

FIG.3 Grid cell representation of the sub-basin corresponding to streamflow station 030302 on the Yamaska river, as used by the CEQUEAU model.

Table 1. Comparison of land-use classifications as determined from LANDSAT imagery and topographical maps for the basin corresponding to streamflow station 030302 on the Yamaska river. Class identifications are: 1) forested areas, 2) unforested areas, 3) swamps, 4) water.

COORDINATES				LAND-USE CLASS							
CEQUEAU		UTM		LANDSAT IMAGE				1:250 000 MAP			
J	I	N	E	1	2	3	4	1	2	3	4
10	13	499	67	62,1	28,6	8,3	1,0	56	40	0	4
10	15	499	69	91,5	6,2	2,3	0,0	81	14	0	5
11	13	500	67	52,4	36,0	10,9	0,7	74	21	0	6
11	14	500	68	60,1	31,4	8,4	0,1	63	33	0	4
11	15	500	69	79,3	15,1	5,5	0,1	85	13	0	3
11	16	500	70	89,8	6,8	2,7	0,6	90	4	0	6
12	12	501	66	25,4	65,2	9,3	0,0	38	51	3	8
12	13	501	67	40,3	45,9	13,8	0,0	63	34	0	3
12	14	501	68	56,2	34,8	8,4	0,0	67	26	0	7
12	15	501	69	53,9	24,2	7,7	14,2	55	21	1	23
12	16	501	70	78,7	15,3	4,5	1,5	68	23	0	8
13	12	502	66	18,4	73,5	8,1	0,0	33	56	10	1
13	13	502	67	29,7	59,7	10,1	0,5	47	49	0	4
13	14	502	68	50,0	39,8	10,0	0,2	68	27	0	5
13	15	502	69	59,8	32,2	6,8	1,2	80	17	0	3
13	16	502	70	69,6	23,3	7,0	0,1	81	18	0	1
14	13	503	67	29,6	58,4	11,9	0,1	68	27	0	5
14	14	503	68	42,0	39,1	12,5	6,4	62	34	0	4
14	15	503	69	52,5	36,1	11,3	0,1	68	22	0	10
14	16	503	70	47,8	41,6	10,6	0,0	54	39	1	6

the results also presented in table 1. The cartographic accuracy for each of the four classes is respectively 92, 89, 39 and 100%, with an overall accuracy of 92% (Benmouffok, 1983; Benmouffok et al., 1985). There has been a problem with swamps. A certain number of pixels containing evergreens have been taken for swamp pixels, which explains the low accuracy. As can be seen on table 1, however, relatively large differences appear between the two classifications, even for themes like water and unforested areas, which have no or little tendency to be taken for swamps, on the Landsat imagery. Simulations made with the Landsat based data bank, gave results similar to or better than simulations made previously from the map data. So, it has been shown that remotely sensed data can replace conventional maps avantageously, for the preparation of land-use information for modelling purposes.

Estimation of rainfall by radar

As the CEQUEAU model allows interpolation of precipitation data from meteorological stations to each grid cell representing the basin, using radar data was almost straightforward. The grid size of the radar being different from that of the CEQUEAU model, a change of grid was easily performed to match the CEQUEAU grid and 2-hr maps were summed up to get 24-hr totals, which had to be ajusted with raingauges in and around the basin. The real problem was the presence of echoes arising from anomalous propagation. For operational input to hydrological models, one has to get rid of these as well as those associated with ground clutter. A new method using only one CAPPI level has been developed to detect and correct those echoes. It is mainly based on horizontal gradients and gives very promising results, as can be seen in figure 4. Simulations with uncorrected and corrected radar data show that the algorithm performs very well, since streamflows are simulated with reasonable accuracy after radar

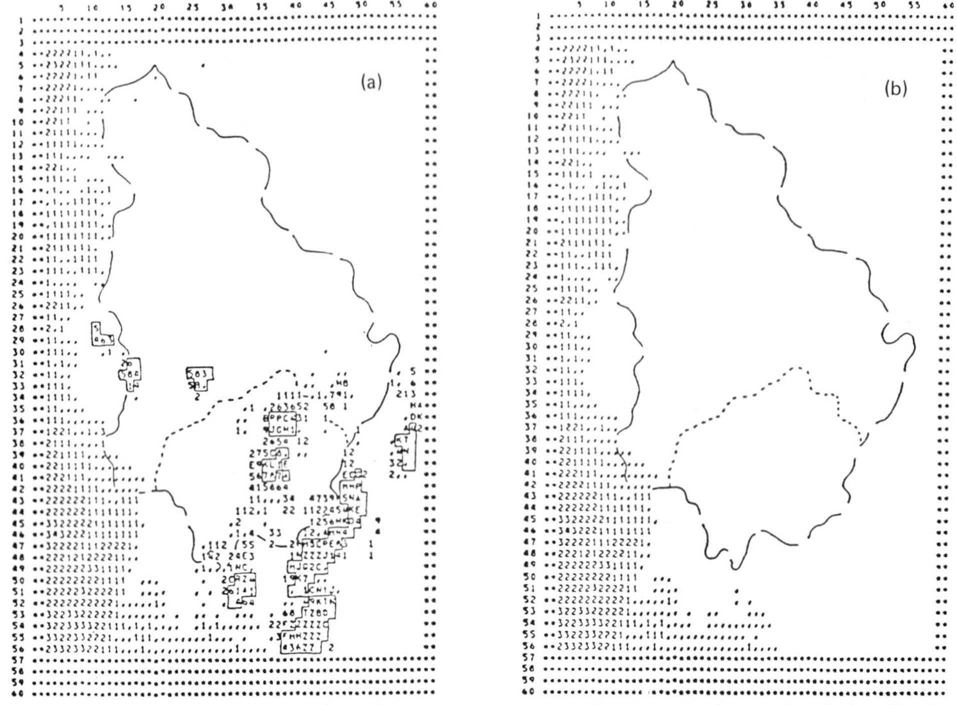

FIG.4 Radar data on the Yamaska basin from 5.00 to 7.00 AM, June 13, 1978. Pixels are 1.6 × 2.5 km in size: (a) uncorrected data; ground echos are identified by closed contours; (b) corrected data.

data are corrected by it (figure 5).

It is thus possible to use radar data operationaly as precipitation input to a forecasting model, with a minimum of human intervention, without having to rely on multi-level information to eliminate "unwanted" echoes.

Updating of the snow cover area and water equivalent

Even if remote sensing can give more information than the snow cover area expressed as a percentage of total basin area, most models can use only that information. On the contrary, at each time step, the CEQUEAU model can issue a map of the water equivalent of the snow cover. That map may easily be compared with the spatial distribution of the snow cover area as estimated from satellite imagery. One can not only compare the simulated snow cover area with that from remote sensing, but also see where the snow line should be in the simulated map and update the snow cover (Fortin et al., 1979 and 1983). It is also possible to update the snow water equivalent from the percentage of snow cover area on each grid cell (Dupont, 1983). In the example presented in figure 6a, percentages of snow cover area for each cell were first obtained from NOAA imagery for grid cells 10 km in size and transferred to grid cells 30 km in size, as used by the CEQUEAU model on the 57500 km^2 Nottaway river basin, a river flowing into James Bay in western Québec. The snow water equivalents simulated by the model (figure 6b) were then modified according to these percentages (figure 6c). It is seen on figure 7, that correction of snow water equivalents using remotely sensed data led to better results, while

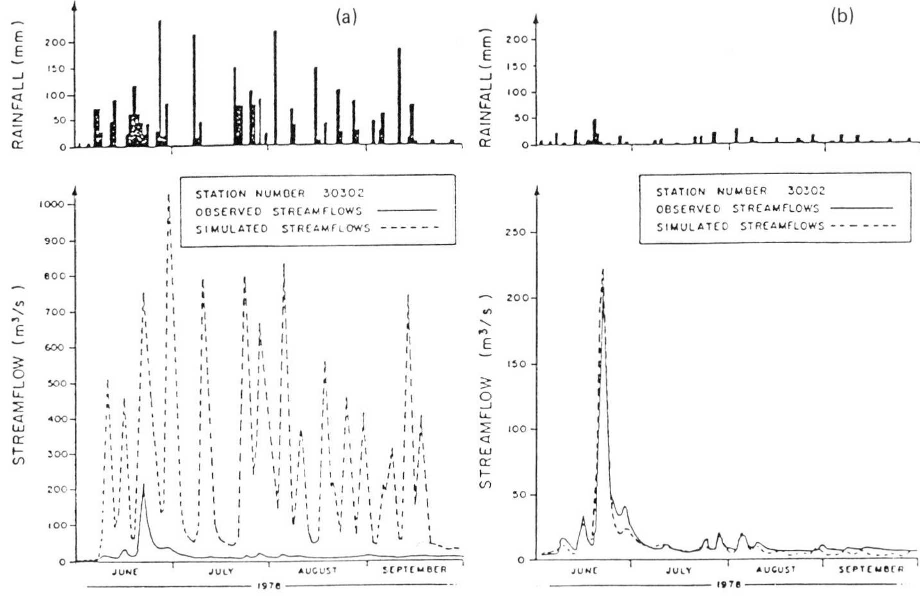

FIG.5 Steamflow simulation on the Yamaska basin, at station 030302 (1270 km^2): (a) uncorrected radar data; (b) corrected radar data calibrated with raingauge observations.

corrections made from snow course data led to results that could be better. It should be said however that the number of snow course stations is very small. Eight stations were available, only three of them being located on the basin itself!

More work is being done to obtain better results and lead to a more general method.

Estimation of actual evapotranspiration

As mentionned above for the EVAPOTRANSPIRATION module, it is possible to estimate actual evapotranspiration from remote sensing (Séguin, 1980;

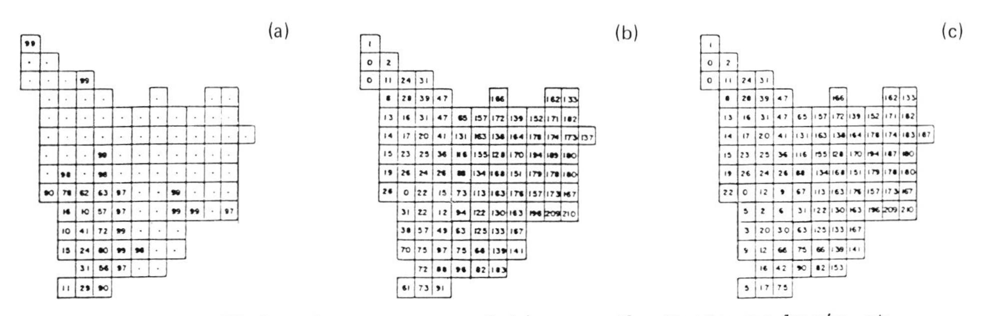

FIG.6 Snow cover updating on the Nottaway basin at station 080701 with NOAA imagery. Grid size is 30 km. (a) Percentage of snow cover on each grid cell on April 21st 1981. A dot (·) indicates 100% snow cover; (b) snow cover water equivalent before updating; (c) snow cover water equivalent after updating.

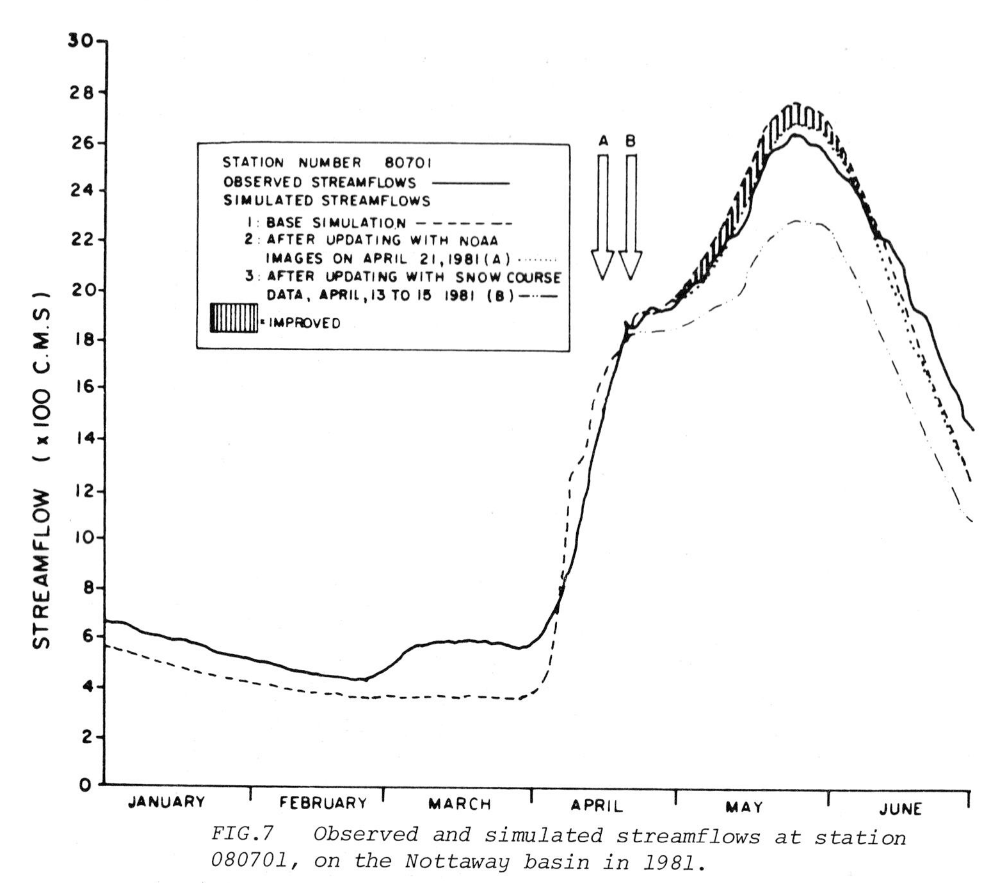

FIG.7 Observed and simulated streamflows at station 080701, on the Nottaway basin in 1981.

Séguin and Itier, 1983; Hatfield et al., 1983). This has the advantage of leading not to point values that have to be interpolated in some way but more directly to the spatial distribution of actual evapotranspiration at the regional or basin scale. Land-use and topographic characteristics can then be taken into account more effectively.

Thermal IR data are available at adequate scales (5 km for Meteosat or GOES and 1 km for the NOAA-AVHRR sensor) and various approaches have been developed for estimating E_a from thermal IR data (Séguin, 1984).

One very simple method well suited to hydrology is based on the computation of daily E_a, using midday surface temperature (Jackson et al., 1977; Séguin et al., 1982):

$$E_a = R_n + A - B\,(T_s - T_a) \qquad \text{eq. 1}$$

where R_n is daily net radiation and T_a is daily maximum air temperature. A and B are constants, mostly dependent upon surface characteristics.

From experiments in southern France, values of 1.0 for A and 0.25 for B have been derived (Séguin et al., 1982). For rougher surfaces (orchards, trees, ...) there are reasons to believe B should rather take values of the order of 0.35 to 0.40. Researches are being pursued on that subject.

Even if it has first been derived by statistical adjustment of E_a-R_n vs T_S-T_a values, it has been demonstrated to be in agreement with the theories of energy balance and turbulent fluxes (Séguin and Itier, 1983). Its accuracy has been estimated to be of the order of ± 1 mm/day by Séguin et al. (1982).

An example of spatial determination of daily E_a is shown for a 130 km E-W x 140 km N-S rectangle subdivided into 520 grid cells (26 x 20), each corresponding to one Meteosat pixel (7 km x 5 km at that latitude) (figure 8). The site is located over the lower Rhone valley.

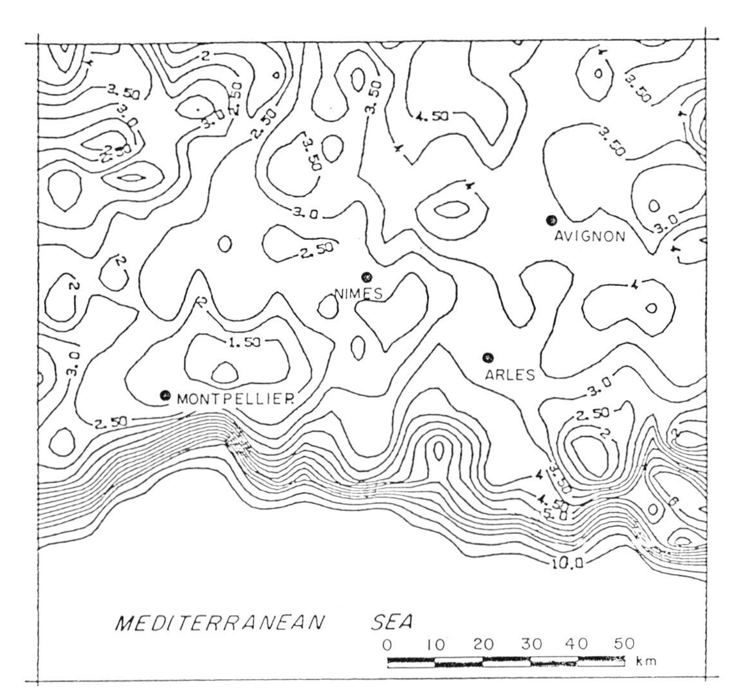

FIG.8 Distribution of actual evapotranspiration over the lower Rhone Valley, in southern France on July 24th, 1979, from METEOSAT data.

Operational use of the model

A model used for daily forecasting of streamflows has to be able to run in a minimum of time with the available data. This is the reason why even if the model is developed so as to make a maximum use of remote sensing it will also be able to run under conditions where remotely sensed data are not available. The model should also be suitable for application to as many basins as possible and not only on well instrumented research basins. This is why it is planned that various algorithms will be selected depending on the data available on a particular basin and day.

The interactive utilization on a microcomputer, together with the appropriate input and output devices, should permit a good man-machine interaction. The microcomputer market is evolving very rapidly so that the exact type of computer and accessories used for the initial version of the model is not yet decided. At the present time, it is planned that a IBM PC-AT or compatible will be used together with an IBM Professional Graphics Display board, under a multi-task operating system. It is believed that the model will be better suited for regional operations than models that have to be runned on mainframes, whereas it should retain most advantages claimed by those, as it will have access to various types of data through the existing data transmission networks.

Acknowledgements

This study is financially supported by grants from Québec FCAR Fund, NSERC of Canada and Environment Canada. Travel allocations from Coopération France-Québec has helped the authors to meet and work on the project.

References

Anderson, E.A., 1973, National Weather Service River Forecast System - Snow Accumulation and Ablation Model. NOAA Technical Memorandum NWS Hydro-17, U.S. Dept of Commerce, Silver Spring, Maryland, 217 p.

Benmouffok, D., 1983, Intégration des données physiographiques obtenues à partir d'images LANDSAT au modèle hydrologique CEQUEAU. Thèse de maîtrise ès sc., Université Laval, 182 p.

Benmouffok, D., J.P. Fortin, L. Potvin and G. Rochon (1985), Estimation des données physiographiques et d'occupation des sols pour la modélisation hydrologique. Colloque: Télédétection et gestion des ressources: aspect opérationnel, 5° Congrès de l'Association québécoise de télédétection, Chicoutimi, 22-23.

Bowley, C.J., J.C. Barnes, A. Rango, 1981, Applications Systems verification and transfert project, v. VIII: Satellite snow mapping and runoff prediction handbook. NASA Technical paper 1829, 87 p.

Cormany, Y., 1969, Relations pluie - débit sur les hauts bassins de l'Authion. E.D.F. Direction des études et recherches no 23/69.

Cormany, Y., A. Guilbot, 1971, Ajustements et réglage des modèles déterministes, méthode de calage des paramètres. La Houille Blanche, no 2, p. 131-140.

Crawford, N.H., R.K. Linsley, 1964, A conceptual model of the hydrologic cycle: IASH Pub. no 63, p. 573-587.

Crawford, N.H., R.K. Linsley, 1966, Digital simulation in hydrology: Stanford watershed model IV. Dept of Civil Engineering, Stanford University, Tech. Rep. 39, 220 p.

Dupont, J., 1983, Utilisation des données acquises par télédétection pour la mise à jour des modèles hydrologiques de fonte nivale. Thèse de maîtrise ès sciences INRS-Eau, 216 p.

Fortin, J.P., G. Morin, W. Sochanska, L. Potvin, 1983, Utilisation de la télédétection pour améliorer la précision des crues de fonte de neige simulées par le modèle CEQUEAU. Symposium on Hydrological Applications of Remote Sensing and Remote Data Transmission (AISH), Hambourg, 1983 (compte rendu à paraître).

Fortin, J.P., J.P. Lardeau, G. Morin, W. Sochanska, J.C. Rassam, 1979, Comparaison du retrait du manteau nival calculé par le modèle hydrologique CEQUEAU au retrait estimé à l'aide des images du satellite ESSA-8. Colloque canadien d'hydrologie: 79 - Hydrologie des climats froids, Vancouver (Colombie Britannique), 10-11 mai.

Girard, G., J.P. Fortin, R. Charbonneau, 1971, Un modèle hydrométéorologique simplifié et quelques applications régionales. Symposium international sur les modèles mathématiques en hydrologie, AIHS, Varsovie.

Girard, G., E. Ledoux, J.P. Villeneuve, 1980, Modèle intégré pluie - eau de surface - eau souterraine. La Houille Blanche, no 4/5, p. 315-319.

Girard, G., G. Morin, R. Charbonneau, 1972, Modèle précipitations - débits à discrétisation spatiale. Cahiers ORSTOM, Série hydrol., v. IX, no 4.

Hatfield, J.L., A. Perrier, R.D. Jackson, 1983, Estimation of evapotranspiration at one time-of-day using remotely sensed surface temperatures. Agricultural Water Management, v. 7, p. 341-350.

Martinec, J., 1982, Runoff modeling from snow covered area. IEEE Transactions on geoscience and remote sensing, v. GE-20, no 3, July, p. 259-262.

Morin, G., J.P. Fortin, J.P. Lardeau, W. Sochanska, S. Paquette, 1981,

Modèle CEQUEAU: manuel d'utilisation. INRS-Eau, rapport scientifique no 93, 449 p.
Peck, E.L., T.N. Keeper, E.R. Johnson, 1981, Strategies for using remotely sensed data in hydrologic models. NASA-CR-66729, 77 p.
Rango, A. (ed.), 1975, Operational applications of satellite snowcover observations. NASA Spec. Publ. 391, 430 p.
Robinove, C.J., 1969, Space Technology in Hydrologic Applications. In: The Progress of hydrology. Proc. First Ont. Sem. for hydrology professors. Urbana, U.S.A., v. 1. New developments in hydrology, p. 88-107.
Séguin, B., 1980, Détermination de l'évaporation réelle dans les bilans hydrologiques par la télédétection en thermographie infra-rouge. Bull. des Sciences hydrologiques 25.2.26, p. 143-153.
Séguin, B., S. Baelz, J.M. Monget, V. Petit, 1982, Utilisation de la thermographie IR pour l'estimation de l'évaporation régionale. 1. Mise au point méthodologique sur le site de la Crau. Agronomie, v. 2, no 1, p. 7-16.
Séguin, B., B. Itier, 1983, Using midday surface temperature to estimate daily evaporation from satellite thermal IR data. Int. J. of Remote Sensing, v. 4, no 2, p. 371-383.
Séguin, B., 1984, Estimation de l'évapotranspiration à partir de l'IR thermique. Comptes rendu, 2° Colloque international sur les structures spectrales d'objets en télédétection, Bordeaux, septembre, éd. INRA, Les colloques de l'INRA, n° 23, G II 3, p. 427-446.
U.S. Army Corps of Engineers, 1975, Program Description and User Manual for SSARR - Streamflow Synthesis and Reservoir Regulation, U.S. Army Engineer Division North Pacific, Portland, Oregon, Program 724-K5-60010.
Villeneuve, J.P., D. Isabel, 1984, Le modèle hydrologique MDOR et sa calibration automatique. Colloque sur la simulation numérique appliquée au domaine de la ressource hydrique. 52e Congrès de l'ACFAS. Université Laval, Québec 9-10 mars 1984.

Hydrologic Applications of Space Technology (Proceedings of the Cocoa Beach Workshop, Florida, August 1985). IAHS Publ. no. 160, 1986.

Estimation of daily runoff based on Meteosat data

HELMUT ROTT
Institute of Meteorology & Geophysics,
University of Innsbruck, Austria

Abstract
The potential of data from geostationary meteorological satellites for continuous simulation of daily runoff in large drainage basins has been investigated. The developed simulation algorithm is based on cloud cover indices which are derived from Meteosat images in 2-hourly intervals and represent an areal measure for precipitation. Taking into account the time-area relationships for runoff, the algorithm was applied to two basins in Central Europe of 26.000 km^2 and 48.000 km^2 area respectively. For 3 periods in summer 1979 daily runoff was calculated one day to three days ahead, starting from measured flow. The first results clearly demonstrate the usefulness of satellite data for runoff modelling, further investigations with increased data sets are planned. Final aim is the use of satellite derived parameters in short-term runoff forecasts.

Introduction

Meteorological and earth resources satellites are continuously providing quantities of data which are useful also for hydrological applications. However, this potential is utilized only to a small percentage and further research is needed to demonstrate the use of satellite data for operational hydrology and water management.

In order to investigate the use of meteorological satellite data for continuous runoff modelling a study was initiated within EARSeL (European Association of Remote Sensing Laboratories) Working Group 10 (Hydrology and Water Management) and sponsored by the European Space Agency. This paper presents first results on this ongoing study in which a method is developed for simulating and as a final goal for forecasting daily runoff volumes in large drainage basins utilizing geostationary satellite data. Presently the investigations are limited to the summer period to focus on rainfall related runoff.

The Test Basin

The drainage basin of the river Danube above Aschach covering an area of 78.190 km^2 was selected for the study. Runoff estimation at this site is of interest for the management of a chain of hydroelectric power plants. A sketch map of the basin is shown in Figure 1.

The runoff simulations presented in this paper were carried out separately for the Danube and Inn basins above the confluence in Passau because the two basins reveal significant differences in topography and runoff regime. The corresponding

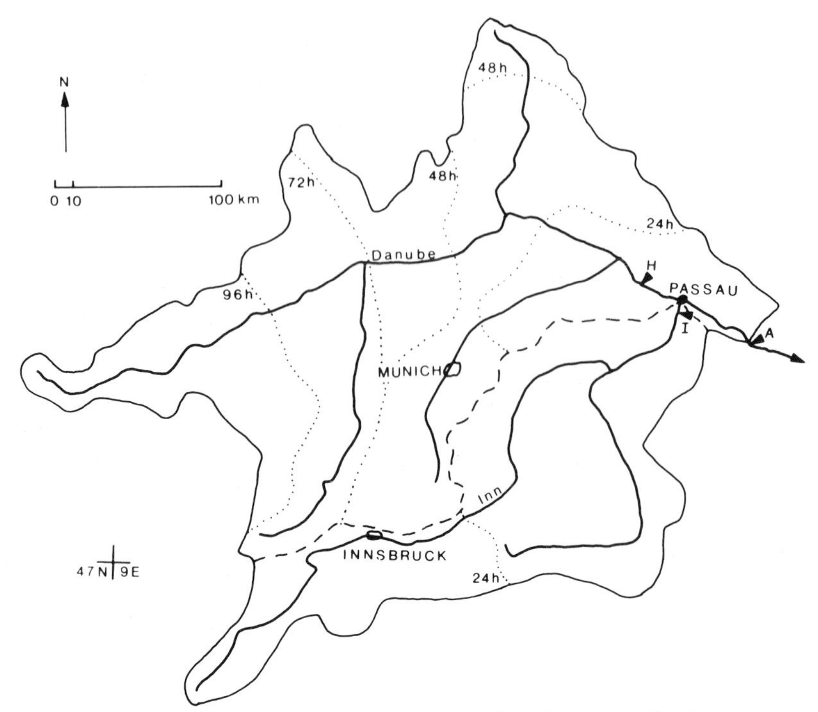

FIG.1 Sketch map of the Danube basin above Aschach. The runoff travel times to Passau for the simulation are indicated by dotted lines. Runoff gauges: A - Aschach, H - Hofkirchen, I - Ingling.

gauging stations are located in Hofkirchen for the Danube (47.496 km^2 drainage area) and in Ingling for the Inn (26.084 km^2). The main part of the Inn basin is situated in the Alps; 2.7 % of the basin are glacier covered so that snow-melt and glacier runoff is of some importance also during the summer season. The Danube basin above Passau includes hilly and undulating terrain in the Pre-Alps, alluvial plains, and to a smaller percentage mountains.

The morphological differences have effects on the slope of the river channels and on the runoff travel time. The time-area relationships for the Danube and Inn basins above the confluence are also shown in Figure 1. Only the 24-hour time intervals are drawn, in the simulation algorithm time steps of 6 hours were employed.

The time-area relation was derived from flow times of the average flood waves which were available for the larger rivers. This was considered an upper limit for the computations. The time lag was increased by 40 percent. Additional information on basin lag was derived from channel slopes and distances. Certainly, wave travel and basin lag are dependent on the intensity of a particular event. Therefore the applied time-area relation can be considered only as a first approximation, which, however, proved useful for the calculation of daily runoff during the investigated periods.

The Basic Concept

A variety of rainfall-runoff models exists, ranking from complete conceptual models to simple regression models. The accuracy of the runoff calculations is not necessarily dependent on the complexity of the model, critical is the quality and availability of the input data. For this study only simple parametric methods were considered because the size of the study is rather limited.

The investigations were focussing on the possibilities of satellite data for runoff modelling, available conventional data were largely neglected. Due to this constraint optimum results can not be expected and further improvements can certainly be achieved when the remote sensing data are combined with conventional data.

During the summer period streamflow in the test basin is primarily controlled by rainfall. This suggests as one possibility for runoff simulation that the areal rainfall data are derived from the satellite data and that these rainfall data are used in a runoff model. This process introduces two sources of errors by i) the transformation of satellite data into rainfall data and ii) the relation of rainfall data to runoff.

Therefore a more direct approach was used by relating satellite derived data on the clouds (cloud indices) directly to daily runoff volumes, taking into account time-area relationships for runoff. The cloud cover index represents a relative measure for areal precipitation. A similar method has been developed by Strübing and Schultz (1985) using NOAA data for the generation of time series of monthly runoff.

The Cloud Cover Index

The investigations were based on Meteosat data, which were used in digital form to utilize the full radiometric and spatial resolution. For the runoff estimation the cloud cover index, which provides a relative measure for precipitation in a given area, was derived from Meteosat data.

Various methods are applied for estimating rainfall based on visible and/or infrared satellite imagery (Barrett and Martin, 1981). For the purpose of long-term monitoring over large areas convective life-cycle techniques do not appear useful because these techniques require very close time sequences of satellite data and sophisticated processing. Moreover, other precipitation types than convective have also to be included.

A simple indexing technique based on infrared satellite data was finally selected, which is consistent during the day/night cycle and which enables automatic data analysis. These are important aspects for operational applications. In the study basin, for example, the cloud cover index was derived for 50 subareas in 2-hourly intervals.

An indexing technique for rainfall estimation based on geostationary infrared satellite data was applied over the GATE area in the Atlantic by Arkin (1979) and Richards and Arkin (1981). The method uses the fractional cloud coverage, given by the cloud top temperature colder than a given threshold, as predictor for rainfall. Comparison with radar estimated rainfall showed good results if the areal and temporal scales are considerably larger than the convective scale.

In mid-latitudes the relationship between cloud top temperature and precipitation reveals considerable variability depending on the synoptic situation and on cloud type. This problem has been investigated for the study periods over the Central European region in a diploma thesis (Aschbacher, 1985) in which the relation between cloud top temperature and precipitation was investigated in connection with synoptic quantities such as geopotential height and vorticity.

In this study satellite derived cloud temperature was used as only variable for the calculation of the cloud index. The cloud cover index CI was calculated for a certain period (12 or 24 hours) and for areas of about 1.000 km^2 size by the following equation which is valid for $T_a \geq T_c$:

$$CI = \frac{A}{N} \sum_{j=1}^{N} (T_a - T_c)^{1/3} \qquad (1)$$

where T_a is a threshold temperature above which the probability for precipitation is assumed to be zero. T_c is the cloud top temperature averaged over the area, N represents the number of Meteosat images (slots) and A is an empirical constant. For the runoff simulations Meteosat images in 2-hourly time intervals were analyzed so that for the calculation of CI over 24 hours N is 12. Relation (1) was derived by comparison of precipitation data from recording raingauges and cloud top temperatures in several subareas of the test basin. The threshold temperature T_c = 260 K was found valid for the investigation periods in summer 1979. The exponent 1/3 is a weighting factor, indicating a certain increase of rainfall intensity with decreasing cloud top temperature.

Equation (1) was derived from a limited data set and the relation between CI and measured rainfall revealed considerable variability depending on the synoptic situation and also due to the problem of representativeness of the surface point measurements. Development of an improved cloud index as rainfall indicator will certainly be possible by including meteorological information, e.g. from synoptic or prognostic charts, but the available data sample was too limited for such investigations.

The Simulation Algorithm

A simple parametric model was developed for simulating the flow in the test basin on a continuous basis. Runoff was separated in base flow QB and direct runoff QD. The calculation of direct runoff is based on the cloud cover index (CI) which is derived for 33 subareas in the Danube basin and 17 subareas in the Inn basin. The subareas are of approximately equal size and were selected according to runoff travel time.

Because it is the final goal to use the algorithm for short-term forecasts of daily runoff, an approach was applied, where the flow $\hat{Q}$ for the time period t+n (n = 1, 2, 3, ...) is calculated from the measured flow Q in the time period t and from satellite data. Time steps of one day were selected.

The estimated daily runoff volume is made up by the base flow and the surface runoff:

$$\hat{Q}_{t+1} = \hat{Q}B_{t+1} + \hat{Q}D_{t+1}$$
$$\hat{Q}_{t+2} = \hat{Q}B_{t+2} + \hat{Q}D_{t+2} \qquad (2)$$
$$\vdots$$

The base flow for the first time step t+1 is calculated from the measured baseflow QB_t, for the next time step t+2 the base flow is calculated from $\hat{Q}B_{t+1}$:

$$\hat{Q}B_{t+1} = QB_t \cdot k_1$$
$$\hat{Q}B_{t+2} = \hat{Q}B_{t+1} \cdot k_1 \qquad (3)$$
$$\vdots$$

where k_1 is the recession constant for the base flow. k_1 was determined empirically from runoff during dry periods: $k_1 = 0.97$ for the Danube basin, $k_1 = 0.98$ for the Inn basin for time steps of one day. For days with significant surface flow an increase of QB by $1/k_1$ was assumed.

The direct runoff is calculated from the direct runoff of the previous day and from the cloud index derived runoff $\hat{Q}CI$:

$$\hat{Q}D_{t+1} = QD_t \cdot k_2 + \hat{Q}CI_{t+1}$$
$$\hat{Q}D_{t+2} = \hat{Q}D_{t+1} \cdot k_2 + \hat{Q}CI_{t+2} \qquad (4)$$
$$\vdots$$

k_2 is the recession constant of surface runoff and was determined as $k_2 = 0.65$ for the Danube and for the Inn basin. $\hat{Q}CI$ is derived from the weighted cloud index by superposition of the contributions from the different subareas:

$$\hat{Q}CI_t = \sum_{i=1}^{M} W_{i,t-l} \cdot CI_{i,t-l} \cdot B_i \qquad (5)$$

where M is the number of subareas for which the cloud cover index is derived: M = 33 for the Danube basin, M = 17 for the Inn basin. The time lag l for the runoff is determined from the time-area relationship; l was assumed constant for each subarea. The time shift was determined in 6-hourly steps, CI was calculated for 24-hourly intervals according to Equation (1). B_i is a weighting factor and depends on the size of the area and on the average runoff loss which was taken from hydrological maps (Keller, 1979).

The weighting function W_i represents a measure of antecedent precipitation and is calculated from the cloud index of the preceding days for each area:

$$W_{i,t} = B_o \left[1 + \sum_{d=1}^{D} C\ (CI_{t-d})\ .\ \exp - (d/E)\right] \qquad (6)$$

d represents the time step in days, a system memory of 5 days was considered: D = 5. B_o and E are empirically determined constants: $B_o = 0.5$, $E = 2.5$. B_o represents the basic value of the weighting function; this is when CI is below a defined threshold CIT during the preceding days. E is a time constant and C is a flag:

$$C = 0, \text{ if } CI < CIT \qquad (7)$$

$$C = 1, \text{ if } CI \geq CIT$$

In principle the weihgting function represents a variable runoff coefficient, which is increasing with the amount of fallen precipitation (given by the cloud cover index). All calculations were carried out in percent of mean monthly flow so that the same coefficients of the weighting function could be used for both basins.

Before the simulation algorithm was applied to the large basin, it was tested in two Alpine basins of 270 km^2 and 820 km^2 size respectively. Due to the small basin size no subdivision of the areas was necessary and the calculations were done in 12-hourly and 24-hourly time steps. For comparison runoff was calculated with the same algorithm also from rainfall data recorded at one, respectively two, stations of the basin. The rainfall derived and measured runoff volumes showed good agreement. The runoff calculations using the cloud index revealed significant deviations on some days. These were related to meteorological conditions when the cloud cover index did not provide good estimates of rainfall. However, these errors are largely compensated if the algorithm is applied to larger areas.

Analysis of the Satellite Data

Several processing steps had to be performed before the Meteosat data could be used as input for the runoff calculations, the preprocessing was done on a digital interactive image processing system. The Meteosat infrared data (12 images per day, 512 x 512 pixels) over Central Europe were read to the image memories and navigated with the aid of landmarks and continent boundaries. In the next step the digital counts were extracted from each image automatically for the 50 subareas and the infrared brightness temperatures and cloud indices were calculated. The total area of the test basin is covered by about 1900 pixels in the Meteosat IR channel. Finally the CI-values are time-shifted according to the time-area relation and averaged over 12 images. This provides the input to the specified algorithm.

The Study Periods

Meteosat data over the test basin have been analyzed so far

for three periods in summer 1979, revealing different synoptic situations: 11 to 22 June, 11 to 21 August, 15 to 30 September.

The period in June 1979 was characterized by strong cyclonic activity over Central Europe and the Northern Mediterranean Sea. Cyclones and frontal systems repeatedly brought precipitation to the test basin, very strong precipitation was observed during the days 16 to 18 June, several stations in the Northern Alps and Pre-Alps reported rainfall amounts larger than 100 mm over 3 days.

During the August period the conditions were different; in the beginning a high pressure system was situated over Central Europe. After 15 August weak frontal systems moved over the Danube basin. These caused convective precipitation revealing significant local differences in occurence and intensity.

During the first part of the September period a stable anticyclone was situated over Central Europe. On 20 and 21 September a cold front moved over the area causing sufficient precipitation. A cut-off low developed in the Alpine region, associated with southerly flow over the Eastern Alps on 22 and 23 September. Due to lee effects only moderate rainfall was observed in the Danube basin during these two days. On 24 September surface flow changed to northerly direction and rainfall intensified. After 25 September a high pressure system built up over Central Europe.

Results of the Simulations

Simulated and recorded runoff are compared for the Danube basin above Hofkirchen and for the Inn basin in the Figure 2 and 3, respectively. The simulations are shown for steps of one day and three days in advance, starting from measured flow.

The comparison indicates the degree of agreement which can be achieved between recorded and Meteosat-derived runoff. Because the parameters of the algorithm have been derived from data of the periods shown, independent verification of the algorithm could not yet be performed. For this task additional satellite data will be analyzed.

One weakness of the algorithm becomes evident from the June period in the Danube basin, when very strong precipitation and increase of runoff was observed. 24-hourly precipitation sums between 50 mm and 100 mm were measured on 17 July in parts of the basin, and strong precipitation occurred also during the day before and after. The cloud cover index does not adequately represent these extreme events because they are not connected with a further decrease in cloud top temperature.

For the Inn basin the correspondence between measured and calculated runoff in the June period is better, though some variability from day to day is found. The deviations are partly compensated for the longer calculation period (3 days) indicating that no systematic errors prevail.

For the September period, during which also a significant storm event occurred, the correspondence between recorded and computed discharge is satisfactory for both basins. During the August period the daily runoff variations were small. Marked deviations of computed runoff are observed in the Inn basin for the two last days of the period, for which runoff is overestimated due to persistent cloudiness and comparatively little precipitation over the Alpine area.

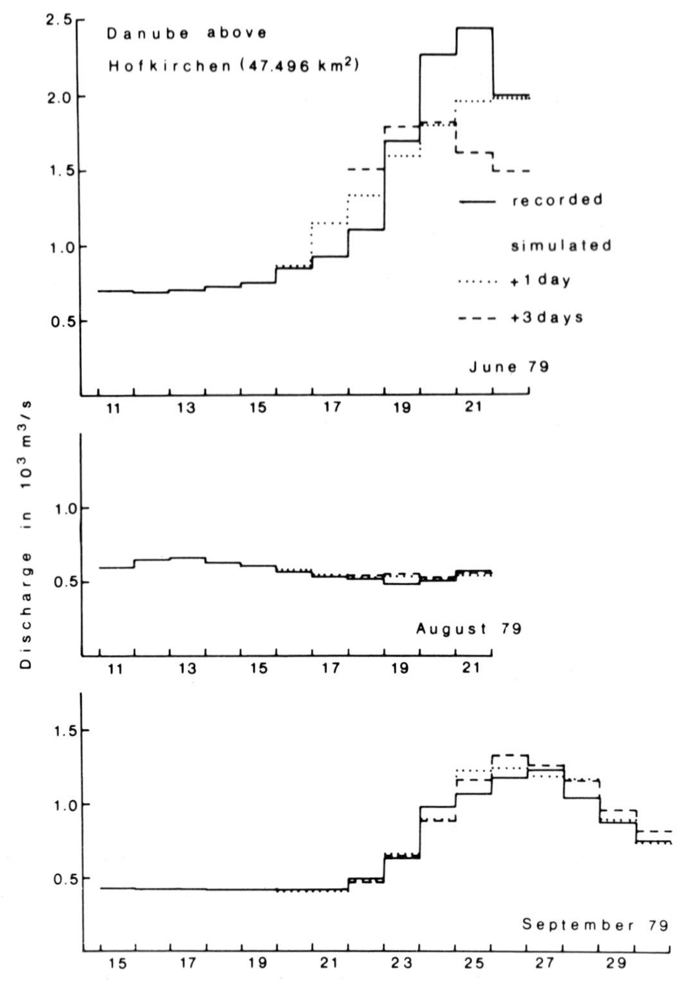

FIG.2 Recorded and computed mean daily runoff for the Danube basin above Hofkirchen.

Conclusions

The investigations were limited to satellite data as model input. Improvements in runoff modelling can be expected by combining conventional and satellite data. The applied algorithm suggests combinations of the cloud cover index as areal indicator of precipitation with point measurements at the surface. Another possibility is to utilize synoptic information for the calculation of the cloud index.

Nevertheless, the investigations performed so far could clearly show the usefulness of meteorological satellite data for continuous simulation of daily runoff in large drainage basins. With the limited data set available it was not possible to optimize the algorithm. Further investigations with increased data sets and for other basins are needed.

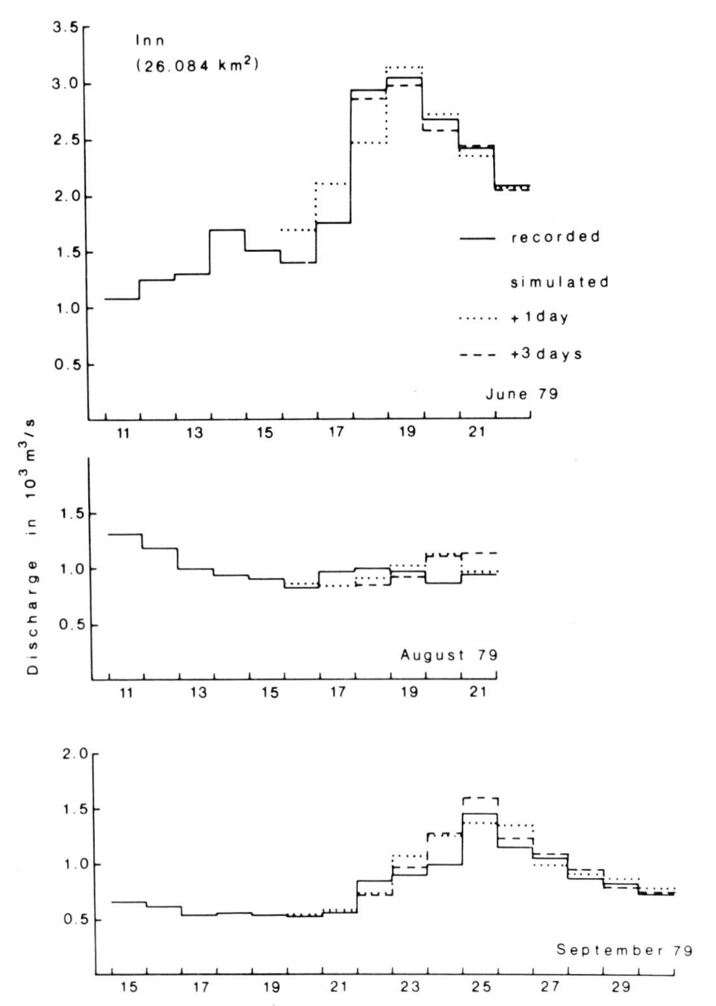

FIG.3 Recorded and computed mean daily runoff for the Inn basin above Ingling.

References

Arkin, P.A., 1979, The relationship between fractional coverage of high cloud and rainfall accumulations during GATE over the B-scale array. Monthly Weather Rev., V. 107, p. 1382-1387.

Aschbacher, J., 1985, Niederschlagsbestimmung aus Meteosat-Daten und synoptischen Größen, Diploma Thesis, Inst. f. Meteorologie und Geophysik, Univ. Innsbruck.

Barrett, E.C. and Martin, D.W., 1981, The use of satellite data in rainfall monitoring, Academic Press, London, 340 p.

Keller, R. (Ed.), 1979, Hydrologischer Atlas der Bundesrepublik Deutschland, Harald Boldt Verl., Bonn.

Richards, F. and Arkin, P., 1981, On the relationship between satellite-observed cloud cover and precipitation. Monthly Weather Rev., V. 109, p. 1081-1093.

Strübing, G. and Schultz, G.A., 1983, Estimation of monthly river runoff data on the basis of satellite imagery.

In: Hydrological Applications of Remote Sensing and Remote Data Transmission (Proc. Hamburg Symp., August 1983), 491-498. IAHS Publ. no. 145.

Hydrologic Applications of Space Technology (Proceedings of the Cocoa Beach Workshop, Florida, August 1985). IAHS Publ. no. 160, 1986.

Integrated modeling and remote sensing of soil moisture

P. C. D. MILLY & Z. J. KABALA
Department of Civil Engineering, Princeton University, Princeton, New Jersey 08544, USA

Abstract

Modeling and remote sensing are two complementary procedures that yield information on the moisture content of the soil beneath the land surface. Each has inherent errors. It is reasonable to expect that a combination of modeling and remote sensing would yield more accurate estimates of soil moisture content and related variables than can be obtained by either approach alone.

We propose that the problem of integrating models and remote sensing be approached using the extended Kalman filter (EKF). The EKF integrates uncertain state dynamics and uncertain measurement models to arrive at an optimal estimate of the system states. The EKF also yields an explicit measure of the accuracy of the state estimates.

In a specific application, we demonstrate the use of the EKF to determine moisture content beneath a bare soil. The use of EKF provides estimates of soil moisture superior to those obtained separately by either remote sensing or modeling alone.

Background

The amount of water in the top meter of the earth's soil is a critical variable that controls a number of hydrologic, biological and meteorological processes (Schmugge et al., 1980). Soil moisture in the top few centimeters governs the partitioning of rainfall into infiltration and surface runoff, the latter being the major source of flood flow in many streams and rivers. The rate of evaporation of water from soil is strongly dependent upon the amount of moisture near the soil surface. Transpiration and growth of crops and other plants depend upon the availability of water to the plant roots. Because a significant quantity of heat is absorbed when vaporization of liquid water occurs, the rates of evaporation and transpiration have a significant influence upon the energy balance of the surface of the earth. Therefore, soil moisture affects weather and climate by controlling the fluxes of water and sensible heat into the atmosphere. Finally, we note that the water yield of a catchment decreases in direct relation to evaporation and transpiration.

The analysis of many of the above-mentioned processes is often complicated by the variability in time and space of the moisture content of the soil. Variations in time result from the dynamic nature of the hydrological cycle, with periodic forcing at the annual and daily scales and with more random forcing due to the passage of weather systems. Variations in depth are intimately related to the temporal fluctuations in forcing. Generally, surface conditions respond to all frequencies of forcing. Deeper soil moisture responds more slowly, due to smoothing by the intervening surface layers.

In order to deal with the problems of soil moisture variability, analyses of the many processes dependent upon soil moisture have often included explicit accounting schemes for that variable. The simplest of these represent the time-varying, depth-averaged moisture content that results from environmental forcing, while more sophisticated models consider the depth dependence. Due to the complexity of natural systems, no model can provide a perfect representation of the actual storage and fluxes of soil moisture. There is therefore a significant amount of uncertainty associated with the calculated values of soil moisture derived from a model.

The other approach to estimation of soil moisture is through measurement, either in-situ or remote. All measurements methods rely on the dependence of some physical property of the soil upon its moisture content. In-situ measurements can yield highly accurate estimates of conditions at a particular site. However, since these estimates are based on relatively small volumes of soil, and since moisture content is highly variable in space and time, good estimates of the average moisture content of large areas require extensive and expensive observation. Remote sensing methods, on the other hand, generally perform areal integration directly in the observation process. Their disadvantages, given the current state of the art, are their inability to sense beyond the surface (0 to 10 cm depth) soil layer and the significant statistical noise in their measurements and in the values of moisture content inferred therefrom.

It is apparent, then, that modeling and measurement are both useful, though imperfect, techniques for the determination of the amount of moisture in the soil. Both are capable of providing estimates of moisture content, but these estimates generally involve significant errors. It is reasonable to expect that a combination of these two approaches, if feasible, would yield more accurate estimates of soil moisture than could be obtained from either approach alone. As Schmugge et al. (1980) have observed, in their extensive review of the problem of estimation of soil moisture,

> "a cost effective soil moisture monitoring program must utilize all... of the approaches and not just one. ... an integrated system should be designed..."

Previous Work

Limitations of space prohibit us from giving a detailed review of the significant contributions that have been made on the problem of integrating models and remote sensing to estimate soil moisture. At the risk of oversimplification, we offer here a few observations concerning the approaches that have been used to estimate moisture content from remotely sensed data.

a. There is clearly information about soil mositure and evaporation contained in measurements of surface temperature, brightness temperature, and backscatter coefficient.
b. There is virtually no dependence of most remotely sensed properties on the moisture content below, say, 20 cm.
c. Remotely-sensed information on near-surface moisture content and on surface temperature is noisy. This is due to measurement error and, in the case of moisture content, to imperfect functional relations between the moisture content and the measured quantity.
d. Simple correlation methods have no way of incorporating prior information into their estimates. However, if we have an idea what the moisture content was yesterday, that information should be somehow relevant today.

e. Modeling methods generally treat the moisture content as being known initially and provide no direct means of correcting subsequent simulation errors on the basis of observations. When the measurements are taken into account, they are treated as perfect measurements.
f. Little work has considered the possibility of multiple measurements, e.g., both thermal infrared and microwave measurements.
g. The uncertainty of the estimates is not dealt with explicitly in most procedures.
h. Few modeling analyses makes use of both the energy and the water balance equations.

In view of item (a), all available observational data should be employed, when possible, for estimation of soil moisture. In view of (b), a simulation model is necessary to extrapolate surface information to greater depths. In view of (c), inferences of the surface state based on remote sensing should be combined with those of predictive simulation models for moisture and temperature, somehow accounting for the error of both. We outline briefly here a framework for estimation of soil moisture that accounts for all of these considerations. In so doing, we avoid all of the shortcomings seen in items (d) through (h).

The Extended Kalman Filter (EKF)

A general framework for the estimation of the states of a dynamic nonlinear system in the presence of model and observational uncertainty is the extended Kalman filter, or EKF (Gelb, 1974). The EKF treats the general nonlinear system

$$\frac{d\underset{\sim}{x}(t)}{dt} = \underset{\sim}{f}(\underset{\sim}{x}(t),t) + \underset{\sim}{w}(t) \tag{1}$$

where $\underset{\sim}{x}$ is the state vector (whose elements might include surface temperature, surface moisture content, moisture content at a depth of 50 cm, etc.), $\underset{\sim}{f}$ is a nonlinear function describing the dynamics of $\underset{\sim}{x}$ and accounting for any exogenous inputs, and $\underset{\sim}{w}$ is zero mean Gaussian noise of spectral density Q(t), accounting for model error. The significance of the term $\underset{\sim}{w}(t)$ is that we realize the model embodied in $\underset{\sim}{f}$ is imperfect. Thus, given an initial value of $\underset{\sim}{x}$, we can predict its future behavior only in a statistical sense. The EKF is a tool that allows us to trace the time evolution of $\hat{\underset{\sim}{x}}$ (which is our best estimate of the true state, $\underset{\sim}{x}$) and of the error covariance matrix given by

$$\underset{\approx}{P}(t) \equiv E[[\hat{\underset{\sim}{x}}(t) - \underset{\sim}{x}(t)][\hat{\underset{\sim}{x}}(t) - \underset{\sim}{x}(t)]^T] \tag{2}$$

where E[ ] is the expectation operator. Equations exist for the propagation in time of $\hat{\underset{\sim}{x}}(t)$ and $\underset{\approx}{P}(t)$, and they are known as the EKF propagation equations (Table 1).

Given that our estimate of x(t) is being continually corrupted by $\underset{\sim}{w}(t)$ in (1), the error covariance is non-decreasing and $\hat{\underset{\sim}{x}}(t)$ becomes less and less reliable. What is needed to reduce the error is an observation of some function of the state. The observation equation for discrete time measurements made at time $\underset{\sim}{t_k}$ is

$$\underset{\sim}{z_k} = \underset{\sim}{h_k}(\underset{\sim}{x}(t_k)) + \underset{\sim}{v_k} \tag{3}$$

where z_k is a vector of measurements (e.g., brightness temperature, thermal infrared radiation, backscatter coefficient) and v_k is the measurement error, having covariance matrix R_k. In general, observed variables are nonlinear functions (h_k) of the state. At the time that the observation z_k is made available, the information contained in it can be combined with the existing information to obtain a new state estimate and a new error covariance. This is accomplished by using the EKF measurement update equations (Table 1). In Table 1, $\hat{x}_k(-)$ and $\hat{x}_k(+)$ indicate estimates of $x(t_k)$ immediately before and after the update. $P_k(-)$ and $P_k(+)$ are similarly defined.

Table 1. Equations of the EKF, from Gelb (1974).

System Model	$\dot{x}(t) = f(x(t),t) + w(t); \quad w(t) \sim N(0,Q(t))$
Measurement Model	$z_k = h_k(x(t_k)) + v_k; \quad k = 1,2,\ldots; \quad v_k \sim N(0,R_k)$
Initial Conditions	$x(0) \sim N(\hat{x}_o,P_o)$
Other Assumptions	$E[w(t)v_k^T] = 0$ for all k and all t
State Estimate Propagation	$\dot{\hat{x}}(t) = f(\hat{x}(t),t)$
Error Covariance Propagation	$\dot{P}(t) = F(\hat{x}(t),t)P(t) + P(t)F^T(\hat{x}(t),t) + Q(t)$
State Estimate Update	$\hat{x}_k(+) = \hat{x}_k(-) + K_k[z_k - h_k(\hat{x}_k(-))]$
Error Covariance Update	$P_k(+) = [I - K_kH_k(\hat{x}_k(-))]P_k(-)$
Gain Matrix	$K_k = P_k(-)H_k^T(\hat{x}_k(-))[H_k(\hat{x}_k(-))P_k(-)H_k^T(\hat{x}_k((-)) + R_k]^{-1}$
Definitions	$F(\hat{x}(t),t) = \dfrac{\partial f(x(t),t)}{\partial x(t)} \Big\vert_{x(t) = \hat{x}(t)}$ $H_k(\hat{x}_k(-)) = \dfrac{\partial h_k(x(t_k))}{\partial x(t_k)} \Big\vert_{x(t_k) = \hat{x}_k(-)}$

Recalling the commentary offered earlier, we see that the EKF appears to provide a valuable mechanism for processing of model estimates and actual measurements of soil moisture and temperature. The uncertainty of both the model and the observations is explicitly considered in arriving at an optimal estimate, and all available information is used. Furthermore, the specification of an appropriate system model -- equation (1) -- allows extrapolation of the estimated near-surface moisture contents to greater depths, depths at which the moisture content is unobservable by remote sensing.

Although we have concentrated on remotely sensed data here, it should be noted that in-situ measurements can be easily incorporated into the EKF framework through augmentation of the observation vector $\tilde{z}$ in (3). This is consistent with our philosophy that all available information should be used.

Application

We have performed numerical experiments using the EKF to estimate soil moisture and temperature in a one-dimensional bare soil column subjected to the atmospheric forcing of rainfall, solar radiation, etc. The system whose states are estimated is not a real physical soil system, but rather an artificial one simulated numerically by solution of a detailed set of governing equations. Likewise, the measurements are based on these simulated states. This synthetic generation of states and measurements has the advantage that the "true" state is everywhere known exactly. Consequently the accuracy of various state estimation procedures can be quantitatively assessed.

The model used for generation of the true states has been described by Milly (1982). The forcing is based on one month of weather data for Dulles Airport in Virginia and the soil is a silt loam (Milly, 1984).

In order to apply the filter, we must define the state dynamics embodied in (1). The filtering procedure is computationally intensive and hence benefits from use of a much simpler model than the one used to generate the true data. For the current analysis, the state set consists of a surface soil moisture content, θ_1, a deep soil moisture content, θ_2, and the surface temperature, T. The dynamics of θ_1 and θ_2 are defined by application of the finite element method (Pinder and Gray, 1977) to the Richards equation for unsaturated flow. We treat the entire profile as a single element and use a special nonlinear set of interpolation functions. The temperature equation is given by the force-restore method (Deardorff, 1970). The final prediction equations involve significant physical and mathematical simplifications of the original equations used to generate the true states and measurements. These discrepancies are modeled by the noise $\tilde{w}$ in (1). We estimate the covariance of $\tilde{w}$ by comparing the predictions of the deterministic part of (1) with the true states.

The filter also requires definition of the measurement equation(s). For the computations described here, we used the relationship between near-surface moisture content and the amplitude of the diurnal soil surface temperature wave (Schmugge et al., 1980). Instead of using published field data for this relationship, we elected to use the simulated truth data to develop the correlation. We found

$$T(1400) - T(0600) = a - b\theta_1(1400) + v \qquad v \sim N(0,\sigma_v^2) \tag{4}$$

where the parenthesized quantities are times of the day, a is 19.3°C and b is 29.2°C.

For the calculations reported here, we employ σ_v equal to 1°C. This is considerably smaller than the value suggested by our simulated data, but makes the estimates of θ_1 based on (4) have approximately the degree of accuracy found in experimental studies. The discrepancy between theoretical and empirical versions of (4) is an interesting area for further research.

We assume that the soil moisture states θ_1 and θ_2, as well as the soil surface temperature, are known exactly at the start of the month. Hence, the error covariance matrix $\underset{\approx}{P}$ is zero at the start. We assume that surface temperature is measured twice daily, at the times required for use of (4). We thus perform a filtering update daily at 1400.

Results

The continuous solid line in Figure 1 depicts the true time variation of θ_1, the surface moisture content. Sharp rises in θ_1 correspond to rainfall periods, while falling θ_1 represents drying periods. The higher frequency oscillations of smaller magnitude represent the influence of various diurnal effects.

The dashed line in Figure 1 represents the estimates of θ_1 made by the simple model used for filtering, but in the absence of measurements. Since the model is an imperfect representation of the true system, there are significant differences between this and the solid curve.

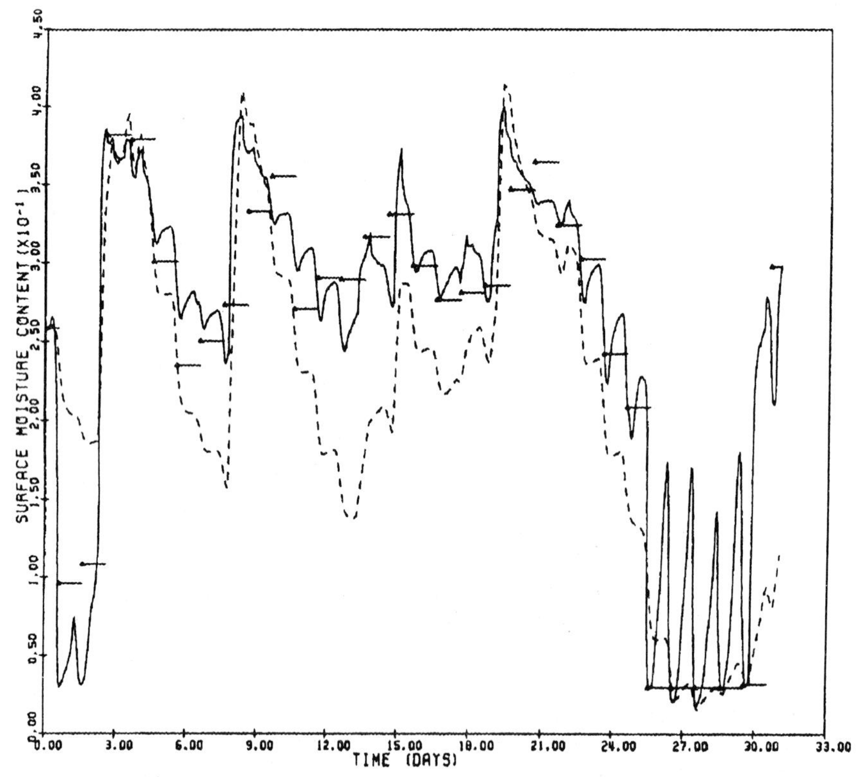

FIG.1 Surface moisture content as function of time. Solid line is true curve, dashed line is from unfiltered model, and horizontal bars are from measurements.

Before illustrating the application of the filter, we call attention to the short horizontal lines in Figure 1. These represent the estimates of θ_1 based on (4) and noisy measurements of the true temperature differences. From (4), these estimates of θ_1 are valid only at one point in time each day. This is marked by the symbol at the start of each segment. The

24-hour horizontal extension of this measurement represents a continuous-time extrapolation of these measurements until a new measurement is available. We shall refer to this as the persistence model.

The result of applying the EKF in this problem for estimation of θ_1 is seen in Figure 2. Again, the solid line represents the true θ_1. The dashed line is the EKF estimate of θ_1. There is a daily jump of θ_1 each time a measurement is made. The filtered $\theta_1(t)$ is clearly superior to the unfiltered $\theta_1(t)$. The estimates of $\theta_1(t)$ in Figure 1 based only on measurements and the persistence model do not appear, on average, to be inferior to the EKF results. However, they do fail to capture the diurnal behavior and would deteriorate with decreasing frequency of measurements.

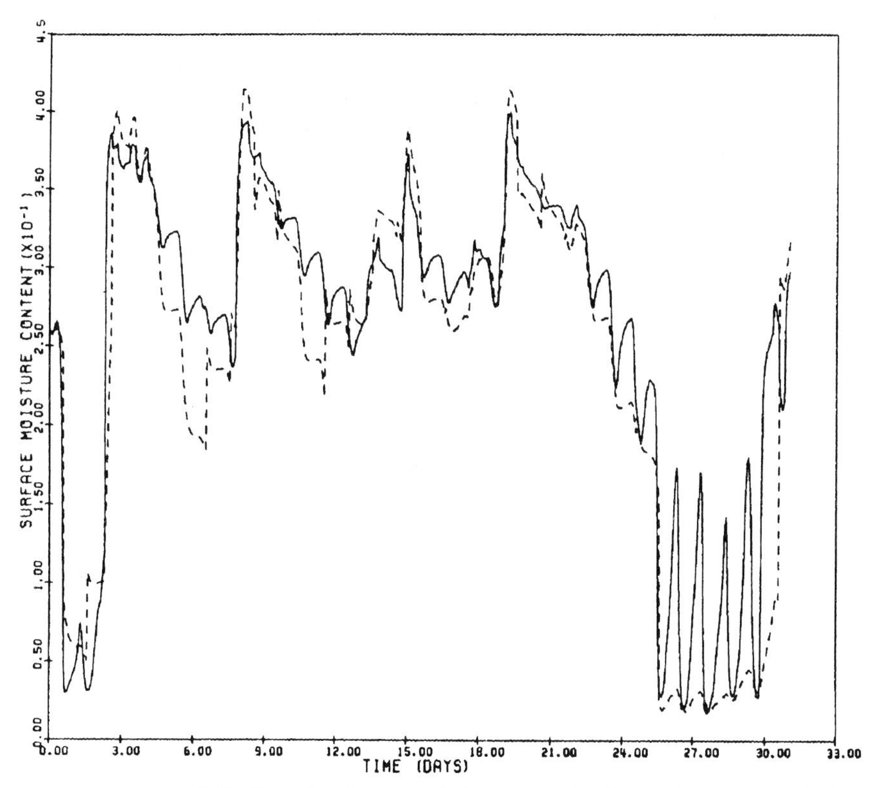

FIG.2 Surface moisture content as function of time. Solid line is true curve, and dashed line is EKF estimate.

Another drawback of the persistence model is that it offers no estimate of how quickly the state covariance will grow after a measurement. In Figure 3 we have plotted the time variation of the diagonal element of $\tilde{P}$ whose value is the error variance for θ_1. The serrated, solid line represents results from the EKF. These are at a minimum whenever a measurement is taken and generally grow until the next measurement. The dashed line depicts the growth of the error in the absence of measurements and corresponds to the unfiltered model predictions of Figure 1. The plotted symbols give the error based on measurements alone. Without knowing the model error of the persistence model, we cannot quantify the accuracy of the persistence estimate between measurements.

Table 2 summarizes the statistics of the cases illustrated in Figures

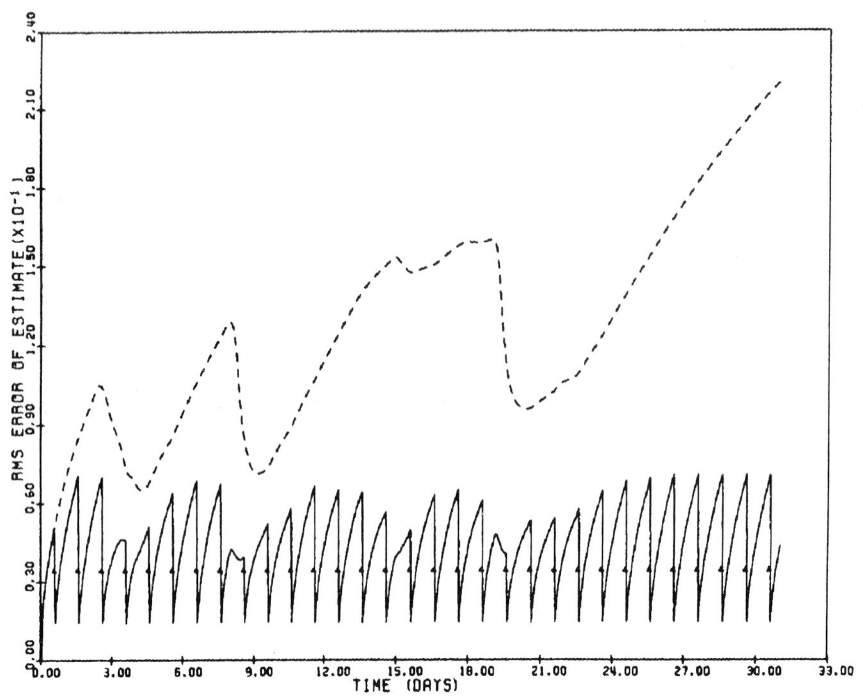

FIG.3 Error of surface moisture content. Solid line is for EKF with daily update, dashed line is for unfiltered model, and symbols are for measurements.

1 through 3. The quantity $(\langle P_{\theta_1\theta_1}\rangle)^{1/2}$ is the square root of the mean value of the theoretical error variance of θ_1 throughout the month. Ths quantity is reduced significantly by filtering in this example. The quantity RMSE (θ_1) is the square root of the mean value of the actual squared error between the true $\theta_1(t)$ and the estimated $\theta_1(t)$ for this particular realization. The improvement in this parameter with filtering parallels that of $(\langle P_{\theta_1\theta_1}\rangle)^{1/2}$, as it should.

Table 2. Error Statistics for Various Estimates of $\theta_1(t)$. Units are the same as those of θ_1, i.e., volume of water per bulk volume of soil.

	$(\langle P_{\theta_1\theta_1}\rangle)^{1/2}$	RMSE (θ_1)
State Dynamics Only	0.125	0.077
Measurement and Persistence	---	0.059
EKF	0.044	0.050

Summary

The extended Kalman filter (EKF) is a potential framework for the integration of remotely sensed data with model predictions to obtain an optimal estimate of soil moisture. It allows the use of all available information, including physical knowledge of the system dynamics. An example shows the benefits of using the EKF instead of either measurements or models alone.

References

Gelb, A. (ed.), 1974, Applied Optimal Estimation, M.I.T. Press, Cambridge, Massachuestts.

Milly, P.C.D., 1982, Moisture and heat transport in hysteretic, inhomogeneous porous media: a matric head-based formulation and a numerical model, Water Resour. Res., 18(3), 489-498.

Milly, P.C.D., 1984, A simulation of thermal effects on evaporation, Water Resour. Res., 20(8), 1087-1098.

Pinder, G.F. and W.G. Gray, 1977, Finite Element Simulation in Surface and Subsurface Hydrology, Academic, New York.

Schmugge, T.J., T.J. Jackson and H.L. McKim, 1980, Survey of methods for soil moisture determination, Water Resour. Res., 16(6), 961-979.

Hydrologic Applications of Space Technology (Proceedings of the Cocoa Beach Workshop, Florida, August 1985). IAHS Publ. no. 160, 1986.

Forecasting snowmelt runoff of Himalayan rivers using NOAA AVHRR imageries since 1980

A. S. RAMAMOORTHI
National Remote Sensing Agency,
Hyderabad 500 037, India

Abstract

The Himalayas are the source for the waters flowing in the Indus, Ganga, and Brahmaputra river systems during the summer months of April to June. Since the snow occurs at very high altitudes in the Himalayas and the snow-covered watersheds of these river systems extend over hundreds of square kilometres, it was not possible hitherto to assess the snow fall conditions and predict the runoff. It is only after the availability of NOAA AVHRR imageries in India, that an effort could be made to map and monitor the snow-covered watersheds.

In this paper is described (1) the regression models relating snow-covered area derived from NOAA AVHRR imageries with the seasonal snowmelt runoffs and (2) the predictions of the quantities of snowmelt runoffs, made by the author, which were less than plus or minus ten per cent different from the discharges that actually occurred and were measured in the years 1980 to 1983.

Introduction

Unlike the rivers of central and southern India, the rivers of north India--namely the Indus, Ganga, and Brahmaputra river systems--are perennial. This is because of the snowmelt runoff from the Himalayas, the abode of eternal snows about 2250 km (1400 mi) in length from the Indus to the Brahmaputra. The Himalayas may be regarded as a double mountain wall of stupendous mountain ranges running nearly east and west, descending into a series of deep valleys towards the north in which the Indus, the Sutlej, and the Brahmaputra rivers gather their waters, while the southern Himalayan slopes drain into the mighty Ganga. The precipitation during winter occurs due to "western disturbances", the extra tropical disturbances moving from west to east originating from the Caspian and Mediterranean Seas and moving across Iran, Afghanistan, and southern USSR. About thirty "western disturbances" occur in a winter with an average frequency of five to six disturbances a month.

The quantity of snowmelt runoff that occurs during the summer months of April to June critically determines the supply of hydropower, irrigation, and drinking water to millions of people living in North India. Hence, there is a great need to get an idea, well in advance, of the quantity of the snowmelt runoff that would occur in these months so that one could plan its optimum utilization vis-a-vis the competing demands.

Development of a model for predicting seasonal runoff from snow covered catchments of Himalayas, using satellite data

In the models that have been developed in the USA for snowmelt runoff studies, the snow-covered areas (SCA) derived from Landsat and/or NOAA satellites (AVHRR) imagery, the daily precipitation, the daily temperature and snowpack water content have been used. These models are based on long term data from a good network of hydrometeorological stations, reliable information about the snowfalls, detailed topographical maps, etc.

In India it has been only in recent years that a systematic and continuous effort has been made in a few basins to collect data required for snow studies. This is because of (1) lack of adequate personnel with an aptitude for snow surveys, and (2) the snow covered watersheds in the Himalayas are situated at very high altitudes and are very large in size varying from about 5,200 km^2 (2000 mi^2) to about 52,000 km^2 (20,000 mi^2); they are inhospitable and hazardous. As is common in a mountain terrain, the snow depths in Himalayas vary very widely from a few inches to many feet within short distances and they constantly change because of frequent spells of 1 to 7 days of snowfall occurring due to "western disturbances." Determining parameters such as snow water equivalent is a formidable task. Considering all these limitations, the author came to the conclusion that if models have to be developed for simulating or predicting snowmelt runoffs of Himalayan watersheds, they have to be based mainly on snow-covered area, which can be distinctly seen and mapped from Landsat scenes or from NOAA AVHRR imagery.

Hence in 1978, the snow covered area in the Sutlej basin was mapped from NOAA satellite AVHRR imagery (of April) of the years 1975 to 1977 obtained from USA and a regression model between the percentage of snow-covered area in the Sutlej basin above Bhakra reservoir and the total runoff of the Sutlej at Bhakra during the months April, May, and June was developed. The Sutlej river was chosen for such a study that was being done for the first-time, not only because of the presence of the Bhakra reservoir--one of the most important major hydropower and irrigation projects in India--but also because correct and authentic observed snowmelt runoff of Sutlej could be obtained at Bhakra for verifying the model. The watershed of Sutlej up to Bhakra is about 43,200 km^2 (16,700 mi^2) and it falls in more than one Landsat scene. On the contrary, from one NOAA AVHRR imagery itself one could get a comprehensive synoptic view of the snow cover and meteorological conditions over Sutlej watershed and adjoining regions. Though NOAA data is of coarser resolution when compared to Landsat data, it is available daily unlike Landsat Data. This is a major consideration in using NOAA data, especially since the snow cover changes occur abruptly and frequently in the Himalayas due to the passage of the "western disturbances".

The setting up of the Earth Station, capable of receiving both Landsat and NOAA satellite data by NRSA in January 1980, was a major event that was responsible for the continuance of snowmelt runoff studies using satellite data. From judiciously selected cloud-free NOAA imagery of January to March 1980, the percentage SCA on the days of very heavy snowfall was worked out and a value to be used for prediction was determined. Using the model developed in 1978 and the percentage of SCA, the likely seasonal snowmelt runoff in 1980 was predicted as 14.20 lakh cusec days. (Ed. Note: lakh = 100,000.) The forecast was checked with the total quantity of runoff of the Sutlej as actually measured at Bhakra reservoir during the snowmelt season. It was found that the difference between the forecast quantity and that which actually occurred (15.17 lakh cusec days) was 6.4 per cent. This result was encouraging and it was felt that this model based on the SCA derived from NOAA imagery could be improved and used for predicting Sutlej flows.

Consequently, during the months of January to March 1981, NOAA imagery was collected (a few images are shown as Figures 1 to 5) and the SCA on cloud-free days in the catchment was determined. The maximum percentage of SCA to be adopted was decided. The actual observed discharge of 1980 was plotted on the regression relationship and after a careful study a new line (model) was drawn. Based on this, the likely seasonal snowmelt runoff of 17 lakh cusec days during 1981 was predicted. The hydrograph of the daily discharge data of the Sutlej (Figure 6) was examined and it was seen that the actual total seasonal snowmelt runoff of Sutlej in 1981 was 16.19 lakh cusec days. Hence, the predicted flow was more than the observed flow by

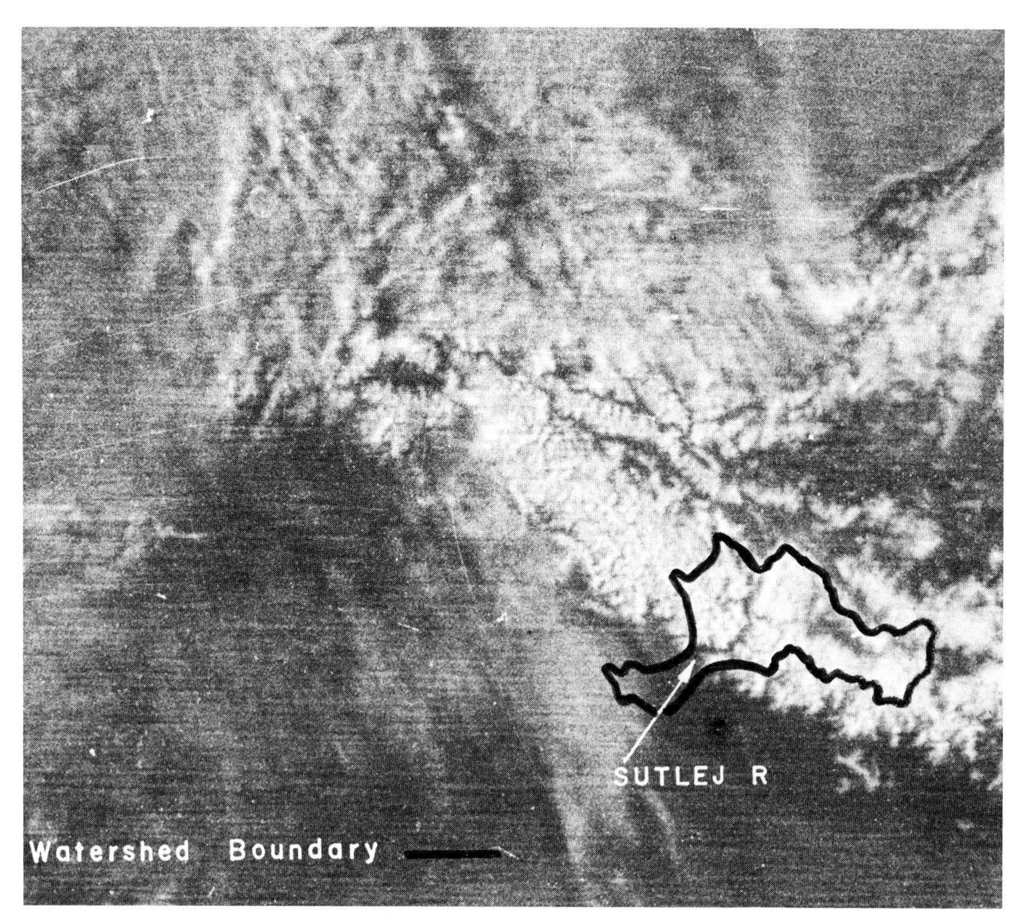

FIG.1 NOAA satellite imagery of 10th Feb. 1981.

about 5 per cent. Taking note of this, the model was revised. The snowmelt runoff studies were continued during the subsequent years. The results obtained are as given below:

Year	Seasonal snowmelt runoff		
	Forecast	Actual	% Difference
1980	14.20	15.17	6.4
1981	17.00	16.19	5.0
1982	16.75	17.77	5.74
1983	20.50	21.02	2.5

The models used are shown in Figure 7. Similar seasonal snowmelt runoff forecasting models with satellite SCA data as input are being developed for other Himalayan rivers.

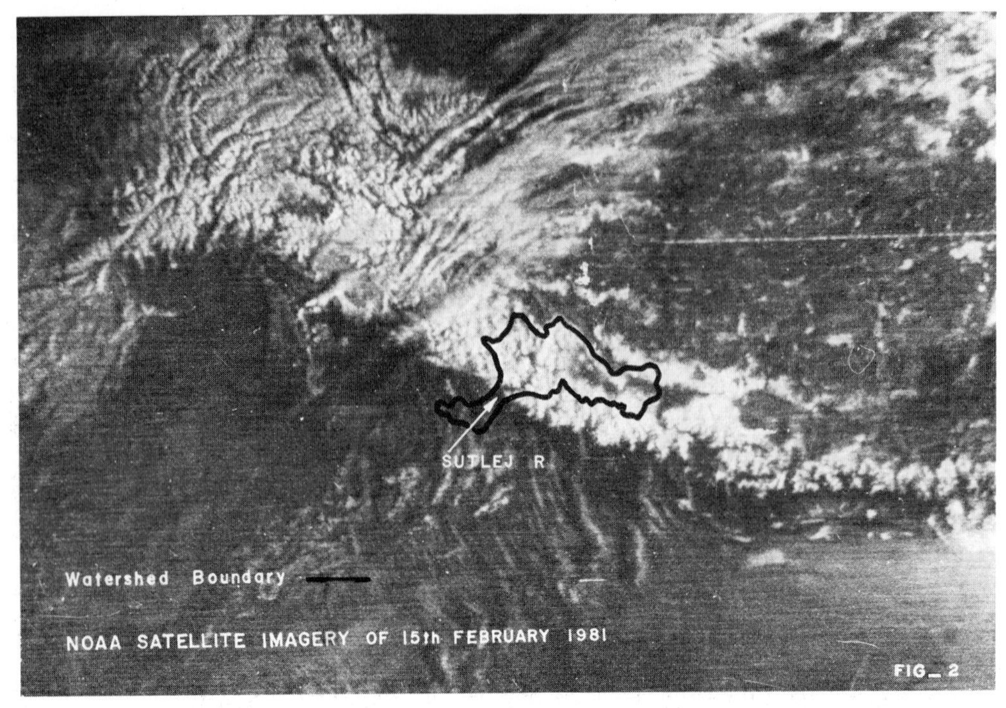

FIG.2 NOAA satellite imagery of 15th Feb. 1981.

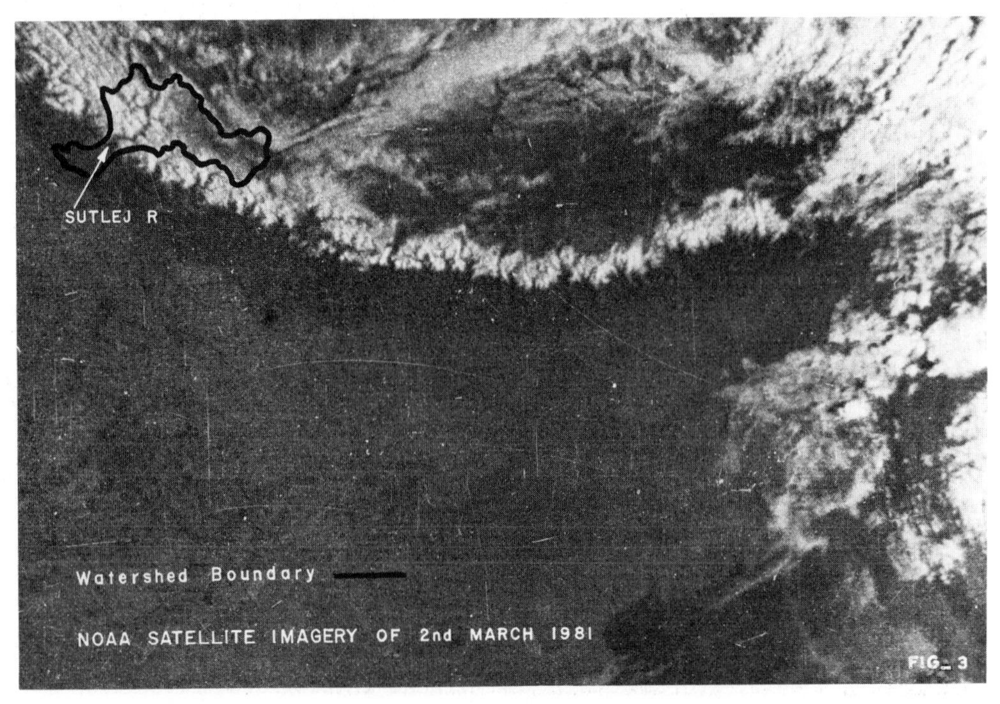

FIG.3 NOAA satellite imagery of 2nd March 1981.

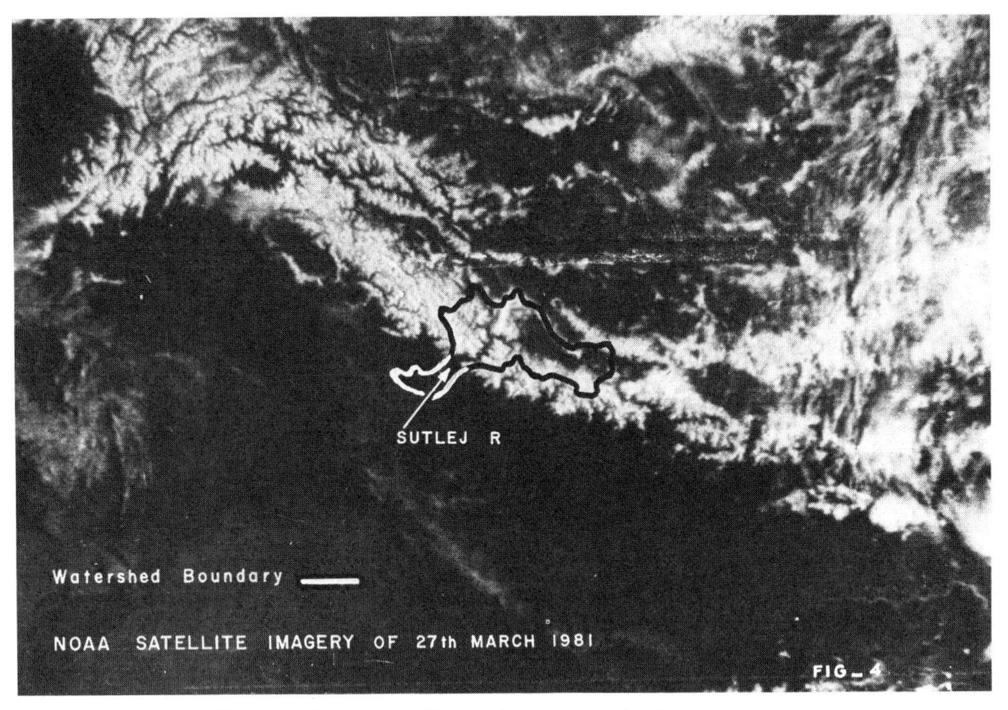

FIG.4 NOAA satellite imagery of 27th March 1981.

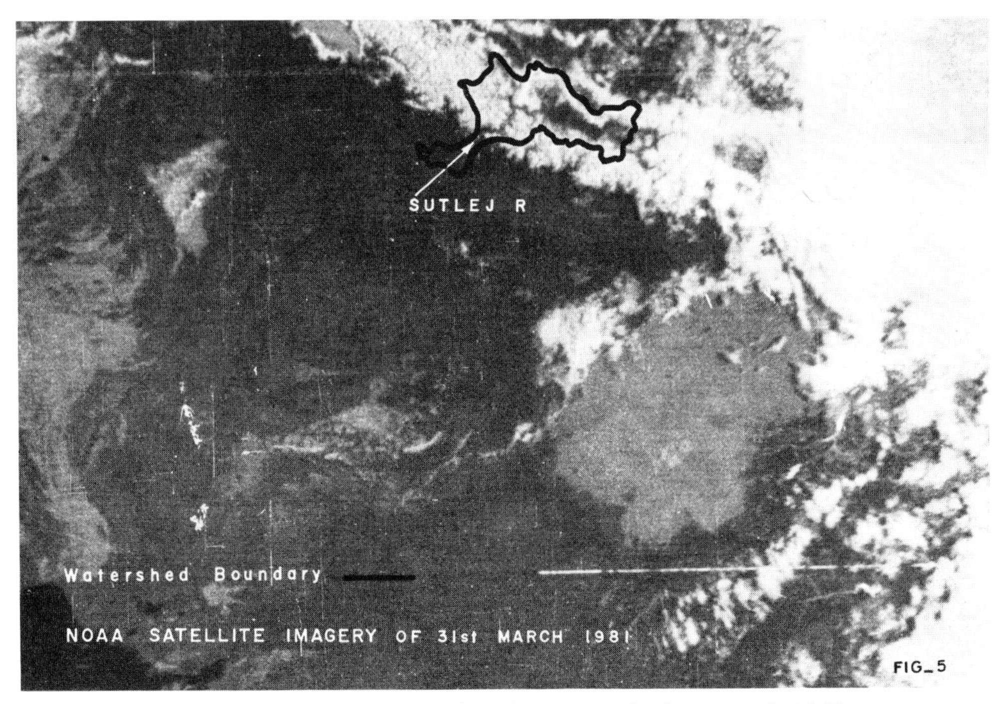

FIG.5 NOAA satellite imagery of 31st March 1981.

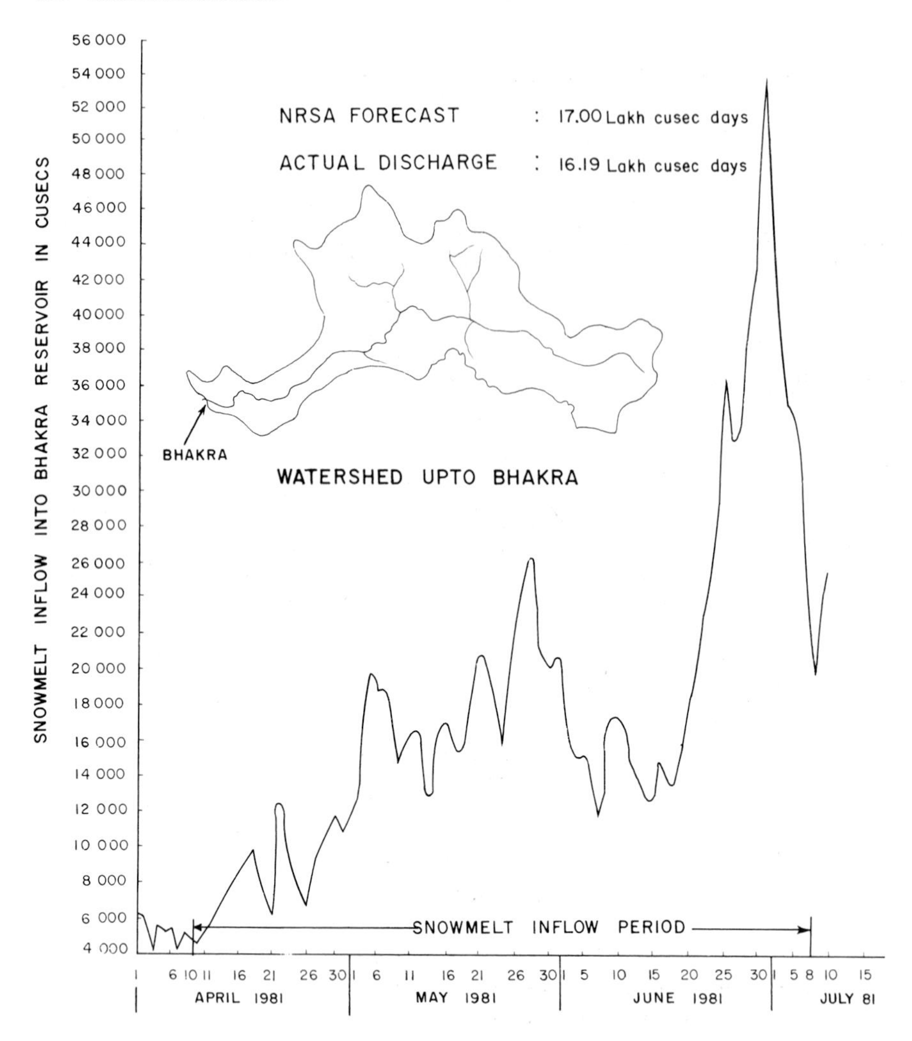

FIG.6 Hydrograph showing snowmelt runoff (1981) from Sutlej River basin into Bhakra reservoir.

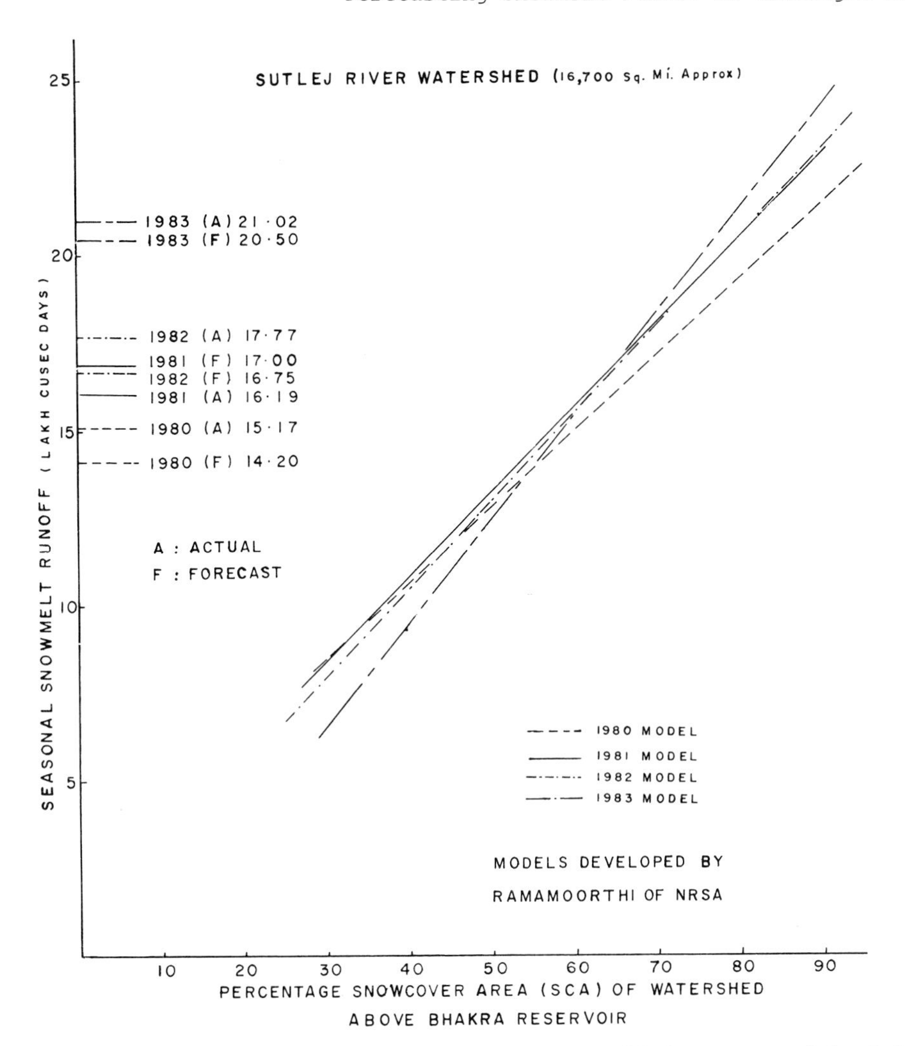

FIG.7 Seasonal snowmelt runoff forecast model, Sutlej River basin.

Hydrologic Applications of Space Technology (Proceedings of the Cocoa Beach Workshop, Florida, August 1985). IAHS Publ. no. 160, 1986.

Satellite data input to Windy Gap computerized streamflow forecasting model

JOHN R. ECKHARDT
Northern Colorado Water Conservancy District, PO Box 679, Loveland, Colorado 80539, USA
CHARLES F. LEAF
Consulting Hydrologist, Sterling, Colorado, USA

Abstract
The basis for timely residual streamflow forecasts for the recently completed Windy Gap Project in Colorado is a remote hydrologic data collection network which utilizes the GOES Satellite for data transmission to project headquarters in Loveland, Colorado. Snowpack, soil moisture, streamflow, precipitation, temperature, and wind data collected at 15 remote sites in the Fraser River Basin are used to update a computerized hydrologic simulation model.

This process-oriented model, developed from Forest Service research and pilot-tested in NASA's recently published Application Systems Verification and Transfer project on satellite snow cover observations, is being used for making forecasts of residual streamflow available to Windy Gap. Forecasts are based on current snowpack and anticipated weather conditions in the basin.

Water diverted at Windy Gap is transported via pumping plant and pipeline to the Colorado-Big Thompson Project for subsequent storage and distribution along the Front Range. Timely short-term forecasts are necessary to minimize pumping costs and to efficiently operate the project in accordance with the water decree.

Introduction

The Windy Gap Project, operated by the Municipal Subdistrict of the Northern Colorado Water Conservancy District, supplies raw water to the Platte River Power Authority and the Cities of Boulder, Estes Park, Greeley, Longmont, and Loveland. Windy Gap is a transbasin project diverting water high in the Colorado Rockies from the Colorado River Basin and by utilizing the Colorado-Big Thompson Project, stores and delivers this water to the users in the South Platte River Basin. The primary components of the Windy Gap Project are a diversion dam on the Colorado River together with a pumping plant rated at 16.8 cubic meters per second and 9.15 km of 2.74-m diameter pipeline.

The diversion dam is located just below a tributary of the Colorado River, the Fraser River, at a location referred to as Windy Gap. The reservoir formed behind the diversion dam has a total live capacity of 393,600 cubic meters and is used only as a forebay to the pumping plant. The pumping plant is located in the right abutment of the diversion dam and contains four vertical shaft centrifugal pumps rated at 4.2 cubic meters per second each. The Windy Gap Project connects with the Colorado-Big Thompson Project through 9.15 km of pipeline.

Data Collection System

The Hydrologic Data Collection System is composed of 15 data collection platforms (DCP) located at remote sites in the Fraser River watershed (see Figure 1). Nine stations measure river stage and six monitor snow and weather conditions. The basic components of the remote sites are a

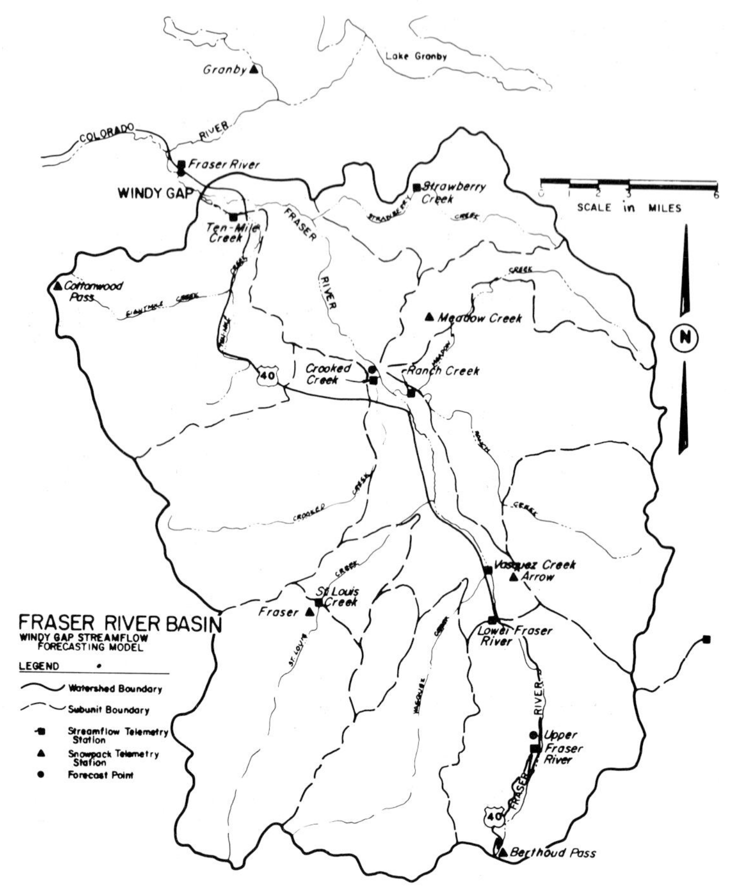

FIG.1 Fraser River subwatersheds and data collection system.

Sutron Model 8004D DCP, battery and associated solar panel, power supply, antenna and cabling, sensors, and shelter. Data acquisition is controlled, stored and transmitted to a goes stationary satellite by the DCP. The satellite used is part of the Geostationary Operational Environmental Satellite Data Collection System (GOES DCS) and is managed by the National Environmental Satellite, Data, and Informational Service (NESDIS).

From this satellite, the data are relayed to a downlink receiver and stored on a computer located at the Northern Colorado Water Conservancy District headquarters in Loveland, Colorado.

Supervisory Control and Data Acquisition (SCADA) System

A State-of-the-Art computer based supervisory control and data acquisition system is used to operate the Windy Gap Project (See Figure 2). The SCADA system is an anticipatory close-looped control system requiring a minimum of human interaction. It operates in a real-time environment to perform the task required to control and monitor the Windy Gap Project.

The basic premise of the SCADA system is to maximize the amount of water diverted while minimizing power cost and meeting the constraints as a result of legal and institutional requirements. The SCADA system utilizes real-time runoff forecasts to establish set point target values for pumping and flow control algorithms. This procedure allows the SCADA system to anticipate streamflows and establish optimum pumping and power schedules.

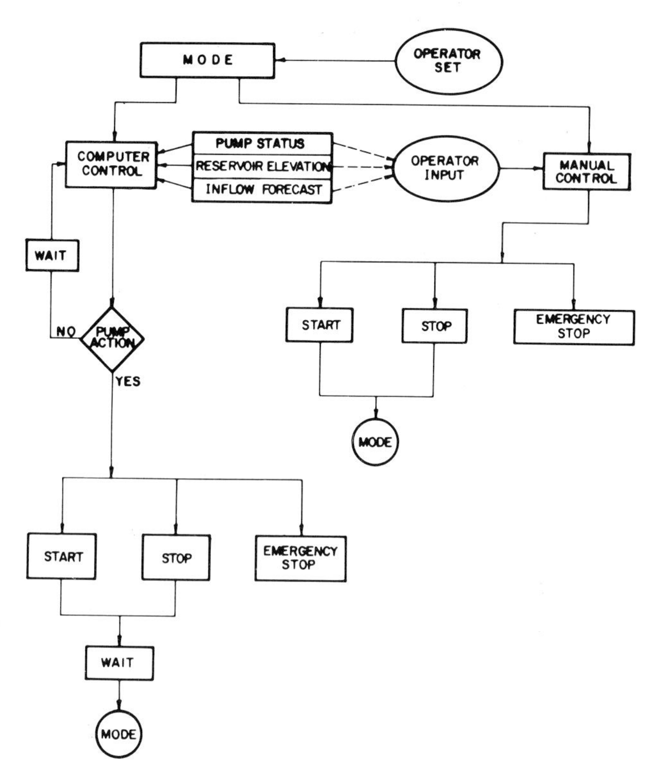

FIG.2 Windy Gap Project, functional flow diagram; Supervisory control and data aquisition (SCADA) system.

Hydrologic Simulation Model

Currently, most forecasts of runoff from the Fraser and other river basins in Colorado are made using statistical correlations between peak seasonal snow accumulation during previous years and resultant streamflow. These forecasts are made each spring assuming that "average" weather conditions will prevail during the subsequent snowmelt runoff season. Extension of these early-season forecasts to a short-term basis using such methods is difficult since precipitation and meteorological conditions during the ensuing melt season can vary widely from year-to-year. However, short-term forecasts are possible using timely information from the GOES satellite data collection network and a dynamic hydrologic simulation model.

Subalpine Water Balance Model

The "Subalpine Water Balance Model" (WATBAL) developed by Leaf and Brink (1973) is being used to forecast residual streamflows to Windy Gap. This model developed from Forest Service research, simulates winter snow accumulation, the shortwave and longwave radiation balance, snowpack condition, evapotranspiration, snowmelt, and subsequent runoff on as many as 25 response units. Each response unit is defined by relatively uniform slope, aspect, and forest cover. Results from all response units are compiled into a "composite overview" of an entire watershed. Recently, WATBAL was modified for use as a streamflow forecasting tool in NASA's Application Systems Verification and Transfer program (See Shafer and Leaf, 1980). Figure 3 is a generalized flow chart of WATBAL.

In the Windy Gap forecasting system, WATBAL simulates snowmelt runoff from eight subwatersheds in the Fraser River Basin (See Figure 1). All are key tributaries that characterize the hydrologic regime of the basin.

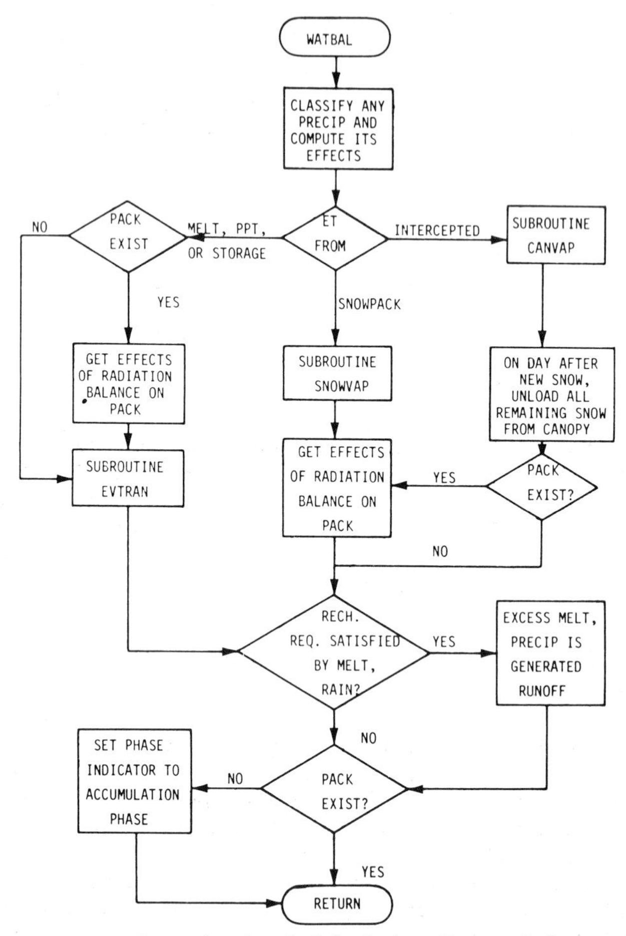

FIG.3 Flow chart of Subalpine Water Balance Model (WATBAL).

Forecasting System Design

The way in which WATBAL is used to update streamflow forecasts has been discussed by Shafer and Leaf (1980). A primary model response is area snowpack water equivalent; this variable is plotted as a function of time in Figure 4. Typically, the seasonal snowpack builds to a "peak" in late spring. To the left of this peak is the winter snow accumulating season (full snow cover) and to the right is the snowmelt runoff (snow cover depletion) season.

Updating the model to reflect existing hydrologic conditions can be achieved through adjustment of simulated water equivalent based on GOES

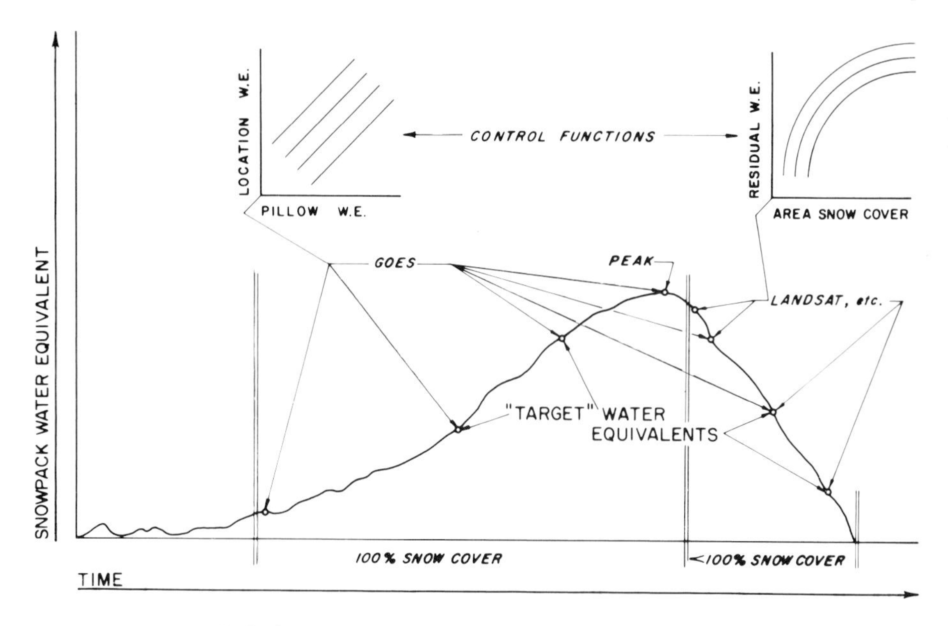

FIG.4 Use of real-time data in updating simulated snowpack water equivalent.

Satellite transmissions of real-time snow pillow data. During the runoff season, additional control can also be achieved using direct estimates of areal snow cover from LANDSAT or other similar remote sensing systems. The control functions shown in Figure 4 are relationships which adjust point measurements to area estimates of snow cover and water equivalent on each response unit.

Operational Forecasts

Basic data inputs to WATBAL are daily air temperature and precipitation. Streamflow forecasts are made using a method similar to one developed by the Corps of Engineers (U.S. Army, 1972). The procedure combines: (a) five-day forecasts of temperature and precipitation (expressed as departures from normal) with (b) the long-term normals, and (c) synthetic sequences of temperature and precipiation derived from frequency analyses (also expressed as departures from normal). The forecast combines (a), (b), and (c) to arrive at an input sequence of assumed future conditions. The forecast system provides for inputting an extended period of record which is updated each day using real-time GOES Satellite-transmitted data. The synthetic data sequences can be either minimum, moderate, or extreme, depending on anticipated weather conditions and objectives of the forecast.

Streamflow Routing

Figure 5 is a line diagram showing a concept plan of the Windy Gap Streamflow Forecasting System. Simulated inflows from the subwatersheds shown in Figure 1 are combined at 4 nodes and subsequently routed down the Fraser River to Windy Gap. A significant impact on streamflow forecasts results from Denver Water Board diversions out of the basin via the Moffat water tunnel. These diversions are subtracted from simulated river flows at node 3. Subtractions will be based on telemetered discharge data from East

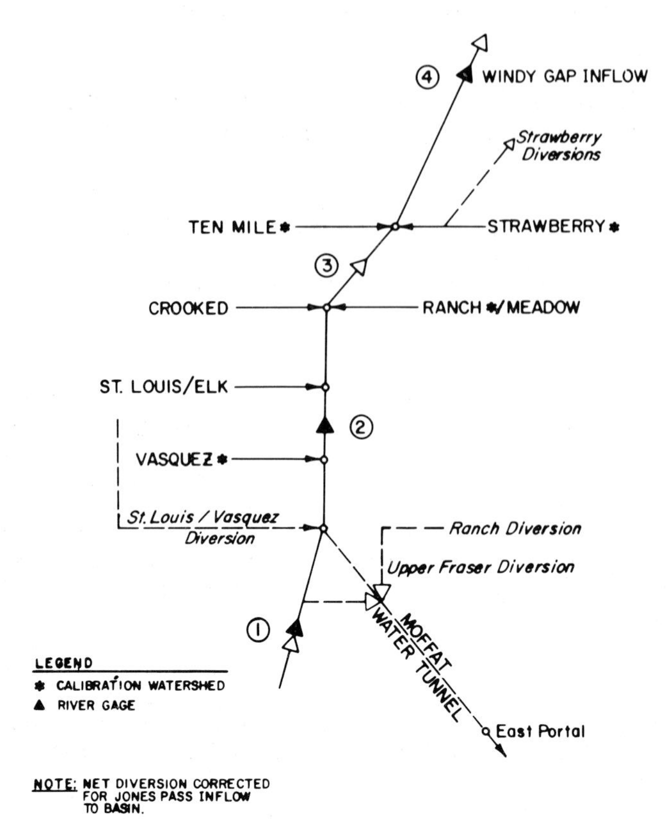

FIG.5 Windy Gap Streamflow routing.

Portal which gages combined diversions through the Moffat system. Telemetered data from river gages at nodes 1, 2, and 4 provide additional controls on model output.

References

Leaf, Charles F. and G. E. Brink, 1973, Hydrologic Simulation Model of Colorado Subalpine Forest: USDA For. Serv. Res. Paper RM-1-7, Rocky Mtn. Forest and Range Exp. Stn., Fort Collins, Colorado, 23 p.

Shafer, Bernard A. and C. F. Leaf, 1980, Landsat Derived Snow Cover as an Input Variable for Snowmelt Runoff Forecasting in South Central Colorado: Final Workshop on Operational Applications of Satellite Snow Cover Observations, NASA Conf. Publication 2116, Albert Rango and Ralph Peterson, Editors, NASA/Goddard Space Flight Center in coop. with Cont. Ed. Univ. of Nevada, Reno, Nevada.

U. S. Army, 1972, Program Description and User Manual for SSARR MODEL: Streamflow Synthesis and Reservoir Regulation. Program 724-K5-G0010, U. S. Army Engineer Division, North Pacific, Portland, Oregon.

Hydrologic Applications of Space Technology (Proceedings of the Cocoa Beach Workshop, Florida, August 1985). IAHS Publ. no. 160, 1986.

Digital analysis of the hydrologic components of watersheds using simulated SPOT imagery

KATHRYN F. CONNORS, THOMAS W. GARDNER & GARY W. PETERSEN
The Pennsylvania State University, University Park, Pennsylvania, USA

Abstract

Systeme Probatoire d'Observation de la Terre (SPOT), a French satellite scheduled for launch in 1985, will have three multispectral bands and a panchromatic band with 20 m and 10 m ground resolution, respectively. In this study, simulated SPOT data discriminate among surfaces with different infiltration and runoff characteristics. Reflectances of features with different hydrologic characteristics are classified using cluster, non-parametric linear discriminant, Bayesian maximum likelihood, and edge enhancement techniques. Simulated SPOT data from a semiarid site in New Mexico discriminate among surfaces with different stabilities that result from differing rates of fluvial and eolian erosion. Simulated SPOT data distinguish components of the hydrologic system disturbed by surface coal mining in a humid temperate site in Pennsylvania. Spectral reflectance and edge characteristics discriminate groundwater recharge and some discharge sites. The digital format of the data allows for ready input into hydrological model data bases.

Introduction

Numeric hydrologic models which predict sediment and water discharge on watersheds require, among other things, data bases containing the areal extent of surface characteristics such as infiltration rate, runoff rate, soil texture, vegetation cover, and surface roughness. Many of the specific components of the hydrologic system of watersheds can be characterized with remotely sensed data (Figure 1). The digital nature of remotely sensed data provides an element by element format that could easily be incorporated into hydrologic models. The first generation of remotely sensed data (LANDSAT-1,2, and 3) has been used to view regional physiography and land use patterns and to grossly classify surface features to an Anderson (1976) Level I. This level of classification, however, is generally not useful in hydrologic modeling. The second generation of satellite remote sensing systems has improved spatial resolution (SPOT), or improved spectral and spatial resolution (LANDSAT-Thematic Mapper) (Table 1) that allow Level II, and III and possibly Level IV classification (Anderson, J. R. et al., 1976). These improvements in resolution may allow for significant improvements in remote sensing input to numeric hydrologic models.

This study evaluates the utility of digital and analog simulated SPOT data to characterize the hydrologic components of watersheds in both semiarid and humid regions. The semiarid data set is located in McKinley County, northwestern New Mexico, northeast of the town of Crownpoint on U.S. Geological Survey 7.5 minute quadrangles of Antelope Lookout Mesa, Becenti Lake, Milk Lake, and Nose Rock. It is situated in the San Juan Basin of the Colorado Plateau Physiographic Province and is centered around Kim-me-ni-oli Wash, an emphemeral, discontinuous arroyo and southern tributary of the Chaco River. Bedrock consists of gently north-dipping

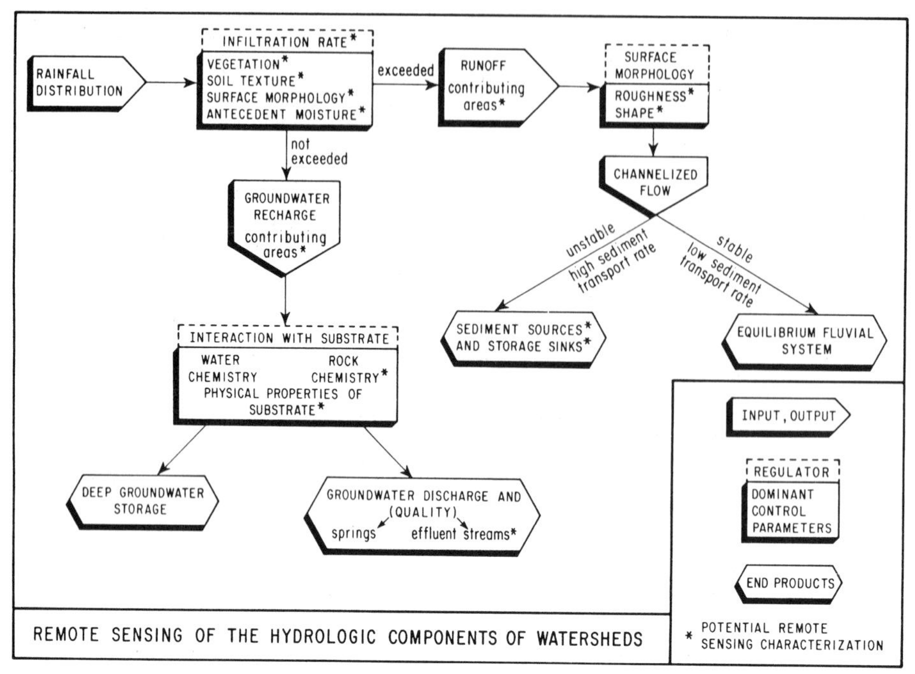

FIG.1 Flow diagram showing watershed components that can be remotely sensed.

upper Cretaceous, continental sandstone, mudstone, shale, and coal of the Menèfee Formation (Hackman and Olson, 1977). Bedrock is discontinuously mantled by Quaternary alluvium and sandy eolian deposits. The climate is high desert, semiarid to arid. Summer precipitation is in the form of high intensity, local thunderstorms. Vegetation consists of rangeland grasses, forbes, weeds, cacti and shrubbery.

Geomorphic processes within Kim-me-ni-oli Wash drainage basin include eolian erosion and deposition, sheetwash, fluvial headward extension, lateral stream migration, piping, pedogenesis, soil creep and rock fall. Detailed field studies (Wells, 1982, 1983; Wells et al., 1983a, 1983b) have produced extensive values for the rates of dominant geomorphic processes in the study area (Figure 2). The upland is characterized by Holocene eolian mantles deposited during high rates of eolian transport and deposition. Radiocarbon dates of the eolian sediment range from 5970+105 yrs BP to modern (Wells et al., 1983a). Present eolian transport rates are low (Wells, 1982; Wells et al., 1983a). Soils are coarse-loamy, mixed, mesic Typic Haplargids. According to Soil Taxonomy (U.S.D.A. Soil Conservation Service, 1977), "..... argids that have an argillic horizon but do not have a natric horizon are formed on late-Pleistocene or older erosion surfaces or sediments." This is consistent with Wells' data which dates the uplands at early to mid-Holocene. These late Pleistocene and early Holocene uplands also show little evidence of erosion and hence, are considered stable. The valley floor component is characterized by locally very rapid tributary headward extension and drainage integration, lateral stream migration, and sheetwash (Mills and Gardner, 1983). Radiocarbon dates of the alluvium range from 3320+60 yrs BP to 390+75 yrs BP (Wells et al., 1983a). Soils are formed on mildly alkaline alluvium and are fine-loamy, mixed, mesic Typic Torrifluvents and fine, mixed, mesic Typic Camborthids. The valley floor of Kim-me-ni-oli Wash has abundant evidence of present day erosion. Work by Mills and Gardner (1983) document a maximum tributary headcutting rate of 12.3 m/yr and a maximum lateral channel migration rate of 5.1 m/yr. Because valley floor soils are young or weakly developed and there is active erosion and deposition; they are considered unstable.

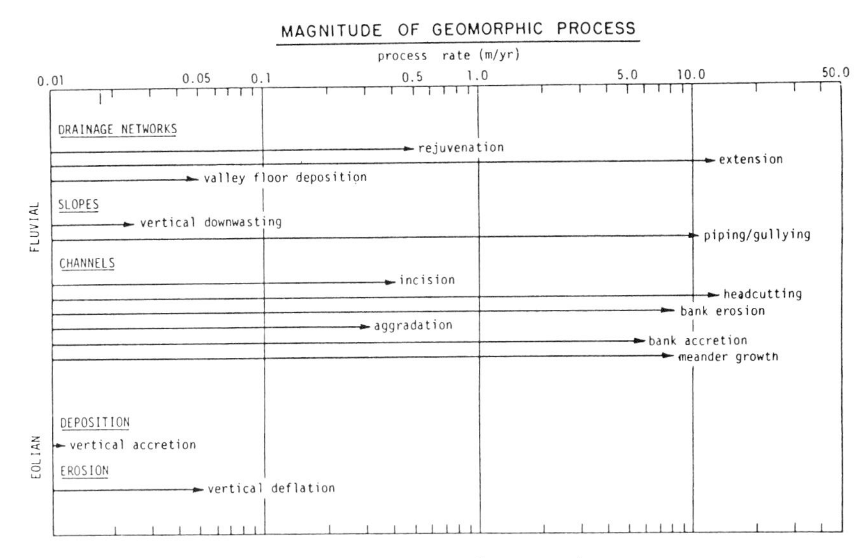

FIG.2 Geomorphic process rates for northwestern New Mexico (from Wells & Gardner,1984).

The humid temperate data set is located in central Pennsylvania in the Allegheny Plateau Physiographic Province on U.S. Geological Survey 7.5 minute quadrangles of Frenchville, Karthaus, Pottersdale, Snow Shoe and Snow Shoe Southeast. The site possesses reclaimed and unreclaimed bituminous coal surface mines, active mines, and unmined watersheds. The surficial bedrock consists of Mississippian age shale, siltstone, sandstone and some conglomerate of the Mauch Chunk Formation and Burgoon Sandstone, and Pennsylvania age sandstone and conglomerate of the Pottsville Group and cyclic sequences of sandstone, shale, limestone, and clay of the Allegheny Group. The area is extensively mined for the Freeport, Kittanning, Clarion and Mercer coals of the Allegheny Group (Berg, 1980 and Williams, 1960). The climate is humid temperature. Natural vegetation consists of second growth mixed deciduous and coniferous forest. Some portions of the study area have been converted to cropland. Mined land is vegetated with grasses and mixed tree cover.

The SPOT Program

SPOT (Systeme Probatoire d'Observation de la Terre) is a French observational satellite. SPOT will orbit circular sun-synchronously at altitudes between 600 and 1200 km with an orbital repeat period of 26 days, but with the capability to observe mid-latitude regions up to 12 times in a 26 day cycle (Chevrel et al., 1981). It will sense in a multispectral scanning (MSS) and a panchromatic mode with high resolution, visible (HRV) range instruments (Table 1). The HRV are composed of 3000 charge-coupled device (CCD) detectors per MSS band and 6000 detectors for the panchromatic band. These detectors are in a linear array and scan in a pushbroom mode as the satellite moves forward along its orbit (Chevrel et al., 1981). Stereoscopic capabilities of the sensor are available because of across track pointability of the HRV. There will be an increase in spatial resolution

Table 1. Comparison of First Generation and Second Generation Satellite Systems: Spectral Bands and Spatial Resolution

	FIRST GENERATION (Landsat 1, 2, and 3)	SECOND GENERATION (SPOT)	SECOND GENERATION (Landsat-Thematic Mapper)
SPECTRAL RESOLUTION (wavelength)	Band 4 0.5-0.6 μ Band 5 0.6-0.7 μ Band 6 0.7-0.8 μ Band 7 0.8-1.1 μ	Band 1 0.51-0.59 μ Band 2 0.61-0.68 μ Band 3 0.79-0.89 μ Band 4(P) 0.51-0.73 μ	Band 1 0.45-0.52 μ Band 2 0.52-0.60 μ Band 3 0.63-0.69 μ Band 4 0.76-0.90 μ Band 5 1.55-1.75 μ Band 6 2.08-2.35 μ Band 7 10.40-12.50μ
SPATIAL RESOLUTION (ground cell)	79 by 57 m	MSS bands 20 m panchromatic band 10 m	bands 1-6 30 m band 7 120 m

of more than an order of magnitude from LANDSAT-1,2, and 3 to SPOT MSS data and of nearly an order of magnitude difference in resolution between the LANDSAT-Thematic Mapper and the SPOT panchromatic data.

In the summer of 1983, SPOT IMAGE Corporation of Washington, D.C., the marketing company for SPOT data sets, sponsored a simulation program to evaluate the potential utility of SPOT. The simulation campaign included 52 test sites throughout the United States. Each site was scanned using a Daedalus AADS 1268 Digital Multispectral Scanner System flown in a Learjet 25-C. Two site types were used to simulate the higher resolution (10 m) panchromatic band (P site type) and the lower resolution (20 m) multispectral bands (S site type). P sites were scanned from an altitude of approximately 6.35 km and S sites from 12.50 km (SPOT IMAGE Corporation, 1983). The semiarid data is acquired from a P site and the humid temperate data from an S site. Because there are considerable differences between aircraft-acquired and satellite-acquired data, several corrections were applied in order to simulate SPOT data (SPOT IMAGE Corporation, 1983).

Computer Classification Methodology

Digital classification of the simulated SPOT data include hybrid, unsupervised-supervised Euclidean distance analysis (New Mexico data), supervised Euclidean distance analysis (Pennsylvania data), Bayesian maximum likelihood classification (Pennsylvania data), and non-parametric linear discriminant analysis (New Mexico data). Comparison of unsupervised Euclidean distance classification of LANDSAT-3 and simulated SPOT data is made for the New Mexico data set. Feature extraction using edge enhancement is also investigated. Accuracy of classification results is evaluated by comparing digitized planimetric area of features on the classification map with a zoom-transferscope-superimposed ground truth map for a small strip of the classified maps.

All computer programs except where otherwise noted are from the ORSER (Office for Remote Sensing of Earth Resources) image processing system. Details on the methods of analysis can be obtained from the ORSER User's Manual (Turner et al., 1982).

Unsupervised Euclidean distance classification is initiated with cluster analysis of portions of the raw, digital, simulated SPOT data using the CLUS program. Final cluster mean relectances in n-dimensional space are termed "feature signatures". Ground surface features that correspond to cluster feature signatures can be determined by comparing the spatial distributions of ground features with the spatial distribution of clustered data.

Supervised methods are used to derive signatures for areas unclassified by CLUS for the New Mexico data set and all of the signatures for the Pennsylvania data set. Blocks of pixels are selected as training fields for each ground feature. Spectral signatures are determined by the STATS program for each training field.

Feature signatures that are similar to one another, have relatively low standard deviations, and representative of ground truth features are used in subsequent classification. Signatures for similar ground features define a feature class. The CLASS program uses feature class signatures and an Euclidean distance classifier for final scene classification. Pixels are assigned to feature classes by signature similarity to input feature signatures. In order to avoid large spectral overlaps between feature classes, signatures with very large standard deviations are not used. The resulting classified data set is cleaned with the DISPLAY program to smooth the appearance of the output map (LMAP program) by retaining only contiguous blocks of a given feature. LANDSAT-3 data analysis is identical to the simulated SPOT Euclidean distance analysis.

The Bayesian maximum likelihood classifier (MAXCLASS program) classifies according to weighted distances of separation between categories. This method is used because although reflectances are theoretically normally distributed, variance is not the same for each band of data. MAXCLASS assumes a multivariate normal distribution and defines hyperellipsoids which describe the distribution of feature classes. Input to MAXCLASS is a covariance matrix for each signature (output from the STATS program). Because some reflectances for the humid temperate data set saturate the sensor on bands 1 and 2, there is no variance for these bands. This classifier cannot use near zero or zero covariances. Feature signatures without variance are not input to this analysis. The DISPLAY and LMAP programs are used to clean and output the classified map as described for the Euclidean distance classification.

The NEIGHBOR procedure in SAS (Statistical Analysis System) (Goodnight and Sarle, 1982) uses nonparametric linear discriminant analysis. Two sets of signatures are used in this procedure: a training set and a test set. A nearest neighbor discriminant analysis defines functions to separate training signatures into user-defined feature classes representative of ground surface features. Test feature signatures are classified by the discriminant functions defined from the training signatures.

Edge enhancement is investigated as a means of feature extraction. Edge enhancement programs were written by J. Ronald Eyton of the Department of Geography of The Pennsylvania State University and include DERIVE, ZHIST, and VTONE. DERIVE determines the first and second spatial derivatives of the data which correspond to the spectral edges, i.e., the rate of change along the ground of pixel reflectance (slope) and the rate of change of the slopes, respectively. The program ZHIST produces a histogram of these derivatives so that tails in the distribution can be deleted and the data can be linearly stretched to expand the number of grey levels over which the data could be displayed with the program VTONE.

Remote Sensing of Watershed Components

Because surface features commonly have unique spectral reflectances, remotely sensed data can be used to distinguish watershed components (Figure 1). Rainfall input to a watershed will result in surface runoff or groundwater recharge depending on the infiltration rate of the surface. If the infiltration rate is exceeded, runoff occurs, interacts with surface morphology, and can result in channelized flow. If the infiltration rate is not exceeded, groundwater recharge can occur, the water interacts with the substrate, and is either stored as deep groundwater or is discharged to the surface.

Simulated SPOT data allow characterization of surfaces with different infiltration rates and several of the parameters that control these infiltration rates including vegetation cover, soil texture, surface morphology and antecedent moisture. This capability is demonstrated with the semiarid data set which separates high infiltration rate, 27 cm/hr (Duffy and Gardner, 1983) moderately well-vegetated, coarse-grained, relatively smooth, dry upland surfaces from moderate infiltration rate, moderately vegetated, medium-grained, hummocky, dry, intermediate surfaces from low infiltration rate, 9.7 cm/hr (Duffy and Gardner, 1983), poorly vegetated, fine-grained, sodium-rich, level, dry surfaces, and from low infiltration rate, well vegetated, fine-grained, level, wet surfaces (Table 2).

Table 2. Nonparametric Linear Discriminant Analysis, Semiarid Site Results

	Percent Classified into Training Field - Defined Classes				
Test Feature Class	Coarse-grained Eolian Mantle	Medium-grained Material	Sodium-rich Fine-grained Material	Well-vegetated Areas	Other
Coarse-grained, Eolian-mantle	83.33	16.66	---	---	---
Coarse-grained, Eolian-mantle	95.24	4.76	---	---	---
Medium-grained material	35.71	52.38	---	---	10.91
Medium-grained material	---	83.34	16.66	---	---
Medium-grained material	7.14	85.71	2.38	---	4.77
Medium-grained material	6.25	81.25	12.50	---	---
Medium-grained material	---	92.86	7.14	---	---
Sodium-rich, fine-grained material	---	4.00	88.00	---	8.00
Sodium-rich, fine-grained material	---	16.67	83.33	---	---
Sodium-rich, fine-grained material	---	45.71	54.29	---	---
Sodium-rich, fine-grained material	---	11.90	80.96	---	7.14
Well Vegetated Areas	1.85	16.66	14.81	59.26	7.42
Well Vegetated Areas	47.62	33.33	16.67	2.38	---
Well Vegetated Areas	---	---	---	88.09	---
Well Vegetated Areas	---	---	---	100.00	---
Well Vegetated Areas	22.86	11.43	---	60.00	5.71

Areas that contribute runoff to the hydrologic system can be detected from simulated SPOT data because the spectral characteristics of these surfaces are influenced by their surface morphology, especially roughness and vegetative cover. The humid temperate disturbed land data set edge enhancement vividly displays this (Figure 3). The bituminous coal strip mine displayed in Figure 2 shows two major surfaces: a mottled surface and a dark surface. The former represents the ungraded, rough microtopography of old unreclaimed mine spoil. The latter represents the regraded, smooth, convex-up slopes of newly reclaimed mine spoil. These smooth slopes are relatively impermeable (Jorgensen and Gardner, in press) and can contribute large volumes of runoff that excessively gully the surface and deleteriously affect adjacent streams (Touysinthiphonexay and Gardner, 1984). Large unstable channels with high sediment transport rates resulting from high runoff volumes (Gryta and Gardner, 1983, 1984) are also detected on edge enhancements (Figure 4). These 7 - 9 m deep, 5 - 10 m wide gullies have transported mine spoil to a 50 by 100 m alluvial fan just beyond the mine edge. The spectral contrast between the mine spoil and surrounding forest (spectral edge) terminates at these gullies. The alluvial fan spectral reflectance is so similar to the mine that no edge appears between them.

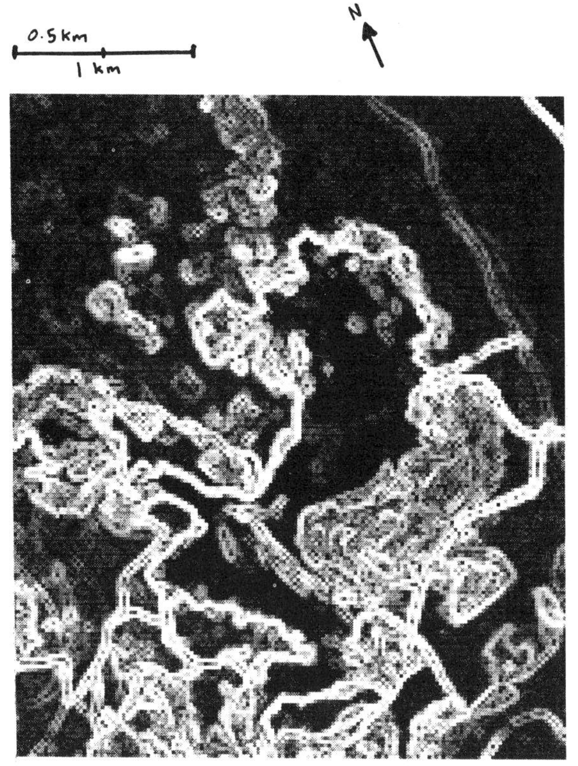

FIG.3 first derivative edge enhancement, channel 2 showing the microtopography of the mine spoil, Snow Shoe Mine, PA. Mottled areas are generally groundwater recharge sites,dark areas have high rates of runoff.

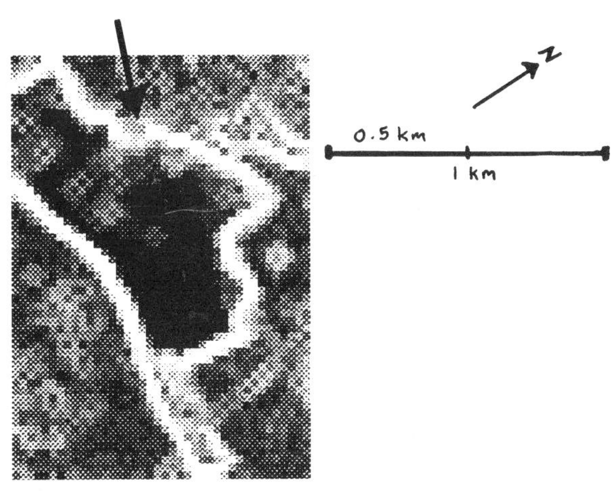

FIG.4 First derivative edge enhancement, channel 1. Arrow shows location of gullies at the Pine Glen Mine, PA.

Relative runoff rates can be discriminated with the semiarid data set with some knowledge of average slope gradients, landscape position, and local geomorphology and remotely sensed information on vegetation cover, soil texture, salt content and microtopography (Figure 5). High runoff rates occur on steep, smooth slopes, surfaces with low infiltration rates, and/or poorly vegetated areas. Low runoff rates occur on level surfaces, areas with high infiltration rates and/or well-vegetated areas.

Groundwater recharge can occur when rainfall rate does not exceed infiltration rate or where local topography detains surface water long enough to allow infiltration. Areas of potential groundwater recharge are located by edge enhancements for the humid temperate data set (Figure 3). The hummocky, ungraded spoil piles, displayed in a mottled tonal pattern in the figure, allow surface water to collect in topographic lows and are thereby internally drained. Infiltrating groundwater interacts with the substrate which in this case is fragmented pyritic shales and changes the water chemistry. The high sulfur content of the shales results in highly acidic groundwater (Williams et al., 1982).

At the toe of many reclaimed surface coal mines, groundwater is discharged as acid mine drainage seeps. Manual interpretation of the simulated SPOT imagery, especially enhanced imagery, located several seeps. Digital classification was less successful presumably because the seeps were generally only one or two pixels in size.

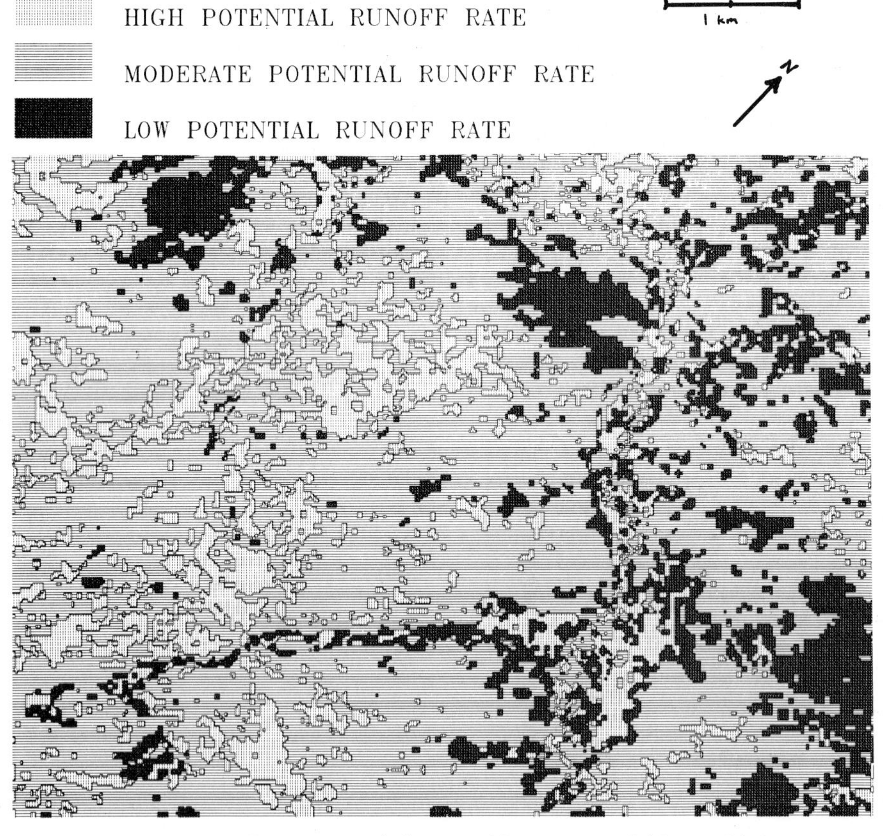

FIG.5 Potential runoff rate Euclidean distance classification map, New Mexico site.

Discussion

Methods of analysis vary in their ability to characterize the landscape surface (Table 3). Four methods of digital analysis of the simulated SPOT imagery are investigated as techniques for extracting hydrologic data: supervised and unsupervised Euclidean distance, edge enhancement, nonparametric linear discriminant, and Bayesian maximum likelihood classification. Details in the results from each of these techniques is discussed in Connors, 1985; summaries of results (Tables 3 and 4) show an Anderson (1976) Level III classification of surface features. All of the methods except edge enhancement successfully discriminate surfaces with different infiltration and runoff rates for the semiarid data set. Infiltration rates are not strongly correlated with spectral reflectance for the humid temperate data set however, and are thus not distinguished well by any of the methods. Sensor saturation due to miscalibration for the very high reflectances of the mine surface severely limits data extraction for this site. Relative runoff rate, on the other hand, can be discriminated by nearly all methods from this data set. Landscape stability classes of the semiarid data set are obvious on enhanced images by manual interpretation. Eolian erosion is readily distinguished by nearly all methods, whereas fluvial erosion is best discriminated with the 10 m resolution of the panchromatic band. Fluvial erosion at the humid temperate site is best discriminated with edge enhancement. Areas of groundwater recharge are also best discerned on edge enhancements of the humid temperate site because recharge areas there have rough microtopography reflected in numerous spectral edges. Groundwater discharge sites are distinguished for some locations on enhanced imagery but are not distinguished well by any method of digital classification.

Conclusions

The high spatial resolution of simulated SPOT data allow surfaces of small areal extent with differing hydrologic properties to be discriminated. Soil and vegetation characteristics and geomorphic features are commonly spectrally distinct and can be determined from this remotely sensed data. The high resolution of simulated SPOT permits the distinction of infiltration rates, runoff rates, groundwater recharge sites, some groundwater discharge sites, landscape stability classes, eolian erosion, and fluvial erosion. Previous remotely sensed data (LANDSAT-1,2, and 3)

Table 3. Evaluation of Digital Classification Methods for the Interpretation of Humid Region Disturbed Land and Arid Land Simulated SPOT Imagery.

HUMID				ARID			
GEOMORPHIC AND HYDROLOGIC CHARACTERISTIC	METHODOLOGY			GEOMORPHIC AND HYDROLOGIC CHARACTERISTIC	METHODOLOGY		
	Unsupervised/ Supervised Euclidean Distance	Edge Enhancement	Bayesian Maximum Likelihood*		Unsupervised/ Supervised Euclidean Distance	Nonparametric Linear Discriminant Analysis	Edge Enhancement
Infiltration rate	N.A./N.A.	N.A.	fair	Infiltration Rate	good	good	N.A.
Runoff rate	good/good	good	fair	Runoff Rate	good	good	N.A.
Areas of Groundwater Recharge	good/good	excellent	fair	Landscape Stability	good	fair	fair
Ares of Groundwater Discharge	poor/fair	N.A.	poor	Eolian Erosion	excellent	good	N.A.
Fluvial Erosion	N.A./N.A.	fair	poor	Fluvial Erosion	poor	N.A.	excellent

* Sensor saturation on two of the bands severely limited this technique.
N.A. = Not applicable.

could not identify all of these geomorphic and hydrologic characteristics (Table 5). Hydrologic parameters such as infiltration rates, soil texture, and vegetation cover can be determined from a combination of field data and remotely sensed data. Field data provide quantitative values for parameters. Where reflectances are high correlated with values of

Table 4. Levels of Land Cover Classification

LEVEL I (after Anderson, et al., 1976)	LEVEL II	LEVEL III*	LEVEL IV*
Humid Data Set			
4 Forest Land	42 Evergreen Forest Land		
	43 Mixed Forest Land		
6 Wetland	61 Forested Wetland		
	62 Non-forested Wetland	Acid Seeps	
7 Barrenland	75 Stripmines, Quarries, and Gravel Pits	Shaly strip mines	Well vegetated Poorly vegetated
		Sandy strip mines	Well vegetated Poorly vegetated
		Topsoiled strip mines	Poorly vegetated
Arid Data Set			
3 Rangeland	31 Herbaceous		
		silty areas very well vegetated areas alluvial clay	
	33 Mixed Herbaceous and Shrub and Brush	well vegetated alluvium	
		coppice dunes	no B-horizon exposed B-horizon exposed
		eolian mantled uplands	
7 Barren Land	71 Dry Salt Flats	salt pans gravel lag silty-salty areas	
	74 Bare Exposed Rock	sandstone mudstone saprolite	

* Levels III and IV are created by the authors for the study.

Table 5. Utility of Data Types in the Investigation of Geomorphic and Hydrologic Characteristics.

Geomorphic and Hydrologic Characteristics	Field Data	Aerial Photography	Simulated SPOT analog/digital	LANDSAT 1,2, and 3 analog/digital
Infiltration Rate	identifiable	identifiable	identifiable	partially identifiable
Runoff Rate	identifiable	identifiable	identifiable	partially identifiable
Ground Water Recharge Sites	identifiable	identifiable	identifiable	partially identifiable
Ground Water Discharge Sites	identifiable	partially identifiable	partially identifiable	not identifiable
Landscape Stability	identifiable	identifiable	identifiable	partially identifiable
eolian erosion	identifiable	identifiable	identifiable	identifiable / partially identifiable
fluvial erosion	identifiable	identifiable	identifiable / partially identifiable	partially identifiable
Hydrologic Model Parameter-ization	identifiable	identifiable	identifiable	partially identifiable

▬▬ identifiable with data type
▬ ▬ partially identifiable with data type
not identifiable with data type

hydrologic parameters, remotely sensed data can provide the location and areal extent of these values. The digital format of remotely sensed data allows for ready input into hydrologic model data bases.

Acknowledgments

This research was supported under agreement No. DE-AC02-83ER60182 by the U.S. Department of Energy as part of the REFLEX program. Dr. Frank Wobber of the Office for Health and Environment of the U.S. DOE is especially acknowledged. George Baumer of the Office for Remote Sensing of Earth Resources and Dr. J. Ronald Eyton of the Geography Department, The Pennsylvania State University, were very helpful in image processing.

References

Anderson, J.R., E.E. Hardy, J.T. Roach and R.E. Witmer. 1976. A land use and land cover classification system for use with remote sensor data: U.S. Geol. Survey. Prof. Paper 964: 22 p.

Berg, T.M., Chief Compiler. 1980. Geologic Map of Pennsylvania: PA DER.

Chevrel, M., M. Courtois, G. Weill. 1981. The SPOT Satellite Remote Sensing Mission: Photogrammetric Engineering and Remote Sensing 47(8):1163-1171.

Connors, K.F. 1985. Simulated SPOT Imagery for the Investigation of Geomorphic Features and Hydrologic Processes: Masters Thesis, The Pennsylvania State University, University Park, PA: 147 p.

Duffy, W.J. and T.W. Gardner. 1983. Soil characterization, headcut erosion and LANDSAT classification in the San Juan Basin, in Wells, S.G., et al., eds., Chaco Canyon Country, American Geomorphologial Field Group Field Trip Guidebook: American Geomorphological Field Group:67-77.

Goodnight, P.T. and W.S. Sarle. 1982. Neighbor, in Ray A.A., ed., SSAS

User's Guide: Statistics: SAS Institute Inc., Cary, NC:397-404.
Gryta, J.J. and T.W. Gardner. 1983. Episodic cutting and filling within gully-fan systems in disequilibrium: Geol. Soc. Amer. Abst. with Prog. 15(6):587.
Gryta, J.J. and T.W. Gardner. 1984. Complex response and sediment allocation in disequilibrium gully-fan systems: EOS Trans., Amer. Geophys. Union. 65(16):217.
Hackman and Olson. 1977. Geology, Structure, and Uranium Deposits of the Gallup 1° x 2° Quadrangle, New Mexico and Arizona: USGS Map I-981:U.S. Geol.
Jorgensen, D.W. and T.W. Gardner. In press. An analysis of soil and surface properties which affect infiltration and runoff on minelands: Proc. Wetlands & Water Management on Mined Lands, School of Forest Resources, The Pennsylvania State University.
Mills, A.M. and T.W. Gardner. 1983. Effects of aquifer dewatering on an ephemeral stream, San Juan Basin, NM, in S.G. Wells et al., eds., Chaco Canyon Country, American Geomorphological Field Group Field Trip Guidebook: American Geomorphological Field Group: 57-66.
SPOT IMAGE Corporation. 1983. 1983 U.S. SPOT Simulation Campaign Auxiliary Information Package: SPOT IMAGE Corp., Washington, D.C.:90 p.
Touysinthiphonexay, K. and T. Gardner. 1984. Threshold response of small streams to surface coal mining, bituminous coal fields, central Pennsylvania: Earth Surf. Proc. and Landforms 9:43-58.
Turner, B.J., G.M. Baumer and W.L. Myers. 1982. The ORSER Remote Sensing Analysis System: A User's Manual: Office for Remote Sensing of Earth Resources, The Pennsylvania State University, University Park, PA.: 265 p.
USDA Soil Conservation Service. 1977. Soil Taxonomy (Agric. Handbook No. 436):U.S. Govt. Printing Off.: Washington, DC. 754 p.
Wells, S.G. 1982. Geomorphology and surface hydrology applied to landscape reclamation in the strippable coal belts of northwestern New Mexico. Tech. Rept. 2-68-3311, 1: New Mexico Energy Research and and Development Institute: 298 p.
Wells, S.G. 1983. Regional badland development and a model of late Quaternary evolution of badland watersheds, San Juan Basin, New Mexico, in S.G. Wells, et al., Chaco Canyon Country, American Geomorphological Field Group Field Trip Guidebook: American Geomorphological Field Group: 121-132.
Wells, S.G., T.F. Bullard, L.N. Smith and T.W. Gardner. 1983a. Chronology, rates, and magnitudes of late quaternary landscape changes in the southeastern Colorado Plateau, in S.G. Wells, et al., Chaco Canyon Country, American Geomorphological Field Group Field Trip Guidebook: American Geomorphological Field Group: 177-185.
Wells, S.G., D.E. Jercinovic, L.N. Smith, A.A. Gutiernez, J. Pickle and D.W. Love. 1983b. Instrumented watershed in the coal fields of northwestern New Mexico, in S.G. Wells, et al., Chaco Canyon Country, American Geomorphological Field Group Field Trip Guidebook: American Geomorphological Field Group: 177-185.
Wells, S.G. and T.W. Gardner. 1984. Geomorphic Criteria for Selecting Stable Uranium Tailings Disposal Sites in New Mexico NMERDI2-69-1112, Vol. I: New Mexico Energy Research and Development Institute: 353 p.
Williams, E.G. 1960. Marine and freshwater fossiliferous beds in the Pottsville and Allegheny Groups of western Pennsylvania: J. Paleo. 34(5):908-922.
Williams, E.G., A.W. Rose, R.R. Parizek and S.A. Waters. 1982. Factors controlling the generation of acid mine drainage. Final Report on Research Grant No. G5105086 Bureau of Mines, U.S. Dept. Int.: PA Mining and Min. Resources Research Inst.: 265 p.

7 Remote data transmission

Hydrologic Applications of Space Technology (Proceedings of the Cocoa Beach Workshop, Florida, August 1985). IAHS Publ. no. 160, 1986.

Satellite data transmission as an aid to hydrological telemetry

R. W. HERSCHY
*CNS Scientific & Engineering Services,
20, Eldon Road, Reading, UK*

Abstract

The paper describes the European Space Agency (ESA) METEOSAT system for the transmission and reception of hydrological data. The data collection platforms (DCPs) transmit, via METEOSAT 1, hydrological data such as river level, river flow, rainfall and evaporation information. These data are received at the European Space Operations Centre (ESOC) in Darmstadt, West Germany and retransmitted via METEOSAT 2 to the user. The user receives the data by means of a small 1.5m diameter receiving dish.

If weather imagery is required this can be accomplished by the addition of a standard display and processing equipment which presents an image every half hour. Weather images and DCP data can be viewed together.

The paper also describes briefly the technical details of the DCPs, the receiver unit, the antenna unit and the mechanical configuration of the system. This development of fast, cheap hydrological telemetry has made data collection, transmission and reception by satellite a cost effective alternative to existing terrestrial methods.

Introduction

At most of the world's stream gauging stations hydrometric data are collected by one of three methods.

1. By an observer reading the staff gauge and either telephoning the reading to base, or filling up a weekly or monthly postcard of staff gauge readings taken once or more times per week. The postcard, when completed, is mailed by means of the normal postal service.

2. By weekly or monthly autographic chart. The chart is then either mailed or manually transported to base.

3. By monthly digital punched paper tape. The tape is then either mailed or manually transported to base as in the case of charts.

Data collected by the above methods are therefore essentially historical. Indeed in the case of monthly charts or tapes, some of the data may be about 6 weeks old before being processed. Such data may therefore be of use mainly for planning or design purposes.

When data are required for operational purposes, however, such as flood control or other water management control purposes, in relative real-time, transmission by means of telemetry is normally employed. However it is quite possible that if most of the data, now classed as historical because of their late arrival at base, were available in relative real-time much more use could be made of the data for management control purposes.

Telemetry usually takes the form of transmission by terrestrial means namely telephone land line or radio. Although such systems are quite common in telemetering hydrometric data, because of the usually harsh environment surrounding streamflow stations, terrestrial methods may suffer from several disadvantages. They may be expensive to install and maintain, they may be prone to interference and installation can be a fairly lengthy process depending on terrain. Radio frequencies are becoming extremely difficult to obtain and both systems are liable to failure during floods when reliability could be crucial.

The introduction of communication satellites now offers a reliable and cost effective alternative to terrestrial systems.

Satellite Telemetry

The satellites GOES (US), GMS (Japan), GOMS (USSR) and METEOSAT (European Space Agency) form a system of geostationary satellites with both a remote sensing and telecommunications facility. These satellites are placed in orbit coincident with the earth's equatorial plane at a height of about 36,000km and since they rotate at the same speed as the earth, appear to be stationary.

METEOSAT 1 was launched in 1977 followed in 1981 by METEOSAT 2. Generally the telecommunications mode of the satellite is designed for a life of about five years but METEOSAT 1 is still operating in the telecommunications mode. Polar orbiting satellites, on the other hand, orbit the earth several times a day generally at a height of less than 1000km, and although providing a higher resolution in the remote sensing mode, only provide a mutual view of the transmitting and receiving stations for a small percentage of the time - namely a few minutes every 2 hours or so.

It is expected that METEOSAT 1 will be replaced by GOES 4 in late 1985. This arrangement between NOAA and ESA will continue until the launch of METEOSAT P2 in 1986.

The satellite itself is composed of a main cylindrical body on top of which a screen-shaped section and two cyclinders are stacked concentrically. The satellite is 2.1m in diameter and 3.2m long. The weight at the beginning of life in orbit was 293kg; this will gradually fall to 245kg as the hydrazine propellant is used during its lifetime. In orbit the whole satellite spins at 100 revolutions per minute about its main axis which is closely aligned to the earth's north-south axis.

The main cylindrical body contains most of the satellite subsystems, including the radiometer. The cylindrical surface is covered with solar cells for power supply. The spacecraft has four main (25 N) thruster motors and two vernier (2.5 N) thrusters. All six are fed by hydrazine popellant contained in three interconnected spherical tanks having sufficient capacity for a five-years lifetime. This system is used to control METEOSAT's attitude in space and to make small changes in its orbit, principally to move the satellite in its orbital plane to make fine adjustments to the longitude over which METEOSAT is stationed (METEOSAT 1 longitude 10°, METEOSAT 2 longitude 0°). The motors are operated by telecommands from the ground station and normally several months elapse between manoeuvring operations.

METEOSAT together with other geostationary satellites perform three principal functions or missions.

a) A microprocessor which starts the transmitter at a preset time, formats and spectral bands (infra-red and visible).

b) Retransmission (dissemination) of computer processed image-derived data by landline and via the satellite to users' ground stations.

c) Data collection via the satellite the environmental in situ measurements using land based, ship or airborne DCPs.

Data Collection Platforms

Operational studies on hydrometric data collection by geostationary satellites have been successfuly carried out in recent years, notably in the USA, Canada and Europe. These studies have confirmed that a satellite telemetry system is reliable and cost effective.

The device which transmits the data to the satellite for retransmission to the ground receiving stations is known in satellite terminology as a data collection platform. The satellite used for hydrometric data transmission in North America is GOES and METEOSAT is used in Europe and the African continent. Many hundreds of hydrometric DCPs are now in operation in North America and many hundreds more are proposed. The first METEOSAT DCP was installed some 5 years ago in the UK to record river water level at a streamflow station. The number of DCPs in Europe using METEOSAT however still falls short of 100. Indeed Europe has been slow to take advantage of the system.

A DCP is essentially an electronic device containing a small UHF low power 6W transmitter operating at 402MHz.

There are three types of DCP offering a range of possible applications.

a) Self-timed DCPs where the data are transmitted in buffered blocks of data at fixed intervals.

b) DCPs which provide an immediate alert transmission when a critical data value has been reached.

c) Interrogable DCPs where the DCP receives a command message from the control centre via the satellite.

The DCPs intended for use with meteorological geosynchronous satellites have been designed to an international specification and are adaptable to all of the satellites listed above.

Whatever the form of the DCP, it has to be approved and certified by the satellite owner, in the case of METEOSAT, by the European Space Agency (ESA).

Self-timed alert DCP

The DCP used in the UK and other European countries is a combined self-timed alert DCP and includes the following features.

a) A microprocessor which starts the transmitter at a preset time, formats the data, and adds the preamble and end of transmission code around the data; a shutdown timer is included to turn off the transmitter in the event of controller failure.

b) A highly stable crystal-controlled clock and oscillator which provides the timing signals to initiate transmission and a stable signal defining the transmission radio frequency.

c) A radio frequency modulator (phase modulator) and low power transmitter (6W at 12V).

d) An alert facility.

e) A narrow beam aerial (antenna) directed to the satellite.

f) A source of power; battery or mains.

The most common DCPs are the self-timed variety which transmits the previously collected data, usually of 3 to 24 hours duration, at a preset time. By allocating to each transmitter a specific time slot, as well as one of about 60 radio channels on METEOSAT, the satellite can relay up to 40,000 messages per day. Each DCP message starts with a unique code to allow identification of its source and its destination.

An alert DCP is used where a hazardous situation may arise which requires data to be sent immediately a measured value falls outside a preset limit or rate of increase. It would be unusual for a DCP to be exclusively alert so an alert DCP is arranged to operate normally as a self-timed DCP, the alert procedure only operating when necessary.

The DCP may be fixed, as in the case of a hydrometric DCP, or mobile. A fixed unit has a small directional antenna which points towards the satellite, in the case of METEOSAT 1, at 10° longitude and zero latitude.

A mobile DCP, normally used on buoys or ships, has the same configuration if the antenna can be mounted on a stabilized structure to ensure that it points to the satellite, or a broad beam antenna to eliminate the need for stabilization. The latter DCP requires a higher transmitter power of 50W to compensate for the lower antenna gain. Both forms may be operated either by battery or mains electrical power, the former having about six months' life.

All except the aerial and the source of power are housed within a single compact box which may be free-standing or mounted on a rack.

There is sufficient space available within the DCP to fit a set of printed circuit boards (PCBs) for a microprocessor-controlled data store and interfacing may be made with up to six sensors simultaneously. The DCPs used in the UK have 8-bit or 16-bit parallel data interfaces and use either two or four inputs. The data format is in the international WMO(SX) code. At the preset time of transmission, sensor data are passed to the DCP where they are modulated on to a radio carrier and transmitted. To prevent interference between transmissions from different DCPs, each DCP in the network is arranged to transmit in a particular radio channel at a particular time. Typically one satellite DCP transponder provides about 4,800 time slots of about one minute within 30 discrete radio channels during one day. Each DCP transmits a preamble code to identify itself, the data and an end of transmission code to complete the message.

Hydrometric Sensors for DCP Transmission

By various combinations of plug-in modules, data from up to 24 sensors (or 120 with an extension unit) can be collected, processed, formatted and transmitted to METEOSAT.

Sensors may be of many different types, having either analog or digital outputs. In the UK the hydrometric sensors most commonly used include digital punched paper tape recorders for river level measurement, tipping-bucket rain gauges for rainfall measurement, sensors for the measurement of potential evaporation, ultrasonic and electromagnetic streamflow gauges and water quality sensors.

Data can be input in any of three ways.

a) The DCP transmitter can request data from the sensors at regular time intervals.

b) The DCP transmitter accepts data from the sensors when available.

c) By an interactive mode, using a visual display unit, whereby the DCP transmitter requests data from the observer who types in the data manually.

A mixture of the above data entries is also possible.

Prior to transmission, the raw data can be processed and formatted by the microprocessor. This can include various calculations, notably the processing of stream discharge from stage by entering the stage-discharge relation into the microprocessor; or potential evaporation from an array of sensors from an automatic climate station which measures windspeed, wind direction, temperature, wet bulb depression, solar radiation, net radiation and rainfall. In this case readings are taken every five minutes and these are used to produce average or total values for a three-hour period. Using five of these measurements, the potential evaporation is calculated from the Penman equation. The resulting data are transmitted once per day, complete with station name, headings etc.

The time intervals and microprocessor software can easily be changed and additional sensors can be added if required.

The DCP transmitter is designed to include self-monitoring and test facilities, thus simplifying commissioning and fault diagnosis. A compact hand-held unit is available to synchronize the real-time clock in the DCP transmitter, and also to perform on-site testing of the DCP, sensors and batteries. The self-monitoring facility also allows measurement of battery voltage, clock accuracy etc from the user's base via the satellite.

The reliable transmission of data by DCPs enables the detection of faults at the hydrometric station. Faults such as blocked intakes, fouling or sticking float tape may be diagnosed by inspection of each received message. This fault-finding capacity enables quick action to be taken which would not normally be taken until the regular site visit.

The receiving system

The receiver is designed on a modular basis giving a variety of possible user options in display and storage and contains two major assemblies, the antenna unit and receiver unit.

The DCP data are transmitted via METEOSAT 1 to ESA at the Darmstadt ground station. After minor processing at ESA the data are retransmitted to METEOSAT 2 for relay to the user's own ground station receiver. Two satellites are necessary in this case since METEOSAT 2 does not have a DCP facility and METEOSAT 1 does not have a WEFAX facility. In a fully operational system one satellite would be adequate. The antenna unit consists of a 1.5m diameter dish and associated down converter. The latter amplifies the received signals, filters and down converts to VHF (from 1961 MHz to 133-9MHz). Cross-site transmission to the receiver unit is carried out at this frequency. The receiver unit consists of the following parts.

a) The second down converter introduces a further conversion to an intermediate frequency of 10.7MHz. This section also provides automatic frequency control and signal strength indication.

b) The demodulator and bit conditioner recover the baseband signal and process it to produce digital data and clock signals.

c) The format decoder detects the presence of retransmitted data in the incoming bit stream, strips of all format coding and forwards the derived DCP data for storage and processing. The DCP data are also routed to a high speed interface.

d) The storage and processing section performs the essential processing and storage required to interface the incoming DCP data with a variety of output options. Buffer storage is provided to ensure that, with the worst case data rate, the output options function without loss of data.

User facilities

Certain options are available in modular subunits such as a mini-floppy disc unit which provides a mass storage medium for DCP data for up to 1,500 DCP messages, a high speed printer which provides hard copy of received DCP data and a user terminal which enables full control of the receiver facilities and interfacing via an RS232 port. If METEOSAT imagery is required this can be accomplished by the addition of standard display and processing equipment. Weather images and DCP data can be viewed together.

Mechanical configuration

The antenna and down converter assembly are mounted on a 120mm OD rod with the down converter enclosure below it. The location is such that a 'line of sight' is available to METEOSAT 2. The dish antenna may, however, be up to 100m from the receiver unit.

The receiver unit is housed in a small case which is located indoors in a position convenient to a power socket and to the printer or computer or other terminals. The front panel contains various status indicators for signal reception, a channel selection switch for use with other geostationary satellites, an alert indicator, a DCP data indicator and stored data and image data reception. The rear panel holds all the interface connectors for VHF input, high speed interface, printer output, terminal interface, floppy disc unit, video output, power input and alert message.

Comparison with Existing Telemetry Systems

A variety of telemetry networks is springing up in Europe based on landlines, line of sight radio or a mixture of both. This has inevitably led to local independent systems which often prove expensive because of the high installation and maintenance costs of relay stations, cables and hardware redundancy. It is expected that by the end of the decade these systems will become even more expensive to maintain with high redundancy. Such systems have often suffered from lack of reliability during severe weather conditions when the need for the data is greatest. Satellite systems on the other hand do not necessarily suffer from any of these disadvantages and because of the largest potential international market are expected to become more cost effective with time.

Conclusions

The development by the European Space Agency of the DCP telemetry system now offers the hydrometric user a low cost method of hydrometric telemetry. The data can be received by the user within a period of two to six minutes of transmission by installing a 1.5m dish antenna receiver. A variety of options are available for recording, displaying or archiving the data. The system offers the following facilities:

a) compact, low cost electronics package;

b) direct interface to a wide variety of hydrometric sensors;

c) versatile data acquisition and processing capability ideally suited to remote locations;

d) simple installation taking a few hours;

e) wide operating temperature range;

f) low power requirements - battery, solar power etc;

g) built-in self monitoring;

h) transmission over any distance, needs no repeaters and can transmit from bottom of valleys, between buildings etc;

i) electronics package needing no routine maintenance;

j) data transmission in WMO code, ASCII text, or 8-bit binary data formatting, with DCP name, heading etc;

k) direct data reception by user's 1.5m diameter receiving antenna;

l) data return typically 95 to 100%;

m) no licence required.

The system will operate anywhere in the area covered by the European Space Agency's METEOSAT satellites and offers a cost effective alternative to terrestrial telemetry.

Bibliography

European Space Agency 1981, Introduction to the METEOSAT System (Paris: ESA).

Herschy, R.W., 1980, Hydrological data collection by satellite. Proc. Inst. Civil Eng. 68(1) pp 759-71.

Herschy, R.W., 1982, Towards a satellite-based hydrometric data collection system. In: Advances in Hydrometry (Proc. Exeter Symp., July 1982), pp 285-296.

Herschy, R.W., 1985, Collection of data using the METEOSAT DCP retransmission system. In: Hydrological Applications of Remote Sensing and Remote Data Transmission (Proc. Hamburg Symp., August 1983), 109-117. IAHS Publ. no. 145.

Herschy, R.W., 1986, New Technology in Hydrometry, (Ed.). Adam Hilger, Bristol, UK.

Hydrologic Applications of Space Technology (Proceedings of the Cocoa Beach Workshop, Florida, August 1985). IAHS Publ. no. 160, 1986.

Making use of the Meteosat data collection system for representative and experimental basins in Provence (France)

R. E. QUELENNEC
Bureau de Recherches Géologiques et Minères (BRGM) Marseille, France
ANDREW ROBSON
European Space Angency, Darmstadt, F.R.Germany

Abstract

The Data Collection System installed on the Meteosat geosynchronous meteorological satellites provides an effective and economical means for Users to obtain environmental data from remote sites. The system is described together with an important application for the study and evaluation of erosion, sediment and water flux in experimental basins in the South of France. Additional project objectives defined by BRGM/ORSTOM include experience gathering and equipment development in the use of satellite Data Collection System.

The Meteosat Programme

The Meteosat Data Collection System (DCS) has been in use since November 1977.

A data collection transponder is mounted on the Meteosat satellites which have three missions to fulfill.

1. The acquisition of images of the earth's disc every half hour in the visible and infrared parts of the spectrum. From these images a variety of meteorological parameters are determined e.g. wind vectors, sea surface temperatures, cloud top heights, etc.

2. The dissemination of corrected and annotated images and data collection reports to User ground stations after retransmission by the satellite.

3. The collection and distribution of environmental data gathered by terrestrial platforms.

The first two satellites were part of a pre-operational programme conducted by ESA. This programme was funded only until November 1983 which tended to restrict use of the DCS to experimental and experience-gathering activities. In 1983, European meteorological services agreed to start an operational Meteosat programme which covered the continued operation of the first two satellites, the launch of an early prototype and the procurement, launch and operation of three new satellites. This programme will provide uninterrupted satellite services up to 1995 and hence the Meteosat DCS has become a truly operational system.
The programme is being executed by ESA on behalf of the European meteorological services. At the time of writing, Meteosat 1 is providing Data Collection Services and Meteosat 2 relays the da-

ta to User receiving stations. From July 85, Meteosat 1 will be substituted by GOES 4 of NOAA/NESDIS until the launch of Meteosat P2 in June 1986.

The Meteosat Data Collection System

Because Meteosat is a geostationary spacecraft, it provides a data link that is permanently available to all compatible data platforms within its field of view (about 80° of great circle from subsatellite point). This is an important advantage over the data collection systems of near earth-orbiting satellites, for which the platforms are in view for only very limited periods.

The Meteosat Data Collection System (DCS) has been designed to have similar characteristics to the data collection systems carried by the other geostationary meteorological satellites presently in operation, namely the GOES series of NOAA/NESDIS and Japan's GMS spacecraft. This coordinated design approach permits the substitution of Meteosat 1 by GOES 4 for 1985/1986 and also data collection from mobile DCPs.

Nominally Meteosat is located over the equator and the prime meridian and therefore has telecommunication contact with the geographical area shown in Fig. 1. However, for operational reasons GOES 4 will be located over the 10°W meridian.

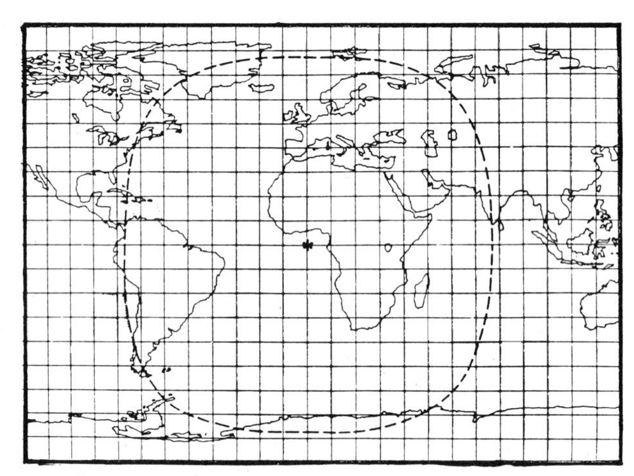

FIG.1 Coverage of the Meteosat Data Collection System.

There are two basic types of DCP:

1. "self-timed" which transmit their data at regular intervals based on an internal clock;
2. "alert" which transmit a small amount of data whenever the value of a particular parameter has been exceeded.

For hydrological applications it is often appropriate to combine both features into a single DCP.

The DCP's transmit to Meteosat on any one of sixty-six 3 KHz reporting channels in the 402 MHz band. After conversion to the 1675 Mhz band, the satellite retransmits the messages to its central ground station, in the Odenwald in Germany. From there, data is either fed to the European Space Operations Centre

(ESOC) in Darmstadt for processing and distribution on the WMO Global Telecommunication System or is transmitted back to a Meteosat after a short delay, for retransmission to User stations.

The data message a DCP may transmit through Meteosat is restricted to a particular format and bit rate. The transmission begins with 5 seconds of unmodulated r.f. carrier which, after relay through the satellite, permits a central ground station receiver to acquire and lock onto the transmission. This is followed by a 2.5 second preamble of alternate ones and zeroes at 100 bps to allow the data reconditioning equipment to lock onto the data stream. Then follows a synchronizing and address code which permits the computing system to (1) know that it is indeed a Meteosat DCP (it could be an interfering signal) and (2) which DCP is actually transmitting. With these basic functions completed, the DCP then transmits the environmental data which has been encoded into a digital bit stream. For "self timed" DCPs this can be up to 5192 bits long (649 characters) but for "alert" DCPs it is restricted to 184 bits (23 characters).

For many Users, the most practical and quickest method of obtaining their data, is to receive the retransmissions from the satellite. At the moment, this feature is unique to the Meteosat DCS. After reception at the central ground station, messages are stored until a break in WEFAX image transmissions occurs. Due to the schedule and format of these image transmissions, these breaks occur for 23 seconds every 4 minutes. During this time, the stored data is transmitted back to a Meteosat at 12.5 Kbs i.e. 125 times the original data rate and retransmitted by the satellite at high power. This permits User reception stations equipped with antennae between 1.5 and 2 m diameter and simple receivers to acquire the data. Interfacing to a personal computer is very straight forward and hence a complete data acquisition and processing station can be procured at a relatively low price (less than 20 K$).

The capacity of the Meteosat DCS depends on how the transponder is used. For fixed location platforms reporting every 3 hours the number of platforms which can be supported using the present 2 minute time divisions would be around 3000. However, as more User platforms are admitted to the system, the time division will probably be reduced to enable over 4000 platforms to use the system.

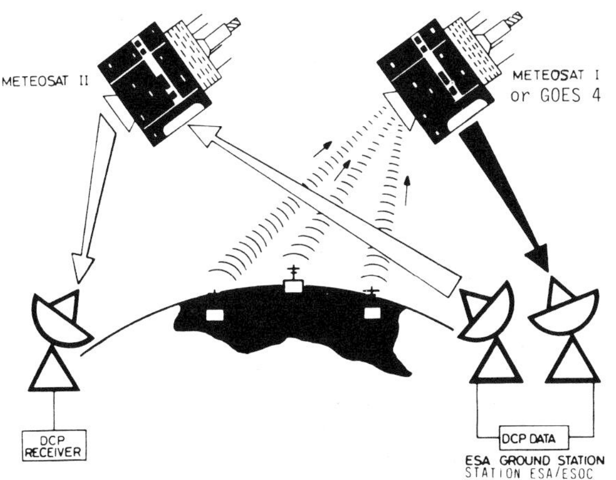

FIG.2 Principle of Meteosat Data Collection System.

Fig.2 provides an outline diagram of the current system. Note that the reason two satellites are used at the moment is due to a failure in the DCS an Meteosat 2. In future, the same satellite will be used for data collection and retransmission.

Data Collection, Satellite Tele-transmission for Experimental Basins in the South of France

The research project of the B.R.G.M./O.R.S.T.O.M research group is concerned with the study and the evaluation of erosion, sediment and water flux in experimental basins in the South of France. The project is supported by the French Ministry of Research and Technology, the Regional Authority "Provence-Alpes Cote d'Azur" and ESA.

Additional project objectives are training, equipment development and testing on a pilot study site, as well as obtaining experience in the use of satellite data collection systems in order to determine their applicability to environmental monitoring.

Four small bad-land type watersheds, with areas ranging from 2 to 450 ha, are situated on erodible black marls geological formation in the Durance river basin near Sisteron in Provence. Fig. 3 shows their location.

FIG.3 Location of experimental basins.

During 1984 they were equipped with several sensors such as rainfall and hydrometric stations for hydro-meteorological in situ mesurements.

Due to the small experimental watershed denudated surfaces, which leads to small runoff concentration times, data acquisition must be done on site with a high frequency, especially during flood times.

Time lag measurements ranging from 1 to 5 minutes lead to a significant load of data: several thousands for one watershed per day.

In order to solve the data collection and management problems, hydro-meteorological data are recorded on site; the rainfall meter and the water level recorder used in the project, were developed by ELSYDE/France. They are equipped with EPROM memory cartridges which allows for regular data transfer to MICRAL desk computers via a RS.232 connexion.

In order to prepare for remote data transmission, B.R.G.M. made a comparative study of available systems: Meteosat data collection system (DCS) was prefered to other systems such as ground telecommunication system, radio and low orbital satellite DCS (ARGOS) for length of messages, alert mode and meteorological image availability, wide coverage receiving possibilities, data acquisition and running costs, etc.

In order to make use of the Meteosat DCS, the following additional equipment will be installed:

a special designed interface unit for data transfer to a data collection platform
a data collection platform with power supplies
an antenna
The general equipment arrangement is shown in Fig. 4.

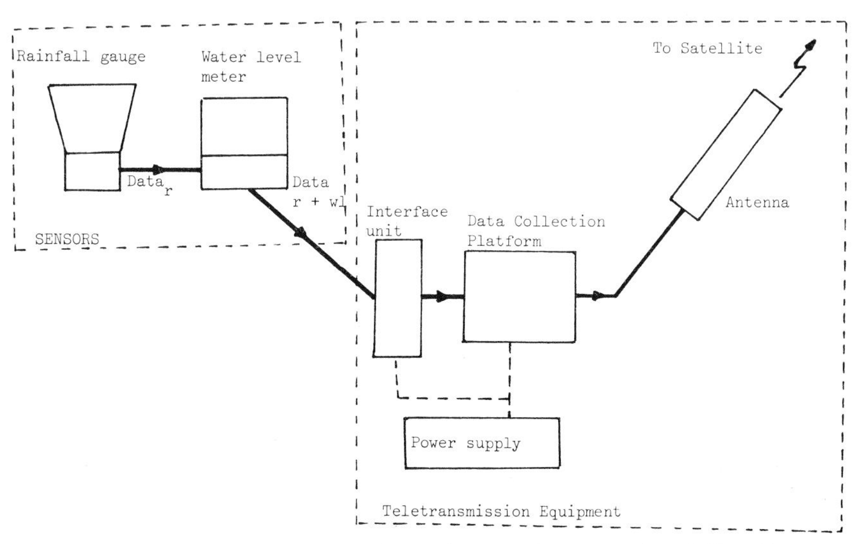

FIG.4 General equipment layout at a DCP site.

The measurement units provide data at 5 minute intervals. The number of bucket tips of the rain gauge is transmitted via optical couplers to the water level meter where they are multiplexed with its measurement of water level, temperature and conductivity. These data, in digital form, are fed to the interface unit which then provides the data together with time of the last measurement and the number of measurements for control purposes. The interface was specifically designed for B.R.G.M. by ELSYDE. Data collected between the three hourly period transmissions are transmitted by the DCP to Meteosat or GOES 4. Alert messages are also generated and transmitted whenever the rain measurement exceeds a certain threshold.

There will be two types of DCPs in use. Both types can also transmit "alert" messages which are on a different radio frequency to the "self timed" messages.

The low power DCPs (5W) obtain their power solely from batteries which require recharging at intervals in excess of 6 months. They transmit via directional antennae of about 1.20 m in length. The high power DCPs (40W) obtain their power from two solar panels (37x68cm) combined with a small battery for non-illuminated conditions. An omni-directional antenna of 30 cm height is used. Both DCPs are the same size (23x33x11cm). By employing two different types of DCPs, experience should be gained to indicate the most suitable for this type of application.

The overall systems were tested in May 1985 and field installation will be carried out during the summer.

The Meteosat receiving station is already installed on the roof of the B.R.G.M. office in Marseille. It is composed of:

1 parabolic antenna, 1.2m diameter, with a pre-amplifier and a converter (1,7 GHz to 137 MHz);
a receiving station developed by EMP/France with a "recepteur démodulateur" and a synchronizer connected to a desk computer with standard peripherals.

The receiving station has been tested using messages from the available reference Meteosat DCP and has proven reliable.

During the next summer period (1985), the four DCPs will be installed in the experimental basins, and hydrometeorological data will progressively feed the B.R.G.M. data-base, on a 3 hourly basis.

Such remote sensing data transmission will allow for an automatic computer processing of the collected data as well as a "télésurveillance" of the equipment installed in the field, 200 km from the B.R.G.M. office. It is also expected that such possibilities will reduce the number of field missions by knowing almost in real time if hydro-meteorological events requiring in situ man-made control programs have occurred in the remote experimental basins.

Use of the Meteosat Data Collection System

In principle there are no restiction on the use of the DCS except that the data to be collected must be classified as "environmental". Nevertheless, there are certain rules which have to be observed. Before a DCP can use the Meteosat Data Collection System, it has to be admitted to the system. This involves allocating an identifying address and reporting frequency to the DCP, and making arrangements for data handling and dissemination. A prerequisite for admission is that the DCP set be type-certified and has therefore undergone a stringent test programme. This ensures that the platform will function successfully within the DCS and more importantly that it will not cause interference to other system users, even under extreme operating conditions. For platforms to be used solely within the Meteosat coverage area, ESA conducts its own certification testing. Type--certified DCPs are commercially available from several European manufactures.

The use of the system is free of charge to authorities of states which participate in the Meteosat Operational Programme. Other authorities and commercial interests are permitted to use the system but are charged according to their use of channel time. As an example a single platform transmitting at 3 hourly intervals would cost 1280 European accounting Units (AU) for the first year of operation and 390 AU for subsequent years (the current exchange rate is 1 AU equivalent to 0.82 US $).

Conclusion

The assurance of operational status of the Meteosat Data Collection up to 1995 has opened up the possibility economic environmental data retrival from sites in an area of almost 40% of the earth's surface. The retransmission of the data permits Users to have access to their data within minutes of its transmission to the satellite.

Transmissions can be according to a schedule (a data-logging mode) or initiated directly by a measurement ("alert" mode).

The use of the system in the B.R.G.M. experiment will provide not only the benefits of rapid data collection but will enable a near real time technical monitoring of site equipment thus reducing dramatically the need for routine inspections. Additionally the decision to use the DCS has led to the development of special interfacing equipment which should find use in other aplications.

Hydrologic Applications of Space Technology (Proceedings of the Cocoa Beach Workshop, Florida, August 1985). IAHS Publ. no. 160, 1986.

Automatic weather station and river level measurements telemetered by data collection platform via Meteosat

I. C. STRANGEWAYS
Institute of Hydrology, Wallingford, Oxfordshire OX10 8BB, UK

Abstract
The Institute of Hydrology (IH) developed its first automatic weather station (AWS) in 1965 and a network has since been installed worldwide. In 1982 an AWS was linked to a data collection platform (DCP) transmitting via Meteosat I to evaluate the usefulness and reliability of satellite telemetry. This evaluation is described and the advantages of DCP telemetry are compared with those of on-site data logging. In view of the good results obtained during the two-year evaluation, a satellite Receiver/Processor and ten DCPs were purchased in early 1985. The provisional results obtained with this equipment are described and future plans outlined.

Relative advantages of logging and telemetry in hydrological data collection

Hydrological measurements can either be logged on site, the data being stored on magnetic tape or in solid state memory for transport physically to base, or they can be telemetered directly. The first IH instrument developments in the mid-1960s used magnetic tape to store data from an AWS (McCulloch and Strangeways, 1965, Strangeways and McCulloch, 1966). Since then, IH has developed a range of other instruments all either logging or telemetering their data.

While hydrological research does not require data in real time, flood forecasting and river management does and the data must be telemetered. However, even for the collection of data for research purposes there is value in telemetry; it dispenses with the need to transport the records physically, often across or between countries. To visit sites can be expensive and incovenient but if the data are telemetered visits are necessary only when maintenance is required. Telemetered data are also received quickly so that it is possible to detect failures rapidly; these might well go undetected for weeks if the data were logged. Until the availability of satellite telemetry, however, it was not economic or very practical to telemeter data from the majority of IH's experimental sites. Being remote, most would require the use of UHF links, often with repeaters, to get the data out and to a telephone line. Telemetry, therefore, was used only when essential. However, now that the cost of satellite telemetry has fallen and that suitable equipment is commercially available, it has become a viable and economic alternative to both data logging and to line-of-site UHF radio links. Considering the usefulness of satelite telemetry to data collection, why is the technique being adopted ratherslowly by hydrologists in Europe? A conservatism against new technology may be responsible, for it certainly represents a big change in the way of thinking. It may be felt to belong to the next, rather than to this, century, although hands-on experiences soon dispells any such feeling. It may be thought, incorrectly, to be prohibitively expensive. The fact that the data can be received by anyone with a receiver may deter others, although it can be coded for privacy. Others may fear that the satellite will fail or that it is not completely under user control. Nevertheless, along with a few other European organisations, IH has opted to exploit this new technique.

Pilot study of a DCP used with an AWS

A standard IH AWS comprises a conventional solarimeter and net radiometer, three platinum resistance thermometers for the measurement of temperature and wet bulb depression for humidity, a contact-closure anemometer, a wind direction sensor and a tipping bucket raingauge. At most of the IH AWS sites the data are logged on a Microdata Compact Cassette logger, type M200, an instrument designed specifically for the purpose by Microdata Ltd between 1966 and 1970, to IH specification and with IH funding. This design, with periodic up-dates, has served well for over 15 years and many are in use. They have been used to log not only AWS data but a wide range of other hydrometeorological variables, such as river level, water quality, rainfall and soil moisture tension. Following the development of the prototype AWS in the late 1960s, the manufacture and marketing of the sensor system was licensed to the Didcot Instrument Company Ltd. and an extensive network of stations, totalling about 60, has since been installed throughout the UK and worldwide. Two decades of experience have now been aquired in the design, development, installation and operation of AWS in a range of climates from tropical rain forest through desert to high altitude sub-arctic conditions (Strangeways, 1972, 1976, 1985).

In December 1982, a standard AWS was installed at Wallingford coupled to a DCP (Mc Michael Ltd) to evaluate the reliability and usefulness of satellite telemetry in hydrology. In this first installation, the Microdata logger was incorporated as an integral part of the system, use being made of its sensor interface unit and much of its logic circuitry. The raw data produced by the logger were subsequently processed by the DCP toconvert them into real units, to reduce them to three-hourly means and totals, to format them into columns with headings and to transmit them once a day (Figure 1).

84-09-08 10:08
*
849365 HYDROL G
849801 WEABK G
171 28359
SXXX21 EESA 080908

IOH W'FORD

TIME	TEMP		RADIATION		WIND		RAIN
TO	DRY	DEPN	SOLAR	NET	RUN	DIR	FALL
1200	9.1	0.4	18.1	10.7	9.0	NNW	0.0
1500	13.1	2.2	30.2	17.2	12.8	NW	0.0
1800	14.6	2.2	20.6	11.3	16.0	N	0.0
2100	11.6	0.1	1.2	0.2	9.2	N	0.0
0000	10.1	0.0	0.0	0.0	5.3	N	0.0
0300	9.5	0.0	0.0	-0.1	6.0	N	0.5
0600	8.9	0.0	0.0	-0.1	4.5	N	0.5
0900	8.7	0.0	1.4	0.6	8.6	N	0.0
TOT	----	----	71.8	40.0	71.9	---	1.0
MEAN	10.7	0.6	-----	-----	-----	---	-----

PE IS 2.09 MM
=

FIG.1 Listing of AWS data telemetered via Meteosat.

The system was installed on December 13 1982. After 12 months of fault-free operation, it was considered sufficiently well proven to be relocated in a harsher environment. Because IH already had a presence in the Cairngorm area of NE Scotland (Strangeways, 1981, 1984, 1985), the station was moved to a site at Coire Cas on the northern slopes of Cairn Gorm at an altitude of 600m, where a standard AWS had been in operation for several years (Figure 2). Over the next 12 months, it performed as well at the new site as it had at Wallingford, despite the harsher climate. The system was considered proven.

In Europe, DCPs transmit their data to Meteosat I, these data being received by the European Space Agency (ESA) at Darmstadt in West Germany. In the 1982 tests, ESA telexed the AWS data to the UK Meteorological Office at Bracknell, who retelexed them to Wallingford; this took some 20 minutes.

Occasionly no telex was received, but for the 24 month test period, only isolated days were lost, totalling around 1%. The cause of these losses is not known, but the complex route which the data followed may have led to some human error along the chain. However, ESA do not claim 100% success in reception of data and this may be the cause. Two other losses of data occurred, both due to operator error. The first loss was due to battery failure at Wallingford before the correct frequency of battery change had been established, the second, at Coire Cas, was due to a momentary loss of power at the time of battery change, which caused the clock-synchronismn to be lost and the system to shut down automatically, until resynchronised.

Extension of the DCP network

The signal level radiated by Meteosat I is very low and requires a large dish and complex electronics to receive it. Coincidental with the two-year evaluation, however, was the launching of Meteosat II. With this, it became possible for the data received from Meteosat I, by ESA, to be retransmitted to Meteosat II for radiation at a much higher signal level. The dish to receive this need be only 1.5m diameter and the electronics more modest, bringing the cost of a receiving station within the budgets of users like IH. Also coincident with this, IH had been developing flood forecasting scheemes for two UK Water Authorities (Brunsdon and Sargent, 1982) and these experiences had shown that UHF radio links could present problems over some terrains. Because radio bands are so full, there is also the problem of obtaining a UHF frequency for each project. At the same time, IH was also planning its future strategy on logging, and this had a bearing on decisions regarding telemetry. All of these factors contributed to the decision to adopt DCPs as a routine means of data collection. A positive approach was made by the purchase of a Satellite Receiver/Processor (McMichael), this being installed in early 1985 (Figure 3), allowing data to be received at Wallingford from one-third of the earth's surface centred on lat. 0°, long. 0°. At the same time, ten DCPs were purchased to enable a start to be made in establishing a network of out-stations (Figure 4).

There are four models of this make of DCP: The first accepts five analogue voltage inputs, the second is programmed to receive serial digital data in RS232 form, the third is a single-channel pulse-counting system intended primarily for use with tipping bucket raingauges, while the fourth is dedicated to telemetering river level (using the DRS Ltd. sensor). The former two are of greatest interest to IH since there is a need to telemeter the full range of hydrological variables. A mix of analogue and digital DCPs was therefore purchased, all programmed to transmit at three-hourly intervals. Each DCP has a time-slot of one minute in which to transmit its data, which it must do at a rate of 300 bauds. With housekeeping data (such as battery and transmitter voltages,

FIG.2 AWS in the Cairngorm mountains, NE Scotland, telemetering via Meteosat.

FIG.3 The satellite receiver dish at Wallingford (above)

The Receiver/Processor with terminal (below)

FIG.4 All DCPs were first tested at this site at Wallingford before deployment at their operational sites.

station name, headings to identify the five analogue channels, and the time of the first scan), time is available to send about 100 numbers relating to data. If all five analogue channels are in use, for example, a sampling time of 10 minutes is possible, each number taking the form of a voltage between 0.00 to 5.00 in 0.02 volt steps, that is to 8-bit discrimination.

Application of the DCPs

The analogue DCPs were purchased so that some of the existing IH sensors could be used with a minimum of development, in particular the river level sensor developed for use with the Microdata M200 logger (Strangeways and Templeman 1974). This sensor was designed to measure a large change of level (5 to 10m) to a high discimination (1mm) while being limited to the logger s 8-bit accuracy; the same technique is equally applicable to the 8-bit DCP. To achieve this, a float turns three continuous-rotation potentiometers, two rotating once per turn of the pulley with one turn representing a 20 cm change of level, producing a signal change offive volts. The two are positioned 180° out of phase, mechanically, to avoid error due to the 5° gap in their windings. The third potentiometer is driven via a reduction gearbox, rotating once for each 4m change of level. Two such systems are now in operation with DCPs. The first of these was tested at Wallingford and then installed at a gauging site on the River Wye in IH's experimental catchment area at Plynlimon, Central Wales. Figure 5 illustrates one three-hour period of data received from this station. The second level system is currently on test at Wallingford, prior to installation at the IH Balquhidder catchment in Scotland.

```
     DAY      HRS     MIN     SEC                 DCP ADDRESS

     189       16      50      15                 16827694

DCP DATA :-

VOLTAGES AT WYE LEVEL 1

06 MINUTE READINGS STARTING AT 13:53 GMT.

++ V1 ++

1.70 1.68 1.68 1.68 1.68 1.68 1.66 1.66 1.66 1.66
1.66 1.66 1.66 1.66 1.66 1.66 1.64 1.64 1.64 1.64
1.64 1.64 1.62 1.62 1.62 1.62 1.60 1.62 1.62 1.62

++ V2 ++

3.82 3.82 3.82 3.80 3.82 3.82 3.80 3.80 3.80 3.80
3.80 3.78 3.80 3.78 3.78 3.78 3.78 3.78 3.78 3.78
3.78 3.76 3.76 3.76 3.74 3.76 3.74 3.76 3.76 3.74

++ V3 ++

0.38 0.38 0.38 0.38 0.38 0.38 0.38 0.38 0.38 0.38
0.38 0.38 0.38 0.38 0.38 0.38 0.38 0.38 0.38 0.38
0.38 0.38 0.38 0.38 0.38 0.38 0.38 0.38 0.38 0.38

BATT: 12.3 VCO: 02.9 =
```

FIG.5 Listing of DCP data from the level sensor at Plynlimon, Central Wales. A change of 0.02 volts, in the top two voltages, represents a change of level of 1mm.

A five-channel DCP is also being used with AWS sensors. In the two-year test of the first DCP from 1982 to 1984, the Microdata logger comprised part of the the system. To simplify the design and to cut costs, new analogue circuits have been developed to convert the sensor outputs to the five volts required by the DCP, without the use of the logger. The prototype of this is currently on test at Wallingford, measuring solar and net radiation, temperature and humidity. Under development is a digital to analogue convertor to allow windspeed and rainfall sensors to be added. To accommodate these, the solar sensor will be eliminated. Seven or more channels would be useful for applications such as this, although the loss of solar radiation is no problem since the net sensor is used for evaporation calculation with solar acting only as back-up. Wind direction is not often required in hydrology and its omission presents no problems.

A water quality station was recently developed for use with the M200 logger and the two prototypes are in operation at Plynlimon measuring pH, conductivity and temperature, with disolved oxygen to be added. The system is submersible and includes analogue interface circuits producing voltages directly compatible with a DCP. It is intended to link a DCP to one of these water quality stations, in the near future, operating it in parallel with, but independently of, the M200 logger. There are clearly many potential uses to which the analogue DCPs can be put.

In the longer term, however, the RS232 serial digital DCP offers greater versatility, because an intelligent interface unit can be interposed between the DCP and the sensors. Since designs for this are not yet complete, only a brief outline of the intended path of development will be given. Following any necessary analogue preconditioning of the signals, such as amplification or bridge circuitry, an intelligent (microprocessor/microcomputer-based) unit will enable the digitised analogue signals to be manipulated in any desired way prior to input to the DCP. Because the DCP requires only a string of numbers or words to be input, these can take any desired form. It is possible, therefore, to have any desired number of sensor inputs, to sample them, say, once a minute and to mean or total the measurements over an hour or longer, to read maximum and minimum values to convert the raw data into real units and to reduce the data to their most compact form so as to make the best use of the one-minute transmission time-slots.

The next in the IH series of low-cost data loggers is being designed to perform as both logger and intelligent DCP interface, including all of the necessary analogue interfacing. The cost of the unit will be kept low, in line with similar earlier developments (Strangeways, et al, 1980, Strangeways 1984). Should the time come that analogue DCPs are no longer required, they can be changed to the RS232 form simply by changing their control program (in ROM) since all the DCPs are identically wired, differing only in how they are programmed. However, there are always likely to remain applications for the analogue types.

WEFAX pictures

The satellite Receiver/Processor also receives WEFAX picture data of cloud cover in the visible band and images in two bands of infrared. By the addition of a Scan Convertor and a colour monitor, the pictures become available at a relatively small additional cost (under £1000). This facillity is being added since the images will be of value to IH in its increasing involvement in remote sensing. Because the picture information is received only slowly, as an audio signal, it is possible to record the data on a low-cost cassette recorder for later, off-line, replay. If very rapid picture access is not required, this presents a low cost alternative to the more expensive disc method of storage. Pictures can also be stored as 35mm transparencies.

Conclusion

While a decade ago data logging would have been used for the collection of historic data for research, and UHF radio or telephone for flood forecasting, the recent availability of reasonably priced satellite telemetry equipment makes it possible to extend the use of telemetry, with its attendant benefits, to all such applications. It is now possible to collect data from one third of the earth s surface with one modestly priced receiver and to transmit data from anywhere within the same area using a DCP costing about the same as a data logger. This is invaluable to IH's need to collect data from across Britain and from many overseas sites, as well as to collect data in real-time for flood forecasting. It is clear that satellite telemetry will become increasingly commonplace during the next decade and that it will not be restricted to difficult or remote sites only, but will find uses wherever telephones are impractical, where UHF links are inconvenient and frequently where loggers may formally have been used. We hope our colleagues in the UK and in the rest of Europe and elsewhere in this third of the world will join us in exploiting this useful new technology.

References

Brunsdon, G. P. and Sargent, R.J., 1982, The Haddington flood warning system: Proc. IAHS Symp. Advances in Hydrometry, Exeter. pub. no. 134, p. 257-272.

Mc Culloch, J. S. G. and Strangeways, I. C., 1966, Automatic weather stations for hydrology: Proc. WMO Tech. Conf. on Automatic Weather Stations, Geneva. Tech. note no. 82, p. 262-264.

Strangeways, I. C. and Mc Culloch, J. S. G., 1965, A low priced automatic hydrometeorological station: Bul. IAHS Xe Annee no. 4, p. 57-62.

Strangeways, I. C., 1972, Automatic weather stations for network operation: Weather, vol. 27, no. 10, p. 403-408.

Strangeways, I. C. and Templeman, R. F., 1974, Logging river level on magnetic tape: Water and Water Engineering., vol. 178, no. 936,

p. 57-60.
Strangeways, I. C., 1976, The long term performance of a network of automatic weather stations and the factors affecting this: Proc. COST Tech. Conf. on Automatic Weather Stations, Reading University, p. 24-45.
Strangeways, I.C., Turner, M. and Insell, W. S., 1980, A simple instrument system: WMO Bul. vol. XXIX, no. 1, p. 16-19.
Strangeways, I. C., 1981, Instruments for mountainous areas: Nordic Hydrology, no. 12, p. 289-296.
Strangeways, I. C., 1984, Low cost hydrological data collection: Proc. IAHS Symp. Challenges in African hydrology and water resources, Harare, Publ. no.144, p. 293-333.
Strangeways, I. C., 1984, The development of an automatic weather station for cold regions: Proc. Western Snow Conference, Sun Valley, p. 12-23.
Strangeways, I.C., 1985, Automatic weather stations: John Wiley and Sons Ltd. Facets of Hydrology, Vol. II, Ed. Rodda, J. C., p. 25-68.
Strangeways, I. C., 1985, A cold regions automatic weather station: J. of Hydrology, vol. 79, in press.

Hydrologic Applications of Space Technology (Proceedings of the Cocoa Beach Workshop, Florida, August 1985). IAHS Publ. no. 160, 1986.

A totally electronic water stage meter for use with a satellite transmitter

GARY G. STRINGHAM & PAUL A. WHEELER
Utah State University, UMC 41, Logan, Utah 84322, USA

Abstract
This paper reports the development of a water stage meter to provide real-time measurements of water levels via satellite for a computer-based research project at Utah State University. This device provides the data reliably and without periodic human intervention. The device is based on an ultrasonic transducer with a temperature sensor to compensate for the change in the speed of sound due to temperature. It has an RS232 port for external communication. The device proved to be accurate to its resolution of 0.05 ft (1.52 cm) and capable of detecting bad measurements. It eliminates periodic maintenance and can be used in remote locations. It can also be used to detect levels of other materials or for distance applications.

Introduction
Water stage meters, devices that measures the level of the water in rivers, canals, or reservoirs, are widely used today. The data they collect are used to make a historical record of measured events, to forecast coming events, and to make management decisions. This paper describes the research and design of a new and different water stage meter needed for remote and maintenance-free data-collection applications.

Measurement of water levels in rivers, reservoirs, and canals in local and remote locations is needed for a computer-based research project at Utah State University. The water stage meter described in this paper will be useful in this project and for water resource management, keeping historical records of hydrological and meteorological information, and early warning systems.

The design must take into consideration a few factors. For example, when sensing from above the surface, care must be taken to ensure that waves and debris do not interfere with the readings yielding erroneous heights. If sensed from under the surface, suspended sediment or sediment deposited on the sensor could affect the reading. The sensor must also be protected from possible damage caused by floating debris.

Another requirement of the sensor is that it must be a "stand-alone" unit, that is, it must operate independently from external support devices because it will be installed in remote locations. Problems of power source, maintenance, and reliability must also be addressed. The collected data need to be transmitted to a computer as often as possible to permit real-time access. Also, mounting, necessary construction at the site, and allowances for water level and weather extremes must be considered.

Literature research yielded information about various water level sensors; some commonly used, and others for research and development. They are listed below:

The Stephens Float Gage is the most common sensor in use today. It consists of a float connected to a pulley which records the liquid level on a strip chart or punched tape. The chart or tape is driven by a spring-wound clock. The chart or tape must be changed and the clock rewound on a weekly or monthly interval. A stilling well is required to provide a still water surface for the float. The stilling well is generally off to one side of the river or canal with an underground, connecting pipe. The unit is enclosed in a shelter to keep the rain and snow off the paper and other sensitive parts (Grover and Harrington, 1943).

An acoustical sensor available on the market has an ultrasonic transducer mounted on the top of a 0.5-in (1.27-cm)* diameter plastic tube. The tube is partially immersed

* Due to instrument constraints, all the measurements and readouts are based on the British system of units. Hence, everything in this paper is in British units, followed by the SI units in parenthesis.

in the water, creating a stilling well. The transducer and associated electronics measure the distance to the water level in the tube (Bartex).

Bezverkhniĭ and Konovalova (1980) reported an attempt to sense the water level by sending a laser beam to the water surface at an angle slightly off of vertical and then measuring the horizontal travel of the beam with an array of sensors. As the level of the water varies, the horizontal travel of the laser beam varies, causing it to reflect to a different location in the sensor array.

Spomer (1981) reports of a method using a bielectrode probe to sense when the liquid has reached a certain level. It is simple, inexpensive, and versatile and uses at most ten components.

Dedrick and Allen (1981) reported using a capacitance method for sensing the water level. It consists of two plates, or a probe and a plate, immersed in the water with a high-frequency circuit attached to the two plates. The plates form the plates of a capacitor. The water between the plates become the dielectric. As the water level changes, the dielectric constant of the water capacitor changes, causing the capacitance to change, which in turn causes the frequency of the circuit to change. The frequency can be measured and from that, the level of the water is calculated.

Dedrick and Allen (1981) also reported using a bubbler, or manometer. It consists of pressurized air tanks, pressure transducer, pressure regulator, and flexible tubing. The pressurized air from the tanks passes through the pressure regulator to reduce it to a lower pressure and then into the tubing which is laid in the water. The air flows through the tubing and out the bottom end where it escapes into the water. The air pressure at the end of the tubing in the water corresponds to the pressure of the water. That pressure can be sensed by the transducer at the top end of the tubing. The transducer output signal is recorded onto a strip chart or processed into any desired electronic signal.

Kort, et al. (1982), reported about an encoder attached to the pulley of a float gage. The encoder yields binary data which is stored in non-volatile RAM. The RAM is on a removable board. Periodically, the board is taken to a computer and the data dumped.

Herschy (1978) has collected several articles written by specialists regarding various aspects of traditional and new techniques for measuring water flow in a channel. Some of these techniques have just been discussed. Others were not as applicable for this project.

Other potential methods follows:

Measuring the round-trip delay of an acoustical sound wave was discussed in the previous section. Laser or electronic waves could be used as the medium for measuring round-trip delay. Or it could be used with amplitude modulation. By adjusting the frequency of modulation and detecting nulls and phase shifts, the distance could be measured.

A gamma ray source placed on the channel bed and a counter overhead could detect the water level. As the level rises, the attenuation is greater, yielding a smaller number from the counter. One of the features of this method is that accuracy can be increased simply by increasing the sample time, which also eliminates noise introduced by waves and debris. Self-calibration to compensate for the half-life of the source is possible by placing another counter underground where the medium between the source and the second counter remains a constant.

A simple and inexpensive method is to put a pressure transducer on the bed and any associated electronics on the bank.

The method that is chosen must satisfy the two main objectives of this project:

1. Design a water stage meter that will be totally electronic, thereby increasing reliability and eliminating periodic maintenance.
2. Permit real-time access to data by allowing simple interfacing to data collection platforms.

The method chosen to sense water levels was an ultrasonic transducer. The reasons for choosing this method are as follows:

1. The method chosen will be flexible in mounting, as it will not require a vertical mount such as a pier post or wall but could be mounted under a bridge or anything rigid over the water.

2. No part of the sensor developed will be in the water, eliminating damage due to corrosion and debris.
3. Ultrasonic transducers and associated electronics are readily available. They need only the interfacing and controlling electronics to use them.
4. The speed of sound is slow enough that it can be measured with digital electronics currently available.

Experiments

As stated above, one of the reasons for choosing the ultrasonic method is the existence of ultrasonic transmitters and receivers on the market. The Polaroid transducer was chosen because of its wide distance and temperature range, high frequency, and fine resolution. The transducer obtained came in an experimental kit. Experiments were conducted with it before implementing it into the water stage meter. It displayed the distance in feet with a resolution of 0.1 ft (3.05 cm).

The accuracy was tested at various distances between 0.9 ft and 6 ft (0.27 m and 1.83 m) and was found to be precisely what was displayed.

Experiments were conducted over rivers with surface variations from still to turbulent and with distances from 2 ft to 12 ft (0.61 m to 3.66 m). It was found to yield consistent results as long as the direction of travel of the pulse was vertical.

One idea for flexibility in design was to aim the beam on an angle towards the water surface. Experiments were performed on a smooth floor and a river surface. The smooth-floor experiments were performed from the balcony of a racquetball court. The transducer was aimed straight down to the floor of the court and then tilted slowly until the transducer could not sense the returning pulse. This was done several times. The angle where the beam was lost was typically close to when the direction of travel was 15° from the vertical.

Similar experiments were conducted on water at various locations with varying waves. The rougher the water, the greater the tilt of the transducer was possible. The major problem was that the readings were sporadic. The distance measured was the distance from the transducer to whatever wave could bounce back the signal first. The conclusion was drawn that using the transducer on an angle greater than about 15° would be unpredictable, sporadic and unreliable.

An experiment was conducted to determine the beam width. The transducer was place in a fixed position aiming down to the floor. The distance to the floor was displayed on the LED readout. A stiff sheet of paper was used to move around the edge of the beam path to observe where the transducer detected it. The orientation of the paper was adjusted to achieve maximum possible reflection of the signal. The locations were noted where the edge of the beam was determined. Using these locations relative to the transducer, simple geometry was used to determine the beam width, which was calculated to be about 15°. This sounds reasonable considering that the specifications states that it is approximately 20° (Polaroid, 1981).

Experiments were conducted to determine if rain has any effect on the ultrasonic sensor. These experiments were conducted in actual rain storms which were moderately heavy for the area. The transducer was aimed horizontally with no object within the 35-ft (10.7-m) range. If the rain was capable of reflecting the ultrasonic pulse, the LED display would have displayed a number less than 35.0. During the experiment the LED stayed at 35.0. No interference was observed. Experiments were also conducted to determine if rain would scatter the beam, causing the transducer to not sense a returning pulse. This was done at 6.0 and 10.4 ft (1.83 and 3.17 m). There was no observable interference.

Design and Function

Figure 1 shows the enclosure built to accomodate the prototype water stage meter. The case, made of aluminum sheet metal, was designed for easy opening and closing and

After the power is turned on and everything is initialized, the water stage meter is waiting for commands on what to do. It needs to know when and how often to take measurements and what to do with the data. The water stage meter can be connected to equipment ranging from terminals to dumb recorders through its RS232 port. A

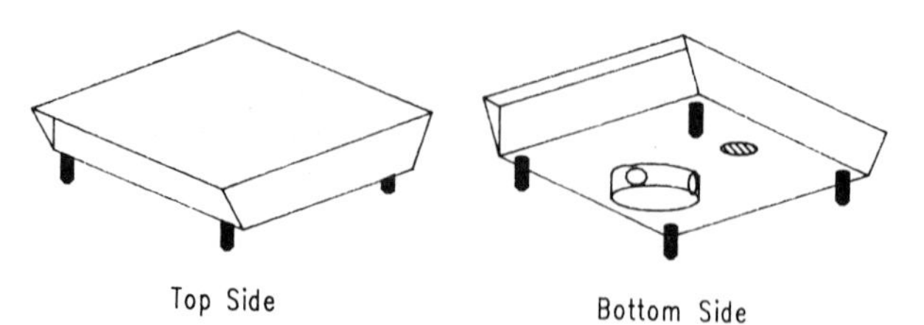

FIG.1 Outside views of the water stage meter.

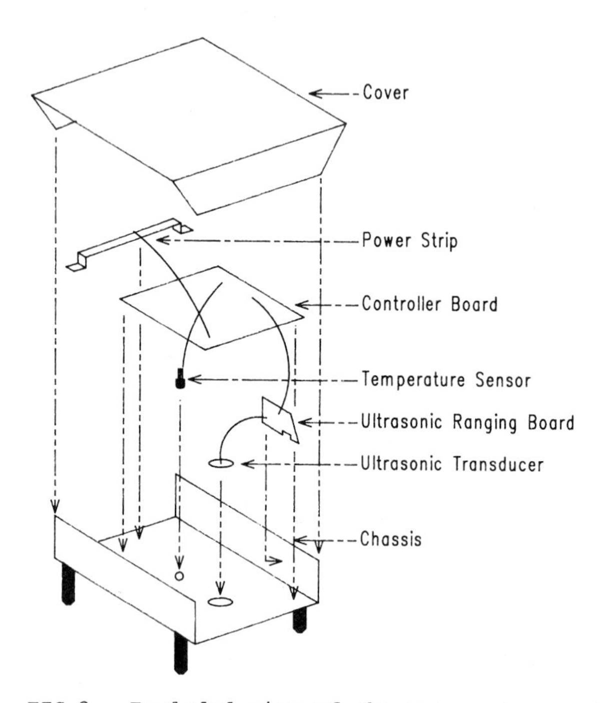

FIG.2 Exploded view of the water stage meter.

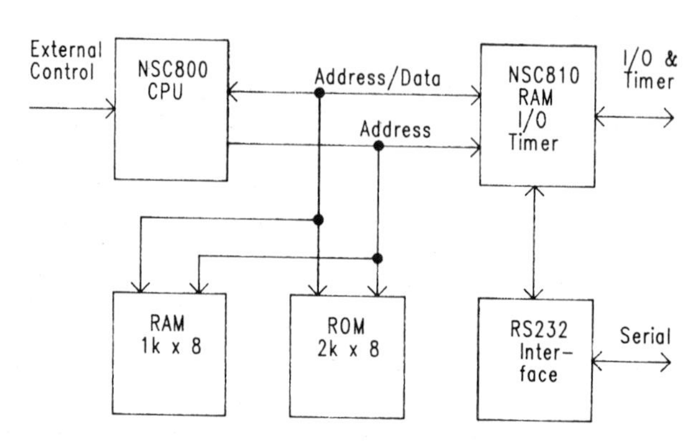

FIG.3 Block diagram of the NSC888 evaluation board.

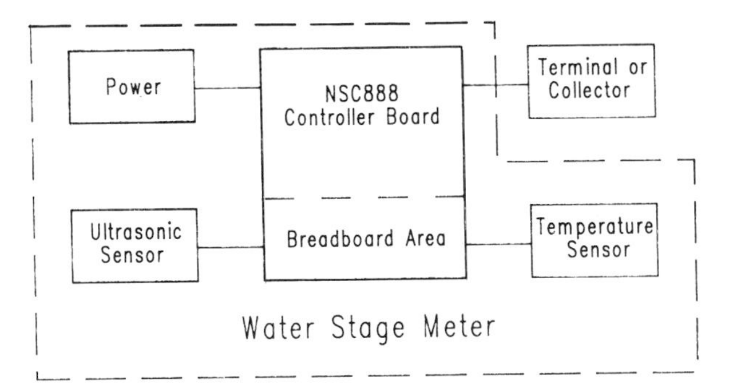

FIG.4 Block diagram of the water stage meter.

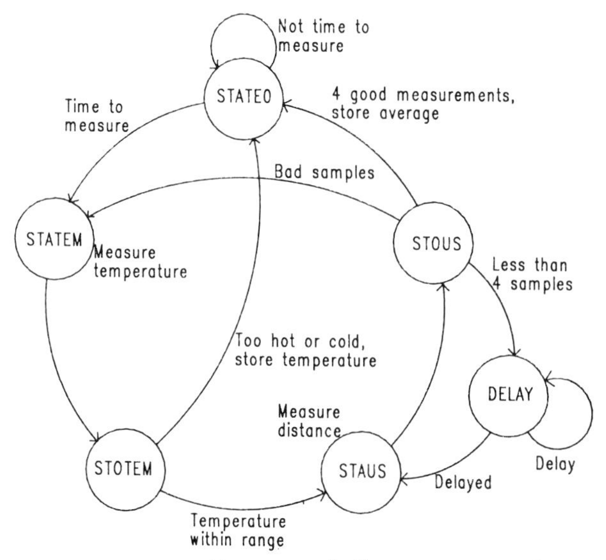

FIG.5 State diagram of the measurement process.

terminal is needed to allow the user to execute commands to do the following:*

1. Set the day and time.
2. Set the first measurement time and repetition rate.
3. Specify where the data is to be stored.
4. Tell it to start taking measurements.

Commands consist of one-letter instructions which is executed when received.

Once the tasks in the list above are accomplished, the terminal can be disconnected. If a simple recorder is to be connected, one that is not capable of sending commands to the device, then the device can be instructed to send the data out the port when it is collected. A data-collection platform, such as one used to collect data to send via radio or satellite, can also be used to receive the data from the device. Since the platform may be busy collecting data from other sources, the water stage meter can be commanded to store the data internally until the platform sends a command requesting it.

Once the device has been commanded to take measurements, a recorder can be connected or the user may leave the terminal connected to receive the data. Commands are provided to allow the user to show the current time, the next time a measurement

* Another device with sufficient capabilities can be used to set up the water stage meter instead of a terminal.

is to be made, and the results of the previous measurement. The user can also ask for the stored data and tell the device to stop taking measurements. This is useful for evaluation and experimentation purposes.

The measurement process involves stepping through several execution states. A state is executed every 0.1 s, after the real-time clock has been updated. Each state executes its job and decides what the next state will be. Figure 5 is a state diagram of the measurement process.

Every minute, the CPU checks if it is time to take a measurement. If it is, it will set a flag. It then jumps to one of the states shown in figure 5.

State STATE0 in Figure 5 turns on the power to the sensors if the take-measurement flag is set.

The ability for the CPU to turn the power to the sensors on and off was designed into the water stage meter to conserve the limited power. The ultrasonic sensor itself consumes 150 mA in quiescent mode (Polaroid, 1981), much more than the 30 mA minimum for the controller board (National, 1981).

Biber, et al. (1980), reported that only the temperature has a significant effect on the speed of sound. The effect caused by humidity, pressure, and frequency is negligible. The speed of sound in air is given by the following equation:

$$Speed = 331.4\sqrt{\frac{T}{273}}\frac{meters}{sec}$$

The only parameter required is T, the temperature in °K. The speed of sound at −30° and 70° C differs by almost 20%.

A temperature sensor was implemented to allow the CPU to compensate for the temperature.

State STATEM starts the temperature measurement process by causing the CPU to start counting the frequency of the temperature sensor. State STOTEM turns off the frequency counting and reads the result from the counter which is the temperature. If the temperature is out of range, (−30°–70° C,) then it will store the temperature and not measure the distance. If it is within range, then it will use the temperature value to look in a look-up table for a temperature-dependant time constant to be used in measuring the distance.

Results

The water stage meter functioned as expected. One of the experiments conducted several times was to:

1. Set up the water stage meter.
2. Disconnect the terminal.
3. Take the device to some location.
4. Measure the distance a few times.
5. Take it back to the terminal.
6. Dump the collected data.

This worked with very few problems. Other experiments were conducted by leaving the terminal connected and having the water stage meter send the data immediately to the terminal.

The preciseness of the distance measured with the software and hardware of the device was evaluated and found to be accurate to within 0.05 ft, (1.52 cm,) the designed resolution.

The temperature measured was accurate to within 1° C when compared with another thermometer.

Power consumption of the device was measured to be an average of 43 mA between measurements. The device is not always in power-save mode during this time. Ten times a second it leaves power-save mode to update the real-time clock. When taking a measurement, the current drawn was at least 200 mA. Capacitors on the controller board decrease this current spike when the ultrasonic ranging board draws a large amount of current during pulse transmission.

Conclusions

This project showed the feasibility of a totally electronic water stage meter. The design allows flexibility in mounting methods. It can be mounted in such places as under a bridge, on the side of a vertical wall, on a rigid overhanging beam, or in the top of a storage tank. The device does not require to have any part of it immersed in water, eliminating the possibility of damage from debris and corrosion.

The serial port on the device permits it to pass the collected data to data recorders or to collection platforms to be transmitted by radio or satellite to computers. This feature will save resources by not sending someone to each recording station to collect the data, especially the remote stations. This feature also permits a real-time data collection system, which could be used as an early-warning system.

This device could also be used to monitor levels in storage tanks, such as water, oil, or gasoline tanks. It does not necessarily have to monitor liquids. It could also monitor levels in grain elevators or snow depths at ski resorts. Or it could be used for distance or positional sensing in an automated factory environment.

Of course, the device has some limitations. It must be mounted on a very rigid structure. If mounted on a bridge, for example, vertical movement should be minimal as traffic crosses on it or as temperature changes causes contraction or expansion. The range is limited from 0.9 to 35 ft (0.26 to 10.7 m). Modifications could be made to the ultrasonic ranging board to adjust the range window closer or farther away. The device was designed with a resolution of 0.05 ft (1.52 cm). The ultrasonic transducer and ranging board are capable of a finer resolution. The controlling board would have to be designed different to handle it.

Estimated cost of the parts required to build a sensor is around $500.0 or $600.00.

The ultrasonic transducer proved to be a practical and economical solution for the objectives of the project. The electronics used with the transducer provided a sensor that is reliable, needs no periodic maintenance, and can interface with other equipment for real-time data collection.

References

Bartex, Inc., WLMS Primary Sensor AQUATRAK® Series 3000: Annapolis, MD, p. 2–4.

Bezverkhniĭ, Sh. A., and Konovalova, S. A., 1980, Discrete Laser Level Meter: Vestnik Sel'skokhozyaĭstvennoĭ Nauki, v. 1, p. 115–118.

Biber, C., et al., 1980, The Polaroid Ultrasonic Ranging System: Audio Engineering Society Preprint 1696(A-8), p. 3.

Dedrick, A. R., and Allen, R. F., 1981, Open Channel Flow Sensing for Automatic Control: ASAE Paper No. 81-2562, p. 4.

Grover, N. C., and Harrington, A. W., 1943, Stream Flow — Measurements, Records and their Uses: Wiley, New York, NY, p. 107–113.

Herschy, R. W., 1978, Hydrometry, Principles and Practices: Wiley-Interscience, Bristol, Great Britain.

Kort, R. L., et al., 1982, A Microprocessor Based Water Level Recorder and Sampler Controller: Transactions of the ASAE, v. 25, no. 5, p. 1282.

National Semiconductor Corp., 1981, NSC888; NSC800 Evaluation Board User's Manual: Handbook.

Polaroid Corporation, 1981, Ultrasonic Ranging System for Distance Measurement Applications: Information Brochure.

Spomer, L. A., 1981, Simple, Inexpensive Solid State Liquid Level Detection and Control: Agronomy Journal, v. 73, p. 139–140.

Hydrologic Applications of Space Technology (Proceedings of the Cocoa Beach Workshop, Florida, August 1985). IAHS Publ. no. 160, 1986.

Use of Meteor Scatter telemetry for hydrometeorological data collection networks

RISTO KALSKE & ILKKA LAHTEENOJA
Surface Weather Systems Division, Vaisala Oy, Post Box 26, SF-00421 Helsinki, Finland

Abstract

This paper describes the use of Meteor Scatter (also known as Meteor Burst) telemetry in hydrometeorological data collection network. The system presented is intended for the transmission of hydrometeorological data as short messages from a network of Automatic Remote Stations to a Central Data Collection Station.

The Meteor Scatter telemetry uses ionized meteor trails burning in the earth's atmosphere to reflect or reradiate VHF radio signals between two points up to distances of 2000 km (1250 miles). No repeater stations are required between the two points.

Advantages of the method include independence from external agencies in operation, one Central Station to cover an area with a diameter of 4000 km (2500 miles), easy network formation, low probability of data interception and automated data collection.

Relevant factors in network planning and implementation are studied. These include Central and Remote Station design features. A typical Automatic Remote Data Collection Station consists of the hydrological data collection equipment, power supply, telemetry terminal and 6-element Yagi antenna.

The operational experience from existing networks and test links is described.

General Description of Meteor Scatter Telemetry System

A Meteor Scatter telemetry system is basicly a VHF radio link capable of transmitting digitally coded information up to a distance of 2000 km. The communication range of conventional VHF links is limited to the line of sight since the electro-magnetic waves of these frequencies propagate straightforward and do not bend to areas beyond the horizon.

The Meteor Scatter telemetry uses ionized meteor trails as reflectors for the transmitted radio signal. Due to the nature of meteors this communication path is usually available for very short periods at a time. Therefore the information intended to be transmitted has to be sliced into relatively small blocks. At the receiving end the complete message is reconstructed from the separate blocks. This basic property of all Meteor Scatter telemetry systems sets special requirements to the communication software in order to achieve the maximum use of available meteor trails.

A typical application of Meteor Scatter telemetry is collection of environmental parameters from remote sites to a Central Station where the data is stored and analyzed. Current operating Meteor Scatter systems transmit data such as wind speed and direction, air temperature, humidity and pressure, solar radiation, water level, water temperature and water conductivity.

The largest network implemented so far is SNOTEL which is owned by the United States Department of Agriculture. The SNOTEL network contains over 500 Remote Stations measuring accumulated snow, precipitation and air temperature. These parameters are collected daily.

Data can be collected more frequently if needed. VAISALA has implemented a Meteor Scatter network in which four Remote Stations measuring water conditions, such as temperature, level and conductivity, in addition to atmospheric pressure and power supply voltage are polled within a ten-minute interval. The environmental parameters are expressed by their instant, average, minimum and maximum values.

A typical Meteor Scatter network is presented in Figure 1.

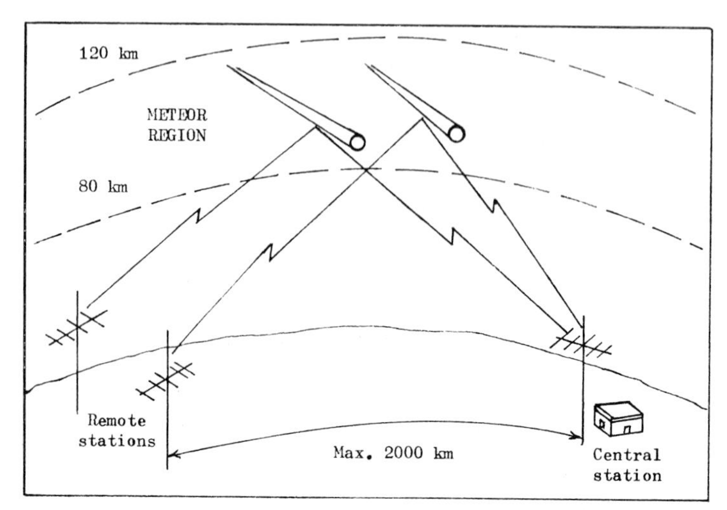

FIG.1 General structure of Meteor Scatter network.

Theoretical Background and Equipment Used in a Meteor Scatter Telemetry Link

More than 10 billion meteors penetrate the earth's atmosphere daily. When reaching the altitude of 120 km, they begin to burn due to the friction caused by the air. Simultaneously they generate an ionized trail which is used to reflect the radio signals. A large majority of these meteors are too small to generate a sufficiently strong reflection or are unfavorably positioned with respect to one particular Meteor Scatter link in order to establish a radio communication path between the link end points. However, useful trails occur at the rate of 2-3 trails/minute with lifetimes ranging from a few microseconds to several seconds. These figures depend on factors like noise level, transmission power, antenna gain and demodulator performance. The optimum frequency range for Meteor Scatter telemetry has been found to exist between 40 MHz and 50 MHz.

The altitude of the ionized trails determines the maximum distance between the two points which can be connected via this particular trail. As the altitude of the useful trails ranges from 80 km to 120 km (50 - 75 miles), the range of a single hop Meteor Scatter link is limited to 2000 km. This limit can be overcome by using a Relay Station which stores the data from one direction and transmits it further to the other direction. Figure 2 on the following page illustrates the altitude distribution of ionized meteor trails (Chu, 1980).

A distinct seasonal and diurnal variation in meteor trail density can be observed. The seasonal variation has been found to be 3:1 with the peak value occurring in July and the minimum value in February. In the daily variation the most active time is morning hours between 05:00 and 08:00 hrs and the lowest meteor activity occurs in the evening between 17:00 and 20:00 hrs. The magnitude of the daily variation is approximately 4:1.

A Meteor Scatter Communication Station (Central or Remote) consists of the telecommunication equipment and of a host device. The telecommunication equipment in VAISALA Meteor Scatter system is always identical and independent

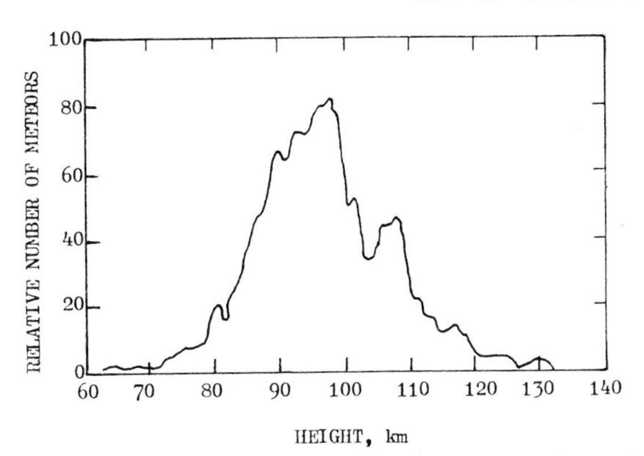

FIG.2 Altitude distribution of meteor trails.

of the type of the station. The MS (Meteor Scatter Telemetry Terminal) is a microprocessor controlled radio transmitter/receiver which takes care of the communication via the meteor trails. The Telemetry Terminal communicates with the host device through a standard RS 232 serial communication port. The host device is, at a Central Station, typically a microcomputer with a disk storage and printer and, at a Remote Data Collecting Station, an Automatic Weather Station. Alternatively a plain terminal with a keyboard and video or paper printout can be used.

The system uses a single 6-element Yagi antenna both for reception and transmission. The power consumption of a Meteor Scatter Station depends on the desired communication rate and is low enough to be supplied with solar panels.

The transmitted radio signal is modulated with a modulation method called Fast Frequency Shift Keying (FFSK), which is a developed version of the conventional FSK (Frequency Shift Keying). This modulation type was selected because of its efficient use of the radio spectrum. The narrow bandwidth which is characteristic to FFSK allows the instantaneous data rate to be as high as 10000 bits/second. As the system used the same frequency both for transmission and for reception the final data rate to bandwidth ratio is high. In other words, the system is able to pass a relatively high amount of information in a narrow (25 kHz) radio communication channel.

The hardware of the system is designed for high reliability and low power applications. The fact that all Telemetry Terminals in a network are equal reduces the system complexity and increases reliability. The number of spare parts is lower and maintenance is faster and more cost-effective than in systems using unequal Master and Remote Stations.

System Software

The system software is divided into four separate tasks. These are the radio communication task, the host device communication task, the statistical calculations task and the system monitoring and diagnostics task. The software is programmed mainly in a high-level programming language. The time-critical parts of the software are programmed using machine language which enables considerably faster execution of the program. The software resides completely in one EPROM chip and is not altered due to power-downs or other interferencies. The software is designed to minimize the host devices overhead activites.

A Meteor Scatter link can be viewed as a slow-speed modem from the host devices point of view. The host device communication task implements this interface. Being strictly a modem natured communication link, the system processes data transparently. All data, text or numbers are processed equally. This universal nature of the link software makes the interfacing protocol problems significantly easier. The host device interface is designed to be used by a human operator. The data is entered with one command and as soon as the message is transmitted and acknowledgement is received from the other end of the link, a "message through" -text is displayed/printed.

The radio communication task is the most demanding part of the software. The data received from the host device, a weather station or a terminal, is divided into blocks and each block is transmitted separately. At the same time data blocks are received from the other end of the link and these blocks are combined to form a complete message to be output to the host device. Each data block is secured with a unique check information which enables the receiver to detect a very high percentage of errors occurred during the transmission. In this part of the link, hardware or software, is the only difference between a Central Station and a Remote Station. The Central Station is responsible for sending the periodic probe signals to detect a usable meteor trail. The central or remote selection is implemented with a jumper switch. The software is identical and thus any Remote Station can be used as a spare part at the Central Station.

The statistical calculations task keeps track of the link performance. The total number of transmitted and received data blocks can be obtained with a "STAT" command.

The system monitoring and diagnostics task continuously monitors the state of the radio equipment. The reflected power from the antenna is monitored as well as the power supply voltage and states of the phase-locked oscillators. An alarm message is generated in case a device fault is detected.

Meteor Scatter Network - Planning and Implementation

The basic structure of a Meteor Scatter Network is a star. One station functions as a Central Station which can communicate with any of the other Remote Stations.

Typically a Central Station collects environmental data from the Remote Stations and sends back short messages to the Remote Stations if necessary. At a Central Station there usually is a computer with at least one serial line in use. The computer usually also processes the data, generates reports, etc. The data which are stored on floppy disks can also be processed elsewhere. A typical Central Station is presented in Figure 3.

A Remote Station may consist of the Telemetry Terminal itself and of an Automatic Weather Station as a host device. The weather station periodically measures environmental parameters and sends the data to the Telemetry Terminal which transmits it to the Central Data Collecting Station. The Central Station can also send instructions to the weather station if needed. The electric power at the Remote Station is usually generated with solar panels. A typical Remote Station is presented in Figure 4.

One Central Station can cover an area of 4000 km (2500 miles) of diameter. Practical beam width of the antenna is 60 degrees. If the Remote Stations are to be located more than 60 degrees apart, at least two separate antennas have to be used. An antenna switch also has to be used to select the antenna. The antenna mast height depends on the distance between stations. To achieve the maximum antenna gain in the optimum direction in 700 km communication distance the antenna height is 6 meters. If the distance is greater then the height is greater and vice versa.

Signal levels in Meteor Scatter telemetry are low. This is due to atmospheric attenuation and the attenuation in the reflecting meteor trail. The Meteor Scatter stations have to be located in an area with low noise level in 40-50 MHz band. The worst noise generators usually are power lines and ignition systems. Sensitivity to noise is not usually problem at a Remote Station, which often is naturally located in a quiet area. If a station for

FIG.3 Meteor Scatter central station.

this reason has to be located in an unconvenient location where the respective host device (computer etc.) cannot be located, the serial interface between the Telemetry Terminal and the host device can be lengthened using a telephone or radio modem.

Performance and Operational Experiences

The performance of a Meteor Scatter System can be characterized with the following two parameters. The first and most important is the average data rate. The second is the average wait time between successive data transmissions. Wait time expresses the system's smoothness in data transmissions i.e. does it transmit large amounts of data at a time with long delays between transmissions or does it transmit data frequently in small blocks. The latter case with shorter wait times is desirable.

The quality of the data has to be taken into consideration when judging system's performance. With the average data rate the bit or symbol error rate has to be expressed.

In the VAISALA Meteor Scatter System the average data rate is approximately 20 bits/second adding together the data rates in both (Central to Remote and Remote to Central) directions. The bit error ratio of this data is less than 1.6×10^{-5}. The average wait time is less than two minutes. These figures can be expressed with an example. A typical message generated by an Automatic Weather Station containing station number, time of day, date and twenty values of measured parameters with five-digit accuracy each can be transmitted to the Central Station in less than five minutes as an yearly

FIG.4 Meteor Scatter remote station.

average. Or, an average A4-sized paper with 2000 characters of text is transmitted in less than 20 minutes. Simultaneously, the same amount of data can be sent to the Remote Station.

Data collection networks using Meteor Scatter telemetry are in operation in the United Stations and in Europe. The first and most well-known is SNOTEL which is earlier described in this paper. It consists of two Central and 500 Remote Stations. Another network called the Alaskan Meteor Burst Communication System (AMBCS) is performing data acquisition and message communication applications in Alaska, U.S.A. Its Central Station is located in the city of Anchorage. In Europe there is one network for geological data acquisition and one system for message communication applications.

Several tests have been carried out to prove the operability of Meteor Scatter Telemetry. These tests, carried out in Finland, Indonesia and Latin

America, have demonstrated clearly that Meteor Scatter telemetry is a reliable means of communication from 70 degrees of north to 70 degrees of south latitudes.

Summary

The Meteor Scatter telemetry can be used to solve the telecommunication problems in many environmental data collection networks.

Advantages of the Meteor Scatter Telemetry are the following:

- The system is totally independent of the external agencies.
- No recurring satellite or other leased circuit fees have to be paid.
- Access to data is near real time.
- One Central Station can cover an area with 4000 km of diameter.
- The System cost is low in comparison with any other method of communication with similar coverage.
- Network formation is easy.
- All stations operate with one common frequency, the directivity of the meteor trail reflection implements natural multiplexing.
- Communication security is high due to the reflection geometrics and digitally coded messages.

As a limitation of this communication method can be mentioned the data rate, which is restricted by the short duration of meteor trails. However, this does not pose a problem in most applications where moderate data rate can be tolerated. Meteor Scatter telemetry system requires low noise level at the vicinity of the station. At a remote station the noise level is not usually a problem but a Central Station is often located near cities and other noise sources.

Applications of Meteor Scatter telemetry range today from conventional environmental data collection networks to message communication.

Reference

Chu, T.M., 1980, Evaluation of DCS III Transmission Alternatives - Phase IA Report., TRW Inc., Defense and Space Systems Group, Redondo Beach, p. 1044.

Hydrologic Applications of Space Technology (Proceedings of the Cocoa Beach Workshop, Florida, August 1985). IAHS Publ. no. 160, 1986.

Operational experiences in meteor burst telemetry — eight years of SNOTEL project observations

ARTHUR G. CROOK
Soil Conservation Service, Portland, Oregon, USA

Abstract

Communication over long distances using meteor trails has recently been applied to large scale data acquisition projects.

The U.S. Department of Agriculture Soil Conservation Service's SNOTEL meteor burst telemetry system consists of 510 sites located in high mountain areas of the Western United States.

The SNOTEL system consists of two master stations which initiate interrogation and receive data transmissions and forward their data to a central computer system. A typical SNOTEL remote data site is equipped with sensors which provide snowpack, rainfall, and temperature data.

Meteor burst communications are a reliable alternative to other types of telemetry. The SNOTEL system accurately senses and transmits data to a central facility. Data users can conveniently access the system.

Data from the SNOTEL meteor burst system are used operationally in snowmelt runoff forecasting and many other ways. The Soil Conservation Service is reducing its traditional manually measured snow course networks and placing increased reliance on SNOTEL data.

Introduction

Communication over long distances using meteor trails has been used for many years. The technique of using these trails for communication was discovered by ham radio operators who, under certain conditions, found themselves talking to someone halfway around the world. The principle gained widespread attention when radio contact with astronauts was temporarily lost during reentry. A shield of ionized gasses around the space capsule during time of reentry repelled the radio signals.

The U.S. Department of Agriculture Soil Conservation Service initiated a meteor burst telemetry system called SNOTEL in 1977. By late 1980, there were 475 sites operating. Currently, there are 510 sites located in high mountain areas of the Western United States. The SNOTEL system is the world's largest known application of this method of telemetry.

Meteor burst telemetry

Meteor burst technology takes advantage of the billions of meteorites that enter the Earth's atmosphere daily. These meteorites range in size from cosmic dust to rock. As each particle enters the Earth's atmosphere, it burns, producing an ionized trail of gasses in a zone 80 to 120 kilometers (50 to 80 miles) above the Earth's surface. (See figure 1.)

These trails diffuse rapidly, usually disappearing within seconds. During their brief existence, however, they will either reflect or reradiate radio signals, particularly those in the low end of the VHF range of 40 to 100 megahertz (MHz). The height of these trails allows radio communications from a transmitter to be received as far as 1,920 kilometers (1,200 miles) from the source (Leader, 1974) and also either eliminates or substantially reduces the adverse effects of local terrain obstacles.

Meteors--defined as extraterrestrial objects in elliptical orbit around the sun--are divided into two classes: shower and sporadic. Shower

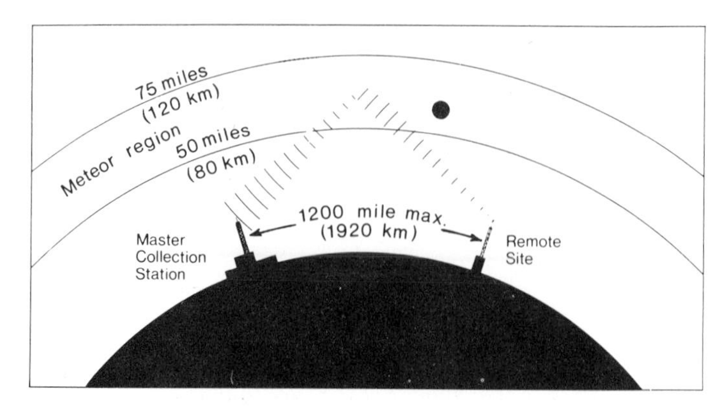

FIG.1 Meteor burst data acquisition system.

meteors are groups of particles all moving with the same velocity in well-defined orbits around the sun. They enter the atmosphere in spectacular fashion and appear to observers on Earth to be radiating from a common point in the sky. Sporadic meteors move in random orbits around the sun. Most meteors used in radio work are in this class. Although their random entry points make them less predictable than shower meteors, certain characteristics are known. Intersection of their orbits with the Earth's orbit is most frequent in August and least frequent in February, at a ratio of about 4:1 due to the tilt of Earth's axis. The forward motion of the Earth sweeps about four times more meteors into the atmosphere in the morning than during the evening, resulting in a significant diurnal variation in available meteor trails. (See figure 2.)

The ionized trail of gasses is composed of positively charged ions and free electrons. The electrons reflect or reradiate the radio waves,

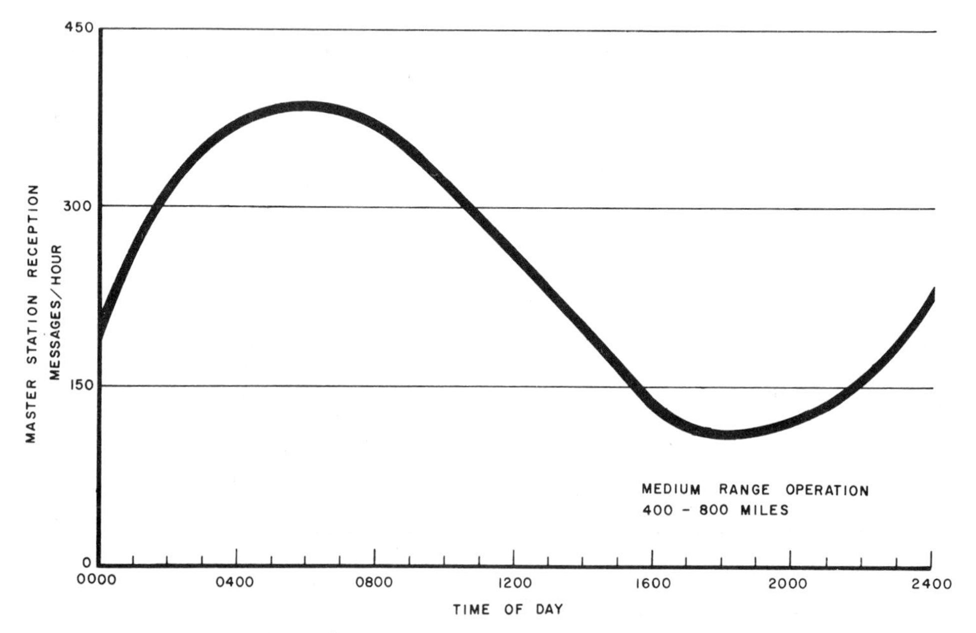

FIG.2 Diurnal data rate variation in meteor burst communication.

depending on the density of the trail. Typical trails are about 25 kilometers (15.5 miles) long with a radius of about 1 meter (40 inches). Low electron line densities (underdense trails) result in reradiation of the radio signal. Overdense trails reflect the radio signal. Signals from underdense trails rise to an initial peak volume in a few hundred microseconds, then typically decay within from a few milliseconds to a few seconds.

Other ways in which the meteor burst principle can be used to communicate include reflection of the radio signals off of objects such as airplanes at distances of less than 160 kilometers (100 miles). These reflections usually last several seconds and are characterized by a great deal of signal fading. The E region, from 100 to 125 km above the Earth's surface, provides long periods of communication time. However, the sporadic nature of the E region limits its usefulness.

Communication over an operating range of up to 1920 km (1200 miles) is possible. Sites in close proximity to each other can be reached via line of site radio signals, or ground wave. Curvature of the Earth and terrain features generally limit this type of communication to about 160 km (100 miles), although ground wave has been observed to extend up to 240 km (150 miles) from the transmitting station to the receiving location. Beyond the ground wave signal, the number of messages per unit of time that can be expected is a function of the amount of sky that can geometrically reflect signals from the master to the remote site. This is referred to as "common sky." The common sky is less at closer distances, increases to its maximum in the range of 800 to 1,280 km (500-800 miles), and then reduces with distances beyond 1,280 km (800 miles). (See figure 3.)

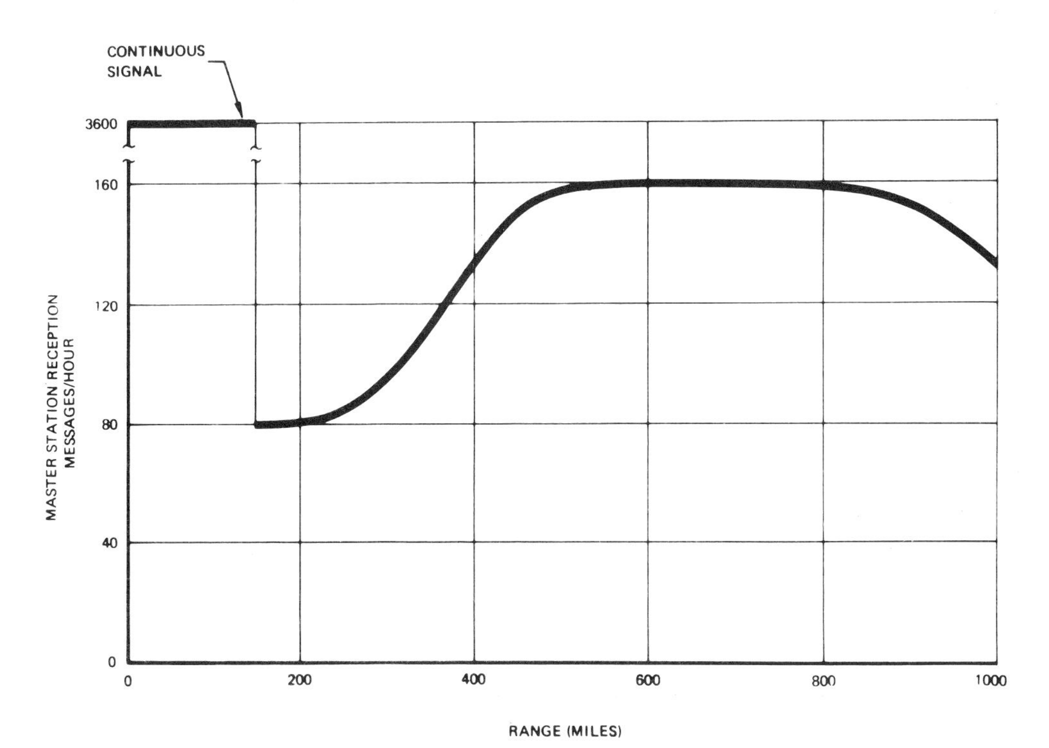

FIG.3 Relationship between meteor burst communication rate and range in distance between master and remote.

It was not until the advent of microprocessor based communication equipment that the meteor burst technique became useful in large scale data transmission projects. Prior to the age of rapid computer processing, requirements of such a system could not be satisfied by manual operators.

SNOTEL

SNOTEL has been in operation in the Western United States since 1977, when the first remote site data were telemetered via very high frequency (VHF) radio using meteor burst technology. This system's primary function is to sense and transmit hydrometerological data from remote mountainous sites to the central data collection station in Portland, Oregon.

By October 1980, 475 sites had been completed and the network was fully operational. Since then, 35 more sites have been added, bringing the total operational sites to 510.

The SNOTEL system is composed of two types of stations: remote data acquisition sites, and master stations--one near Boise, Idaho, and the other near Ogden, Utah. The entire network of remote sites is within communication range of each master station. Using two master stations enhances system performance and substantially reduces communication failures resulting from problems at the master stations.

An optimum SNOTEL remote site is situated in a small clearing in the timbered high mountains. The surrounding forest canopy provides a sheltering of the catchment area. Therefore, snow accumulates uniformly, and precipitation falls in a nearly vertical path for optimum gage catch. The site is also sheltered from winds, thus minimizing transport of the snowpack either onto or away from the measurement area. The site aspect is typically flat to north facing, minimizing solar radiation effects on the snow. The slope is gentle, allowing for free water drainage, but not steep enough to permit snow creep. Stainless steel "pillows," about 3 cm (1.2 inches) thick and 1.8 m^2 (20 ft^2) in surface area, are used to hydraulically sense the weight of the snowpack. Pillows are normally placed in configurations of 3 or 4 units which are connected together to function as a single weighing platform. Precipitation is collected in a 30.5 cm (12 inch) diameter cylinder. The height of the gage is a function of the annual amount of rainfall expected, as well as of the depth of the winter snowpack. Both the water equivalent of the snowpack and the amount of accumulated precipitation are measured by pressure transducers. Air temperature is also sensed at the site. An analog signal is relayed from the transducers, converted to digital format, and forwarded to a storage buffer within the communications unit every 15 minutes. Data are then transmitted to a master station upon receipt of a valid probe.

All sites in the network are interrogated once daily during a 3-hour period from 0500 to 0800, Pacific Standard Time. Additional polls can be conducted on either a scheduled or ad hoc basis, depending on data needs. Newer models of remote site electronics have microprocessors capable of acquiring additional data. These upgraded sites can be programmed to store and report several observations per day, such as total 24-hour wind run, maximum, minimum, and average wind speed and temperature during a 24-hour period, and other predefined functions.

Another recently implemented feature of the new models is the daily transmission of data regarding the operational characteristics of the site. Such diagnostic parameters as signals received, transmissions, master station acknowledgment received, battery voltage under load, and transmit forward and reverse power are now available to field maintenance technicians. Using this information, the technician can detect operational problems and perform repairs prior to failure of the site.

The SNOTEL system was designed to provide maximum control and flexibility to the operational offices. Data are collected at the master stations in response to either scheduled or unscheduled polls. On a set fifteen minute cycle, all data are forwarded to a central computer facility in Portland, Oregon. The data are filed and kept on line and available for up to 14 months. This allows access to the current water year's (October 1 through September 30) data plus two months. The five Soil Conservation Service offices charged with responsibility for remote site operations and data quality are able to readily access the central system via remote computer terminal. They examine the "raw" data, make editing adjustments, and perform analyses. Other agencies and organizations which require SNOTEL data for their operations may also gain access via terminal.

At the conclusion of the current water year, the data are subjected to a final examination, and editing is performed to assure that the final record diverges no more than $\pm$ 10 percent from the onsite "true" value. When this process is completed, the data are placed in an archival data base at the U.S. Department of Agriculture's computer facility in Fort Collins, Colorado.

Data Reliability

The performance of the SNOTEL system is evaluated based on three criteria: The first criterion relates to the consistency with which data are received from all sites during the regularly scheduled, or nominal poll. The goal is to acquire data from at least 90 percent of the sites. See table 1 for a summary of nominal poll performance. Hardware and software failure accounts for virtually all performance problems, with very little failure attributable to lack of adequate meteor bursts. The reader will note a marked improvement in system performance during mid-1985. This improvement is attributed to two factors. First is continued improvements in field servicing. Both the quality of service equipment and the skill of the field technicians continues to improve. Second is improvement in software designed to conduct master station to central computer communications and to process the data. The inevitable bad data files, which must be anticipated to occur occasionally, are now being processed using improved data recovery techiques, thus salvaging some data reports that previously would have been lost and treated statistically as non-reporting sites.

Table 1. Systemwide response to nominal polls
Monthly average percentage of sites reporting

	Daily nominal polls				
	1981	1982	1983	1984	1985
January	--	81.6	89.3	79.2	88.4
February	74.1	78.8	88.2	82.5	87.5
March	80.2	83.8	91.1	85.4	91.5
April	82.5	85.6	90.0	87.5	93.4
May	82.7	90.4	89.5	90.5	96.1
June	80.4	89.2	91.6	90.8	96.5
July	81.7	88.8	90.9	89.4	
August	84.1	86.6	89.4	90.1	
September	--	87.7	88.9	89.9	
October	85.7	89.7	90.2	89.3	
November	86.0	88.7	86.5	90.7	
December	85.5	87.2	80.6	89.5	

The second criterion is the diurnal stability of data. Sensors and electronic communication equipment are maintained to keep diurnal change at, or less than, 0.3 percent of full scale capacity of the sensor, i.e., 7.6 mm (0.3 inch) in a 2,540-mm (100 inch) device. A majority of the data channels meet this standard of acceptability, as table 2 illustrates. The targeted minimum percentage of data channels meeting this criterion is 80 percent. The sensitivity of electronic and mechanical components to temperature changes is illustrated by the more stable diurnal fluctuations in the winter months when snowpacks insulate equipment and daily temperature ranges are small. During the summer when equipment is exposed to large daily temperature ranges, data channels fluctuate more widely.

Table 2. Diurnal fluctuation of data channels

	Percentage of channels with 0.3 percent or less diurnal fluctuation				
Month	1981	1982	1983	1984	1985
February	80.4	85.4	90.9	84.7	90.4
June	80.0	67.6	74.1	75.0	73.5
October	80.4	75.6		92.0	

The third criterion sets the required accuracy of sensors and data transmission. Data stored at the central computer facility should be within 10 percent of actual onsite conditions. Conditions are measured periodically by survey crews and these measurements are compared with telemetered data. If SNOTEL data are outside the ± 10 percent limits, those data are edited and brought into conformance with the observed values. The predominance of data errors appear to be caused by system component malfunctions, with a lesser percent attributable to sensor problems.

Snow pressure pillows tend to systematically overweigh the accumulated snowpack, as reported by Smith and Boyne (1981). The magnitude of measurement error is dependent primarily on snowpack physical properties. Ice lenses can cause temporary over or under weight, lasting from a few hours to a few days. A well located, properly installed pillow system should be expected to yield data which are no more than about 5 percent greater than actual or true values as determined by excavation and weighing of the snowpack on the pillow surface. This systematic overweight is generally equivalent to the systematic bias in the commonly used Federal snow sampler. Thus, measurements by both techniques should be equal (Work, et. al, 1965).

In a critical test of 5 years of SNOTEL performance, Schaefer and Shafer (1982) studied telemetry and sensor performance in the Colorado-New Mexico part of the system. They concluded that there was no appreciable systematic error, that is, observed and telemetered values were equivalent. In their study random error resulted in an average expected difference of about ± 1.25 centimeters (0.5 inch) between observed and telemetered data. They compared data gathered by snow survey teams using standard Federal snow samplers to telemetered snow-water data and found a nearly 1:1 correspondence in arrays of four metal pillows and about a 5 percent systematic overweigh in three-pillow systems.

Using SNOTEL data in streamflow forecasting

SNOTEL data are retrieved by computer terminal for a wide variety of uses. The principal use by the Soil Conservation Service is in forecasting snowmelt season volumes, and hydrograph recession on snowmelt streams. These forecasts are generated primarily for irrigation water management and reservoir operations.

Much of the justification for the existence of the SNOTEL system and the resultant streamflow forecast is based on recurrent drought in the Western United States. The most recent severe drought occurred in 1977. Streamflow forecasts were widely used to optimize the use of all the region's available water. The severity of any drought needs to be judged objectively so that mitigating water management actions can be taken. The recently developed Surface Water Supply Index (SWSI), described by Shafer and Dezman (1982), is a method of evaluating the severity of water supply problems, using SNOTEL data, streamflow forecasts, and reservoir storage data.

SNOTEL data are used operationally in streamflow forecasting by SCS in three ways. The first use is in physical process modelling of streamflow. SNOTEL derived snowpack, precipitation, and air temperature data are being input as parameters in hydrologic basin models. Selected forecast points are currently being calibrated and tested. Output from these models includes peak flow, time of peak, recession characteristics, low flow, seasonal volume, and other hydrograph features. More widespread use of these models is anticipated in 1986 as additional forecast points are calibrated.

Secondly, SNOTEL data are being used to improve the accuracy of the snowpack variable in regression forecasting procedures. Traditional regression procedures have used the first of the month snow course data as one of the most significant independent variables. A problem arises when the maximum seasonal accumulation of snow occurs at the snow course between the scheduled measurements. This situation is presumed to occur commonly between April 1 and May 1, but prior to the availability of daily SNOTEL data, could not be confirmed and quantified. Now with SNOTEL, the forecasting hydrologist can make the needed adjustment to the first of the month measurement, thus improving the resultant forecast reliability. A variation of this theme is the revision of snowpack data based on SNOTEL observations and recalculation of forecast values when major short duration storms are detected over the watersheds catchment area.

The third way that SNOTEL data are being used operationally is in substituting SNOTEL data for manually observed snow course data. This procedure requires a correlation of SNOTEL and snow course data. A regression equation is then used to estimate snow course values from SNOTEL reports. These estimates are used in lieu of measured snow course data in the existing regression procedures to forecast streamflow volumes. This method is being used extensively by the SCS pending the accumulation of sufficient data history that SNOTEL data can be used directly in multiple regression analyses.

Conclusions

Although meteor burst communications has been a useful technique for many years, it was not until the advent of high speed computer processing that the technology became a viable data telemetry option. In 1977, the SCS began installation of what became the world's largest known meteor burst telemetry system--a project called SNOTEL.

Eight years experience with SNOTEL leads to the following conclusions. Data can be collected in a highly reliable and accurate fashion using meteor burst technology. An analysis of the system performance has shown that the required 90 percent of all sites can be expected to respond to scheduled polls. Diurnal fluctuation of the data is generally less than or equal to 0.3 percent of the sensor's full scale capacity. Data transmitted by SNOTEL can be expected to vary no more than 10 percent from the actual value.

Data from the SNOTEL meteor burst system are used operationally in a variety of ways. Snowmelt runoff in Western U.S. streams is routinely forecast, irrigation applications are being scheduled, and critical water supply shortages have been evaluated and contingency plans formulated. The Soil Conservation Service is reducing its traditional manually measured snow course networks and placing increased reliance on SNOTEL data.

References

Leader, Ray E. 1974. Meteor Burst Communications. Proceedings of the 42nd Western Snow Conference, p. 29-36.

Schaefer, Garry L. and Bernard A. Shafer, 1983. A Critical Analysis of Five Years of SNOTEL Performance in the Rocky Mountains. Proceedings of the International Symposium on Hydrometeorology, Denver, Colorado, Amer. Water Resources Assoc., p. 31-37.

Shafer, B.A. and L.E. Dezman 1982. Development of a Surface Water Supply Index (SWSI) to Assess the Severity of Drought Conditions in Snowpack Runoff Areas. Proceedings of the 50th Western Snow Conference, p. 164-175.

Smith, F.W. and H.S. Boyne 1981. Snow Pillow System Behavior for SNOTEL Application. Colorado State University unpublished report to the Soil Conservation Service.

Work, R.A., H.J. Stockwell, T. G. Freeman, and R. T. Beaumont, 1965. Accuracy of Field Snow Surveys in the Western United States, Including Alaska, CRREL Technical Report 163, 43 p.

Hydrologic Applications of Space Technology (Proceedings of the Cocoa Beach Workshop, Florida, August 1985). IAHS Publ. no. 160, 1986.

On merging satellite and meteor burst communications with real-time event reporting technologies

DAVID C. CURTIS
International Hydrological Services
Bloomfield, CT 06002, USA

Abstract
Automated environmental data collection systems are being implemented for a variety of purposes at locations around the world. VHF/UHF radio, geostationary satellite, polar orbiting satellite, and meteor burst telemetry systems are commonly used to transport data. Each system has characteristics that define its relative scale of operation. VHF/UHF systems tend to be local, meteor burst systems tend to be regional, and satellite systems can range from regional to global in scale.

This paper briefly discusses each telemetry type and how it is normally used. Also a configuration is discussed that allows efficient interfaces between telemetry systems, particularly when merging local automated systems with systems operating on larger scales.

1.0 Introduction

Real-time event reporting technology has enabled the development of very cost-effective environmental data collection and monitoring systems. Such systems have been implemented in projects around the world for flood warning, water supply, irrigation, and reservoir operation applications. Real-time event reporting systems have proven to be especially effective in monitoring rapidly changing environmental conditions such as flash flooding since data reporting rates are directly proportional to the intensity of the monitored event.

These systems commonly use VHF or UHF radio communications between remote sensor sites and the central data collection site. However, radio communication at these frequencies is generally line-of-sight which has limited the systems to local or sub-regional scales.

Data communications in real-time event reporting systems have been designed to serve the local user first on the assumption that, in time-critical situations, the local user has the greatest need for information to support local decision-making. However, this may not solve the need for data in an appropriate time frame from these systems at the regional and national levels where professional analysts are often located.

To handle regional and national data communications needs, satellite or meteor burst systems are often employed. Unfortunately, these systems often preclude real-time data reception at local levels due to the high cost of the data receiving equipment. Local communities must then rely on a secondary and often less reliable communication links to monitor developing storm conditions.

This paper presents an approach that merges real-time event reporting systems with either satellite or meteor burst technologies to provide both local data reception in real-time and timely data communications for regional and national purposes. The approach discussed is cost-efficient, simple, and, at least conceptually, relatively independent of equipment type. Satellite techniques could be employed where reliable satellite links are available and meteor burst techniques could be used where satellite links are economically or politically infeasible.

The following sections briefly review four data telemetry methods - namely VHF/UHF line-of-sight, geostationary satellite, polar orbiting satellite, and meteor burst. Next a network configuration will be discussed that can easily serve both local and regional/national interests.

2.0 Data telemetry systems

2.1 VHF/UHF Radio-- VHF/UHF radio communications for data telemetry are primarily land-based systems. At frequencies in the VHF/UHF bands, the communication path between transmitter and the receiver must be line-of-sight. In other words, the receiving site must literally see the transmitting site. If not, reliable communication cannot occur.

Where line-of-sight radio paths do not exist, it is still possible to communicate between two sites through intermediate radio repeaters. A repeater would receive radio signals from a remote site along one line-of-sight path and retransmit those signals to the target receiving site along a second line-of-sight radio path. (See Figure 1)

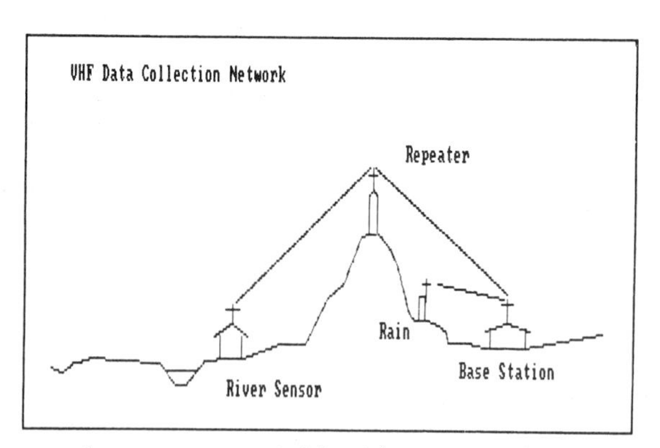

FIG.1 VHF Data Collection Network.

Limiting data telemetry to line-of-sight radio paths and to terrestrial repeater sites can make data communication over large areas difficult. As the areal extent of a VHF/UHF system expands, the number of repeaters required to enable communication can become excessive. Multiple repeaters linked in series make communication with significant portions of the network vulnerable to the failure of any one of the repeaters. Thus VHF/UHF systems have most often been used in local or sub-regional applications.

One of the great advantages of VHF/UHF radio telemetry systems is that the user normally owns the entire system and doesn't have to share system resources with anyone else. This allows the user to totally control the way information is transmitted on the telemetry network. Such flexibility allows the user to take advantage of transmission protocols, data sampling rates, transmission schedules, etc. to precisely meet the needs of individual applications.

For example, a rapidly growing number of communities are implementing automated data collection systems to aid their response to flash flooding. With VHF/UHF radio, these communities can take advantage "event-reporting" technologies to maximize available response time.

Event-reporting systems self-initiate a radio message when a monitored variable changes status. In the case of rainfall, change of status could be defined as the measurement of an additional increment of rainfall (e.g. one millimeter). The beauty of an event-reporting system is that the system responds at a rate that is directly proportional to the intensity of the storm. During fair weather no rain is accumulating and the status of the rain gage remains unchanged. When rain begins, the status of the rain gage changes when one millimeter of rainfall has been measured and a radio message to that effect is transmitted. During heavy rainfall, rain gage status is changing rapidly and radio transmissions are generated frequently. Event reporting exactly identifies the high intensity portions of storms that are so critical to time-sensitive situations such as the potential development of flash flooding.

In summary, VHF and UHF radio telemetry systems offer excellent responsiveness due to total user control of transmission protocol and due to the normally constant real-time availability of the network resources. Line-of-sight requirements for radio communication pathways, however, restrict the application of VHF/UHF systems to local or sub-regional scales.

As long as the data needs are local in nature, the limitations placed on the scale of application for VHF/UHF systems are not a problem. However, if there is a need to retrieve data from wide areas (regionally or nationally) in a timely fashion, other transmission methods are often employed.

2.2 Geostationary Satellite-- In many large scale data collection applications, it is necessary to forego land-based radio repeaters in favor of repeaters on board earth satellite platforms. Located at altitudes high above the earth's surface, satellite based radio repeaters dramatically expand potential areas of communication.

Geostationary satellites orbit the earth at an altitude of approximately 35,600 km (Bras et.al. 1982). At this altitude, the satellite's orbit is synchronized with the rotation of the earth and the satellite appears to remain at a fixed point above the earth's surface.

Radio repeaters on board geostationary satellites enable communications over vast areas. For example, one satellite located above the equator at 105 degress west longitude can cover an area extending east-west from the mid-Atlantic to the mid-Pacific and north-south from the arctic fringe to Antarctica. (MacCallum and Nestlebush, 1983) In other words, all of the North and South American Continents except for the western edge of Alaska could communicate through one geostationary satellite.

Data can be retrieved from almost anywhere within view of a geostationary satellite. Large scale data acquistion such as from major river basins like the Mississippi or the Amazon Rivers is made possible by satellite relay. Low power data collection platforms can be placed in very remote areas. Data are periodically beamed to the satellite and retransmitted to the appropriate ground station.(See Figure 2)

Geostationary satellites offer a tremendous asset in wide areal coverage. However, such wide areal coverage generates a large set of potential users and the satellite is a limited resource. The U.S. operated GOES (Geostationary Operational Environmental Satellite) data collection system maintains space craft with 200 domestic channels and 33 international channels each. (MacCallum and Nestlebush, 1983) The domestic portion is capable of handling only 12,000 messages per hour. This works out to 60 windows per hour over the 200 channels (60 x 200 = 12,000).

To control the usage of satellite and ground station resources, tight controls are imposed on the scheduling of data transmissions to and from the DCP's. Normally data are transmitted from each DCP through its assigned one minute window once every three hours.

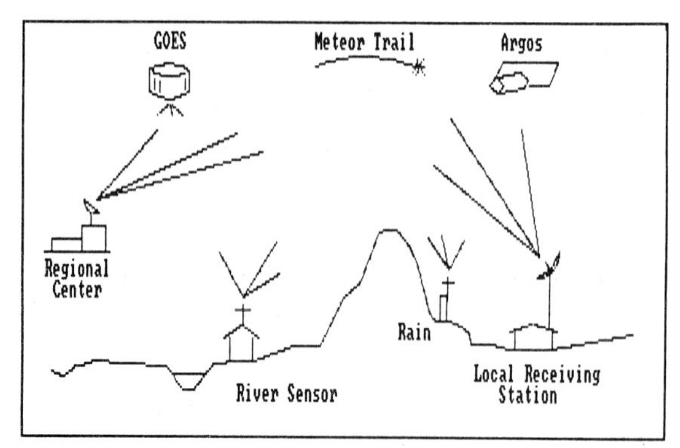

FIG.2 GOES, Meteor Burst and Argos Data Collection systems.

Three hour data collection intervals are adequate for many applications but for some time-sensitive applications three hour intervals may not be sufficient. In those cases where shorter intervals are required periodically, some DCP's can switch to a secondary channel and transmit in an accelerated mode. Usually some criterion is set for a monitored variable such that normal three hour transmissions occur when the sensor value is below the criterion. When the monitored variable rises above the preset criterion, transmission is initiated on the secondary channel with reporting intervals calculated to more accurately reflect rapidly changing field conditions.

Although the introduction of the accelerated reporting mode for DCP's makes the satellite data collection system more responsive to rapidly changing field conditions, the cost of the satellite ground station still prohibits wide spread use at the local level. As a result satellite ground stations are normally maintained at regional or national centers. Local users must then rely on secondary communication channels (telephone, microwave, etc.) to obtain the necessary data. Reliance on secondary communications links may negate the system response gains afforded by the accelerated data reporting mode.

2.3 Polar Orbiting Satellite-- Not all areas of the globe have access to operational geostationary satellites. Even in areas with access to geostationary satellite systems, political, economic, and technical issues may preclude their use. Polar orbiting satellites offer another alternative.

The United States and France jointly administer the Argos Data Collection System which includes two satellites of the Tiros-N series in polar orbit. These satellites orbit at low altitude (approximately 850 km.) and each takes about 101 minutes to complete one near circular orbit. (Service Argos, 1984)

As the satellite passes over a data collection platform, the data message is transmitted to the satellite for on-board storage. When the satellite passes over the appropriate ground station, the stored data is retransmitted down to the ground station. (See Figure 2) Thus, data can be acquired from platforms located anywhere on the globe.

Data retrieval schedules are governed by the location of the data collection platform. Platforms located near the North and South Polar regions will "see" each satellite once every orbit. Since each satellite makes 14 orbits per day, platforms near the poles will be in satellite contact 28 times daily. Near the equator, platforms will only see 6 to 8 satellite passages per day.

Due to slight differences in orbital parameters between the two satellites, the time between successive satellite passes over a particular data collection platform is variable. The irregular data retrieval schedule makes real-time and other time-sensitive applications difficult. For example, at latitudes of approximately 30 degrees North or South platforms are serviced 8 to 12 times per day by the satellite. However, the irregularity in the timing of the satellite passes means that successive satellite passes could be as long as 7 hours apart. If only one of the two satellites was operational, successive passes could be as many as 11 hours apart.

2.4 Meteor Burst Communication -- Meteor burst communication employs an interesting technology that permits data collection at regional scales of operation. In addition, the regional scale operation can be totally independent of equipment operated by outside or foreign interests.

Meteor burst technology uses the properties of trails left in the atmosphere by meteors. Every day billions of meteors ranging in size from a few microns to a few centimeters in diameter enter the earth's atmosphere. These pieces of cosmic dust collide with the atmosphere at speeds of 10 to 75 kilometers per second. The meteors slow due to the friction of the atmosphere and their kinetic energy is transformed into heat. As the meteors vaporize, trails of positive charged-ions and free electrons are left behind. (Day, 1982) These trials are short-lived with only the most dense trails lasting as long as a few seconds. Most of the useful meteor trails occur in the region 85-115 km above the earth.

Meteor trails have a very important property. When a radio signal of the appropriate frequency is directed to them, meteor trails can reflect or re-radiate the incident signal. To communicate with remote data collection platforms, a master station continuously scans the skies for useful meteor trails. When a trail occurs at the correct location, the signal from the master station is re-directed downward to the remote data collection platform. The DCP responds immediately by transmitting its data by the reverse pathway before the meteor trail becomes too weak to sustain radio communication. Using this technique, a single master station can retrieve data from platforms from up to 2000 km away.

Total data throughput for a meteor burst telemetry system depends on how often usable meteor trails become available. Usually the waiting times for usable trails are on the order of a few seconds or minutes. Typically a 30 character message will have a waiting time of 90 seconds or less 95 percent of the time. (Sytsma, 1982)

Short messages can be transmitted on a single trail while longer messages can be pulsed through as usable trails become available. Typical meteor burst systems are expected to average better than 100 words per minute of data throughput around the clock and throughout the year. (Morgan, 1983)

3.0 Meeting Data Needs at Multiple Scales of Interest

Quite frequently, data collection networks are designed to meet the parochial interests of a single agency. A flood prone community may choose a real-time event reporting VHF radio communication system to meet its time sensitive needs at the local level. At the same time, a regional agency operating a large flood control structure may choose a satellite based system to gain wide areal coverage; perhaps including the area covered by the local real-time VHF network.

Unfortunately the above example is not a rare case. Furthermore, experience suggests that the data sets are rarely shared and most certainly not shared in real-time. VHF telemetered sensors and satellite telemetered sensors may even cover the same area which amounts to an inefficient duplication of resources.

Other data transportation problems can occur within a single agency that has responsibilities at different levels. For instance, a meteorological forecasting agency requires local real-time data at field offices to support the its community warning function. Similarly, a regional or national office specializing in severe weather analysis may need the same data to support broader areal forecast and warning objectives. Often neither office has reliable convenient access to the real-time data even when the community data collection system is within the forecast offices areas of responsibility. Valuable information about rapidly changing storm conditions may remain at the local level - lying out-of-reach from regional forecasters.

The basic problem is one of scale. It makes sense for a local community to use a VHF radio system to satisfy a real-time reporting need. It also makes sense for an agency with regional or national interests to use a satellite or meteor burst system to meet its needs. However, where these systems co-exist, it seems imperative that the local real-time data should be elevated to help support broader regional and national data needs in a timely fashion as well.

Currently, the only way local data is elevated to higher levels (beyond practical distances afforded by a series of VHF/UHF repeaters) is through telephone or microwave links. Reliability issues during severe weather for telephone, and the costs associated with microwave networks have limited their application.

Ideally, the best solution would be to somehow merge locally-based real-time systems with larger scale systems like satellite or meteor burst. Unfortunately, the transmission protocols of these systems are all incompatible with one another. However, there may be a way to solve this problem in a cost effective way that is relatively independent of the data collection system configuration.

Each local real-time data collection system normally has a mini or microcomputer as the primary data collection, management, analysis, and display device. All the data in the system is concentrated at this point and is available in real-time. Why not put an interface to the regional/national data collection system at the local data concentration point? For example, one or more data up-links could be attached to the local computer to periodically transmit through satellite or meteor burst to a regional data collection center. (See Figure 3) In addition to its local functions, the computer would translate the data from the real-time format to the format required by the up-links.

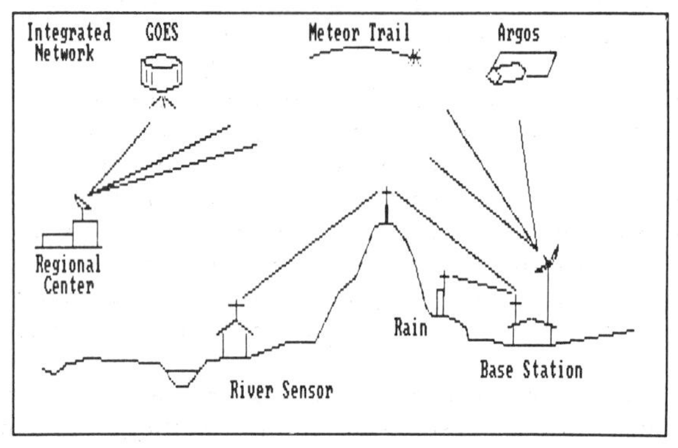

FIG.3 Integrated networks.

Using this simple approach to merge data acquisition systems, local users get their data in real-time and regional users get timely data from the same group of sensors at a cost of just one or two up-links. Both users would reliably get the data in time to support their individual needs. In addition, by concentrating the data before being up-linked, satellite resources in particular are much more efficiently used.

Consider a VHF real-time network with 100 different raingage sites. To collect these data by satellite, 100 different DCP's would normally be required. Each DCP would require its own one minute window every three hours to transmit data for a total satellite usage of 100 minutes every three hours.

To see how much information could be transmitted through a concentration point DCP, the satellite communication capacity must be reviewed. Data is transmitted through the U.S. operated GOES satellites at 100 bps (bits per second). The transmission window is 60 seconds long but only about 50 seconds should be considered usable due to drift in timing mechanisms etc. A total of 5000 bits (50 sec x 100 bps) could be transmitted during the 50 second interval. The transmission of one character of information requires 10 bits which limits data messages through the 50 second window to 500 characters. Assuming that say 50 characters are used for message overhead (date, time, station identification, etc.) 450 characters of capacity remain to carry data.

Rainfall accumulation in millimeters for a three hour period could be easily described using three characters. The information may be more valuable if it were described in three hourly increments which would require a total of nine characters. Thus, one DCP could be used to transmit the hourly rainfall totals for 50 sensors once every three hours. For the example of a 100 raingage system, a minimum of two DCP's would be required but three DCP's would probably be used to allow for expansion. Now instead of 100 minutes of satellite time required to obtain data from these 100 raingages, only 3 satellite minutes are required every three hours.

The responsiveness of the satellite portion of the merged system can be further enhanced in the 100 raingage example with no impact on satellite data collection system resources. From a system resource point of view, there is little difference between three DCP's each reporting through its own one minute window once every three hours and one DCP reporting once per hour during the same three hour period. Both situations consume three minutes of satellite time.

In the example above, three characters could describe one hourly rainfall total. Thus, 300 characters would be required for 100 hourly rainfall totals. Since a 450 character message capacity exists for each DCP, only one DCP would be required to transmit rainfall data each hour for this example. Total satellite resource time would remain at three minutes for each three hour interval but the timeliness of the acquired data would improve due to more frequent reporting.

To improve the reliability of satellite message throughput, messages are sometimes repeated during the one minute transmission window. If this procedure were followed in the above example, the amount of data that can be handled by a single DCP would drop accordingly. If two messages were sent, perhaps only 40-45 sensor data values could be handled. If three messages were sent, perhaps only 20-25 sensor data values could be transmitted per DCP. In any case, the data can be transmitted to a regional or national facility in a timely fashion with a minimum use of satellite resources.

The example merged data collection system described above focused on a combination of VHF and geostationary satellite telemetry systems. The same idea can be applied to polar orbiting satellite and meteor burst combinations as well.

Merging data telemetry systems at the concentration points can be done quite easily with existing off-the-shelf hardware. Many DCP's currently have the capability to accept input through an RS-232-C serial communications port and the required memory to store information until transmission time. All that has to be done is to connect the RS-232-C output port on the local computer to the DCP and have the computer automatically update the DCP at the required times.

4.0 Summary

Four types of data telemetry techniques in common use have been presented and their important characterisitics were briefly reviewed. The rapid growth in the expansion of existing data systems and the deployment of new systems is creating situations were multiple scales of data needs in the same region are being meet by different data collection techniques.

An example was given showing how a VHF and a satellite network could be merged. Data from a local network can be acquired by a regional center through a satellite up-link at the local data concentration point. Data retrieval can be achieved in a timely fashion with minimum number of DCP's.

The VHF/satellite network combination is just one example combination. Other configurations could easily arranged using VHF, geostationary satellite, polar orbiting satellite, and meteor burst telemetry systems. By judiciously combining systems, inaccessible data and sensor duplication can be avoided.

5.0 References

Bras, Rafael L.; Donald Grossman; David Schafer, A Methodology for Analyzing the Effect of Hydrometeorology of the Contiguous United States on the GOES Random Data Collection System, Final Report - Contract Number DACW33-82-C-0011, U.S. Army Corps of Engineers, Waltham, MA, Aug 1982.

Day, Willis E., "Meteor Burst Communications Bounce Signals Between Remote Areas",Electronics, International Edition, McGraw-Hill, Inc., Dec 29, 1982.

MacCallum, Douglas H.; Michael J. Nestlebush,The Geostationary Operational Environmental Data Collection System, NOAA Technical Memorandum NESDIS 2, Washington, D.C., June 1983.

Morgan, Edward J.,"The Resurgence of Meteor Burst",Signal Magazine, June 1983.

Service Argos, Location and Data Collection Satellite System User's Guide, Toulouse, France, 1984.

Sytsma, Donald, "Meteor Burst Data Transmission Practical for Remote Locations",Resource Development, Spring 1982.

8 Geographic information systems

Hydrologic Applications of Space Technology (Proceedings of the Cocoa Beach Workshop, Florida, August 1985). IAHS Publ. no. 160, 1986.

The development of a component of NASA's Pilot Land Data System to support hydrological research

R. D. PRICE
Laboratory for Terrestrial Physics, Goddard Space Flight Center, Greenbelt, Maryland, USA
R. M. RAGAN
Remote Sensing Systems Laboratory, Department of Civil Engineering, University of Maryland, College Park, Maryland, USA

Abstract

The Pilot Land Data System (PLDS), a state-of-the-art data system under development by NASA's Goddard Space Flight Center (GSFC) to support land sciences research, contains a hydrology-oriented component. The PLDS hydrology component provides access to extensive data sets and computing tools of interest to the hydrological sciences research and applications community. Specifically, this component has the capability: to store satellite-, aircraft-, and ground-acquired data; to remotely access this data and information about the data; and to transmit the data to distant geographical locations. Additionally this component offers access to image data analysis tools, hydrological models, and intensive computing systems.

NASA expects to make the PLDS-Hydrology component initially available in 1986 to researchers participating in the International Satellite Land Surface Climatology Project, the science project selected to drive the PLDS concept and design. One of the objectives of this research project is to investigate the effects of soil moisture, evapotranspiration, heat flux, and other portions of the hydrologic cycle on climate.

During the first year, the following developmental activities are being undertaken. An online data base is being established of Landsat Thematic Mapper, NOAA-7 Advanced Very High Resolution Radiometer, and NIMBUS-7 Scanning Multifrequency Microwave Radiometer satellite data taken of the mid- and southwestern portions of the U.S. from 1978 to the present. Weather station data on parameters such as temperature, humidity, wind speed, etc. covering the same time period for the same geographical area are also being entered into the data base. A data base management system utilizing a natural language query structure is being developed to catalog, describe, store, and retrieve these data of relevance to hydrology research. A very high speed (1.5mb/s) optical fiber data transmission link interconnecting two VAX mini-computers in two different buildings at GSFC which house the PLDS hardware and the hydrology researchers respectively, is being installed. A high speed communications link is also being implemented between the PLDS at GSFC and the University of Maryland's Remote Sensing Systems Lab which is participating in both the PLDS development, and hydrology research and applications in water runoff and streamflow modeling. Through a computer networking scheme, the PLDS will offer access to a comprehensive and sophisticated image data analysis software package called the Land Analysis System (LAS), and to a unique NASA developed supercomputer called the Massively Parallel Processor on which is being implemented a "parallelized" hill slope model for very high speed calculation of runoff in a watershed basin.

Future developmental efforts to complete the prototype system include: the installation of capability for geographic data entry; the development of software for front end data processing such as reformatting and registration algorithms, and the connection of the PLDS to other investigators' facilities participating in the demonstration research project, and to other selected data bases necessary for the success of that research.

Introduction

NASA research in the land sciences is entering an era of attacking large-physical-scale, long-temporal-scale problems that require teams of scientists from many disciplines to solve. An example of such a research problem is a recent research initiative, called the International Satellite Land Surface Climatology Program (ISLSCP), (Murphy 1983; Ohring and Sellers 1984; Toll and Witt 1984) into the study of land-atmosphere system interactions, where the emphasis will be on developing an understanding of the relationship of climate to natural and anthropogenic alterations of the land surface i.e., land surface climatology. The hydrologic cycle, a pictorial representation of which is shown in Figure 1, is an intimate part of the land-atmosphere system through its subset of mass, energy, and momentum interactions such as soil moisture evaporation, latent and sensible heat fluxes, and rainfall and snowmelt runoff. Such a problem needs hydrologists, biologists, meteorologists, soil scientists, and remote sensing scientists to examine the full range of energy, mass, and momentum exchange processes which occur between the land surface system and the atmospheric system.

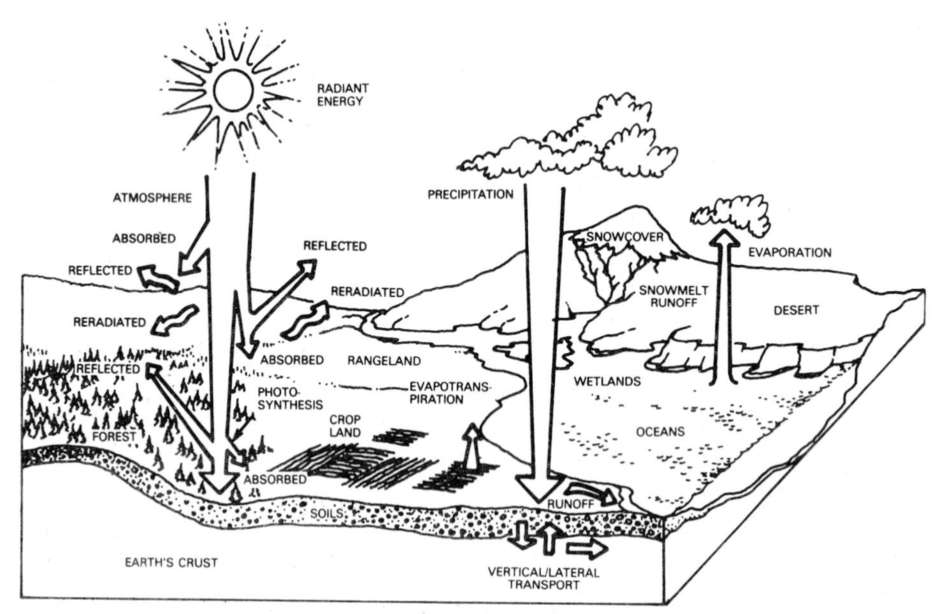

FIG.1 A pictorial model of the hydrologic cycle showing the many mass, momentum, and energy exchange processes.

The land sciences community is currently large and geographically dispersed, and it is not expected that such a collection of scientists can, or even should, be assembled in one place to press the attack on such a research problem, at least because of the size of community and the amount of computing and other resources, facilities, and services required, in addition to the length of time that will be required to study the problem. The scientists will use an enormous amount and variety of data in an experimental approach to such a research problem. Because NASA is chartered as a space technology agency, particular emphasis will be placed on the utilization of remotely sensed data, i.e., earth observation data acquired from space satellite platforms. These data will be transformed into land science knowledge through an extensive and complex set of data preparation, analysis, and information extraction processes.

Example - Future Hydrology-Oriented Research

As indicated, part of NASA's future hydrological research in land processes will be in the area of land surface climatology and will be pursued through a program called the International Satellite Land Surface Climatology Program (ISLSCP). ISLSCP is aimed at determining the influence of land surface properties on climate. Climate is typically studied through the use of models, called general circulation models (GCM), which contain land surface parameters such as soil moisture, vegetation cover, surface albedo and radiation fluxes. One of the major problems involved in the use of climate GCM's in particular, is characterization of those models with hydrological parameters, such as soil moisture, which are an important part of the models. Soil moisture is especially important because soil moisture content influences the rate of evapotranspiration (ET). ET, in turn, is a key parameter in climate models since it is a major component of surface energy balance. Recently developed soil-plant-atmosphere (SOPLAT) models, which represent land surface-atmosphere interactions, also indicate that soil moisture content is a crucial element of the model.

One of the objectives, then, of ISLSCP research, which was formulated specifically to address this problem, is to determine if remotely sensed data, satellite data in particular, can be used to quantify the spatial and temporal variability of surface soil moisture over large areas (regional/continental/global size) at grid scale sizes appropriate for GCMs, SOPLAT Models, etc. Soil moisture content is revealed through surface skin temperature, through diurnal sensible and latent heat fluxes, and through microwave brightness temperatures. Therefore, an attempt will be made to develop a methodology for quantifying surface soil moisture at these scales from a combination of visible, near-, short-wave, and thermal infrared, and microwave satellite sensor data, and to document the accuracy with which these determinations can be made. Previous research has already indicated that a relationship exists between soil moisture content and microwave brightness temperatures as observed using aircraft sensors (Schmugge 1983). Preliminary results from analysis of NIMBUS-7 Scanning Multifrequency Microwave Radiometer (SMMR) sensor data shows that a useful soil moisture index may be derivable in large homogeneous areas of sparse vegetation cover (Wang 1983).

Data sets of radiance values observed by satellite sensors, such as NIMBUS SMMR, GOES VISSR, Landsat MSS and TM will be compared to point surface observations of the same characteristics to determine if hydrological parameters such as soil moisture can be estimated using satellite data. Algorithmic techniques need to be developed to extend point ground observations to area measurements comparable to the areas in which the satellite sensors integrate their signal, utilizing aircraft sensor measurements such as the Thematic Mapper Simulator, Airborne Imaging Spectrometer, and scatterometers to aid in the interpolation/integration between points. Several experimental comparisons of this kind will need to be performed in areas of different vegetation cover at different times of the year. An estimate of the type and amount of satellite, aircraft, and ground data already acquired to support land surface climatology research is given in Figure 2. It is hoped that standard methodologies can be developed for converting satellite measured radiances into quantitative areal estimates of hydrological variables such as soil moisture in land surface-atmosphere surface models.

SENSOR PLATFORM	DATA TYPE	AMOUNT OF DATA
SATELLITE	LANDSAT MSS/TM	3610 MB
	NOAA-6,7,8,9 AVHRR LAC/GAC	
AIRCRAFT	TM/LAPR-2	250 MB
	AIS	
	TIMS	
GROUND	METEOROLOGICAL (PRECIPITATION, SURFACE TEMPERATURE, HUMIDITY, WIND SPEED)	44 MB
	DIGITAL TERRAIN/TOPOGRAPHY	
	FIELD SPECTRAL REFLECTANCES	

FIG.2 Initial estimate of type and amount of data needed to support Land Surface Climatology Research.

System Concept

The scope of the research problems, the dispersion of the research community, the size of the data sets, and the range of data processing involved in land sciences, with land surface climatology and its hydrology component being just one representative example, all indicate that an extensive data system must be developed and emplaced to support land sciences research. NASA has embarked on just such a systems and technology development program, the goal of which is to establish a prototype, state-of-the-art data and information system to support research in the land sciences which will lead to a permament research tool. This program is called the Pilot Land Data System (PLDS) program, and will use the ISLSCP as a system requirements driver and science demonstration project of the PLDS.

Analysis of the data system drivers involved in ISLSCP research indicate that the system concept for the PLDS will have to include functional capabilities in: data management, because extensive sets of satellite, aircraft, and ground data will be utilized by ISLSCP hydrology researchers; analysis software tools, because significant data preparation and manipulation, and image processing will be performed; computing system access capabilities, because large physical system models will be used in information extraction; and networking and communications, because groups of researchers will be physically separated from each other, from the computing resources, and from the data sources. As shown in Figure 3, the PLDS Program has been organized to contain these functional elements as technical development areas.

An on-line data bank is now being established which will contain extensive sets of satellite, aircraft, and ground data. Data sets of utility include retrospective, current, and future earth observations from the following satellite sensors: Landsat Multispectral Scanner (MSS) and Thematic Mapper (TM), NOAA Advanced Very High Resolution Radiometer (AVHRR), NIMBUS Scanning Multifrequency Microwave Radiometer(SMMR), GOES Visible and Infrared Spin Scanning Radiometer (VISSR), TIROS Operation Vertical Sounder (TOVS), and SPOT multispectral radiometer. Already about 100 MSS and TM scenes, and about 25 AVHRR scenes acquired from 1978 to the present over

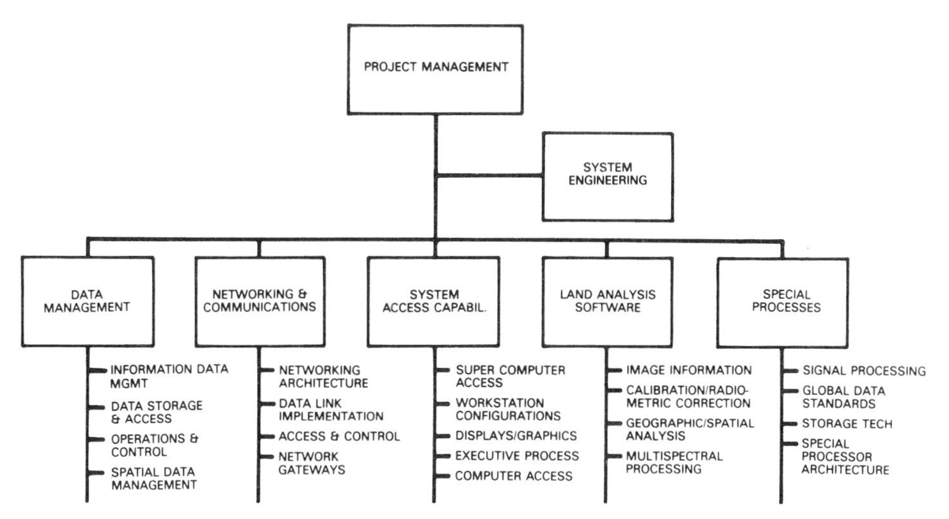

FIG.3 Organization and content of the functional elements of the Pilot Land Data System Development Program.

the midwestern Great Plains and southwestern desert of the U.S. have been assembled and prepared for entry into the data bank. The data bank will also hold data from NASA aircraft multispectral scanners (Thematic Mapper Simulator, Airborne Imaging Spectometer, Linear Array Pushbroom Radiometer) and NASA passive and active microwave radiometers (L-band radiometer, L-band synthetic aperture radar, and L- and C-band scatterometers). Ground biophysical data (vegetation index, canopy temperature, biomass, soil type) and micrometeorological data (surface temperature, pressure, windspeed, humidity) have been, and will continue to be, acquired and entered into the data bank also.

It is clear from this discussion that a significant challenge resides in the development and implementation of a data base management system that can ingest, track, and provide these data to users in a "friendly", minimal-response-time fashion. To satisfy the user friendly requirement, a natural language query structure has been installed and is being evaluated at Goddard. To satisfy the minimal-response-time requirement, research is being performed in the use of quad tree structures for data arrangement, the use of digital optical disk media for data storage, and data base machines for data access and retrieval.

Utilization of large amounts of these disparate data requires a sophisticated, comprehensive set of analysis software tools. These tools must be capable of performing preprocessing functions such as reformatting, processing functions such as geometric and radiometric correction, and analysis functions such as land surface feature separation and classification. An image data analysis software system, called the Land Analysis System (LAS), containing over 200,000 lines of code, has already been developed at the Goddard Space Flight Center to perform many of these functions. While this analysis tool contains many capabilities for analysis of spectral and spatial data, its functionality and performance will continue to be augmented and enhanced with the addition of routines to perform radar data signal processing and geographic modeling, and selected algorithms will be implemented on other-than-serial architecture computers.

One such algorithm, a hill slope model for calculating runoff in a watershed basin, is being implemented on Goddard's parallel architecture computing machine called the Massively Parallel Processor (MPP). This supercomputer, a schematic of which is shown in Figure 4, has 16384 separate processing elements each performing a given operation in lock step fashion. This gives the MPP the capability to perform approximately 10^9

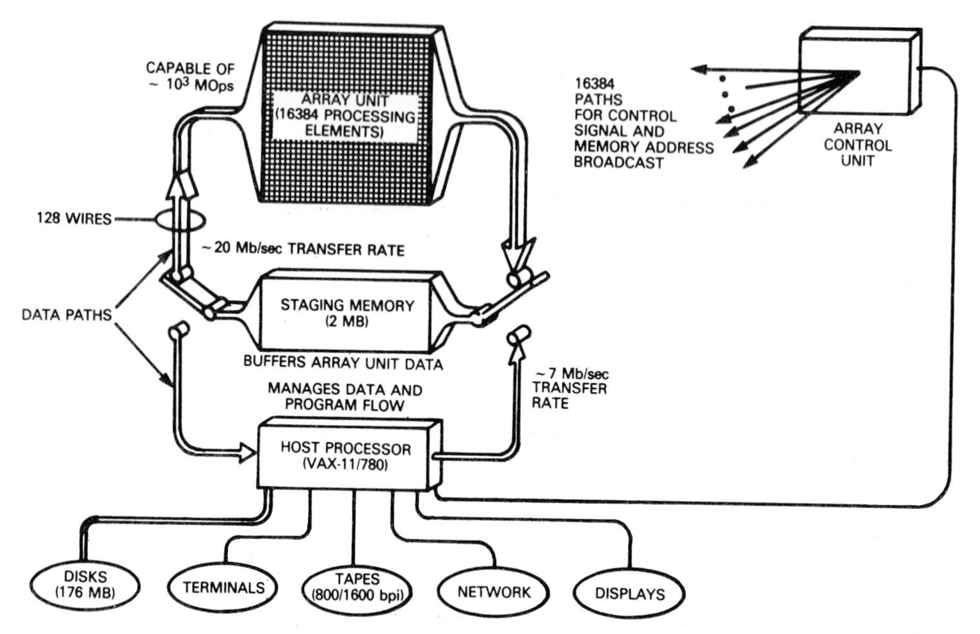

FIG.4 Schematic representation of NASA'S Massively Parallel Processor.

operations per second. The parallel architecture of the MPP is ideal for the implementation of the hill slope algorithm, and is also ideal for image processing and analysis functions. Access to this computing machine will be offered through the PLDS.

The MPP is just one example of access to NASA's superclass computers that the PLDS provides to ISLSCP investigators. Investigators at GSFC have been provided access to the center's Cyber 205 vector processing machine and its IBM 3081 high speed serial machine. In the future, access will be provided to the Cray vector processing machine at the NASA Ames Research Center as well (ARC). In addition to access to intensive computing engines, PLDS will provide access to the LAS image data analysis software which resides on a DEC VAX 11/780 minicomputer at the Goddard Space Flight Center.

Networking and communications form the final functional area in the system concept for PLDS. The geographical dispersion of the data sources, computing engines, and hydrology researchers requires the ability: to remotely locate and retrieve data, and information about the data from on-line data banks and data directories/catalogs/inventories; to remotely access hardware and software systems for intensive computing; and to transmit to, and receive from, distant geographical locations reduced data, text messages, and other research results. A local area network, which allows the interconnection of VAX minicomputers, which are part of the PLDS hardware, and hydrology researchers in different buildings at GSFC, has been completed. This network utilizes Ethernet coax cabling and DECnet protocol intrabuilding and a very high speed data transmission (~1.5 mb/s) optical fibre cable interbuilding. This network is extended to GSFC's large computing facilities via gateways to the facilities. This network is also connected to the University of Maryland (UMD) via a dedicated high speed link (~ 56 kb/s) which utilizes the TCP/IP protocol. This link is being implemented between the GSFC and the UMD since the UMD's Remote Sensing Systems Lab is a funded participant in the PLDS systems development and in the ISLSCP hydrological research. A representation of this network is shown in Figure 5. NASA's Program Support Communications Network (PSCN) will ultimately be used to provide network connections to other NASA centers including the ARC.

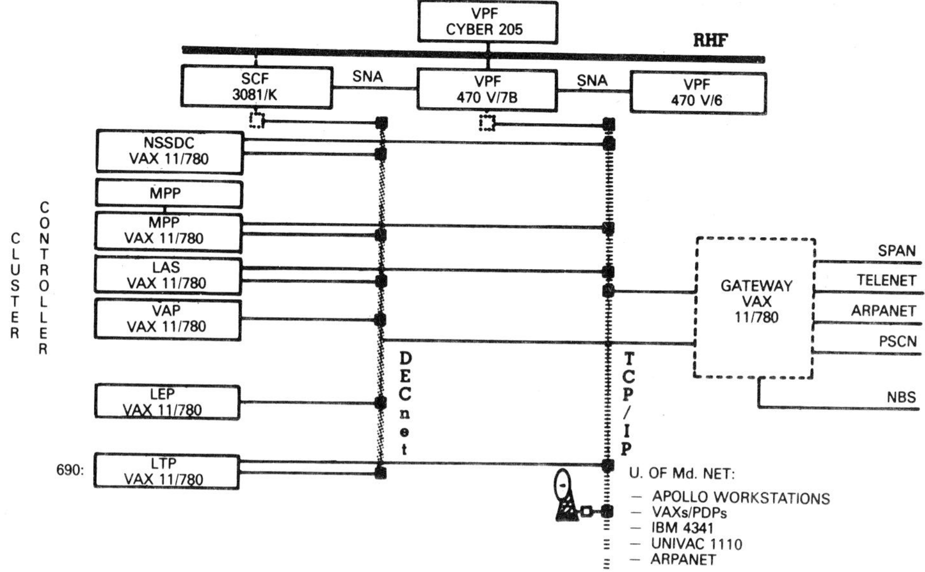

FIG.5 A block diagram of the Space and Earth Sciences High Speed Data Network (SESnet).

Future Evolution

It is projected that as many as a dozen universities will be participating in various portions and phases of ISLSCP research. In addition, sources of data such as the Water Resources and National Mapping Divisions of the USGS in Reston, Virginia, the National Meteorological Center in Ashville, North Carolina, the EROS Data Center in Sioux Falls, South Dakota, and the NOAA Environmental Satellite Data and Information Service in Suitland, Maryland will need to be electronically accessed in order to allow timely accurate transmission of data via PLDS links to ISLSCP researchers.

PLDS communications links amongst the additional research nodes at NASA centers and universities, and the data nodes will be implemented. Future developmental efforts to complete the prototype system include: the installation of capability for geographic data entry; the development of software for front end data processing such as reformatting and registration algorithms, and the utilization of workstations tailored to specific computational activities.

References

Estes, J., July 1984, The Pilot Land Data System; Report of the Program Planning Workshop. NASA Technical Memorandum #86250.

Ohring, G. and P. Sellers, December 1984, Report of the Design Workshop for the First ISLSCP Field Experiment.

Rasool, S., June-December 1983, Development of the Implementation Plan for the International Satellite Land Surface climatology Project (ISLSCP) Phase I.

Schmugge, T., July 1983, Remote Sensing of Soil Mositure: Recent Advances IEEE Transactions on Geoscience and Remote Sensing, Vol. GE-21 #3, p. 336-344.

Toll, D. and R. Witt, October 1984, Report from the North American Working Group Meeting on the ISLSCP Retrospective Analyses Project.

Wang, J., 1983, Passive Microwave Sensing of Soil Moisture with Satellite Sensors: The Efforts of Soil Bulk Density and Surface Roughness, Remote Sensing of the Environment 13, p. 327-344.

Hydrologic Applications of Space Technology (Proceedings of the Cocoa Beach Workshop, Florida, August 1985). IAHS Publ. no. 160, 1986.

A geographic information system for prediction of runoff and non-point source pollution potential

WANADA B. POTTER & MARTHA W. GILLILAND
Department of Civil Engineering,
University of Nebraska, Lincoln Omaha,
68182-0178, USA
M. DAVID LONG
Remote Sensing Applications Laboratory,
Department of Geography - Geology,
University of Nebraska, Omaha,
Nebraska 68182-0178, USA

Abstract

Many of the parameters required to model runoff and non-point source water pollution potential are geographic in character and are obtained from geographic sources; for example from soils maps, topographic maps, land use maps, and aerial photographs. Modelers frequently extract these spatially organized data manually, only to input them to a non-spatially organized model. In the process of translating information about slope, slope length, soil types, land use, basin characteristics, and meteorological characteristics from primary sources to a model, the geographic character is stripped from the primary data.

In contrast, a computer based geographically structured information system (GIS) can manipulate primary data in a spatially structured environment. A GIS, aimed at predicting runoff and pollution potential, was developed and calibrated on a portion of the Elkhorn River Basin in Nebraska. The system accepts digitally mapped information on soil type, topography, and land use; calculates characteristics such as slope, and slope length; and relates these characteristics to soils and land use parameters in order to produce three dimensional maps of runoff potential, sediment pollution potential, and fecal coliform pollution potential. While validation in other river basins is needed, the system has the potential to promote better communication between researchers and those with money for non-point pollution mitigation and may improve our ability to allocate mitigation resources efficiently.

Introduction

Non-point sources are now the major sources of criteria pollutants in surface waters. Non-point sources contribute significant percentages of such pollutants as BOD (57%), nutrients (87% of phosphorus and 88% of nitrogen), total suspended solids (98%), and bacteria. Sediment and sediment-attached pollutants have been recognized in particular as "...the most widespread source of pollutants discharged into the nation's surface waters." Agricultural sources, particularly cropland, pastureland, and rangeland, produce almost 64% of the sediment discharged to surface waters (Gianessi and Peskin, 1981). In Nebraska, the single most prominent pollutant which precludes the attainment of "swimmable-fishable" national water quality goals, as set forth in the 1977 Clean Water Act, is coliform bacteria (Nebraska Department of Environmental Control, 1982).

Non-point source pollution from agricultural sources originates on the land, and different parcels of land exhibit different potentials for pollution production. Non-point source pollution potential for a parcel of land is typically a function of the use and management of land by people, of the physical properties of the land, and of the hydrologic and meteorologic properties of the area. Non-point source pollution models typically represent these factors with several parameters, most of which are geographic in character. Yet, during modeling, that geographic character is frequently lost. For example, soil characteristics, topographic parameters, vegetative cover, and information on erosion control practice are often taken from maps, aerial photos, and/or landsat data. In the process of transferring such information into a mathematical model, the geographic character is stripped from the information.

The goal of this study was to develop a geographically based tool for analyzing and communicating non-point pollution potential, with special emphasis on bacteria pollution. Such a tool allows the geographic character of information to be retained, can deal with diverse parcels of land, and is responsive to the bacteria pollution problem in Nebraska.

The study area is located in the lower Elkhorn River Basin, in Western Douglas County, Nebraska (Fig. 1). Fecal coliform bacteria standards are violated regularly in this river, with sources being municipal sewage treatment plants, feedlots, and livestock grazing. For example, feedlots number in the thousands in the Basin. Livestock grazing is extensive and is commonly associated with small streams. The specific study area for this work included parts of a one square mile section (2.59 km^2) of land, each part representing a distinct land use: a large feedlot, a pasture, and a cornfield.

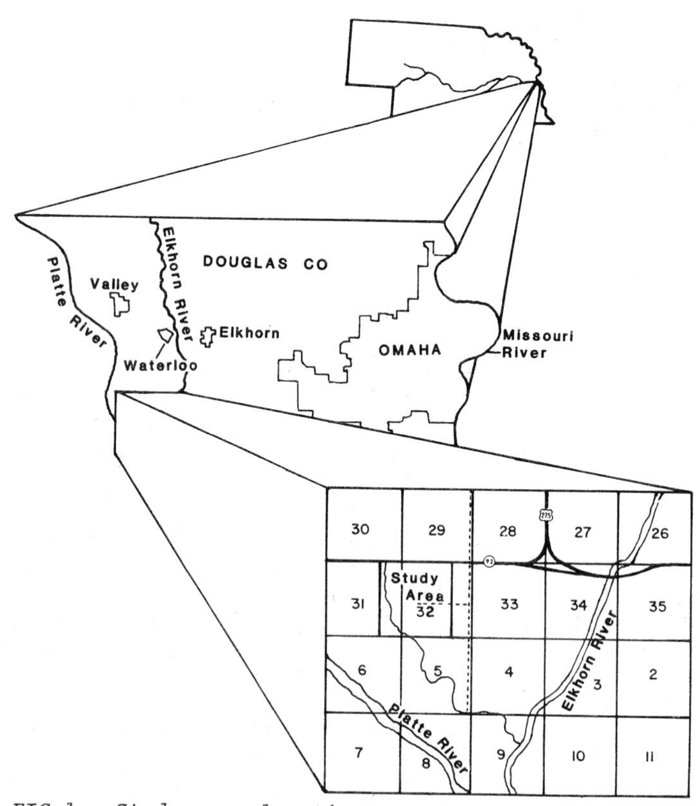

FIG.1 Study area location.

The geographic information system (GIS) utilizes a raster format and is somewhat unique in that it is modular, transportable, and expandable. For each cell, a set of parameters are input and manipulated according to three equations that deal with distinct dimensions of non-point pollution. The output is three-dimensional pollution potential maps useful for analysis, communication, and planning.

This paper summarizes our results in 5 parts: (i) the predictive equations are described; (ii) the unique aspects of the geographic information system are delineated; (iii) implementation of the equations into the GIS is discussed; (iv) model calibration techniques are summarized; and (v) two output maps are provided as results.

Predictive Equations

This study utilized three accepted predictive formulae: (1) the Soil Conservation Service Curve Number technique (SCSCN) for the prediction of potential runoff; (2) the Universal Soil Loss Equation (USLE) for the prediction of potential erosion; and (3) a simple loading function for the prediction of bacterial densities in runoff.

The SCSCN technique was developed by the U.S. Department of Agriculture - Soil Conservation Service (SCS) in the 1950's. The SCS National Engineering Handbook (U.S. Soil Conservation Service, 1972) contains a full description of the development and use of the technique. Application of the technique requires solution of the equation:

$$Q = \frac{(P-0.2S)^2}{P+0.8S} \qquad (1)$$

where

Q = total runoff (inches or cm)
P = precipitation (inches or cm)
S = maximum potential difference between P and Q (inches or cm)

The value of S, as expressed in equation 2, is a function of the variable CN (runoff curve number or soil-cover complex number).

$$S = \frac{1000}{CN} - 10 \qquad (2)$$

Evaluation of CN is based on the assessment of 3 parameters: 1) antecedent soil moisture conditions (AMC); (2) soil hydrologic type; and (3) land use and treatment class. Assessment of AMC is based solely upon 5-day antecedent precipitation. The SCS has devised a hydrologic soil classification system which divides all identified soils into 4 hydrologic groups on the basis of minimum infiltration exhibited by a soil after prolonged wetting. Land use and treatment classes were developed to consider the effects of the surface conditions in a watershed on runoff potential. Class assignments are based type of cover (e.g. contour or straight plowed, good or poor crop rotations, and terracing). Both hydrologic soil type and land use treatment class are geographic in nature and may vary spatially within a watershed. Soil type information is normally mapped and land use and treatment classes can be identified from aerial photographs.

The USLE is an empirical equation designed to compute long time average soil losses due to sheet and rill erosion across the land surface. The equation ignores sediment yields from gully, streambank, or streambed erosion. Wischmeier and Smith (1978) give a full description of the development and use of the equations. The USLE groups the many interrelated physical and management parameters which influence erosion into six factors such that erosion is the product of those factors as follows:

$$A = RK(LS)CP \quad (3)$$

where

A = soil loss per unit area per unit time
(tons/acre/unit time or t/hectare/unit time)
R = a rainfall factor which is a product of the total storm energy and maximum 30-min. intensity. R expresses erosive potential as a number of erosion index units (EI) per unit time. (100 ft-tons-in/acre-hr/unit time, 100 t-m-cm/hectare-hr/unit time)
K = soil erodibility factor: soil loss rate per erosion index unit (tons/acre-EI, t/hectare-EI)
(LS) = a terrain factor which considers slope length and steepness (dimensionless)
C = a cover and management factor (dimensionless)
P = a support practice or erosion control practice factor (dimensionless)

Five of these six factors may vary spatially within a watershed and are geographic in nature. They are K, (LS), C, and P. The K factor is related to soil type which is normally mapped. The (LS) factor is a function of the terrain, and can be interpreted from an hypsography map. The C and P factors can be identified from aerial photographs.

Certain bacteria have been identified as indicator organisms for assessing the possibility of fecal contamination in surface waters. The U.S. Environmental Protection Agency (EPA) has established bacterial density standards for total coliform bacteria (TC) and fecal coliform bacteria (FC); specific numerical limits vary according to the type of beneficial use designated for the surface water. For example, the total coliform standard for partial contact recreation (such as canoeing) is 2000 organism/100 milliliters (ml). In contrast, total coliform concentrations in the Elkhorn River are commonly over 100,000 organisms/100 ml.

Stocking rates, age and type of fecal deposits, antecedent conditions, temperature, season, and rainfall intensity are some of the many factors which affect bacterial densities in runoff. The relationship of these factors to bacterial densities are not well defined and not quantified. McElroy (1976) has suggested that bacterial densities in runoff from feedlots might be approximated by using typical density values from the literature. This approach, extended to other types of land uses, was used here. This is clearly a simplication since it ignores the very factors (other than land use) that can cause extreme variations in bacterial density.

Description of Geographic Information System

The basic geographic information system utilized in this study is the Raster Geographic Information System for Mapping (RGISM) developed by the Remote Sensing Applications Laboratory at the University of Nebraska at Omaha. In developing the design philosophy for RGISM, Peterson and Long (1984) identified three goals; the system was to be: (1) modular rather than monolithic, (2) transportable, and (3) flexible and expandable. These goals led to a unique system design that utilizes the standard operating system file structure of the host processor rather than utilizing an internal filing system. With this approach, a significant amount of programming, common in more monolithic GIS's, is eliminated. RGISM is organized as a family of free standing program modules written in standard Fortran 77. Each module performs a specific process on, or manipulation of, data files. This approach is distinctly different from the conventional organization of monolithic GIS's which compile all manipulation programming in one large program. The module approach eliminates the necessity of loading unused programming into the host processor's core memory, and in general makes more efficient use of system resources. Other GIS's may use a chained modular approach, but often they rely on non-standard programming and so are very system specific; that is they are not transportable. Because all RGISM program modules are written in standard Fortran 77 and rely on no system specific commands, RGISM is a highly transportable system requiring only that the host processor be equiped with a Fortran 77 compiler and virtual memory. Although the programs were written to be run interactively, they might easily be executed in a batch mode.

To meet the goal of flexibility and expandability, user specified operations were added to the list of available map manipulations. To add an operation to RGISM the user must only write a program module to perform that operation. Due to the free-standing structure of RGISM, editing and debugging a monolithic master GIS program is not required in order to incorporate the new operation. To aid the user in the development of a new program module, a library of subroutines and functions has been developed. Most of these library operations are I/O operations. However, there are also library operations which read and display comments from input files, and insert comments into output files. These can be called by the user from within the new program module. The only programming burden which is left to the user is the description of the new manipulation to be performed, frequently less than ten lines of programming.

In order to use this raster based system, two program modules are available to convert digitized vector (x, y, z) data to raster format. The first, POLLYFILL, converts a digitized polygon vector file to a raster format. The second, ELEVMOD, converts a terrain file consisting of digitized contour lines and/or randomly spaced elevation data to an elevation model (or raster hypsography map). Since all raster mapped data are stored as integer type data, it may be desirable to multiply elevation data which are recorded in less than one foot intervals by a factor of ten or 100 to assure that the decimal data are not lost in the rasterization process. Both of these programs are written to be able to read vector files that are output from a Numonics digitizer. Once rasterized, maps can be edited on a cell by cell basis. Presently, neither photo-digitized nor LANDSAT data may be entered into the system. Yet the raster data structure of RGISM is highly compatible with both LANDSAT and photo digitized data, and the development of a program module to read and reformat such data for use in RGISM would be a straight forward matter.

RGISM presently has four options for map display. OVERPR creates an over printed grey-shade map with up to sixteen levels. The limits of the map dimensions are those of the line printer. GISPRINT creates a print file in which the different raster cell values are represented by single character symbols, specified by the user in response to a program prompt. The dimension limitations are the same as the limits of OVERPR. SCREEN produces the same output that GISPRINT does, but rather than writing it to a file to be printed, it is written to the user's terminal. TRIDGG will produce a three-dimensional depiction of the specific map on the user's terminal, provided that the user is equipped with a graphics terminal. TRIDHI produces a plot file which can be plotted on a pen plotter to obtain a hard copy of such a three-dimensional representation.

Implementation of the Predictive Equations in RGISM

Each of the three predictive equations discussed above were implemented through a separate program module in RGISM. The program module implementing the SCSCN technique is named RUNOFF, and produces a map of storm runoff potential in inches. The program module implementing the USLE is named USLE, and produces a map of storm erosion potential in tons per acre. The program module implementing the extension of McElroy's approach to estimating bacterial densities is named GERMS and produces maps of potential bacterial densities in runoff in TC organisms per 100 ml and FC organisms per 100 ml.

All three of the predicitive equations utilized contain some type of land use factor: the land use and treatment classes used in evaluating CN in the SCSCN technique might easily be represented in a land use map; the C (cover) and P (erosion control practice) factors used in the USLE for the prediction of potential erosion might also be portrayed in a land use map; and, in the extension of McElroy's approach, bacterial densities in runoff are related directly and exclusively to land use. However, implementation of each of the predictive equations requires a slightly different land use classification system. In order to avoid the necessity of compiling and digitizing three separate land use maps, a full purpose land use classification system was devised. A single land use map was then compiled and digitized to become the data base land use map. Each of the three program modules is equipped to interpret the land use information needed by that module from the common land use map. The starting point for developing this full purpose land use classification system was the "cover" classification system set forth in the National Engineering Handbook (U.S. Soil Conservation Service, 1972) for use in the SCSCN technique for runoff prediction. The SCSCN classes were then harmonized with classes used in the USLE which are described by Wischmeier and Smith (1978) and Novotny and Chesters (1981), and with land use distinctions which affect bacterial densities in runoff. The final full purpose classification system contained 46 classes.

A similar approach was used for inputing soils information related to soils characteristics. A single soils map is consulted by both the RUNOFF and the USLE program modules; each module is equipped to interpret the soils data required for its operation from the soils map. It was not necessary to devise a full purpose soils classification system because the basic data base soils map was digitized directly from a published SCS soils survey, and the standard soils map unit map proved to be sufficiently full purpose. In the case of both the land use map and the soils map, which are used in the data base, the single full purpose map serves as a source of basic data for more than one program module. The basic map necessarily contains more information and detail than any one of the program modules might require.

The complete data base consists of four maps: land use, soils, elevation, and a base map. The land use information was compiled from aerial photographs and field scouted information. The soils map is a digitized version of the SCS Soil Survey map. The digital elevation model was produced using the ELEVMOD program to interpret a compilation of: contour information from a US Geological Survey 7.5' quadrangle, additional estimated elevation data obtained from field observation, and surveyed elevation data for critical areas. The base map is an outline of the one square mile (2.59 km) study area and contains locations of match points used to align and rescale other digitized maps before rasterization.

RUNOFF is the program module implementing the SCSCN technique (equations 1 and 2) to predict runoff potential. The module prompts the user to enter the 24-hour precipitation. Then, on a cell by cell basis, the module complete each of the following four steps. (1) The module consults the soils map and interprets hydrologic soils group values. (2) It consults the land use map, and, on the basis of land use class and hydrologic soil type, it determines the CN value. (3) Potential runoff (in inches) is then calculated for the current cell using the formula given in equation 1. (4) The predicted runoff potential is stored in the appropriate location in an output map file. The consult/calculate process is then repeated for each cell until the runoff potential map is complete.

USLE is the program module implementing the USLE (equation 3) to predict erosion potential. This module also prompts the user to enter the 24-hour precipitation. The rainfall and runoff factor (R) is calculated from daily precipitation using an empirical formula developed by Lombardi (1979). Then, on a cell by cell basis the module executes the following five steps. (1) It consults a slope map and a slope length map and calculates the terrain factor (LS) used in equation 3. The slope and slope length maps must have been created using a RGISM program module called SLOPE. (2) The module consults the soils map and assigns a soil erodibility factor (K) based on soil type. (3) The land use map is consulted and a cover factor (C) is assigned. (4) A practice factor (P) is assigned on the basis of land use class and slope. Finally, (5) the predicted erosion potential (tons per acre) is stored in the appropriate location in an output map file. This consult/calculate process is repeated for each cell until the erosion potential map is complete.

GERMS is the program module implementation for predicting bacterial densities in runoff. This module simply consults the land use map, and, on a cell by cell basis, assigns a typical TC and FC density for each land use class. Two potential bacterial density maps are produced, one for TC densities and one for FC densities.

Calibration

Field data were gathered during one spring and fall season. Runoff samples were collected from each of the three distinct agricultural land uses found in the study area. These samples were analyzed for bacterial densities and for suspended soilds. The bacterial density data were used to supplement typical density data from the literature and to confirm the applicability of data from the literature to other settings. The suspended soilds field data were the only data available to calibrate the GIS model. Suspended solids (measured in mg/l) were assumed to be directly related to potential runoff and erosion. The model could then be calibrated by assuming that the suspended solids concentration in runoff from a watershed must be equal to the sum of all erosion from the watershed (mass) divided by total runoff volume. In order to carry out this analysis, the boundaries of the small watersheds from which samples were taken had to be mapped and digitized. A program module was developed which consulted the watershed map, the runoff potential map, and the erosion potential map. Using a given cell dimension, the program then calculated total runoff volume and erosion from each watershed.

Results

The study area, with land uses and sampling sites noted, is shown in Fig. 2. Within the 1 square mile (2.59 km) area, three types of land uses predominate. A large feedlot (capacity 13,000 head) occupies the northeast quadrant; the southeast corner is occupied by lightly grazed pasture; and most of the remaining land (shaded area) is used for corn production. Figs. 3 and 4 are examples of the three dimensional output from this GIS; their orientation is the same as the site map (Fig. 2), with the feedlot in the northeast corner and the pasture in the southwest corner.

Figure 3 shows the study area terrain in three dimensions, with the vertical scale greatly exaggerated relative to the horizontal scale. Actual site elevations range from 1100 to 1125 feet (335 to 343m) above sea level. A low ridge which runs from the south end of the lake to a point beyond the northern boundry of the study area appears as a mountain ridge. The digital elevation model, used to plot this map, formed the basis for the slope and slope length maps needed in the USLE program module.

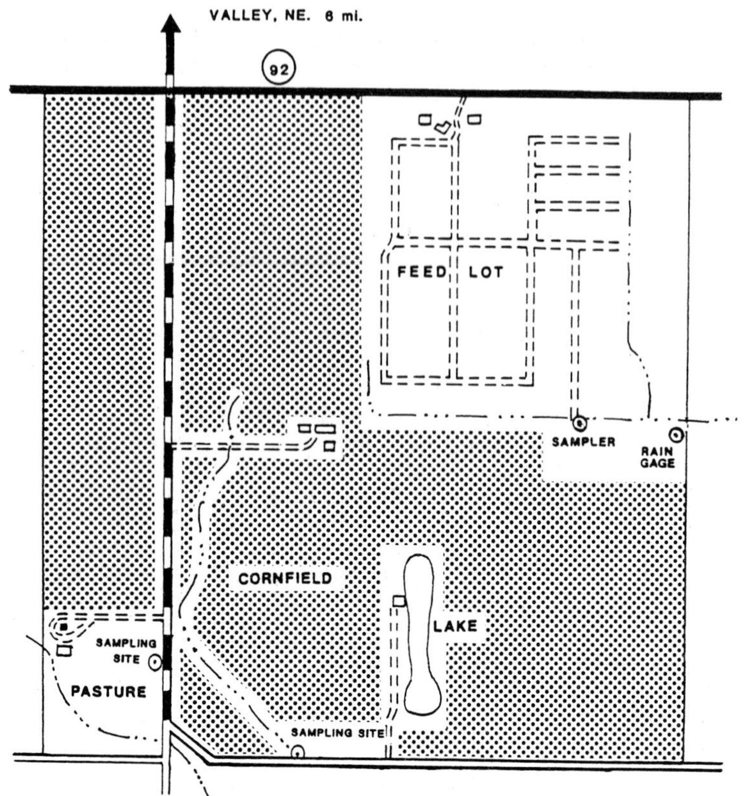

FIG.2 Study area site map.

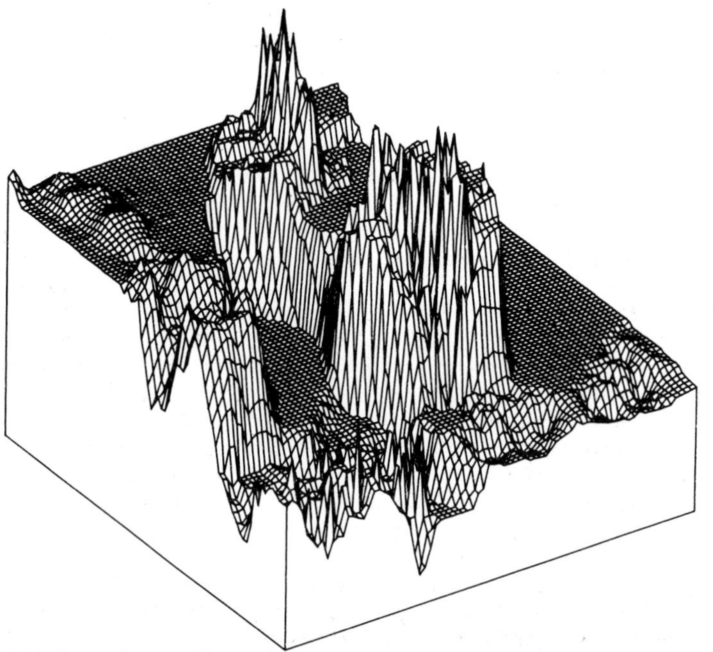

FIG.3 Three dimensional depiction of study area topography.

Figure 4 is a three dimensional representation of the runoff potential of the study area when subjected to 2 inches (5.08 cm) of precipitation in a 24 hour period. Runoff potential ranges from a high of 1.21 inches (3.07 cm) from the feedlot to 0.00 inches (0.00 cm) from the lake.

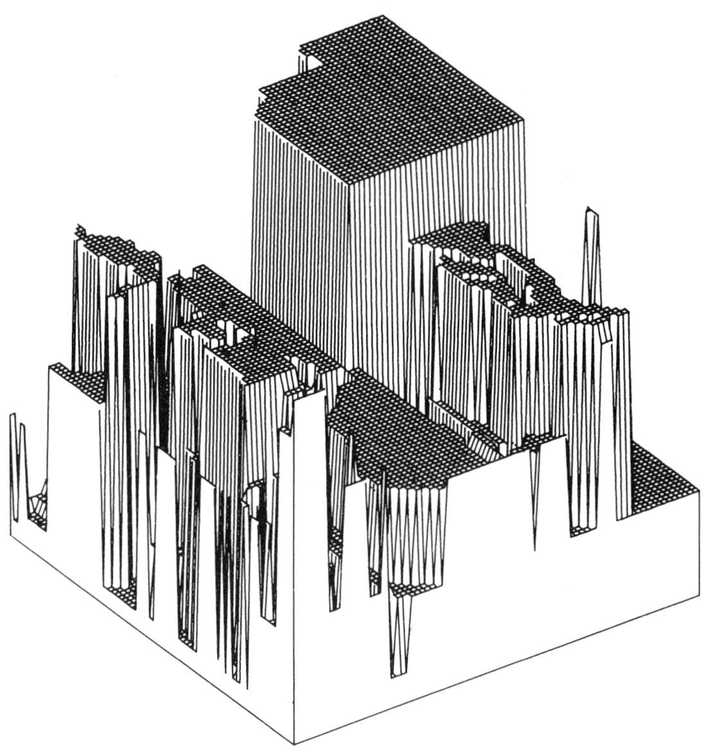

FIG.4 Three dimensional depiction of runoff potential for a 2 inch (5.08 cm) 24 hr. rainfall event.

The variation of runoff potential within the cornfield reflects the effect of soil type on runoff potential. The more highly permeable soils in the southeastern extremes of the cornfield yield much less runoff than the less permeable soils which flank the lake and adjoin the western boundary of the feedlot. Interestly, the pasture does not appear distinctively on the runoff potential map, probably due to the orientation of the map image. One of the difficulties in plotting three-dimensional maps is the lack of a system to choose the "best" orientation prior to plotting.

These three dimensional maps are useful tools for analysis, planning, and, particularly, for communication. For example, the results of a proposed pollution mitigation measure can be "viewed" before it is implemented. Similarly, a land owner can examine a picture (literally) of the relative significance of the non-point source pollution that arises from different parcels of his/her land.

References

Gianessi, L.P., Peskin, H.M., and Young, G.K., 1981, Analysis of National Water Pollution Control Policies, part 1: A National Network Model: Water Resources Research, v. 17, no. 4, 7 p.

Lombardi, F., 1979, Universal Soil Loss Equation (USLE), Runoff Erosivity Factor, Slope Length Exponent, and Slope Steepness Exponent for

Individual Storms: Ph.D. Thesis, Purdue University, West Lafayette, Indiana, as cited by Knisel, W.G., ed., 1980, CREAMS: A Field-Scale Model for Chemicals, Runoff, and Erosion from Agricultural Management Systems: U.S. Dept. of Agriculture, Conservation Research Report No. 26, 640 p.

McElroy, A.D., ed. 1976, Loading Functions for Assessment of Water Pollution from Non-Point Sources:Environmental Protection Agency, Office of Research and Development, Washington, D.C., (EPA/600/2-76/151), 444 p. (Su. Doc. No. EP 1.23/2:600/2-76-151)

Nebraska Dept. of Environmental Control, 1982, 1982 Nebraska Water Quality Report: Department of Environmental Control, Lincoln, Nebraska

Novotny, P.E., and Chesters, G., 1981, Handbook of Nonpoint Pollution: Sources and Management: Van Nostrand Reinhold Co., New York, 555 p.

Peterson, M.P., and Long, M.D., 1984, personal communication, Asst. Professor, Dept. of Geography - Geology, University of Nebraska - Omaha, Omaha, Nebraska, and formerly Computer Co-ordinator, Remote Sensing Applications Laboratory, Dept. of Geography - Geology, University of Nebraska - Omaha, Omaha, Nebraska (respectively).

U.S. Soil Conservation Service, 1972, SCS National Engineering Handbook, Sec. 4, Hydrology, 548 p. (Su, Doc. No. A57.6/2: En 3/ sec. 4/rev.2)

Wischmeier, W.H., and Smith, D.D., 1978, Predicting Rainfall Erosion Losses - A Guide to Conservation Planning: U.S. Dept. of Agriculture, Agricultural Handbook NO. 537. 58 p. (Su. Doc. No. A1.76: 537)

Hydrologic Applications of Space Technology (Proceedings of the Cocoa Beach Workshop, Florida, August 1985). IAHS Publ. no. 160, 1986.

An information system for water resources

R. LEMMELA & Y. SUCKSDORFF
National Board of Waters, Helsinki, Finland

Abstract
A computer based information system for water resources has been developed in the Hydrological Office of the National Board of Waters in Finland. The system contains a central file of all data on watercourses and drainage basins and is compatible with other environment file systems having geographical coordinates or drainage basin numbers as co-ordinating entities. In addition to the central file all the files of the National Board of Waters will be combined to the system. A digital terrain model digitized from maps of scale 1:200 000 is also used. The physiographical factors of a drainage basin are interpreted from pictures obtained from Lansat or SPOT satellites and weather satellites are used to interprete rapidly changing entities such as snow covered area, freezing and thawing of the lakes and the temperature of surface water.

The system will cover the whole of Finland by 1986.

Introduction
There are many factors which have contributed to the development of an information system for water resources in Finland. Firstly, there has always been a need for different combinations of hydrological data for many purposes, for example for research work, for hydrological and water resources planning and for monitoring natural changes. Secondly, in recent years many hydrological registers have been stored in computer memories instead of manually. Thirdly, a very good program for the collection, processing, recording, combining and output of digital data and digital data bases has been developed by the National Board of Survey in Finland. The same institute prepared the base map and digital terrain models of Finland. Finally, it has recently become possible in Finland to use satellite pictures operationally, eg. for interpreting the physiographical factors of drainage basins.

In the following the system is described and some results obtained during its development and utilization are presented.

General description of the system
The system is presented in Fig. 1. It consists of a central file of all drainage basins and a program which collects data from different files, combines and processes it and presents the processed data in tabular and graphical form.

All the registers of the National Board of Waters will be combined into the system. Other registers having geographical coordinates or basin numbers can also be linked. Basin characteristics are interpreted by means of satellite images. The percentage of cultivated land, foresttypes, drained bogs, bogs and lakes in a drainage basin will be interpreted from Landsat images. Weather satellite images will be used for the interpretation of rapidly changing entities, such as freezing

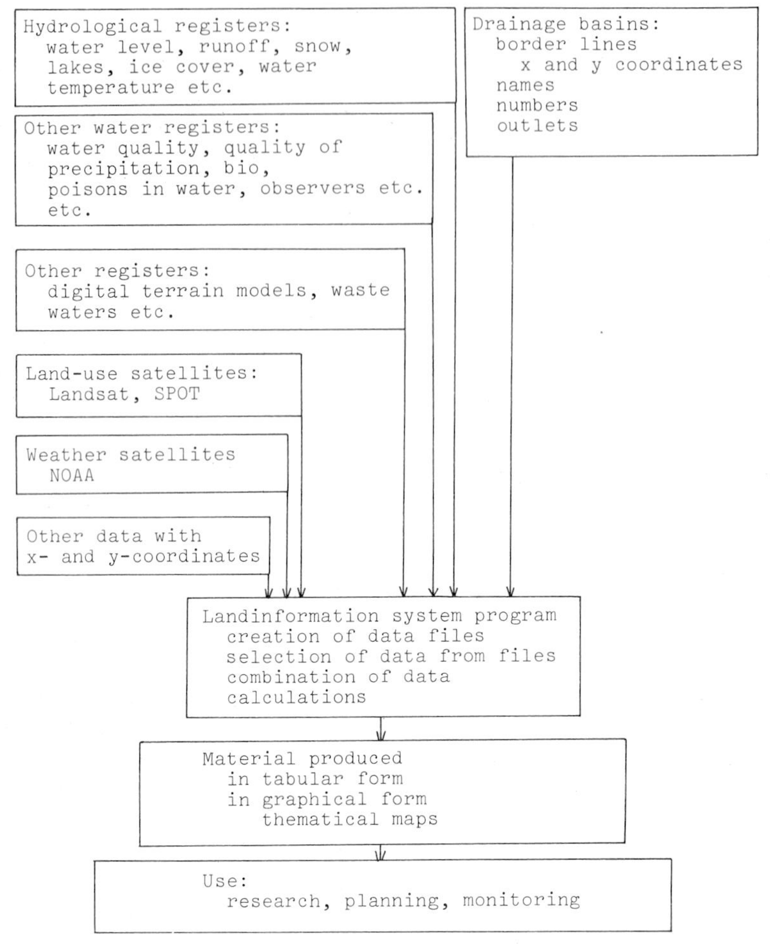

FIG.1 General description of the information system of water resources.

and thawing of lakes, snow cover distribution and the temperature of surface water in lakes.

Drainage basins in Finland

Finland is divided into 74 drainage basins. These main basins are each divided into three smaller area classes, making 9^3 areas in all. The areas of the smallest sub-basins are thus from 20 km^2 to 30 km^2. In addition the coastal areas of Finland are divided into areas of about the same size as the drainage basins.

The divides of the drainage basins are drawn onto maps of scale 1:50 000. These maps are reductions of the base map of Finland, which is originally to the scale 1:10 000 (1:20 000 in Northern Finland). The divides are drawn with the help of topographical contour lines, which are marked on the maps every 2,5 meters in the vertical direction (every 5 meters in Northern Finland). Aerial photographs and field measurements are used in difficult terrains, such as bifurcations and large swamps.

The land information program

The National Board of Waters has obtained a program called FINGIS (Finnish Geographical Information System) (Keisteri and Tuhkanen, 1982) from the National Board of Survey for collection, processing, recording and output of all spatially oriented data. The capability of the program of handling positional information also makes it possible to link different registers together, if the information can be located with coordinates.

Other common links can be used to combine registers, too, for example the numbers of the drainage basins.

The units to be processed in the map data base are points, lines, areas, connections and texts. A line goes from node (end point) to node, and the nodes are linked to all their lines. Areal features are also linked to all surrounding lines.

Digitizing of drainage basin maps

The drainage basin maps are digitized with a digitizer and a microcomputer. All the data is then sent to the master computer and data bases (drainage basins) are generated with the FINGIS-program. Corrections are made with a graphical working station with the help of the same program.

Digitizing starts by orientation of the map by giving the coordinates of the corners of the map and digitizing them. After this every divide line and the sites of the release points and drainage basin numbers are digitized. When digitizing, different meny orders are used, indicating the line type (there are five different line types depending on the drainage basin), outlet, text etc. The numbers of the maps and the drainage basins are also fed to the microcomputer.

In order to make the drainage basin register as compact as possible, extra digitized points of drainage divides are filtered. The digitizing speed is normally 3.2 coordinate pairs per second, at which speed the number of digitized points is on average 9.2 points per kilometer. Filtering is done with a program which calculates ellipses along a digitized line using the points i and i+2. If the point i+1 is within the ellipse it is filtered, otherwise it will be the first point when forming a new ellipse. The perpendicular axis of the ellipse is a given tolerance, which represents the accuracy of digitizing plus the accuracy of the basin divide in the horizontal direction. Seven drainage basins were digitized several times, with a mean areal error of 0.14 %. This corresponds to a tolerance of about 50 m (1 mm on a map of scale 1:50 000). This is the tolerance used in filtering. A greater tolerance could be used, but in that case the accuracy of the basin divide should be known exactly although in fact it varies. The filtering degree is 73 % when using a tolerance of 50 meters, leaving 2.5 points/km. To digitize, filter and transmit one map in the scale 1:50 000 to the main computer takes about four hours. The area covered by one map sheet is 600 km^2.

Height and slope of the watershed

Two digital models were used to calculate the average height, average slope and slope direction. Both models were constructed by the National Board of Survey in Finland. The first model was digitized from maps having a scale of 1:10 000 and a vertical distance between contour lines of 2.5 m. The covering net has a length of 50 m in this model, but a length of 100 m is used in the calculations. The second model, called the "GT-model", is digitized from maps having a scale of 1:200 000 and having a vertical distance between contour lines of 20 m. The net size is 200 m x 200 m.

The models were tested in seven drainage basins with areas ranging from 10.9 to 40.2 km^2. Errors were calculated for some of the above mentioned parameters and differences between the models for some others.

The difference in the average height of a drainage basin between the models was on average 1.7 m and the standard deviation was 1.5 m. The root mean square error of one point in the "GT-model" is 2.15 meters when compared with the height of the nearest contour line. From these numbers it is concluded that both models can be used when calculating the average height.

The mean slope of a drainage basin was calculated in two ways. First, the local slope was calculated with help of a square of 3x3 points. Then the mean slope of the whole drainage basin was calculated as an average value of these points. The difference between these values was on average 58 % when the two models were compared, so the average of local slopes cannot be used. Instead the slope from every divide point to the outlet point was used and the distanceweighted mean of these values was calculated. The differences between slope values of the models in three areas were 0.8 % of the slope, varying from 8.0 to 13.0 %. The standard deviation for the slope was calculated theoretically and was 17 % for the 1:200 000 model and about 9 % for the 1:10 000 model. When all the basin points were used the corresponding figures were 23 and 14 %, respectively. When all the points were used the difference in average slope (GT-model) varied from 1.0 % to 3.3 %. The average slope then became smaller because the slope becomes smaller with decreasing distance from the outlet point. In conclusion both models can be used when the average slope of a basin is calculated. Better results are reached when all the points are used, but it is also possible to use only the divide points. The height of the outlet point should be digitized from a base map and not taken from the terrain model.

The average slope direction should be calculated from local slope directions as a percentage of for instance eastern, southern, western and northern slopes in a basin.

Basin characteristics determined using satellite data

Basin characteristics, such as cultivated land, forests, bogs, drained bogs and lakes will be interpreted from satellite images. Research has been carried out with Landsat images and an operational system has been started this year (1985). Kuittinen and Kauppi (1981) used images from Landsat-2 and compared digitally interpreted land use types with base maps and the national forestry inventory number 6. When they compared land use interpreted from Landsat images with land use interpreted from base maps (16 points per km^2) they found the following correlations: tilled ground outside densely populated areas R^2 = 0.95, tilled ground in densely populated areas R^2 = 0.84, forests and forest-supporting bogs together R^2 = 0.95 and forests R^2 = 0.64. Bogs had a correlation of R^2 = 0.35 because most bogs had a stand of forest.

The amount of growing stock was also interpreted from satellite pictures and was compared with results from the national forestry inventory. The results were 10770 m^3/km^2 from Landsat pictures and 10910 m^3/km^2 from the forestry inventory. The interpreted area was 800 km^2. In smaller areas the error could probably be greater, but this could not be estimated because results from the national forestry inventory method used in Finland cannot be used in areas smaller than 500 km^2.

Research is continuing and operational interpreting from both TM- and MSS-images will start in 1986. Physiographical factors for all river basin parts (area 20...30 km^2) will be interpreted. It is planned to carry out a reinterpreation after 10...20 years in order to monitor changes in physiography of the drainage basins.

The use of weather satellite data

In addition to the above-mentioned permanent or slowly changing data it is planned to file data from the interpretation of rapidly changing entities seen in weather satellite images. NOAA images have been used to determine the snow covered area and provisionally to determine the freezing and thawing of lakes. The temperature of surface water will also be estimated from NOAA images.

Effect of basin characteristics on the quantity of water

Lemmelä and Kuittinen (1976) summarized the effects of basin characteristics on the quantity and quality of water. The results for quantity are mostly from small catchment areas (from 0,07 to 122 km^2) but when the water information system is in operational use results should be available for all sizes of basins. In Finland for example (Mustonen, 1965) the effect of catchment area is such that the maximum runoff in general decreases with increasing area. The effect of the shape of the catchment area on maximum runoff is dependent on the location and length of the watercourse. Increase in altitude and landslope usually increases the maximum runoff. Lakes and artificial waterstorages have a moderating effect on water level variations. Furthermore, when the drainage area and the lake percentage increase, the date of high water is postponed. Reduction of river flood areas increases the quantity of high water in the lower reaches of the watercourse and the date of high water occurs earlier. With increasing permeability of soil the discharge is levelled. However, the permeability of soil may be considerably reduced by frost. Increase and decrease in the volume of growing stock has been found to affect evaporation and runoff. Annual runoff was increased by 7 mm when the cubic volume of growing stock in the area was decreased by 10 cu.m/ha, whereas annual evaporation was increased by a good 10 mm when the cubic volume of growing stock increased by 10 cu.m/ha. Human activity in recent years has been concentrated primarily on the drainage of forests, arable land and peatlands and on regulation of watercourses. It has been found that the drainage of arable land increases minimum runoff. Bog and forest drainage has been found to increase the mean runoff, and particular note has been made of the relatively high increase in minimum runoff. According to investigations carried out in southeastern Finland, the spring maximum runoff was increased on average by 30 % and the summer maximum runoff by 130 % as a result of forest drainage.

References

Keisteri, T. and Tuhkanen, T., 1982, Digital Map Data Base and Application Programs Developed at the National Board of Survey in Finland: XI Cartographic Conference, ICA, Warsaw, p. 1-18.

Kuittinen, R. and Kauppi, L., 1981, Vesistöalueiden fysiografisten tekijöiden inventointiin sopivat tiedostot ("Data bases suitable for inventoring the physiographical factors in river basins", in Finnish only): Vesihallituksen monistesarja, No. 1981:47, p. 1-24.

Lemmelä, R. and Kuittinen, R., 1976, Effect of Climatic and Basin Characteristics on the Quantity and Quality of Water, and an Inventory of these Characteristics: Nordic Hydrological Conference 1976, Reykjavik August 29th - September 1st, Preprints of papers, Nordisk Hydrologisk Forening, p. 1-19.

Mustonen, S., 1965, Meteorologisten ja aluetekijöiden vaikutuksesta valuntaan, MVT 12. Helsinki. (English abstract: Effects of meteorologic and basin characteristics on runoff.)

Hydrologic Applications of Space Technology (Proceedings of the Cocoa Beach Workshop, Florida, August 1985). IAHS Publ. no. 160, 1986.

The role of cell size in hydrology oriented geographic information systems

JACK D. FELLOWS
Office of Management and Budget, Washington, Washington DC, USA
ROBERT M. RAGAN
Remote Sensing Systems Laboratory, University of Maryland, College Park, Maryland, USA

Abstract
Interrelationships among cell size, computer requirements, and accuracy of results are major practical problems facing hydrologists concerned with the use of remote sensing based geographic information systems (GIS). The paper presents the results of a series of sensitivity studies on the performance of a hydrology oriented GIS that can automatically define watershed boundaries from digital terrain data, interface several data planes, and then simulate streamflows with the SCS hydrologic model. The sensitivity analyses provide a series of curves that show the consequences of changing the cell size of a GIS on the hydrologic model parameters. These analyses indicate that the volume of runoff is relatively insensitive to increases in the cell size of accurate land cover and soils data but because of the role of slope in the timing of runoff, significant errors in peak discharge estimates can result as the cell size of digital terrain data is increased.

Introduction
Hydrologists have used empirical models for estimating watershed runoff for many years. The ability to use these models in a timely and effective manner has been greatly enhanced by improvements in data collection and management techniques. Very good quality synoptic land cover, soils, and topography digital data bases can now be created from aerial and satellite remote sensing. In addition, several geographic information systems (GIS) have been developed capable of storing and manipulating these digital data bases. A computer-based hydrologic analysis systems can be created by integrating these data bases, GIS systems, and hydrologic models to produce real-time watershed runoff estimates. The purpose of this paper was to use such a system to examine the sensitivity of these runoff estimates to data resolution.

Hydrologic Analysis Program (HAP)
The HAP system is an interactive computer program designed to determine watershed runoff estimates. Model parameters are derived from data base information contained within a user defined watershed. A HAP data base is represented as a collection of 7 1/2 minute United States Geological Survey (USGS) topographic maps. Each of these maps are divided into a matrix of cells. These cells contain the data necessary to define hydrologic model parameters. Watersheds can be defined by either manually digitizing its boundary or automatically generated by identifying the location of the watershed outfall cell on the appropriate topo map. Watersheds are automatically generated (i.e., "grown") from outfall cell locations by applying an enhanced image processing algorithm to digital

elevation data. Adjacent topos of elevation data are accessed as the watershed propagates across topo boundaries. HAP assembles the appropriate topos of data that contain the watershed, define the necessary hydrologic model parameters from data in cells within the watershed, and route these parameters through the hydrologic model.

The HAP system was designed and implemented for the Environmental Planning offices of the Maryland National Capital Park and Planning Commission in Montgomery County, Maryland. It continues to provide real-time runoff analysis for any user defined watershed within their 1295 square kilometer digital land cover, soil complex, and elevation data base.

Although HAP's modular design permits the usage of any hydrologic model, the version discussed in this paper incorporates the widely used United States Soil Conservation Service TR-55 (SCS-TR-55) hydrologic model (SCS, 1975). This empirical model was designed for watershed areas less than 2000 acres. The SCS-TR-55 rainfall-runoff relationship is defined by:

$$Q = (P - .2S)**2/(P + .8S) \tag{1}$$

Where:

Q = volume of runoff in inches,
P = rainfall in inches,
S = potential maximum storage.

In practice, a runoff curve number, CN, defined in terms of watershed land cover and hydrologic soil types is used as a transformation for S:

$$S = (1000/CN)-10 \tag{2}$$

Traditionally, aerial photos and soil maps have been used to determine the percentage of watershed under various types of land cover and soils. Table 1 is then used to find CN. It has been extremely well documented [Blanchard (1975); Ragan and Jackson (1980); Salmonson, Rango, and Dallam (1977)] that remotely sensed data can be use for model parameter determination, such as a CN, without significant hydrologic model error. HAP uses a similar table to determine runoff curve numbers for a Landsat classified land cover and digital hydrologic soil group data base. The time of concentration, t_c, is that time required for water to move from the most hydraulically distant point to the watershed outlet. The SCS-TR-55 defines t_c as:

$$t_c = (HL**.8*(S+1)**.7)/(1900Y**.5)/0.6 \tag{3}$$

Where:

t_c = time of concentration in hours/sq. miles/inches
HL = hydraulic length empirical relationship
= 209*(watershed area)**.6 for watersheds 2000 acres
Y = average watershed slope

t_c from Equation 3 is entered into the equations listed in Table 2 to determine the watershed peak discharge (q_p) in CSM/inch. The peak discharge in cfs is q_p times the watershed area in square miles times the volume of runoff (Q in Equation 1) in inches.

Table 1.--RUNOFF CURVE NUMBER FOR SCS MODEL (ANTECEDENT MOISTURE CONDITION II, SCS 1975)

LAND USE DESCRIPTION		HYDROLOGIC SOIL GROUP			
		A	B	C	D
Cultivated land: without conservation treatment		72	81	88	91
with conservation treatment		62	71	78	81
Pasture or range land: poor condition		68	79	86	89
good condition		39	61	74	80
Meadow: good condition		30	58	71	78
Wood or Forest land: thin stand, poor cover, no mulch		45	66	77	83
good cover		25	55	70	77
Open Spaces, lawns, parks, golf courses, cemeteries, etc.					
good condition: grass cover on 75% or more of the area		39	61	74	80
fair condition: grass cover on 50% to 75% of the area		49	69	79	84
Commercial and business areas (85% impervious)		89	92	94	95
Industrial districts (72% impervious)		81	88	91	93
Residential:					
Average lot size	Average % Impervious				
1/8 acre or less	65	77	85	90	92
1/4 acre	38	61	75	83	87
1/3 acre	30	57	52	81	86
1/2 acre	25	54	70	80	85
1 acre	20	51	68	79	84
Paved parking lots, roofs, driveways, etc.		98	98	98	98
Streets and roads:					
paved with curbs and storm sewers		98	98	98	98
gravel		76	85	89	91
dirt		72	82	87	89

Therefore, HAP must provide values for precipitation, watershed area, CN and slope to use the SCS-TR-55 hydrologic model. Area is determined by counting cells contained in the user defined watershed. The watershed

Table 2.--HAP EQUATIONS USED TO DESCRIBE THE SCS-TR-55 t_c VS q_p RELATIONSHIP

t_c	Equation
less than 0.25	$q_p = 485(t_c^{-.315})$
0.25 - 0.55	$q_p = 350(t_c^{-.537})$
greater than 0.55	$q_p = 325(t_c^{-.723})$

curve number is produced by overlaying the land cover and soils data planes. Slope is calculated from elevations. Precipitation is determined from 24-hour Type-II storm distribution (SCS, 1975).

Sensitivity Test

HAP was used to examine the SCS-TR-55 hydrologic model parameter estimate errors as a function of watershed area and cell resolution. The area, slope, SCS-TR-55 curve number and peak discharge estimates were calculated for 237 watersheds in data resolutions ranging from 30 to 300 meters. Comparisons were made between parameters calculated from manually digitized and automatically generated watersheds. This test required a massive data base of geophysically distinct terrains and various land cover/soil textures. Because of the difficulty in obtaining and measuring hydrologically distinct land cover/soils data sets, the approach adopted was to acquire 30 meter USGS digital terrain data and then synthetically generate corresponding land cover/soils data. The land cover/soils data was created by a computer program designed to force pseudo-randomly generated numbers into preselected discrete data classes that correspond to the HAP land cover/soil complex table (see Table 1). Three land cover/soils sets were produced and their spatial textures were measured with a second-order gray level probability function (Rosenfeld, 1982) to ensure distinctly different spatial textures.

This 30 meter resolution data base was then aggregated to produce 60, 120, 210, and 300 meter resolution data sets. From these data sets 270 computer plots were generated showing the percent absolute error of SCS-TR-55 model parameter estimates due to watershed delineation method and cell resolution as a function of watershed area and land cover/soil spatial texture. To make the error estimates from these plots meaningful, envelopes of stated statistical confidence were drawn through these data plots. These envelopes were drawn by using the following hypothesis test:

$$Ho = \frac{(Ug - Um)}{Um} * 100 = c \qquad (4)$$

$$HL = \frac{(Ug - Um)}{Um} * 100 < c$$

Where:

U_g = area, slope, curve number or peak discharge mean for a given range of automatically delineated watershed areas,
Um = same as U_g but for manually delineated watersheds,
c = critical error.

Table 3.--TABULATION OF t-TEST INPUTS

Watershed Size (sq.miles)	n	Δ	$t_{n-1,\alpha}$
.06 - 0.20	33	0.72	-1.645
0.20 - 0.30	28	0.79	-1.701
0.30 - 0.40	26	0.81	-1.706
0.40 - 0.50	33	0.72	-1.645
0.50 - 0.80	31	0.75	-1.645
0.80 - 1.50	36	0.68	-1.645
1.50 - 3.00	30	0.75	-1.645
3.00 - 4.00	9	1.50	-1.833
4.00 - 12.00	10	1.40	-1.812

n = Number of Watersheds in each Range
Δ = the Associated Non-centrality Parameter
$t_{n-1,\alpha}$ = the t-distribution value to maintain a level of significance of 95% and power of the test at 99%.
(sq. miles x 2.6 = sq. kilometres)

In an iterative process, a minimum model parameter error due to cell size or watershed delineation technique differences could be selected according to a noncentral t-distribution methodology that would reject the null hypothesis in Equation 4. By picking a range of watershed area and level of significance, one can provide a large enough sample of watersheds to maintain a specified power and critical error value. Therefore, the HAP user would be confident to this power that the parameter error for this range of watersheds would be less than this critical error. The following equations were used for this test:

$$T = (x - U_o)/s \quad n \tag{5}$$

$$c = (x - U_o)/s \tag{6}$$

Where:

x = mean error for a range of watershed size
s = standard deviation
U_o = mean error greater than x
n = number of watersheds in range of watershed sizes
= non-centrality parameter
T = t test statistic

If the T in Equation 5 is greater than the t_{n-1}, test statistic then the null hypothesis in Equation 4 is rejected. Equation 6 was used to determine the critical error value and sample size for each watershed area range to control a 0.05 level of significance and 0.99 power. Once the critical error was determined for each of the nine watershed area ranges shown in Table 3, a polynomial regression was calculated and plotted between the critical error and the mean watershed area.

Results

Figure 1 shows watershed area, curve number, slope, and peak discharge error estimates between watershed delineation methods as a function of cell size and watershed area. For example, a HAP user can be 99% confident that the 30 meter data resolution peak discharge error between "grown" and digitized watersheds is less than 10% for watershed areas greater than 0.15 square miles.

By assuming that the model parameter estimates from the 30 meter resolution data base are correct, the plots in Figure 2 were generated in the same fashion to show model parameter errors of digitized watersheds as a function of cell size and watershed area. Similar plots were made for all three land cover/soil textures and grown watersheds. The dashed portions of these plots represent the watershed areas greater than the 2000 acre SCS-TR-55 hydrologic model limitation.

Conclusion

Interrelationships among data resolution and accuracy of results are a major practical problem facing hydrologists concerned with using regional digital data bases to define hydrologic model parameters. Figures 1 and 2, which show the results of these interrelationship sensitivities on the performance of HAP, provide a data set that may be of considerable value to hydrologists facing these issues.

Increasing a cell size from 30 to as large as 120 meters does not change the estimated curve number by more than 15% for the range of land cover/soil complexes studied, even when the watershed area approaches 0.13 square kilometers. Increasing the spacing of elevations points from 30 to 120 meters and larger produces serious impacts on the estimate of slope and area when the drainage basin size is less than approximately 2.59 square kilometers. Thus, even though the errors associated with curve numbers might be relatively small, the watershed slope and area error can significantly amplify the peak discharge error. Still, sound hydrologic analyses can be anticipated on watershed areas larger than approximately 2.59 square kilometers, for resolutions less than 120 meters.

When the cell size of the elevation data was 30 meters, the results obtained with the automatic watershed delineation technique showed excellent agreement with those obtained by the traditional manual digitizing method. The results of Figure 1 indicate that the automatic delinea-

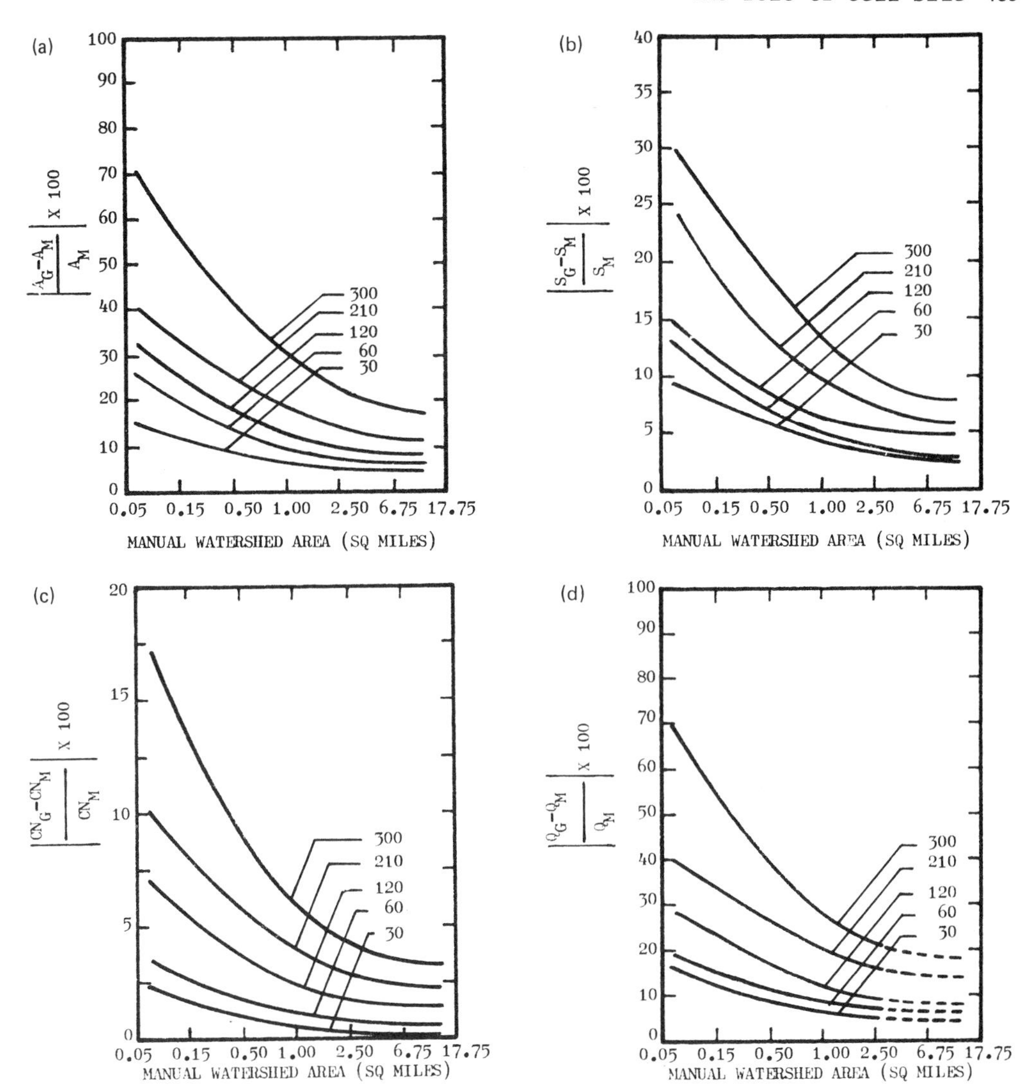

FIG.1 Ninety-nine per cent confidence error envelopes between manual and automatic delineations: (a) area, (b) slope, (c) SCS-TR-55 curve number, (d) SCS-TR-55 peak discharge. (237 watersheds).

tion method should not use a cell size larger than approximately 60 meters. However, the trends indicate that larger cell resolutions might be used when the watershed area of interest is larger than those in the test data set.

References

Soil Conservation Service-USDA, "Urban Hydrology for Small Water sheds," Technical Release No. 55, January, 1975.

Blanchard, B.J., "Remote Sensing Techniques for Prediction of Watershed Runoff," paper W-15, NASA Earth Resources Survey Symposium, Houston, Texas, June, 1975.

Ragan, R.M., and Jackson, T.J., "Runoff Synthesis Using Landsat and SCS

Model," Journal of Hydraulics Division, ASCE, May, 1980.
Salomonson, V., Rango, A., and Dallam, W., "Water Management and Control Applications System Verification and Transfer Project," NASA/GODDARD, Greenbelt, Maryland, 1977.
Roenfeld, A., "Textural Measurements in Digital Pictures," University of Maryland, College Park, Maryland, TR-51, 1982.

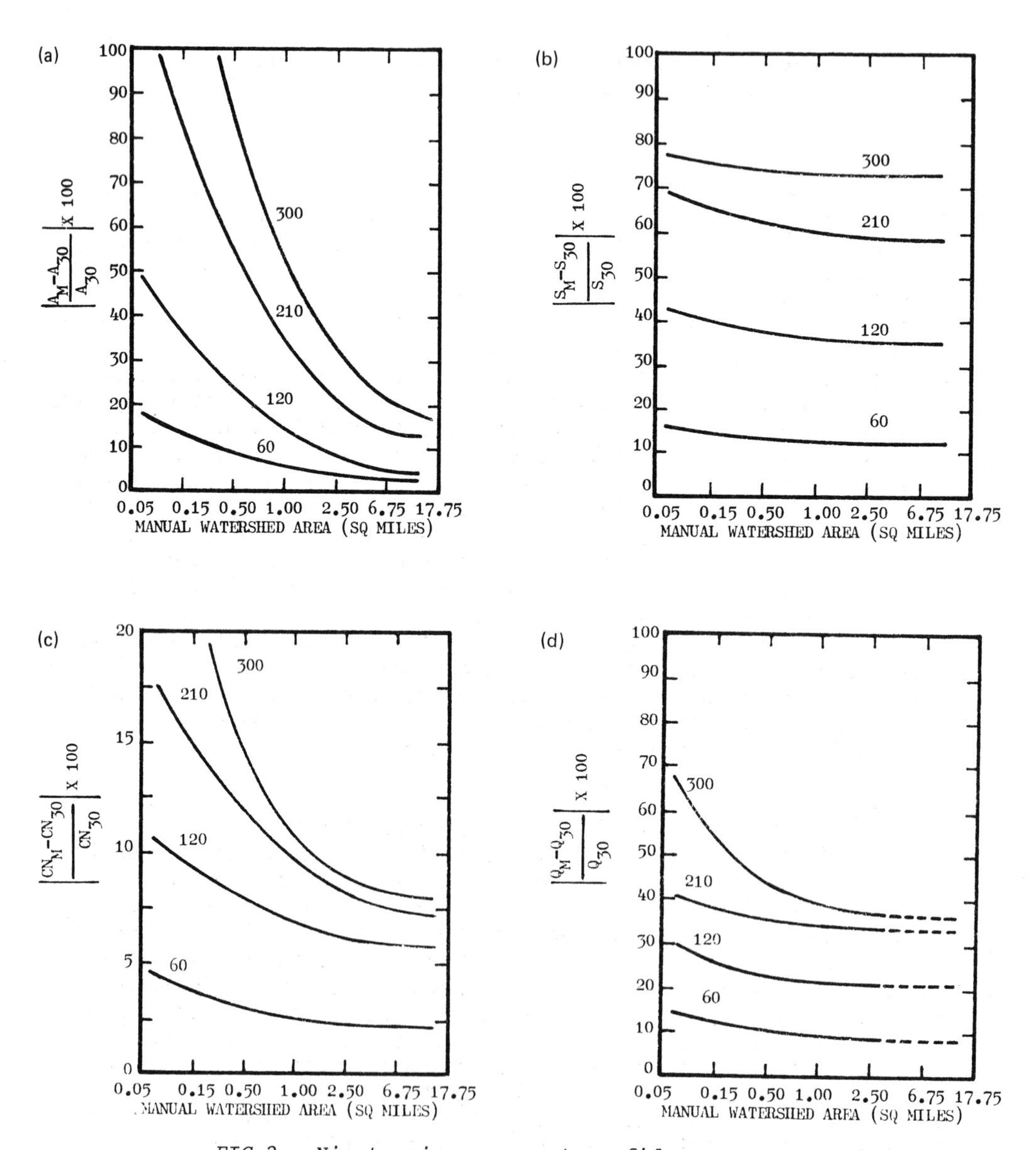

FIG.2 Ninety-nine per cent confidence error envelopes between 30 meter and 60, 120, 210 and 300 meter manually delineated watersheds: (a) area, (b) slope, (c) SCS curve number, (d) SCS-TR-55 peak discharge. (237 watersheds).

Hydrologic Applications of Space Technology (Proceedings of the Cocoa Beach Workshop, Florida, August 1985). IAHS Publ. no. 160, 1986.

Mainframe to personal computer integration for state-wide remote sensing-based hydrologic modeling

R. M. RAGAN, M. J. COLGAN, J. HOLLISTER &
J. K. SIRCAR
Remote Sensing Systems Laboratory, Department of Civil engineering, University of Maryland, College Park, Maryland, USA
E. J. WHITE
Bureau of Research, State Highway Adminis tation Baltimore, Maryland, USA

Abstract
The use of specially configured image processing computers to translate digital format imagery into valuable hydrologic information is well established. Our mainframe computers now have the speed and mass storage capacity to manage the multi-layered data sets required for hydrologic analysis on a regional scale. Still the utilization of remote sensing capabilities by hydrologists at the decision-making level continues to be limited despite extensive research and a number of successful, well-documented demonstration projects. A major factor limiting the use of this important new source of information has been the lack of effective systems that integrate image processing and mainframe capabilities with an easy to use, but still powerful, intelligent workstation on the individual hydrologist's desk. The present paper describes a cooperative project that can provide the international hydrologic community an example of the type of systems integration needed to insure user level utilization of remote sensing capabilities. The objective of the project is to develop and support the necessary data bases and management software that will allow the hydraulic engineers of a state highway administration to use a desk top microcomputer as an intelligent workstation to conduct hydrologic analyses above any point on any stream in the state. The workstation is an IBM PC, XT or AT that can be operated as a stand-alone unit or networked to a supporting VAX or mainframe that provides mass storage, additional computational power and the required data security.

Introduction
Our ability to use specially configured image processing computers to translate digital format imagery into valuable hydrologic information is well developed. At the same time, our mainframe computers now have the speed and mass storage capacity to manage the multi-layered data sets required for hydrologic analysis on a regional scale. Still, the utilization of remote sensing capabilities by hydrologists at the decision-making level continues to be limited despite extensive research and a number of very successful, well-documented demonstration projects. A major factor limiting the use of this important new source of information has been the lack of effective systems that integrate image processing and mainframe capabilities with an easy to use, but still powerful, intelligent workstation on the individual hydrologist's desk. A cooperative project between the Maryland State Highway Administration (MSHA), the Federal Highway Administration (FHWA), and the Remote Sensing Systems Laboratory (RSSL) of the University of Maryland can provide the international hydrologic community an example of the type of systems integration needed to

insure user level utilization of remote sensing capabilities.

The objective of the cooperative project is to provide MSHA hydrologists with an ability to use the SCS family of models to simulate streamflow conditions at any point in the State with a minimum of effort. Thus, the user has a desk top terminal that can quickly assemble the land cover, slope, and soil data within the watershed and then make the necessary interfaces to define the hydrologic parameters and run the model. Providing this capability required integrating the powers of an I^2S Model 70 Image Processing System with the mass storage of a UNIVAC 1100/80 mainframe and IBM desk top computers with digitizing tablets and on-board graphics that serve as intelligent work stations. The system is shown schematically by Figure 1.

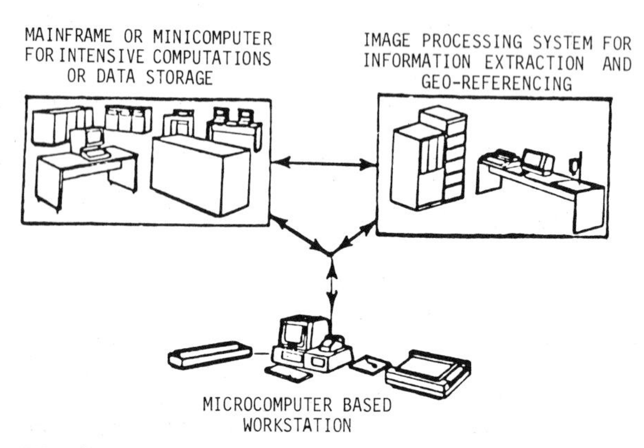

FIG.1 System integration for remote sensing based hydrologic modeling.

The I^2S Model 70 can be used to register Landsat derived land covers with digital format elevation and soil data on a USGS quad-sheet basis. The MSS can be used in the rural areas of the State and the Thematic Mapper can be used in the highly developed Baltimore-Washington corridor. The 3200 square km, three county test area includes a very heavily urbanized region that was developed by digitizing themes derived from high altitude photography. By reformatting the data into 5 second cells, a 1200 baud telephone line provides an acceptable mechanism for transferring the I^2S developed data sets onto the UNIVAC 1100/80. The UNIVAC provides the permanent storage and data security required by the MSHA. The test program has concluded that the general purpose UNIVAC system will be replaced by a VAX 11/730 that will be dedicated to the support of the hydrologic modeling system.

Phase I of the project, in which a three county area covering approximately 3200 sq. km. was used for systems development, testing and personnel training has been completed. Phase II, under which the Statewide data base is to be developed and a minicomputer of the VAX class capable of supporting 4 workstations is to be configured, will require approximately 30 months to complete. The present paper centers on the operation of the workstations that are built around the IBM PC, XT or AT networked to a minicomputer or mainframe through a 1200 baud smart modem.

Use of the Intelligent Workstation

When the project was originally proposed, it was planned to have all of the data and applications software on a mainframe with access through a standard dumb terminal. By the time the contracts were signed to start the MSHA project, the IBM PC-AT with a 20 M-byte hard disk had been introduced and software was available that would allow a microcomputer to duplicate the operations of a mainframe-based hydrologic analysis program described by Ragan and Fellows (1980). Thus, the decision was made to adopt this new software and build the MSHA approach around desk top personal computers that would allow the hydrologist to perform his computations and store data for several counties without having to connect to a central computer.

Because of its graphics capabilities, and to allow practicing civil engineers to easily modify the program in the future, the software adopted for the workstation was written in BASIC. In order to optimize the core storage, the various functions of the workstation are performed by a series of relatively small compiled subprograms that are brought in as needed through chaining procedures. The operation of the desk-top workstation is illustrated by Fig. 2. Figure 3 shows the sequence of subprograms that are implemented to perform the tasks outlined in the subsequent paragraphs.

In a typical problem, the hydrologist wants to run an SCS model on a watershed somewhere in the State. He types in the name of the county (or counties) and the names of the USGS 7.5 minute quadrangle sheets that define the watershed boundary. The data base management system on the PC then examines a catalog to determine if all of the land use, soil, and slope data required are stored on the PC disk. If this check shows that the data is there, the program proceeds as described in the next paragraph. If the data is not available on the PC, the user is advised on the screen display and asked if he wants to obtain the data from the mass storage device on the UNIVAC or VAX. If he decides to continue the analysis, the screen prompts will allow him to automatically dial into the supporting computer through the 1200 baud smart modem. A data base management system on the supporting computer is automatically implemented and the screen prompts take the user through the steps necessary to bring the needed data down to the personal computer and check it for transmission errors.

Following a series of prompts on the color graphics CRT, the hydrologist will input the boundary of the watershed from a digitizing tablet. These coordinates interface with a Geographic Information System on the PC that assembles and stores the data within the boundary as a series of sequential and random access files. If the hydrologist wants to examine the impact of any changes in land use or other watershed characteristics, these proposed conditions are input from the digitizer or keyboard. Files for these altered watershed conditions are then developed and stored. The Curve Numbers are computed and the hydrologist can either accept SCS default values or, for example, he can enter travel times from the keyboard that he has computed through detailed hydraulic analysis. The workstation then follows the computational steps set forth in the SCS manuals to execute the models. Color maps, such as the photo reduced dot matrix copy shown in Fig. 4, are displayed on the CRT to show the spatial distribution of the current and proposed land use, soil type, and slope. At the same time, 1:48,000 symbolic maps and statistical summaries are output on the dot matrix printer. The color CRT can then display the computed hydrographs while the dot matrix printer outputs the tabular data, as shown in Fig. 5.

In addition to running the SCS programs from the workstation or supporting computer, the hydrologist has an onboard relational data base capability that allows him to look at relationships among the watershed parameters. For example, he can easily assemble the land use, soil type and slope data for the watershed of interest and develop a color CRT display such as that illustrated in Fig. 6 that shows the location of those areas that are either forest or grass on a C or D hydrologic soil group where the slope is greater than 10%.

Because the software is compiled, speed is not a problem. In this example, the SCS-TR-55 was run for existing and altered land use conditions

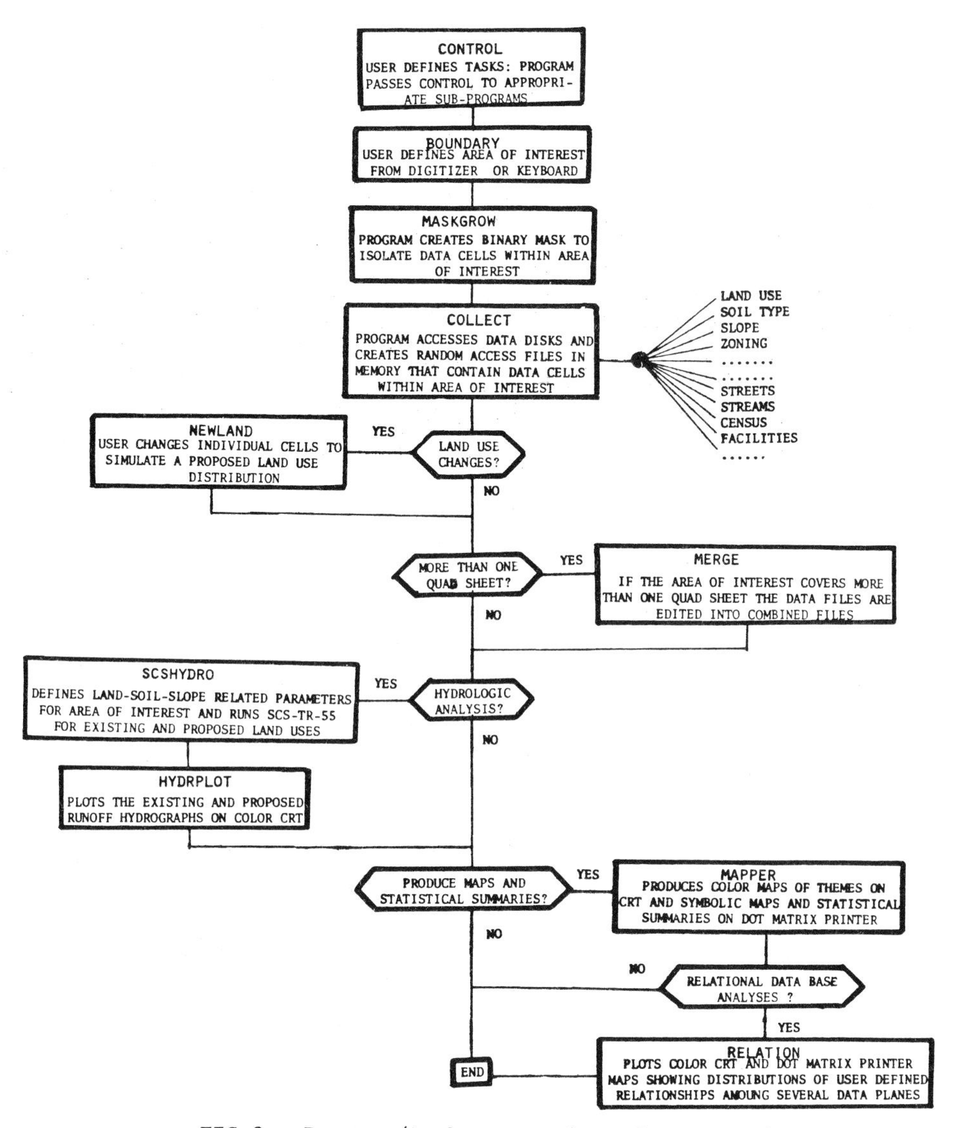

FIG.3 Program/task sequencing of workstation software.

on a 2084 acre watershed. All computations including the generation of four dot matrix printer maps and four color CRT maps required 7.25 minutes on the IBM-AT.

The Data Base

At present, land use, soil type and slope data for three counties of the Statewide MSHA project are complete. The data are stored in blocks of 90 x 90 cells referenced to USGS quadrangle sheets. The quadrangle sheets are then grouped by counties. Thus, the county and quadsheet names become "pointers" that quickly move the computer to the specific data sets required. Depending on the intensity of development, the land use data is defined from either high altitude aircraft or Landsat MSS/TM. The hydrologic soil groups are developed by digitizing the county soil maps. Thus far, the slope maps have been developed by either manual digitizing or an

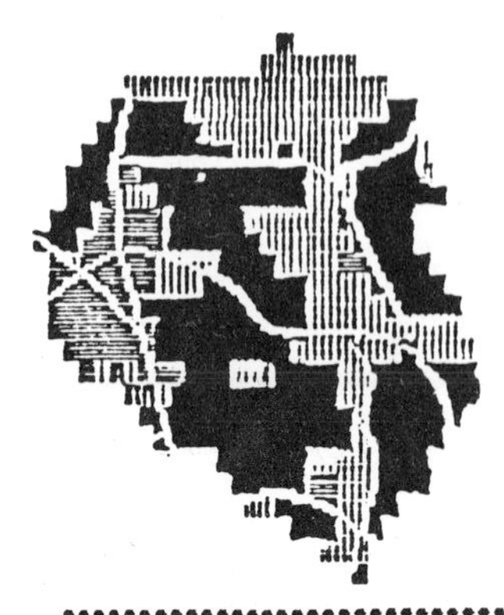

UPPER SLIGO
EXISTING
LAND USE

SINGLE HOMES
TREE CANOPY
GRASS
LOW DENSITY
HIGH DENSITY
COMM/INDUST.

SYM	CLASS	ACRES	%
B	GRASS	142.29	6.83
C	CULTIVATED FIELDS	0.00	0.00
F	FOREST	422.28	20.26
J	RURAL RESIDENTIAL	0.00	0.00
K	COMMERCIAL INDUSTRIALL	243.27	11.67
L	SINGLE FAMILY HOUSING	1156.68	55.51
M	LOW DENSITY	32.13	1.54
N	HIGH DENSITY	87.21	4.19
	TOTAL	2083.86	100.00

FIG.4 Dot-matrix printer copy of color CRT display of watershed land use map & statistical summary.

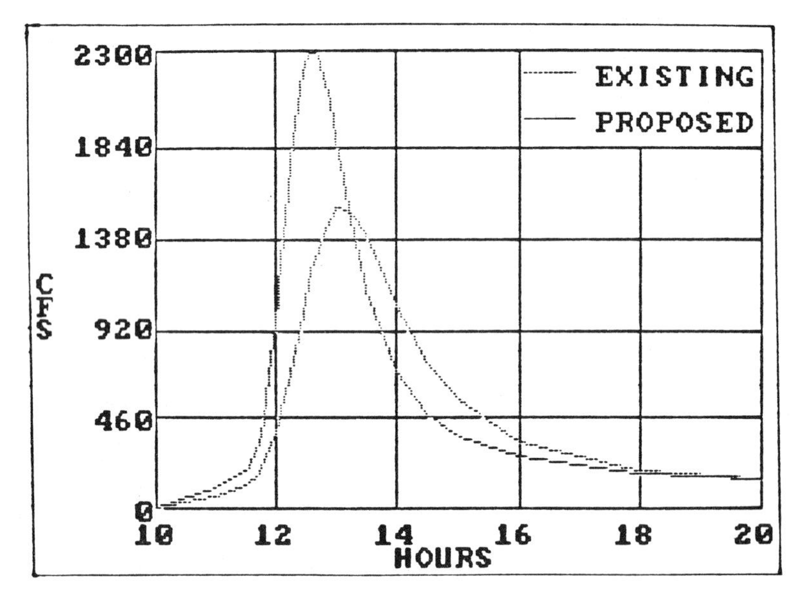

****** SCS-TR-55 HYDROLOGIC ANALYSIS ******

**** RUNOFF HYDROGRAPH FROM TYPE II STORM DISTRIBUTION ****

PROJECT TITLE: UPPER SLIGO CREEK
24 HOUR RAINFALL (INCHES) 4.80

AREA(ACRES)= 2083.86 SQ.MILES= 3.256032

QUANTITY	PRESENT	PROPOSED
CURVE NUMBER	74.77	77.26
PERCENT IMPERVIOUSNESS	34.20	40.19
AVERAGE PERCENT SLOPE	3.30	3.30
TIME OF CONCENTRATION (HOURS)	1.90	1.20
VOLUME OF RUNOFF (INCHES)	2.27	2.48
PEAK DISCHARGE	1503.96	2293.74

FIG.5 Dot-matrix printer copy of color CRT display of hydrographs & portion of tabular data.

FIG.6 Dot-matrix copy of typical relational analysis.

experimental scanning technique using a Vidicon camera interfaced with the I^2S System 70.

Reference

Ragan, R.M. and Fellows, J.D., "A Data Base System for Real-Time Hydrologic Modeling," Proceedings of the ASCE Specialty Conference, Civil Engineering Applications of Remote Sensing, University of Wisconson, August 13-14, 1980.

Hydrologic Applications of Space Technology (Proceedings of the Cocoa Beach Workshop, Florida, August 1985). IAHS Publ. no. 160, 1986.

Implementation of geographic information systems in the Water Resources Division of the United States Geological Survey

WALTER L. RENNICK
US Geological Survey, 445 National Center, Reston, Virginia 22092, USA

Abstract

The Water Resources Division (WRD) of the Geological Survey has linked its national, regional and state office computers in a X.25 telecommunications network using leased communication circuits and switches from public communication vendors such as AT&T. This distributed network of computers is referred to as the Distributed Information System (DIS) and is used to process hydrologic data locally, and to interface with national hydrologic data bases. Recently, the need to input, analyze, and display hydrologic data in a spatial domain has increased due to realization that the results of data processing can be easier to interpret and understand by others if presented in a graphic form, specifically in the spatial domain.

To meet this need WRD has procured a proprietary geographic information system (GIS) for evaluation. This GIS was selected after extensive analysis of the needs of WRD personnel which resulted in a Request For Proposal with detail GIS specifications for a system to be evaluated at four WRD regional offices and one district office. This evaluation is currently underway, using the GIS in support of numerous hydrologic applications. Several concerns related to the use of a GIS are already being identified for future consideration in making a GIS more usable in hydrologic applications. One general concern relates to the maintenance of a national cartographic data base with the appropriate quality control, standard formats (to insure that users can use it easily), and that the data is "correct". Other concerns relate to the use and transfer of GIS data sets across the network in an usable manner, and the size requirements of a usable GIS data base.

Introduction

The Water Resources Division's Distributed Information System (DIS) began implementation in October 1982 to provide more efficient computing support for of the Water Resources Division (Posson, etal., 1985). The DIS now consists of over 60 Prime super minicomputers installed in district offices across the nation and linked through a telecommunications network providing computing services for nearly 3000 users. The mission of the Water Resources Division (WRD) is to provide hydrologic information to appraise the Nation's water resources. To accomplish this mission WRD:

- Collects Data
- Conducts Investigations and Analyzes Data
- Coordinated Water Data Acquisition
- Disseminates Data and Information
- Conducts Research on Hydrologic Principles and Processes

In support of these objectives WRD has developed major software systems (eg. WATSTORE, WAter-data STorage and REtrieval system) for the management and analysis of hydrologic and related data. This effort supports data collection, in cooperation with State and local agencies, or other Federal agencies, of information pertinent to the identification, location, and physical description of over 250,000 sites. These locations include over 15,000 stream gauging stations, 1000 lakes and reservoirs, 30,000 water level observation wells, 12,500 ground water quality wells and 1,000 sediment stations. The numbers for active sites varies from year to year. When the number of parameters measured at each site is considered along with the historical records that are maintained, the need for improved methods of accessing and using the data presents a tremendous challenge to the data base managers in WRD. Rough estimates of the amount of computer storage media required for these national data bases are five to ten gigabytes and growing! This challenge is complicated by the need to keep much of the data on-line so that it can be readily accessed by users through out the Nation.

Acquisition of a Geographic Information System

With the implementation of the DIS, WRD began several major studies to evaluate methods to distribute the support and maintenance of its national data bases to district offices and still maintain the integrity of the data. Also with the acquisition of super-mini computers in each district office as part of the DIS network of computers, hydrologists were able to process more data locally and needed software to support this increased demand. This demand, mainly involved being able to retrieve selected subsets of the national data base, integrate that data with new data locally, and then easily display results in a variety of graphical forms for water resources managers to review.

One result of these studies was the recommendation to acquire an integrated geographic information system for test and evaluation. Many of the data base systems that WRD has developed for the management and analysis of hydrologic data can be considered geographic information systems. However, it was realized that while these systems strongly supported the data storage and retrieval aspects of WRD's mission objectives, they did not provide or support recent technological capability to digitize data, analyze data spatially, and display graphically the results in an integrated and interactive manner.

A primary specification for the procurement of a geographic information system was that it provide an integrated approach to data processing. Another primary specification was the support of both interactive graphic displays and drafting quality plotter graphics. Finally, the system had to provide a direct link between the spatial (coordinate) data and the associated attribute (a water level measurement) data so that processing of spatial (geographic) data would produce corresponding results in the attribute data. Secondary considerations were compatiblity with existing hardware and software already in use by WRD.

No GIS considered met all the specifications included in the Request For Proposal, especially in the support for links to existing hydrologic models used by WRD , and in the support for integration of vector based spatial data with raster (gridded) based data. The GIS procured by WRD is now being tested and evaluated for its ability to support hydrologic applications related to WRD's mission objectives. The GIS under evaluation was acquired from Environmental Systems Research Institute (ESRI)1 Inc., and is called ARC-INFO. This name reflects its integration of a coordinate data management system, ARC, using an arc-node data structure (derived from the USGS Digital Line Graph format) and a general purpose relational database, INFO. INFO is a relational data base marketed by Henco, Inc. INFO had coincidentally been purchased for use in the WRD-DIS as a data base system for the creation, analysis and management of small hydrologic and administrative data bases. This reduced the initial cost to government of the ARC-INFO system since the license for INFO had already been purchased.

GIS Evaluation

Evaluation projects have included a demonstration project in cooperation with the State of Connecticut involving the automation of over 30 spatial data layers and associated attribute data for two 7.5 minute map quadrangles in Connecticut. The results of this project were demonstrated at the annual meeting of the Association of American State Geologists in June 1985 at Mystic, Connecticut. This effort involved inter-divisional cooperation within the Survey, with the State of Connecticut Department of Natural Resources, and with other Federal agencies. Both existing digital cartographic data and newly digitized cartographic data along with the attribute data were converted or automated, and then integrated using ARC-INFO. Several scenarios were developed to test the capabilities of the system. These included an industrial siting procedure, a public water supply well siting procedure, a low flow run-off model, and the generation of an initial data base for a ground water model. The results of this project are still being evaluated. The general results were quite favorable in showing the capabilities of an integrated GIS. Most exciting were the interactive retrievals of all attribute data associated with a map feature, achieved by placing the cursor on or near a digital map feature (a well site) as displayed on a color graphics terminal. This project identified several areas of concern related to utilization of a GIS. These included the amount of time required to build the digital data base, the space required for storage of temporary results and final results, the ease of using existing digital cartographic data bases. These concerns will be discussed more below. A second project evaluating the ARC/INFO system is the WRD National Water Summary. This project produces an extensive annual publication each year summarizing national water resources data on a state by state basis and uses hundreds of thematic maps illustrate conclusions and facts about water quality and quantity for each state. This project hopes to automate these graphic summaries using ARC-INFO. It plans to use the 1:2,000,000 Digital Line Graph (DLG) files prepared by the National Mapping Division (NMD) of the Survey for printing the National Map Atlas as a digital base map for the generation of map graphics for use in its yearly publication.

This project has raised concerns about the general utility of the present DLG file structure. The DLG files produced by NMD are an excellent source of digital coordinate data, but were developed more for the expediency of map printing. The difficulties encountered with the DLG files can be corrected with functions provided in the GIS, although improvements to the GIS in treating mismatched boundaries in the DLG need to be made. These concerns also raise the issue of the maintenance of a national digital cartographic data base, since users are now acquiring the tools to add and modify the coordinate data. (If improper use of statistics can distort or deceive, the improper use of digital graphic maps based on poor quality coordinate data is even more susceptible!)

Another project using the ARC-INFO system in WRD is, the John Day River Basin in Oregon. This joint USGS and State of Oregon GIS project was developed on a raster-based image processing system, but used INFO as its main data base manager. While this project was quite successful in demonstrating many features of a geographic information system, the lack of integration between the INFO data base and the raster mapping display has resulted in the decision to convert much of the spatially related raster data to the ARC-INFO arc-node format in the second phase of this project. A WRD project in Arizona will be using ARC-INFO to analyze data digitized from radar images of the Colorado River basin. A water use project in California will attempt to use the GIS to summarize water use information derived from local accounting units after conversion, using the GIS, to national accounting units used by WRD. An administrative project is using the GIS to build a data base that can be used to manage and display graphically information related to the performance and structure of the WRD-DIS network. A digital map display of the telecommunications links can be produced indicating by color the amount of transmission load each link carries, providing a geographic perspective of the network traffic data. This digital map can then be used as an interactive interface for retrieving the attribute data associated with each mapped network feature.

Concerns Related to the General Use of a GIS

The above projects have raised several concerns about the implementaon of a GIS in a distributed network. A partial summary of these concerns includes:

1. Size of computer storage required for practical applications.
2. Impact on other computer users and resources.
3. Maintenance and distribution of digital cartographic data bases.

This issue involves the concern that a digital cartographic data base must be topologically "clean", for example all polygon boundaries representing a closed area must be topologically closed, no holes or gaps, in the boundary. Unfortunately many existing digital data sets do not meet this requirement. ARC-INFO provides the functions to correct this, which must be done to allow the spatial analysis functions to work properly. These functions can be quite time consuming for both user and computer resources if the coordinate data in the digital map is dense. A second aspect of this problem is the problem of digital coordinates from geographic layers digitized from different sources (eg., a political boundary manuscript and a stream network manuscript), if a line representing the same boundary is digitized once in each layer, when they are overlaid, using the GIS they are not identical. Again ARC-INFO has functions to repair this problem, but it introduces ambiguity in the data. This problem can be minimized during the creation of new digital coordinate data bases by digitizing features representing the same boundary only once.

4. Remote usage of the GIS system from other sites in the DIS network.
5. Lack of GIS commands to easily accomplish certain data manipulation tasks.

This includes data format conversion functions between different GIS data files and data files from different computer systems,and more intelligent commands to help resolve data inconsistencies when "cleaning" a digital map.

Conclusion

Tentative conclusions related to the utilization of a GIS in support of WRD mission objectives are encouraging. The present evaluation effort is helping identify potential problems that must be resolved before the general use of a GIS is possible by more casual users who may and should be able to use a GIS in the future. Problems with existing digital cartographic data bases and procedures in creating new digital cartographic data bases must be resolved. In addition to problems with the data, improvements in the GIS system, including consistent command syntax, complete documentation, and development of new commands are being identified for future modifications.

References

Kilpatrick, M. C., 1981, WATSTORE: A WAter Data and STorage REtrieval System: Popular Publications of the U. S. Geological Survey.

Posson, D. R.; Nethaway C. D.; Harbaugh, A. W.; 1985 Design and Implementation of a National Distributed Information System: Proceedings of the National Prime Users Group Conference, Vol. II, p 521.

Note

The use of firm, trade, or brand names in this report is for identification purposes only and does not imply endorsement by the U.S. Geological Survey.

Hydrologic Applications of Space Technology (Proceedings of the Cocoa Beach Workshop, Florida, August 1985). IAHS Publ. no. 160, 1986.

The APPS-IV analytical stereoplotter with superposition graphics: a unique tool to build and revise GIS data bases

DAVID C. GOODRICH
Autometric, Inc. 5205 Leesburg Pike/Suite 1308
Falls Church, VA 22041, USA

Abstract

The APPS-IV with Superposition Graphics (SUPER-P) interfaced with a minicomputer and the AUTOGIS geographic information system (GIS) provides an ideal facility to collect, update and analyze digital database information. The database information can be compiled from stereophotography obtained from a large number of sensing systems ranging from frame photography to some of the most complex dynamic imaging systems including Space Shuttle photography.

The Superposition Graphics subsystem of the APPS-IV allows direct overlay of computer graphics onto the stereophotography. Within the system the operator can view stereographics and stereophotography simultaneously while moving throughout the stereo model. The stereographics can be displayed while digitizing new imagery or can be generated and displayed from coordinates maintained in previously compiled GIS database. This provides the operator real-time verification of feature delineation and identification during database compilation. This paper describes the APPS-IV Superposition Graphics environment and its capabilities. The AUTOGIS software system and its major capabilities are also briefly discussed.

APPS-IV - Superposition Graphics - AUTOGIS Environment

The APPS-IV Superposition Graphics - AUTOGIS™ environment is composed of the following key components:

- APPS-IV (Analytical Photogrammetric Processing System)
- Host Computer
- Vector Automation G-80 Graphics Processor
- High Resolution Monitors and $1/2$ x Demagnifying Lenses
- Registration Board
- AUTOGIS (Automated Geographic Information System) Software

Figure 1 illustrates the APPS-IV and the high resolution monitors. The Superposition Graphics (SUPER-P) is a subsystem to the APPS-IV. To fully appreciate Superposition Graphics and AUTOGIS software functions the capabilities of the APPS-IV must be more fully described.

The APPS-IV:

The APPS-IV is a medium accuracy analytical stereoplotter used to spatially quantify stereophotographs. It is capable of stage position accuracy of 10 micrometers or less after calibration using an affine transformation. The unique stage on stage design of the APPS-IV lends significant compactness to the instrument, as compared to other units of similar accuracy. Common stage motion is controlled by a trackball, and differential x and y stages are controlled by the delta x and delta y thumbwheels (see Figure 1). The x thumbwheel functions as the elevation wheel when automatic stereomodel

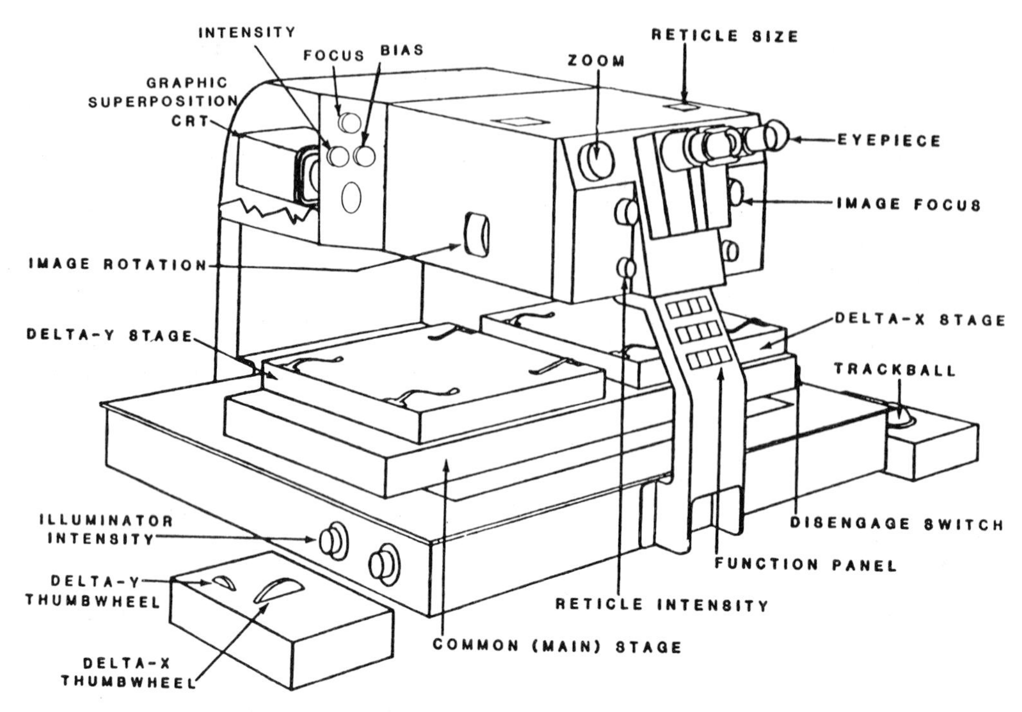

FIG.1 APPS-1V overview Model 4000.

maintenance is engaged. The y thumbwheel can remove any residual y parallax that may exist. This provides improved viewing and pointing accuracy.

The APPS-IV's electronic subsystem contains 13 microprocessors that perform servo monitoring, communications with the central processor, and stereoviewing maintenance throughout the stereomodel (Greve, 1982). Because the APPS-IV microprocessors handle the computationally intensive task of stereo maintenance, the host computer is free to accommodate other users and database management. Once the model parameters have been downloaded into the APPS-IV and stereo maintenance is engaged, the instrument can operate without the host computer. For model setup and data collection the APPS-IV communicates to the host via a standard RS232 interface. Support software is currently available for DEC PDP, VAX, Data General, and Hewlett-Packard minicomputers.

The optical subsystem of the APPS-IV allows zoom magnification from 6x to 36x as well as optical image rotation to allow the setting of pseudo stereo models. The optical subsystem also has a TV camera port which will allow mounting of a TV camera to view imagery and superimposed graphics for training or supervisory inspection purposes. The optical qualities of the subsystem are comparable to the highest quality light table microscope. Detailed photointerpretation tasks can therefore be carried out on the APPS-IV during compilation, rendering additional light table tasks unnecessary.

These APPS-IV features combine to perform many useful functions. One of the most important functions is the ability to accurately measure ground or object space coordinates. This feature is complemented by a vector drive capability in which the APPS-IV can be commanded to drive to a specific object space coordinate in the stereomodel. Profile collection is another key capability. This feature allows collection of three-dimensional object space coordinates along a predetermined line or curve at programmable intervals with a selectable pause length at each point. A complete and reproducible digital model can be produced with this capability. To assist profile and point collection the APPS-IV contains a 150 point buffer so that measurements will be protected against loss if the operator should get ahead of the host's data processing programs. This unique, non-time critical, interface of the APPS-IV allows significant simplification of the software architecture required in the host.

These capabilities allow thorough analysis and mensuration of stereophotography. Current stereophotography accommodated by the APPS-IV ranges from non-metric close range to instantaneous frame to some of the most complex dynamic (panoramic or strip) sensor systems including Space Shuttle photography. The APPS-IV is further enhanced with the addition of the SUPER-P graphics subsystem.

The Graphics Superposition Subsystem:

To accomplish the superimposition of stereo computer graphics into the APPS-IV, two 3-inch diameter high resolution phosphor monitors are placed in the rear bracket of the APPS-IV. The image of the graphics is beamsplit into the optical train using two plate beam splitters (see Figure 2). This allows the operator to simultaneously view photographic and graphics images

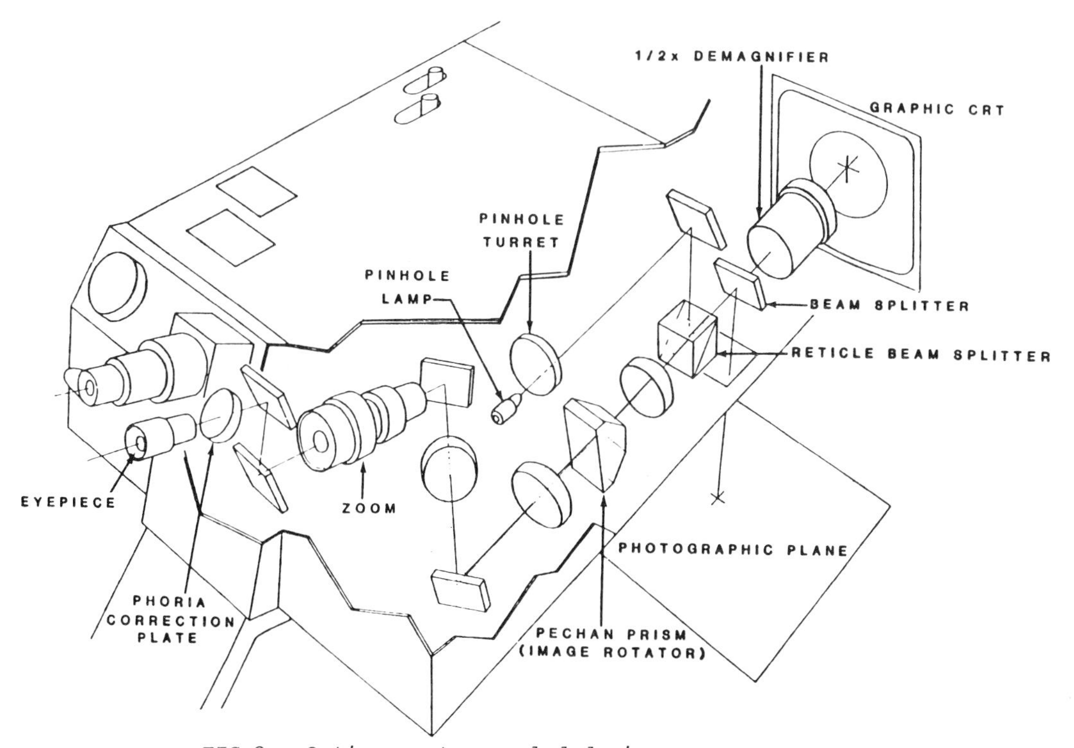

FIG.2 Optics system exploded view.

while looking into the eyepieces. When special design $1/2$ x demagnifying lenses are placed in front of the high resolution monitors the graphics lines observed on the photography are approximately 50 micrometers wide.

The additional graphics "plane" of information increases the information space obtainable in normal stereophotographic analysis. Non-imaged information can be displayed at the geometrically correct photo locations to enhance photo interpretation. The graphics can also be used to correct the inadequecy of current compilation methods where data compiled from photography must be displayed and reviewed on another separate medium (graphics CRT or hardcopy). Using this system the operator can monitor digitizing progress without looking away from the eyepieces.

The Vector Automation G-80 processor stores and controls the graphics information display on the high resolution monitors. This vector graphics processor has 16k x 16k addressability (2k x 2k displayable) and a 30-60 cycles/second refresh rate.

The remaining key component of the Graphics Subsystem is the registration board. This microprocessor resides in the APPS-IV electronics drawer, and maintains continual registration of the graphics to the stereophotography. This is achieved by sensing the stage motions as the operator moves through the stereomodel. These stage translations are transformed to graphics space and sent to the G-80 processor.

The SUPER-P subsystem hardware coupled with a subset of G-CORE compatible software allows display of segments containing vector, symbol and text characteristics with selectable attributes. Major attributes include multiple line styles, intensity variation, highlighting (blinking approximately four times per second) and visibility (on/off). With the visibility attribute on/off toggle, a cluttered graphics overlay can quickly and easily be toggled off by the operator to focus attention on the imagery. A hardware intensity reostat also allows the operator to adjust the graphics so they appear translucent over the imagery. When adjusted properly, the operator can perceive the graphics and yet "look through" them to view the imagery with minimal degradation. Graphics overlays can be displayed in mono or stereo and can be declared either as tracking or stationary. Stationary (non-tracking) segments allow display of operator prompts and/or warnings within the field of view during stage motion anywhere in the stereomodel. This feature, combined with a voice data entry option that is currently being developed, will provide a system where the operator's attention need not be diverted from the primary work environment, namely the graphics and the stereomodel. The SUPER-P subsystem is summarized in Figure 3.

AUTOGIS (Automated Geographic Information System) Software

AUTOGIS software provides an efficient system for input, storage, retrieval, manipulation and display of spatially referenced data. Input to the system can not only be made from photographs using the APPS-IV, but also from existing maps or engineering drawings using an XY digitizer or from remote sensing raster format. During input the features are identified as they are digitized and entered via the voice data entry option or on an alphanumeric terminal. The software system also provides a simple mechanism for tying together features that cross stereomodel boundaries. All information in the AUTOGIS digital database is referenced to easily reproducible ground space coordinates.

AUTOGIS consists of two major software subsystems. The first is the Analytical Mapping System (Niedzwiadek and Greve, 1978). This subsystem allows full photogrammetric block adjustments of aerial photographs to obtain photoposition and orientation. This information is stored in a photographic database. When retrieved, this information can be used to set up a stereomodel on the APPS-IV. Once the stereomodel is set, accurate three-dimensional ground can be obtained to form point, line, or polygon data for input into the Data Base Management System (DBMS).

DBMS is a subset of MOSS, the second major subsystem of AUTOGIS . MOSS,

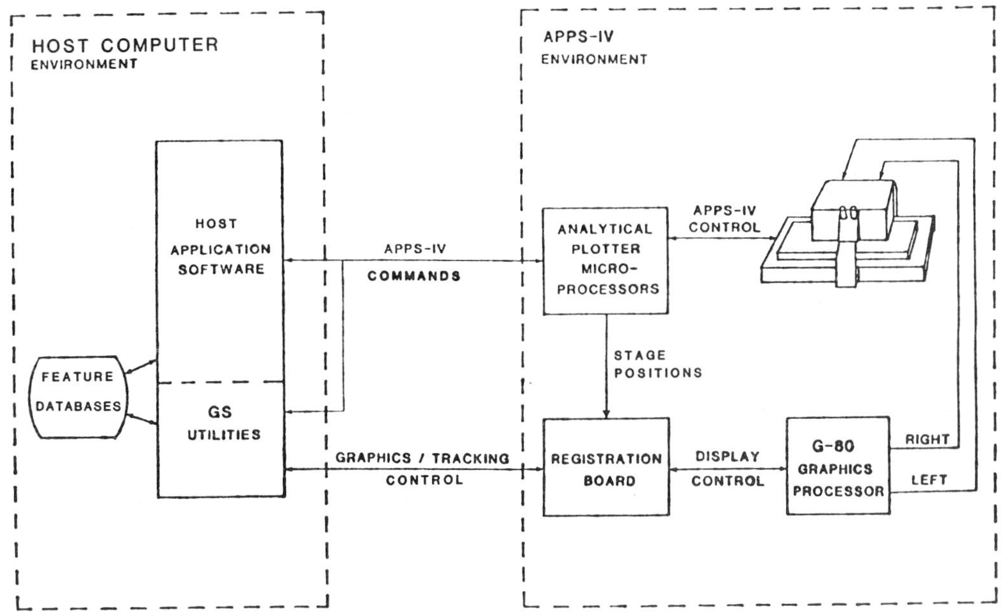

FIG.3 SUPER-P subsystem.

the Map Overlay and Statistical System, was designed around a set of constraints and user needs of natural resource planners in the Department of the Interior. These constraints and needs are applicable to many other users including the hydrologist. They include the ability to accept input data in several formats including remote sensing raster format and the ability to perform a large number of spatial analysis tasks to handle hydrologic and natural resource planning problems. For the additional design constraints and a more thorough overview of MOSS the reader is referred to Reed (1984).

Applications

The SUPER-P subsystem in the APPS-IV environment provides definite advantages in numerous applications. When coupled with the AUTOGIS software, major operational advantages are realized during compilation and revision of informational databases. The entire system provides a complete tool for cartographic feature delineation, identification, editing and subsequent statistical analysis.

During database compilation the operator has real-time verification of compilation via superimposition of graphics which represent the features digitized thus far. The operator can readily check for feature omission and properly joined feature boundaries. "This capability permits 'direct digital editing' of information to be accomplished and at the most efficient point during the data handling process" (Greve, 1983).

Existing database information can be graphically overlaid onto new imagery for edits and updates. Feature additions and deletions can be readily made by comparing new photographs to the graphics generated from the existing database. This is accomplished by converting the ground coordinates to photo-image coordinates which are used to generate the graphics. The process of converting existing ground coordinates to image coordinates is the inverse of the normal photogrammetric mapping function. This process employs the mathematically well defined collinearity equations whose inverse transformation exists. In simplified matrix notation, image coordinates are computed from

$$\vec{x}_I = 1/s \; [M] \; [\vec{X}_G - \vec{X}_o] \qquad (1)$$

where

$\vec{x}_I$ = vector of image coordinates
s = scale factor (i.e. mm/m)
[M] = the 3 x 3 orthogonal ground (object) to image space rotation matrix
$\vec{X}_G$ = vector of ground coordinates to be transformed
$\vec{X}_o$ = vector of ground coordinates of the camera station at the instant of photography

Once image coordinates are transformed into film space, a six parameter affine transformation defined in the fiducialing process is applied to the image coordinates to obtain APPS-IV stage coordinates. Through a graphics registration process another six parameter affine transformation is established. This transformation relates APPS-IV stage coordinates to graphics coordinates in the display space. Once these transformations are established, graphics can be generated so the operator may perceive

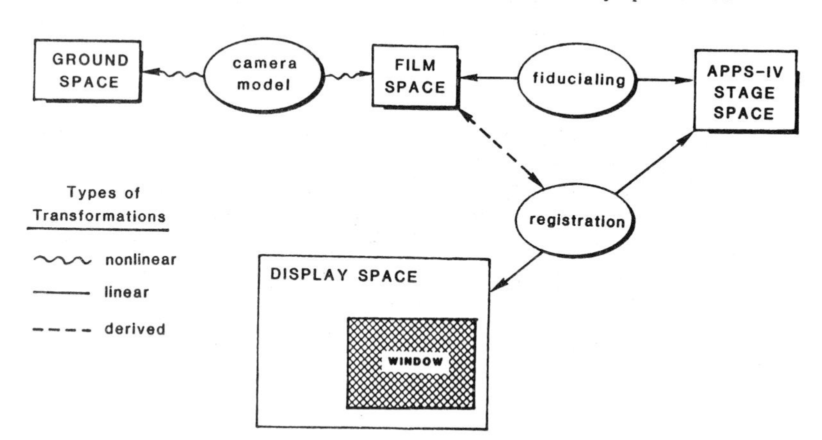

FIG.4 Spatial relationships.

positionally correct three-dimensional graphics while looking through the APPS-IV optics. The transformation process from ground coordinates to graphic coordinates is summarized in Figure 4.

With superimposed graphics from a previously compiled database properly registered to new imagery, database updates are readily accomplished via visual change detection. The new imagery used for the database update process need not be from the same sensor or camera system. As long as the ground (object) to image space transformation exists, superimposed graphics can be generated from previously compiled databases. The compilation, update, and edit capabilities of the APPS-IV with SUPER-P graphics are currently being applied in diverse fields where positionally accurate information is required.

The U.S. Fish and Wildlife Service is using the APPS-IV, SUPER-P , and AUTOGIS system for identification and quantification of the nation's wetlands. Current defense applications use the system for graphical fusion of intelligence information onto imagery. The system is also being evaluated for databasing interiors of large power plant construction using terrestrial close range photography.

Conclusions

The APPS-IV with AUTOGIS software allows exploitation of an extremely large database of existing aerial photography to identify and quantify drainage basin characteristics. This database continues to grow and will soon be supplemented with orbital based Space Shuttle photography. Spatial relationships within this stereophotography are accurately measured using the APPS-IV analytical stereoplotter. These measurements are logically and efficiently stored by AUTOGIS software. AUTOGIS software can then perform complex spatial analysis of the collected data.

The APPS-IV - AUTOGIS system is further enhanced with the Superposition Graphics subsystem which allows direct overlay of three-dimensional computer graphics onto the stereophotography. The fusion of this additional "plane" of graphics information into the well defined spatial environment of the APPS-IV provides a unique tool for GIS compilation, verification, and updating from stereophotography.

Acknowledgments

Mary Ehlers and the clerical staff of Autometric, Inc. also deserve special thanks for the typing and graphics presentation of this paper.

References

Greve, C.W., June 1982, "APPS-IV, Improving the Basic Instrument": Photogrammetric Engineering and Remote Sensing., v.48, no.6, pp.903-906.

Greve, C.W., 14 April 1983, "Superposition as a Tool for Intelligence Fusion and Targeting": Military Electronics/Countermeasures.

Niedzwiadek, H.A. and Greve, C.W., Feb. 1978, "The Wetlands Analytical Mapping System": Proc. 44th Annual Meeting of the American Society of Photogrammetry, Washington, D.C..

Reed, C., 1984, Map Overlay and Statistical System (MOSS), System Reference Manual, prepared by Autometric, Inc., Falls Church, VA, p. 1-1 to 2-33.

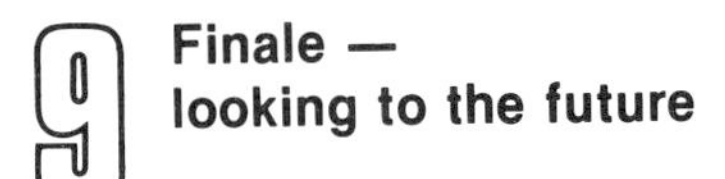

9 Finale — looking to the future

Hydrologic Applications of Space Technology (Proceedings of the Cocoa Beach Workshop, Florida, August 1985). IAHS Publ. no. 160, 1986.

Closing discussion

ARTHUR J. ASKEW
Hydrology and Water Resources Department,
World Meteorological Organization, CP No.5,
CH-1211 Geneva 20, Switzerland

At the close of the workshop the participants were invited to express their views concerning the general trends that had emerged during the week of technical discussions. The session was led by a panel composed of T.E. Andersen (Norway), J. Mwanje (Kenya), R.W. Paulson (USA) and V.V. Salomonson (USA), with A.J. Askew (WMO) acting as moderator. A summary of the discussion at this session is presented below.

Remote Sensing Systems

In a number of ways the use of remote sensing for hydrology has reached a turning point in its development. The number of operational satellite systems is increasing and greater reliance can now be placed on the future availability of many data. It cannot be denied that the transfer of some systems to commercial operators raises questions concerning administrative and financial implications which, at this point in time (August 1985), have yet to be clarified. Nevertheless, a basic set of sensors is now well established and potential users in the hydrological community await with interest any new developments. In particular, will these follow present trends or will they be departures from the past and use, for example, laser technology? New sensors, carried on experimental satellites are important research tools, but their value to operational practice can only be realized once they are carried on a routine basis and the necessary procedures for data collection and interpretation have been perfected. There is some evidence of a narrowing of the gap between research and operational practice in this field, and this is to be welcomed. In particular, one can foresee a significant role for satellite derived data in routine work in operational hydrology and water-resource development. Routine applications require that data be provided consistently over many years and that the data meet the requirements of the hydrological community. It is important therefore that these requirements be spelled out and the work being undertaken by various national committees or by regional groups, such as the European Association of Remote Sensing Laboratories, or by the World Meteorological Orgnization at international level, is to be welcomed.

The main emphasis of the workshop was on satellite based systems, but the continuing and oft increasing value of aerial surveys and radar measurements was not ignored. Satellites have taken over the role of aircraft and radar in many instances, but not in all. A clear trend is emerging in which all three modes of data collection are employed in conjunction with one another and tied jointly to ground-truth measurements instead of, as in the past, being seen as mutually exclusive options. One outcome of this is to increase still further the importance of ground-truth measurements. Remotely-sensed data build on and enhance the value of data obtained from ground-based instruments, but do not replace them. In fact, while it may be possible to reduce somewhat the number of conventional measurement stations because of the availability of remotely-sensed data, those that remain need to be more reliable, more carefully located and maintained, and must provide more accurate measurements on a larger number of parameters.

Applications of Remotely-Sensed Data

Frequent references were made to the International Symposium on Hydrological Applications of Remote Sensing and Remote Data Transmission that had been convened by IAHS in Hamburg in August 1983 (IAHS Publ. Nc. 145, 1985) and to the significant progress in the application of remote sensing that had been achieved in the intervening two years. This progress has not been uniform. Mapping of snow cover is now routine in many services and attention has shifted to the optimum use of such data, particularly in hydrological models. Work on soil moisture and groundwater, however, has as yet not benefited to such a great extent from remote sensing. This may be due, at least in the past, to the fact that the data obtained from current sensors cannot be interpreted so directly in terms of soil moisture and groundwater parameters. The estimation of precipitation from remote sensing is considered to be in an intermedite stage. There is an increasing number of instances of the routine estimation of areal precipitation being based, at least in part, on satellite-derived data. This serves to emphasize the difficulties faced in cases where the corresponding ground-truth data are collected by different agencies, provinces or even countries, or where there are no such data available for all practical purposes.

Spatial resolution has increased steadily and this has greatly enhanced the value of the observations for most uses. However, together with an increase in the number of sensors, this is resulting in the collection of an ever greater volume of data. This poses serious problems regarding the storage, analysis and timely distribution of data. In the past, hydrological modellers have called for more and more data; the cry of the future may be for more models which can make full use of the remotely-sensed data that are already available. These data allow lumped estimates to be made at a higher level of detail and on a more sound basis than do conventional data. They also contain a wealth of information on spatial variability which cannot be used to much advantage until more and better distributed models have been developed.

Many of the algorithms presented at the workshops are very site specific and will need to be generalized if their full potential is to be realized. Such developmental work should involve a careful consideration of the information content of conventional ground-based measurements and the operational value of current analytical and modelling techniques. New operational procedures based on remote sensing should only be introduced when and where their advantages over current techniques can be clearly demonstrated on both technical and economic grounds. For example, a distributed model using remote-sensed data may not give as good results as a well-tried lumped model using accurate ground-based measurements.

Data Transmission

In the field of remote hydrologic data transmission, emphasis is now being placed on the operational characteristics and feasibility of the various systems available. Many options are available: direct wire, telephone, line-of-site radio, micro-wave telemetry, satellite relay, meteor-burst, etc. All are operational and well-tried, questions therefore concentrate on their relative merits, in particular their costs. As the systems become more widely used, their costs usually decrease but it is hoped that means will be found to reduce costs even beyond this. A comparison of costs, however, is likely to show quite different results for different applications, depending on the specific requirements in each case.

While accepting that general statements cannot be made as to the relative merits of the different systems, one must emphasize the universal importance of good forward planning. Many mistakes in planning have been made in the past and authors are encouraged to present papers at future meetings describing these mistakes as a basis for offering advice to others faced with similar problems. One of the most important factors to plan for is system maintenance. Far too many systems fail because insufficient attention has been paid to the logistics and costs of maintenance, including the provision of spare parts and availability of trained technicians. Good planning will help users to focus on system life-cycle costs, rather than just on initial capital costs. Due consideration of this will often result in the selection of a different data transmission system or a revised configuration of the system that has already been chosen.

Geographic Information Systems

Some five to ten years ago a considerable amount of analytical work was still being undertaken manually, in particular as regards the extraction and preparation of data. The impact of the micro-computer is now very evident and this has led to a very real interest being shown by the hydrological community in computer based geographic information systems (GISs). These are seen as potentially valuable tools for the systematic compilation and joint analysis of a wide variety of water-related and land-use data. GISs store these data on the basis of geographic location and can easily accept and interface with remotely-sensed data. The availability of a number of tried and tested GISs for general application is welcomed, particularly in view of the immense effort required to develop any new system. However, the selection and use of any GIS should take account of its particular design, limitations and in-built assumptions. Potential users should be wary of being driven by a specific GIS to collect and analyze data demanded by the system, unless they are confident that the output will be what they really need. An important early decision is the choice of grid cell size and the selection of standard formats for input and output, particularly as data compilation and input are usually more difficult and costly than the acquisition and operation of the GIS itself. The rapid expansion in use of GISs raises the question of standardization in hydrological practice, and does so with a greater sense of urgency and on a larger scale than has previously been the case. It is hoped that the standards established will be robust and mutually compatible as regards data formats and efficient with regard to algorithms.

More Wide-Spread Application of Remote Sensing And Geographic Information Systems

Reference was made at the workshop not only to the expansion of remote sensing and GISs in hydrology but also to the use of such technology in a larger numer of countries. Countries which do not themselves operate satellite systems are now using satellite-derived data on a routine basis and are developing new techniques for the analysis and application of such data. A major influence on such developments is the extent to which the data are received directly in the country or are rapidly re-transmitted from a receiving station in a neighbouring country. This poses serious problems for many developing countries, particularly those in Africa where there are few receiving stations.

Once the data are available, the micro-computer offers a very cost-effective tool for their analysis and application. Practically all national agencies can afford to purchase a micro-computer, but its purchase alone does not ensure its efficient and long-term use. Some software is prohibitively expensive and digital analyzers are costly items. If current trends towards automation and digital processing continue, will there still be a placed for manual processing? A total commitment to automation and computer-based techniques could place future developments well beyond the reach of many developing countries because of the related requirements for hardware, software and trained manpower. An appropriate mix of manual and automatic procedures and basic and sophisticated techniques needs to be identified and made available. In this way, the great potential of micro-computers and remote sensing for developing countries can be made to bear fruit.

Conclusions

In both developing and developed countries there exists a wide range of scientific and technical ability and achievement and it is not easy to establish the current status on a global basis or identify trends. There is general agreement, however, that most progress has been made in recent years in the development of techniques for applying remotely-sensed data and GISs. Far less effort has as yet been directed to scientific research in the fields concerned and, above all, the implementation of the application techniques in operational practice has been regrettably slow. Individual experts often prefer to develop ever more sophisticated procedures rather than engage in the much less stimulating task of transferring existing knowledge and technology to potential users and formalizing new techniques for routine application. However, given the will and the resources, we can expect to see a significant increase in the operational use of remotely-sensed data and GISs in the coming years.

After a long period of technical development, we have now reached the state where remote sensing for hydrology has come of age and will start to be used widely in operational practice. This shift from development to operation depends, not only on the data and services that can be provided by the satellite operators, but also on the ability and willingness of the hydrological and water-resource community to revise their operations to take advantage of the benefits offered. The shift should be governed by a realistic assessment of the long-term benefits and costs of the new technology. It should not be seen as a panacea for all past problems but as a tool to be used in improving our ability to assess and manage the water resources at our disposal and to limit the death and destruction caused by the floods and droughts which all-too-frequently ravage the world.

Individual Membership of IAHS

INTERNATIONAL ASSOCIATION OF HYDROLOGICAL SCIENCES

WORLD CATALOGUE OF MAXIMUM OBSERVED FLOODS

Prepared by
J. A. Rodier & M. Roche

384 pages
price $30 (US)
IAHS Publication No. 143
(published 1984)
ISBN 0-947571-00-0

World Catalogue of Maximum Observed Floods is a follow-up to the *World Catalogue of Very Large Floods* published by UNESCO in 1976. The collection and collation of the data for the new Catalogue were undertaken by the International Association of Hydrological Sciences with support from UNESCO as a contribution to project A.2.7.2 of Phase II of the International Hydrological Programme. With the help and cooperation of IAHS National Committees and National Representatives, IHP National Committees, national agencies and individual hydrologists and consultants, data were assembled from 95 of the 110 countries approached, including 34 of the 35 countries which had provided information earlier for the UNESCO Catalogue. A particular effort was made to include data from arid regions such as the southwest part of the USA, countries bordering the Sahara, and Australia.

Data include maximum observed flood discharges for 1400 stations/observation sites and also all the maxima published previously in the UNESCO Catalogue. As such, this publication is extremely comprehensive and invaluable to those working in water resources management.

In addition to information on maximum floods, details are given of the procedures used for estimating the floods and the accuracy of these estimates. Basin characteristics and details of each station are also listed to enable an understanding of the hydrology and the formation of floods in each area.

The new Catalogue includes 105 new long time series of anual maximum floods for major rivers or stations with interesting statistical distributions of annual maxima.

Orders This publication may be ordered from the following addresses:

Office of the Treasurer IAHS
(Attn: Meredith A. Compton)
2000 Florida Avenue NW
Washington, DC 20009, USA

IUGG Publications Office
39 ter Rue Gay Lussac
75005 Paris
France

IAHS Press
Institute of Hydrology
Wallingford, Oxfordshire
OX10 8BB, UK

Please note that unless instructed otherwise the publication will be sent by surface mail and delivery to some destimations outside Europe and North America may take up to six months. Air mail postage is extra. Pre-payment is welcomed but not obligatory.

SEA LEVEL ICE and CLIMATIC CHANGE

Edited by **Ian Allison**

Proceedings of the Canberra Symposium, December 1979
471 + xv pp.; price US$10; published 1981 by the International Association of Hydrological Sciences as IAHS Publication no. 131

The International Symposium on Sea Level, Ice Sheets, and Climatic Change was held at Canberra, Australia, on 7 and 8 December 1979 as part of the 17th General Assembly of IUGG. The symposium was sponsored by IAHS, IAMAP and IAPSO and was organized by the International Commission on Snow and Ice of IAHS, with support from the Local Organizing Committee for the IUGG General Assembly.

The major objective of the symposium was to review current ideas and recent results on the processes and the effects of interactions between sea level, ice, and climatic change on time scales of 100 to 10 000 000 years. While the cryosphere has been the subject of considerable speculation regarding the climatic past and future, the exact causal relationships between cryosphere phenomena and sea level in the past remain uncertain. Description of those changes in sea level and ice sheets which had causes and effects other than climatic, would hopefully define a residue of features with direct climatic implications, and help to identify interconnections between the three phenomena.

As might be expected with a symposium theme of such general scope, the contributed papers cover a very wide range of topics, and it is hoped that this will highlight the complexity and multidisciplinary nature of the study of relationships between sea level, ice, and climatic change. The papers have been grouped into two major sections, each divided into subsections.

ICE AND SNOW AS ELEMENTS IN THE WEATHER AND CLIMATE SYSTEM AND AS INDICATORS OF CHANGE
The record of climate change in glaciers
The climatic role and environmental effects of snow
Sea ice as a climatic element
Evidence of the past climatic change from large ice sheets

FEATURES AND INTERACTIONS OF SEA LEVEL, ICE AND CLIMATE IN THE QUATERNARY
The global record of the late Quaternary changes of sea level, ice and climate
Processes of interaction between sea level, ice sheet and climate
Sea level, ice, and climatic change: invited summary reviews

The book is available from either the Office of the Treasurer IAHS, 2000 Florida Avenue NW, Washington, DC 20009, USA or the IUGG Publications Office, 39 ter Rue Gay Lussac, 75005 Paris, France. A catalogue of all IAHS publications is available free of charge from either of these addresses or from the IAHS Editorial Office, Institute of Hydrology, Wallingford, Oxon OX10 8BB, UK.

INTERNATIONAL ASSOCIATION OF HYDROLOGICAL SCIENCES

INTEGRATED DESIGN OF HYDROLOGICAL NETWORKS

Edited by Marshall E. Moss

415 + x pages
price $40 (US)
IAHS Publ.no.158
(published July 1986)
ISBN 0-947571-75-2

A Symposium on the Integrated Design of Hydrological Networks was held in conjunction with the Second Scientific Assembly of IAHS at Budapest, July 1986. This volume of pre-published proceedings is dedicated to the memory of Walter B.Langbein, who for nearly 30 years was pre-eminent in the conceptualization, development, and implementation of network design technology. The 36 papers in the volume come from 15 countries, and are divided into three sections:

1. Spatial sampling
2. Sampling frequency and its joint optimization with space-sampling schemes
3. Efficient utilization of information

In the first section, the keynote paper by A.J.Hall uses the highly variable hydrology of Australia to illustrate the philosophies required to make efficient use of data-collection resources in a large country with varied demographies. Many of the papers in this section deal with interactions of spatial dependency in hydrological fields and the resulting spatial density of measurements required to describe the fields.

The papers in section 2 tend to be more in a research vein and also demonstrate more of the integrated nature of networks for hydrological data collection. It would appear that integration of hydrological networks is a concept that has remained of interest to researchers in this field but it has not yet made a significant impact on the day-to-day planning and management of hydrological data networks.

Section 3 shows that guidance provided by the WMO *Guide to Hydrological Practices* for minimum network densities still seems to be dominant in procedures for evaluation of data-collection programmes around the world. Other papers in this section stress the tools of data collection and utilization, e.g. microcomputers and remote sensors.

13. JUN 1989
30. NOV. 1989
10. MAR. 1993
-6. FEB. 1996
12. JUN 1997
11. JUN 1998
26 MAY 2003
CANCELLED